F. Barch

Phone 6-1100

MB Tex. Dust.

AN INTRODUCTION TO
TEXTILE FINISHING

By the Same Author

An Introduction to the Chemistry
of Cellulose (1938)
(*In conjunction with* Dr. F. C. Wood)

▲

Mercerising (1941)

▲

An Introduction to Textile
Bleaching (1946)

▲

Textile Science (1948)

AN INTRODUCTION TO
TEXTILE FINISHING

By

J. T. MARSH

M.Sc., F.R.I.C., F.T.I.

FIFTH IMPRESSION

LONDON
CHAPMAN & HALL LTD.
37 ESSEX STREET W.C.2
1953

First published in 1947
Second impression 1948
Third impression 1950
Fourth impression 1951
Fifth impression 1953

PRINTED IN GREAT BRITAIN BY JARROLD AND SONS LTD., NORWICH

CATALOGUE NO. 321/4

To
the Immortal Memory of
JOHN MERCER
Father of Textile Chemistry

PREFACE

THE rise of the textile industry—the greatest British industry—precipitated the Industrial Revolution; this fact is not always appreciated.

Mechanisation of the domestic crafts was accomplished by a few inventions and the use of water-power; the industry was well established on a factory basis before steam-power led to the formation of a chemical industry.

Although the steam-engine of Newcomen was largely used for pumping in mines, it could not be adapted to rotary motion and was unsuited to the needs of factories; the steam-engine of Watt and Boulton was first used in mines, but as water-power was already in use in the textile industry, the way was prepared for steam-power in the factory. The textile industry made use of one-third of the steam-engines produced by Watt and Boulton.

The parent of the modern chemical industry was sulphuric acid manufacture, and its first commercial application was in connection with the bleaching of linen. The manufacture of alkali, as distinct from wood-potash, was made possible by the availability of sulphuric acid; the use of alkali was, and is, essential in the textile industry, so that an immediate market was soon assured. By a curious coincidence, Watt was in communication with Berthollet at the time of the discovery of chlorine and was informed of its bleaching properties; this information was passed on to Macgregor, his father-in-law, and chlorine was soon employed for the bleaching of linen. The commercial production of bleaching powder by Tennant followed in due course.

The use of coal for power led to the introduction of coke for metallurgy, and the manufacture of coal-gas brought with it various coal-tar products, the investigation of which led to the foundation of the synthetic dyestuffs industry by Perkin.

Hence it may be seen that the rise of modern industry from Lancashire and Yorkshire was due in part to the presence of coal, iron, water-power, and water-transport, but also to the presence of a textile industry on the first factory system. The district possessed its inventors, craftsmen, and its merchants, a combination from which the modern industrial pattern has crystallised on the basis of research—production—selling.

However, all chemists are aware that the first member of a series has rather peculiar properties, and it is not surprising to find that the textile industry has retained its traditional pattern, and cannot be regarded as a modern industry; it is still amorphous and therefore flexible, but not being crystalline it lacks coherence and form, strength, and rigidity.

It has often been stated that the greatest single handicap under which the textile industry suffers is that the selling function is in the hands of a separate community as it was before the Industrial Revolution, and indeed before the textile craft was ever practised in England. If the selling function is separated from the industry, the research function, on the other hand, is almost completely divorced from it. The danger of this course may be seen from the history of the early dyestuffs industry which became obsolescent because Perkin took his profits and retired instead of investing in industrial research. The dyestuffs field came under German control and was nursed into supremacy by careful and painstaking research.

In the early textile industry, the process of manufacture was brought to a high pitch of technical perfection by brilliant improvisation and empirical methods without any regard to research. Trained scientists were not required in an expanding market, but the inventor and technical expert could still expect advancement leading to partnership, as shown by Mercer, for example. Later, however, the control of the industry passed more into the hands of the merchanting community, and its direction became overlaid with nepotism and patronage. It was not realised that many industrial methods soon become technical anachronisms, so that both plant and processes are now threatened with obsolescence.

The question arises, therefore, whether the textile industry— that sprawling and ungainly giant—can be re-erected on to the tripod which supports the modern industries, namely : research— production—selling. The present organisation is not in accordance with the healthy economic development of the industry in relation to the interests of the community. There is no need to look, as the dyestuffs industry had to look, to foreign lands for a rebirth of its fundamental science; the new textile science has arisen in these islands, and has now come of age. For the first time in history, the essential knowledge of the structure of fibres is available to explain and enlighten their behaviour. Provided that the present "sellers'-market" does not obscure our vision, there is no reason why the application of scientific knowledge and of scientific method should not bring about a great textile revolution of which the development of synthetic fibres is only a foretaste. The greatest single obstacle is the failure to appreciate the positive achievements of textile science and the impact of new technical forces propelled by the dynamic power of research.

Although no branch of the textile industry can function efficiently to-day without the constant services of the scientist, the inherent soundness of the policy of a scientific approach to technical problems is realised by very few firms; elsewhere there is apt to be confusion between bricklaying and architecture. Where there is a lively recognition of the potential contributions of science, and faith in a future of constructive effort, prosperity may also be found. Textile scientists should be regarded as the "pathfinders" to the industry. In respect of its social relations, the value of research lies in its benefit to mankind, and textile research has been of great service to the community by improving the properties of our clothing in many and various ways. On a less practical note, the textile scientist may take pride in the fact that research is a great intellectual adventure and one of the highest peaks of human endeavour.

In *An Introduction to Textile Bleaching* the writer has given an account of the occurrence and properties of the chief textile fibres, and the methods adopted for their purification; the present, and companion, volume deals with their behaviour in various circumstances.

For many generations, the finishing of textiles followed a characteristic routine in which secret recipes were handed down, surrounded by such an air of mystery that it was impossible to consider finishing on any rational basis. It must be admitted that the mystery of the craft was often greatly overrated, for many of the finishes disappeared on the first wash.

As future advances will be made on the foundations laid by the present generation of textile scientists, it seems profitable to review the state of our knowledge. Considerable interest and mental energy have been directed to the production of permanent finishes, whereby the fugitive starches and gums have been replaced by resinous condensation products and polymers, and by cellulose derivatives; with our increasing knowledge of the structure of cellulose it has been possible to perform chemical reactions on this substance with the creation of new effects. Equally striking researches have brought about remarkable developments in the production of wetting agents and softeners; work on emulsification has had repercussions on the manufacture of stable preparations of oils, fats, and waxes. Some of the major defects of various textiles have yielded to the advance of science, namely, the creasing of the cellulose fibres, and the felting of wool. The development of rayons brought new problems, many of which have been solved. Some of the older finishes have been the subject of intensive examination, and although no striking alterations may have taken place, yet they are now on a firm basis and thoroughly understood by those with the necessary knowledge illuminated by the modern appreciation of the behaviour of fibres in terms of their structure.

Two criteria have been taken for this work, first, commercial importance, and secondly, scientific and technical interest. Hence, although some of the finishes described in the following pages are of limited application as yet, they may be of some scientific importance. It must also be remembered that mercerising was not practised in Mercer's lifetime, and that Lowe's patent was allowed to lapse for lack of support.

The writer has been privileged to assist, in a modest way, with some of the great advances in textile science; he has also been sufficiently fortunate in his work to have had access to many of the most famous finishing plants in Europe, Canada, and the U.S.A. It has also been the author's good fortune to be acquainted with many of the great pioneers of textile science, and he hopes he has benefited from his numerous discussions with them, as he has from their friendship.

The subject-matter of this book is based on the experiences of the writer during his twenty years' service as a research chemist in the textile industry, and from a careful study of the literature of the subject. Sometimes the literature is contradictory in the extreme and it is often impossible to reconcile conflicting statements, but both sides of the argument have been presented as fairly as possible. Many of the new developments are taken from studies of the patent literature, both British and foreign, and this is no easy matter. Some British patent specifications seem to have little real value and the data would have been better left in the note-book. The patent office must draw a handsome income as a publishing house with material which many technical journals and trade magazines would reject; the authors, or rather the owners of these documents, must pay very dearly for this type of circulation. The only novelty in certain specifications is the coining of some new term for an old property; some specifications claim new effects or different effects from identical processes, and in others the only invention is that of a new property. The British patent system is no longer regarded with the great respect that should be its due, and many industrial scientists and technologists have a poor view of the accuracy and validity of the specifications. A patent is rapidly becoming a dated licence to go to the High Court. In not more than one-half of the patents filed, have the patentees sufficient confidence to pay the first renewal fees; less than 2 per cent. of specifications are upheld for the full period of sixteen years, and of the patents subjected to litigation, only 5 per cent. survive.

The preparation of this book was undertaken because it was thought that there was need of a work dealing primarily with the chemical aspects of textile finishing, and embodying, under one cover, the chief recent investigations. No endeavour has been made to write a treatise on textile finishing in all its branches, and the mechanical aspects are only considered in so far as they are essential for a satisfactory understanding of the whole scheme. Not all things can be set down in writing, and the masterly craftsmanship of the Yorkshire finishers, for example, can only be saluted in passing.

"There are also many other things . . . the which, if they should be written, every one . . . even the world itself could not contain the books that should be written."

Thanks are due to Miss Alexander and Mr. Tankard of Tootal Broadhurst Lee Company, Ltd., and to Mr. Manby of Leeds University, for providing various photographs. Grateful acknowledgment for the loan of blocks is made to the Society of Dyers and Colourists, the Textile Institute, the *Textile Recorder*, the *Silk Journal and Rayon World*, the Bradford Dyers' Association, Daniel Foxwell and Son, Ltd., Arthur Heaton & Co., Messrs. Mather and Platt, Sir James Farmer Norton, Ltd., John Mitchell & Sons, Ltd., Sellers & Company (Huddersfield), Ltd., Messrs. Whitehead and Poole, and Wm. Whiteley & Sons, Ltd. Courteous permission for the reproduction of illustrations has been received with thanks from the Institution of Mechanical Engineers, Messrs. Thomas Broadbent and Sons, Ltd., John Dalglish & Sons, Spooner Dyer & Engineering Company, Ltd., and S. Walker, Ltd.

In conclusion, warm and sincere thanks are given to the friends and colleagues with whom this work has been discussed, and in particular to Dr. C. S. Whewell and to Mr. A. D. J. Piesse, M.Sc., for undertaking the arduous task of reading typescript, galley-slips, and page proofs.

J. T. M.

Manchester, 1946.

CONTENTS

PLATES

There are 161 illustrations numbered in one sequence. The twenty-seven plates contain the following figures:

All other illustrations are in the text

NOTE

Throughout this book the *gallon* to which reference is made is the British Imperial gallon and not the U.S. gallon. The British gallon is equivalent to 1·2 U.S. gallons.

CHAPTER I
GENERAL INTRODUCTION

THE term "finishing" in its widest sense has been held to cover all the processes which fabrics undergo after leaving the loom or knitting machine; from this standpoint, finishing would include bleaching and dyeing, which, indeed, are sometimes regarded as wet-finishing processes.

The object of finishing is to improve the attractiveness and/or serviceability of the fabric. A more restricted view of finishing is that of the third and final stage of the treatment of woven or knitted fabrics to prepare them for the consumer; bleaching and colouring form the first and second stages. Even this definition, however, is open to criticism, for some fabrics are not bleached and others are not dyed or printed; again, many finishing operations, such as the crêping of silk and rayon, the mercerising of cotton, the crabbing of wool, and the cutting of velvets, form part of the first phase of fabric treatment. Subject to these corrections, finishing is best regarded as the final stage in the embellishment of the fabrics, most of which, as they come from the loom, having an unattractive appearance, which persists, although to a less extent, even after dyeing or printing. A simple definition of finishing is the sequence of operations, other than scouring, bleaching, and colouring, to which fabrics are subjected after leaving the loom or knitting machine. The simple processes of damping, smoothing, stretching and ironing, or pressing, as carried out in the home to make articles of clothing neat, fresh, attractive, and presentable, have their counterpart in the treatment of long lengths of fabric which present a rough and crumpled appearance after bleaching or colouring. From these humble finishing processes, many elaborate treatments have been developed to render textile materials more attractive, either by improving their appearance or by imparting some property not normally possessed.

The technique of finishing is capable of wide variation, but in the main it may be held to depend on four factors:

(a) The type of fibre and its arrangement in yarn and fabric.

(b) The physical properties of the fibre, particularly in respect of swelling capacity, as affecting the behaviour when pressure or friction is applied, in wet and dry states and at high and low temperatures.

(c) The receptivity of the fabric for absorbing various finishing preparations.

(d) The susceptibility of the material to chemical modification.

It is obvious that the character of a fabric is determined to some appreciable extent by the fibres from which it is made; silk and linen, for example, have certain intrinsic properties for which they are famous, and require comparatively little finishing to enhance their attraction. The same remarks hold good for wool when the fibres are arranged to make worsted material, but in the typical woollen construction a complicated series of processes is necessary to "finish" the cloth, after which it bears little resemblance to its appearance in the loom. Another example of the effect of yarn and fabric structure with regard to finishing may be seen in knitted fabrics, many of which are not suited to the usual finishing processes, with the exception of a few special finishes. It will be seen, therefore, that the fabric structure plays an important part. With regard to weave, a plain weave is susceptible to many finishing treatments, but a fancy weave does not so lend itself, particularly with cotton; in general, the more complicated the fabric structure, the less the necessity for further embellishment by finishing processes—"a good cloth finishes itself." Although cotton fabrics are often regarded as dull and unattractive, the robust nature of the material offers a fertile field for finishing processes, and an opportunity and a challenge to the more modern developments in finishing technique on a scientific basis.

Most of the simpler finishing processes are merely concerned with the effects of pressure, moisture, and heat, but satisfactory and consistent effects are determined to a large extent by an understanding of the fundamental properties of the various fibres and their behaviour when subjected to these processes. Whereas the "art," or craftsmanship, of finishing can only be acquired by practical experience and not from text-books, a thorough knowledge of the scientific principles involved and the physical and chemical properties of the various materials forms the base for future advances.

It is possible to divide finishing processes into two broad classes:

(*a*) physical,
(*b*) chemical,

using both terms in a very wide sense.

The physical or mechanical processes range from simple drying over steam-heated cylinders, or on a stenter which both dries and stretches the cloth, to a complicated series of calendering operations; special effects may be produced by beetle or schreiner machines. A soft and lofty effect may be produced by raising the surface of the cloth, and a mellow feel by "breaking" the finish of filled goods. Such treatments, however, have been known for a long time, and the machines used for such effects have remained basically the same in so far as finishing technique is concerned, although sometimes improved from the engineering standpoint. One notable exception, however, lies in the modern methods of controlled and compressive shrinkage of fabrics.

Chemical finishing methods, whether by the application or deposition of chemical compounds, or the performance of chemical reactions with the fibre itself, have extended in a remarkable manner. The improvement of the appearance of fabrics by the application of various compounds has been known for many generations, and in particular, cotton material lends itself to treatment with starch, dextrin, glue, gums, china clay, Epsom-salts, glycerol, soaps, and soluble oils, for stiffening, weighting, and softening, as required. Many of these chemical finishes were combined with mechanical finishes, such as calendering, to enhance the effect. A limited number of "styles" were produced, as trade was regular and demands relatively unexacting. Most of these older finishing agents have been cheap and available for many years. The chief criticism of such finishing materials is the ephemeral nature of the effect, and it has been felt by many merchants and finishers that it is illogical to demand increasing fastness of dyes without a similar permanence of finish.

Some well-established finishes, such as the milling of wool, the production of non-felting wool by chlorination, the mercerisation and parchmentising of cotton, were outstanding as highly specialised treatments capable of providing a durable effect.

Lawrie (J.S.D.C., 1939, 55, 350; 1941, 57, 180) has drawn attention to the point that many of the old finishing preparations have not been made specifically for that purpose, but rather represent products which have been cheap and available for a long time. Modern organic research, however, has made it possible to synthesise compounds which are ideally suited for textile finishing purposes—a branch of work which had been ignored during the revolution in dyeing and neglected ever since. One difficulty, however, is the cheapness of the older products, such as starch, compared with the new and expensive organic products; on the other hand, the range of effects from the older products is definitely restricted, whereas there is no limit to synthetic products.

In 1939, there were some 1,500 finishing agents on the market, in addition to the many thousands of ideas incorporated in patent specifications, but not commercially developed. Further, the finisher is anxious to consider and apply new ideas and methods, in strong contrast to the attitude of the old dyers prior to 1914.

With the exception of certain special compounds, these recent developments may be classified as follows:

(a) Long-chain fatty compounds;
(b) Synthetic resins;

    (c) Cellulose derivatives;
    (d) Quaternary ammonium compounds.

The last three groups can be utilised to produce permanent effects in contradistinction to the transient nature of most of the older finishing preparations.

Many textile terms are used with a characteristic lack of accuracy, precision, and elegance, and it is customary to speak of permanent finishing when durable finishing is meant. As pointed out by Smith (J.S.D.C., 1938, *54*, 407), neither permanent finishes nor permanent waving will "endure indefinitely," so that a finish can only be considered *permanent* if it remains unaffected through all the conditions of wear and treatment to which a fabric may be subjected during its life. It is not considered reasonable that a finish should outlast the material to which it has been applied; but, on the other hand if, in spite of wear and tear and laundering, an effect or finish is still evident to a substantial degree when the goods have become unserviceable, then the finish may be termed durable. An alternative meaning of the term permanent in finishing is that the effect outlasts the requirements of the consumer.

The German *hochveredlung* implies a division of finishing into high-class finishes and, presumably, low-class finishes; it may also connote a super-finish.

On the basis of temporary and "permanent" effects, the following may be regarded as transient or impermanent finishes:

    Mechanical. Calendering, beetling, schreinering, embossing and glazing, "breaking" and stretching.
    Filling. Starch, gum, Epsom-salt, china clay, and other mineral fillers.
    Softening. Oils, fats, waxes, soaps, and deliquescent substances such as glucose, glycerine, and magnesium chloride.

There are also many miscellaneous finishes produced by deposition of various substances on the fabric which may be regarded as impermanent, as they are easily removed by washing or dry-cleaning; examples may be seen in many shower-proof finishes which depend on wax emulsions or aluminium salts for their effect, and also numerous delustring effects.

The permanent, or rather, durable finishes are exemplified by the following:

    Mechanical. Milling of wool, various raising and cutting processes, controlled compressive shrinkage.
    Deposition. Cellulose esters and ethers, synthetic resins, both internal and external, rubber latex, bonding, and laminating.

Chemical. Mercerising, parchmentising, immunising, treatments with ethylene oxide, formaldehyde finishes, wet chlorination and other non-felting effects, modern hydrophobic fibres from finishes of the "Velan" type, permanent setting of wool.

No system of classification can be beyond criticism, and it may be argued that raising processes do not give permanent effects, as many of the finishes do not resist water; on the other hand, the original effect is not restored by wetting or washing. Similarly, many of the chemical and deposition finishes may be removed by chemical means, and the permanent set of wool is only permanent within certain limits.

It is interesting to realise that permanent finishing is not a particularly modern development except in respect of the deposition processes as against filling with starch and china clay; the milling of wool has been known for 4,000 years, the mercerising and parchmentising of cotton since 1850, and the chlorination of wool since about 1900. Permanent set, too, is a very old effect in its simpler forms.

Before discussing various special finishes, it is proposed to give a brief account of the general methods employed for different materials. Some knowledge is assumed of the occurrence, properties, and purification of the various textile fibres; in this connection, reference may be made to *An Introduction to Textile Bleaching*, by Marsh (Chapman and Hall, London, 1945).

COTTON

The use of cotton as the prime textile material is by no means entirely due to its cheapness and abundance, but rather to the fact that it provides material whose laundering properties are excellent because of the great resistance to hot alkaline detergents. Compared with other textile materials, cotton survives household treatments of sufficient severity to ruin the fibres, either by disintegration, dissolution, diminished strength, shrinkage, matting and felting, and so forth. Most soiled garments contain a large amount of greasy or fatty matter which is most easily removed by boiling in a mildly alkaline solution, often with rubbing; hence shirts, overalls, children's frocks, handkerchiefs, and many other items of personal apparel are composed of cotton. Another contributory factor to the popularity of cotton is its strength and durability.

Although some special types of cotton, in certain weaves, provide very attractive textile fabrics, yet it cannot be said that a typical cotton fabric has an inherent appeal such as may be found in linen, wool, silk, or rayon; nevertheless, the robust nature of cotton is such that it forms an excellent material on which the main part of the art and science of finishing may be brought to bear. Many of the finishes for cotton arose from attempts to transform this somewhat humble substance into a rather cheap imitation of the fabrics from more expensive fibres; hence methods were devised to improve its lustre to simulate silk, to stiffen cotton to imitate linen, or to impart some of the characteristic features of wool. Without some of these special finishes, cotton has great utility, but little beauty.

At one time it was customary to classify the finishes for cotton under three headings:

    (*a*) pure;
    (*b*) assisted;
    (*c*) stiffened.

The pure finish is mainly for goods which are intended for subsequent printing or dyeing, and is in the nature of an intermediate finish, for the final finishing processes are applied after the colouring of the material; this intermediate pure finish generally consists in opening the cloth which has been bleached in rope-form, washing and drying —during the drying process, the opportunity may be taken to rectify the width of the cloth and to adjust any distortion of warp and weft which may have occurred during bleaching. The white cloth trade, however, demands a more merchantable or attractive fabric than that merely prepared for dyeing or printing, and certain additional "pure" finishes are generally applied which have much in common with the smoothing of fabrics by household ironing, and depend mainly on imparting smoothness and brightness by calendering. At this stage it is not possible to draw a sharp line of demarcation between the pure and assisted finishes, for although the pure finish depends mainly on mechanical methods, such as calendering or breaking and softening, yet the effect is generally enhanced by small amounts of various softening preparations; fundamentally, however, the pure finish is a mechanical treatment including stretching to the required width and calendering to smooth and brighten the cloth, but depending to the minimum on added substances.

The assisted finish relies to some extent on the presence of material other than the cotton, and small amounts of some stiffening or binding agent are applied before the mechanical finish in order to improve the general effect, but these additions should not be obviously apparent.

The stiffened finish relies to a much greater degree on the presence of stiffening, binding, filling, and weighting agents in considerable quantity; most of these added substances are removed again at the first wash, but it must be remembered that many heavily-filled goods are not intended for wearing apparel. On the other hand, there has been a tendency to sell starch and china clay instead of cotton merely to give the effect of a thicker, better, and more robust fabric. Such practices are slowly disappearing as permanent stiffening methods are evolved and the public become educated to the fact that a cheap temporary finish is much more expensive than a dear permanent finish.

Starch is probably the commonest finishing agent for cotton goods, and it may be applied as a stiffening agent, alone or with a little softener; alternatively, it may be applied as a binding material for filling and weighting substances such as china clay and other compounds which would normally "dust out" of the cloth. The function of many of these filling and weighting compounds is more or less self-explanatory, but in general they add "substance" to the fabric, and it has been found over generations of empirical practice that cotton is an excellent vehicle for these applied finishing preparations.

More recently, methods of permanent finishing have been devised whereby it is possible permanently to improve the lustre of cotton, or to soften it, or to stiffen it, and even to apply stiffening and binding agents whose durability far exceeds that of starch, etc. Highly specialised chemical treatments have enabled new durable finishes to be evolved, relying on the chemical stability of cotton to various reagents on the one hand, and its reactivity on the other.

Where a smooth effect is required in cotton goods, it is customary to singe any projecting cotton hairs before bleaching, and even before the finishing processes proper, a heavy calendering finish is often applied by the water mangle to flatten the threads and close the interstices of the cloth, thus providing a satisfactory groundwork on which later to apply binding, stiffening, and filling materials.

The common operations in the finishing of cotton goods include stiffening (or softening) and weighting, damping, stretching, and calendering. The object of the stiffening process is to give the fabric a firmer handle and increased body; softening and weighting agents may be added at the same time to impart mellowness and substance. The degree of stiffness is mainly determined by the nature and consistency of the starch paste, the amount absorbed, and the method of application; these points are discussed in greater detail on page 275. In general, the fabric is passed over tension rails to smooth it before impregnation, and then dried on steam-heated cylinders or on a stenter (which dries and stretches the cloth); often both cylinders and stenter are utilised.

The successful operation of mechanical finishing processes necessitates a proper conditioning of the fabric beforehand, and more than the usual moisture of condition is often added to render the cotton sufficiently plastic to give the best result, which includes an attractive mellowness. Different effects are produced from various calender bowls, which include iron, steel, cotton, and paper; both hot and cold calendering may be utilised. Specialised calenders, such as the schreiner, are capable of providing a high degree of lustre which depends to a large extent on an embossing action. A smooth, lustrous, and "thready" effect may be obtained by a type of pounding or hammering in the beetle machine.

A noteworthy recent mechanical finish, described on p. 248, is directed to obviating the shrinkage on laundering to which cotton goods are prone, by controlled compressive shrinkage methods to give a "Sanforized" product.

In addition to the three classes of applied substances, stiffening and binding agents, filling and weighting agents, softening and emulsifying agents, certain miscellaneous agents are commonly applied to cotton, and these include fireproofing mixtures, mildew-proofing agents, waterproofing agents, and so forth.

A great forward movement in the finishing of cotton goods may be seen in the application of natural and synthetic products of high molecular weight; these specialised and durable finishes include the application of rubber, cellulose derivatives, and synthetic resins, and are described in some detail later.

Apart from the mechanical and deposition processes, both ancient and modern, cotton lends itself to certain chemical finishing methods, of great commercial importance and technical interest. Amongst these are found the improvement of lustre by mercerising under tension with caustic soda solutions, parchmentising and organdie effects with dispersing agents such as acids, salts, and various chemical solvents for cellulose, and the controlled or modified formation of various compounds of cellulose on the cotton itself, such as esterification and etherification, amongst which may be included the modern development of permanent waterproofing or the formation of water-repellent fibres.

Last, but by no means least, cotton has been used not only as a medium with which to form a chemical reaction in textile finishing, but as a substance in which it is possible to synthesise or build up certain synthetic resins in such a way that the major defect of the material, creasability, is radically improved, as in the "Tebilized" branded products.

LINEN

Linen may be regarded as the aristocrat of the cellulose fibres; its inherent appeal as a dress material is such that in 1558 Queen Elizabeth passed an Act to prevent "the deceitful treatment of cotton" in order to safeguard the quality of linen. Such is the superiority of the material that few attempts have been made to improve it by special finishes; on the other hand, there are many processes which aim at providing cotton with a linen-like finish.

The first treatments which are ordinarily given to linen in the loom state are cropping and singeing; in this manner, all projecting fibres and fluff are removed to produce a clean and lustrous surface. Cropping is carried out in the usual manner on a machine which has two, three, or four blades, and functions in a similar manner to the lawn-mower; singeing follows the practice usually adopted in the cotton trade with plate or flame machines.

After bleaching and dyeing, the fabric is usually subjected to the operations of damping, mangling, calendering, beetling, and stentering. These basic processes produce a beautiful lustrous effect with a mellow handle characteristic of linen.

Although linen normally contains more moisture than cotton, this is insufficient for the successful prosecution of mechanical finishes, and extra moisture must be added; if this is not done, then a limp effect is obtained, as there is some evaporation of moisture during processing. As previously indicated, the physical properties of fibres are affected by their moisture content, so that processes which depend on mechanical treatment for their action must operate on material which is in the correct plastic or receptive state.

The actual amount of added moisture depends to some extent on the particular finishing treatment, but an increase of 5 to 6% is generally suitable, although for mangling or cold-calendering 3 to 5% may be adequate. The damping may be effected by the spray or brush machine in the usual manner.

Beetling is of great importance in the finishing of linen, and its object is to close the interstices of the fabric and produce a flat effect with a high degree of lustre. Fundamentally, beetling consists in pounding the fabric with a series of heavy wooden hammers which fall on the beam of cloth directly beneath them. The beam rotates and also moves laterally during the hammering; the fabric becomes a little thinner and stiffer. The effect of beetling naturally varies with the time of treatment and with the length of cloth on the beam. For the best effect, the linen should be free from wax and fat. It is obviously essential that the cloth should be wound very evenly on the beam and entirely free from creases or damage will ensue. The filling and stripping of the beams are done outside the beetle; the process of reversing the direction of the cloth is termed a change. The time of beetling may vary from a few hours to 45 or 50 on the older type of machine, but with the modern all-metal machine, the time may be reduced to about 25%. Montgomery (J.S.D.C., 1938, 54, 351) states that dress linens requiring 22 hours on the old machine may be given the same finish in 5 hours on the new; the finishing of damasks may be reduced from 45 hours to 9 hours, and shirtings from 45 hours to 16 hours.

As the time factor is considerable, many attempts have been made to reproduce the beetle finish by other means, and the hydraulic mangle has been widely utilised for cheaper effects. The mangle finish gives a full, soft and mellow handle, together with a closing of the interstices of the fabric, but the last-mentioned result is determined by the amount of pressure employed. It is often customary to utilise heavy calendering as a preliminary to the beetling process, and although this may result in the saving of considerable time, yet the peculiar stiffness of a good beetle finish is not obtained by a shortened treatment; the characteristic lustre of the calender persists through the beetling process.

It will be realised that mechanical treatments of this type are determined to a large extent by the plasticity of the moist cloth which retains the impression on drying; when the fabric is wetted, as in laundering, a considerable amount of the "finish" disappears, but the effects of beetling are not entirely removed, for the typical compactness of beetled linen persists.

Embroidery linens are usually given a simple finishing treatment, as outlined above, but sheetings are often given a light starching before calendering or beetling. Damasks are sometimes treated with a mixture of starch, gum tragasol, glycerol, and Turkey Red oil, and then almost dried on steam-heated cylinders before calendering or beetling. Dress linens require a somewhat different method of treatment, for although the smooth and sheer effect is wanted, yet the stiffness or crispness must be replaced by a soft handle. The draping properties of the fabric are determined to some extent in the loom, for "a well-woven cloth finishes itself," and if the material is so constructed as to permit good shrinkage in mercerising, then a soft and pliable result may be obtained. After beetling, the material may be impregnated with a suitable softening preparation and stentered to the required width, or it may be stentered and softened mechanically on a button or scroll breaker.

Linen may be finished with some of the specialised treatments such as waterproofing and mechanical processes of compressive shrinkage in much the same manner as for cotton. One of the great disadvantages of linen, however, is the ease with which it creases, but this may be obviated by the crease-resisting finish as outlined on p. 401. For this process to be successful without deterioration of the linen, it is necessary for standards of quality to be fixed below which the goods may not be processed; the solubility number must not rise above a certain maximum. Hence the development and control of a specialised finish has done much to improve the general standard of bleaching and finishing linen even for the ordinary finish, and chemical degradation is now at a minimum.

The finishing of the material from the coarser vegetable fibres, such as hemp and jute, is not very exacting on account of the uses to which such fabrics are put. In general, the simple routine finishing involves shearing, and calendering or mangling under very heavy pressure.

The use of dressing preparations which include starch as a stiffening or binding agent is almost entirely confined to cotton and linen fabrics, and mainly to cotton; most dressings are applied to the back of the fabric. This type of finishing is rarely encountered with rayon, silk, and wool.

RAYON

No textile material demands more care in finishing than does rayon; the strength of the fibre in the dry state is less than that of the parent cellulose, and there is a very considerable reduction in strength when wet. Further, this is accompanied by a high degree of swelling, so that the rayon is very easily deformed when wet. Rayon is much more susceptible than cotton to chemical attack.

Most rayons are composed of very fine individual filaments, and care must be taken to avoid damage. The necessity for imposing the minimum strain on rayon in both wet and dry states has led to the use of machines which, although similar to those used for cotton goods, are much lighter in construction.

Many fabrics composed of 100% filament rayon are processed, as far as possible, in open width on jigs and padding mangles. The general procedure is to de-size the fabric, and then lightly scour in soap and sodium carbonate solution, followed by rinsing. The excess of water is generally removed by a vacuum hydroextractor with the cloth at full width, and the actual drying is carried out on a stenter, taking care to avoid over-stretching; drying on cylinders gives a harsh handle to rayon fabrics, and this is not generally acceptable. An alternative method of drying is on the loop or festoon drier, which may be followed by an adjustment of the width on a stenter fitted with a steam box. Numerous rayon fabrics are finished on the blanket drying machine, sometimes called the Palmer, where the fabric passes around a smooth steel cylinder against which it is held in close contact by a travelling blanket.

Light calenders are also available for finishing rayon goods; these generally have three bowls, the top and bottom bowls being made of wool-felt and paper, whereas the middle bowl is made of steel or chilled iron. Only light tension and pressure should be applied, except where it is required to accentuate the lustre, in which case the middle bowl may be heated.

Rayon filament fabrics are rarely stiffened or filled; even where softening materials are applied, care must be taken or the yarns of the cloth will acquire a tendency to slip and the cloth will "grin."

A very popular type of fabric is that with a cotton warp and rayon weft; this may be treated in rope form, but care should be taken to keep the rope as slack as possible with convenience. The rope may be opened to full width by scutching and the fabric dried on steam-heated cylinders, after which it is generally impregnated with some softening preparation, stentered to width, and finished on the Palmer or on a silk calender.

Spun-rayon fabrics, in the early stages of treatment, may be dealt with in rope form or in open width; the heavier fabrics are perhaps best treated in open width as they are apt to acquire rope-marks, break-marks, and various creases which are not easy to remove in the later stages of finishing. A very common treatment, before bleaching, is to pass the goods through dilute sodium hydroxide solution of about 2% concentration, followed by rinsing. The cloth is generally scoured in soap solution on a wince machine or in the jig; the lighter cloths may be impregnated in full width with soap solution and then scoured in rope form on a wince machine. The purified fabric is then rinsed, extracted, and opened if necessary; drying may conveniently take place on a loop drier after the fabric has been impregnated with a softening material, and the width adjusted by a stenter with steam box, or, alternatively, the impregnated cloth may be dried directly on the stenter, where a soft and woolly feel is required. A smooth and flat finish may be obtained by finishing on the Palmer or on the silk calender.

The golden rule of finishing rayon fabrics is to allow adequate shrinkage during the last drying process; otherwise a thin papery handle is obtained instead of a full supple effect. Many goods are unfortunately finished in strained state and with a potential laundry shrinkage of 10%; on the other hand, the fully shrunk fabrics are apt to be "baggy" due to distortion, unless treated by the crease-resisting process of Foulds, Marsh, and Wood. For untreated rayons, a residual shrinkage of 1 to 2% may be advised.

Many rayon fabrics, filament as well as spun, benefit from a mild calendering between cold steel and paper bowls with a minimum of pressure; the object is to loosen the fibres or filaments and obtain a full handle.

The decatising machine, normally used for wool goods, is becoming increasingly popular for imparting a wool-like finish and a full handle to spun rayon fabrics.

It may be remarked that spun-rayon fabrics in general appear well suited to specialised resin finishes such as those capable of providing crease-resisting effects.

A somewhat detailed account of the finishing of the popular rayon crêpes is given on page 93.

ACETATE RAYON

The rayon from cellulose acetate possesses different properties from regenerated cellulose; the lower density (1·33 as against 1·5) gives greater cover, and the nature of the fabrics is noteworthy for a richness and beauty of a high order. Cellulose acetate, however, although robust from the standpoint of tensile strength in both dry and wet states, is susceptible to change by hot water, alkali, and dry heat; hence during the finishing processes certain precautions must be taken. In particular, a temperature of 80°C. should not be exceeded with any aqueous solution, the use of hot dilute alkali must be avoided, and temperatures over 140°C. must not be used, as the acetate will fuse and give an unpleasant and glazed effect.

It may be remarked in parenthesis that many attempts have been made to raise the "ironing point" of acetate rayon, particularly in view of possible damage with domestic appliances which are not thermostatically controlled. Some of these processes depend on a surface saponification of the acetate; for instance, B.P. 369,586 of British Celanese, describes successive treatments with solutions of diminishing alkalinity, the first solution containing 1% sodium hydroxide solution. Treatments with metallic salts have also been suggested, and according to one of these, B.P. 372,129, the acetate rayon may be treated with a solution of a metallic salt which has a weighting effect, such as stannic chloride or zinc chloride, in presence of a compound such as sodium chloride or calcium chloride, which depresses swelling; the metal is then precipitated as an insoluble salt by dibasic sodium phosphate solution.

For the ordinary finishing of acetate rayon fabrics it is generally advisable to keep the fabric in open width, for any creases which are formed in processing are difficult to remove. The cloth is often stentered as a first process to remove wrinkles; it may be de-sized on the jig with an enzyme preparation at 60°C. and then scoured with soap and a sulphated fatty alcohol at the same temperature; higher temperatures are apt to reduce the lustre of the rayon. After bleaching with slightly acid hypochlorite solution, or with slightly alkaline hydrogen peroxide, the fabric is well washed. The next stage is to remove excess water by a vacuum hydroextractor or by careful mangling, and soften in a suitable mixture, such as one of the modern sulphated or sulphonated products, to which may be added glycerine or diethylene glycol. If a firm handle is required, then dilute gum Tragasol may be used.

The final stentering operation is often combined with a Palmer unit which should not operate above 105°C. or an unpleasant glaze will be produced. On some flat goods, a light calendering treatment is carried out at a temperature of 55° to 80°C., according to the weight of the fabric. Printed acetate rayons may need mechanical softening on the button-breaking machine.

It may be remarked that, as a general rule, all rayon fabrics, whether acetate rayon or regenerated cellulose, should be dried at relatively low temperatures for the best handle.

WOOL

As nature has provided most animals with a clothing material in the form of hair, it is not surprising that man has adapted the best of these for his own clothing. The softness and lightness of wool render it particularly attractive, and the crimped fibre enables the fabric to exhibit valuable warmth properties which are primarily due to the low thermal conductivity of the air entrapped in the interspaces. Wool can also absorb more moisture than any other natural fibre without feeling wet, and this, too, plays a part in its value as a clothing material, for moisture is adsorbed with the evolution of heat, thus protecting the body from experiencing sharp changes of temperature.

The softness and lightness of wool are best displayed in woollen goods where the fibres are arranged at random in the yarn; a firmer and more compact arrangement is seen in worsteds where the wool hairs are in parallel formation in the yarn.

In addition to the thermostatic value of wool as a clothing material, coupled with its softness and lightness, there is an elasticity of a very high order, and also excellent draping properties. The freedom from creasing, compared with other fibres, was unique for centuries, and approached only by silk.

The elastic properties, together with a scale structure, enable very compact fabrics to be made by milling; it is also possible so to treat wool that the milling property is destroyed and the fibres will no longer felt into an entangled matted mass, but will retain their open and "lofty" effect after repeated washings.

The three fundamental factors in ordinary finishing, heat, moisture, and pressure, are employed to good purpose in the finishing processes; indeed, the use of starch and fillers so common with cotton does not find a place in the treatment of wool, and if firmness should be required, a little gum or dextrin is quite adequate. The methods of finishing wool, however, are more complex than with other textiles.

Enterprising use is made of two peculiar properties of wool: (a) the ability to acquire permanent set and (b) the felting phenomenon, both of which depend on heat, moisture, and pressure; for milling, the pressure is intermittent.

The common methods of imparting permanent set, such as crabbing, blowing, boiling, decatising, etc., depend on softening and fixing the fibres. The action of steam or hot water renders the wool plastic, during which state it is allowed to cool under mechanical constraint, usually on a roller where it has been wrapped evenly and smoothly and firmly. In crabbing, for example, this process removes the strains in the woven fabric which would establish distortions such as cockling, puckering, waviness, etc., and gives an even appearance and regular structure to the fabric. This simple method of forming a roll under tension and causing the fibres to yield to the self-pressure in the plastic state is capable of many variations.

The milling or fulling process is well known and is produced by friction, heat, and moisture; the fibres become entangled and draw the material together to consolidate it in a unique manner. The surface thus created may be raised, and the raised pile may be specially arranged or treated for further finishes. Unmilled fabrics, of course, may also be raised.

As previously mentioned, it is possible to utilise wool to form two types of yarn, in one of which long hairs are arranged in parallel formation, and in the other, shorter hairs of varying length are arranged at random; the former gives worsted material and the latter, woollen goods. The difference in yarn and fabric between woollen and worsted is so fundamental that it has been said, "worsteds are made in the loom and woollens are made in finishing."

Worsteds

The natural finish for worsted fabrics is a clear-cut effect where the woven pattern is accentuated; hence worsteds are rarely milled, but may be semi-milled to create a fullness which is lacking in the loom state. No attempt should be made to obscure the pattern. The first stage in the finishing of worsteds is to crab the cloth by passing through hot water under tension on to a roller; heat, moisture, and pressure impart a degree of permanent set to the wool and prevents crows' feet marks, cockles, and other forms of distortion which would mar the fabric. A similar effect may be obtained by blowing with steam (see page 160). The worsted fabric is then scoured, during which process some shrinkage is allowed and the fabric becomes more compact; drying is then carried out on a tenter, which also adjusts the width of the cloth. The next stage in finishing is to brush the fabric and cause any projecting hairs to stand erect; the brushing is often accompanied by steaming or dewing to facilitate the subsequent cutting or shearing to give a smooth, clean surface. A final blowing process straightens the woven fabric and clarifies the design, after which the worsted cloth is pressed.

Some worsteds are apt to exhibit too much lustre after pressing, and this may be removed by steaming. The use of steam in this connection must not be confused with blowing and decatising; with ordinary steaming, the fabric is passed through an atmosphere or mist of hot steam rising from an open trough, and the treatment, which is directed to the removal of harshness and lustre, is on the basis of "little and often."

Pressing is almost essential for the clear-cut finishes, as it improves smoothness and lustre, and gives additional firmness and solidity to the fabric; it has been compared with the calendering of cotton. The press-finish is frequently applied to worsteds, but is only applied to woollens to a minor degree; many cotton linings are press-finished, and also some silks and rayons. It is necessary to condition the fabric before this process, which may be effected in various ways, the commonest of which is to place press-papers between the folds of the cloth and then transfer it to a hydraulic press for 90 minutes to 2 hours. The original method relied on the use of hot iron plates. Many of the older presses were heated by circulating steam through the cavities of the iron plates placed in the press, but later developments produced press-papers cemented over resistances which could be heated electrically. After one pressing, the folds are moved and the papers changed to a different position so as to press the untreated parts of the fabric. Rotary presses are also available.

Woollens

With most woollen goods the sequence of finishing operations may be divided into wet and dry processes. The common wet processes are crabbing, scouring, carbonising, milling, boiling, bleaching, and drying. The usual dry processes are brushing, steaming, damping, cutting, blowing, raising, napping, and pressing.

The wet processes generally precede the dry finishing operations, but it is clear that many variations and permutations of these treatments are possible in establishing a sequence of finishing operations.

A typical woollen finish may be obtained by scouring the fabric and then milling it to obtain a close compact structure on which subsequent finishing operations will be performed. The increased cover obtained by milling enables a pile to be raised on the surface of the fabric by teazles or card-wire; the raised hairs are then cropped or sheared to produce an even surface. The fabric is finally pressed and any strains removed by London shrinkage which is a form of relaxation shrinkage.

With many of the Scotch tweeds, the milling and scouring processes are combined in one finishing step.

Some overcoating materials are napped, that is to say, after the raising and cropping process, the pile is rubbed to give a slight bead effect.

Another interesting wool finish is the Melton type, in which there is no raising, but cover is obtained by a heavy milling. The sequence of steps is to mill, dye, tenter, brush, steam, crop, blow, press, and steam if necessary.

The dress-faced finish is generally obtained by scouring, milling, raising (wet), cutting, brushing and steaming, pressing, boiling, washing, tentering, steaming and raising, shearing, pressing, and finally steaming to remove press-glaze if required. In face-finished goods, the extent of milling or fulling is such that the construction of the fabric is no longer visible.

The velour finish depends to a very large extent on the correct blend of suitable wools in the original fabric, and this enables a very dense but soft pile to be produced. The sequence of finishing operations is to scour, mill, raise (dry), cut, steam, and press.

The fleece finish, as seen in blankets and rugs, is obtained by scouring and lightly milling, followed by raising.

Vicuna finishes depend for their effect on an alteration in the normal order of treatment of woollens; fundamentally, the effect is due to milling on a raised pile, and the fabric is therefore raised before milling.

SILK

Silk may be regarded as the most valued of all the native fibres; its peculiar, characteristic handle and its appearance are the result of careful treatment by bleacher and finisher. The distinctive lustre, high tensile strength, resistance to wear, pleasant handle, and excellent draping properties, together with warmth, softness, and smoothness are such that silk materials are regarded as a demonstration of the artistic taste of wealthy people; in olden times, silk was reserved for persons of high position, and only such people were allowed to wear it.

Until the middle of the nineteenth century, the methods of treating silk were simple but lengthy. The silk-gum was removed by boiling, when the pleasant softness develops, and then the material was bleached by stoving in sulphur dioxide vapours. The bleached fibre was generally mordanted in an acid alum or iron solution and then dyed in liquors made from extracts of dyewoods or roots; although the weighting of silk by metallic compounds and various tanning materials was known, it was not until about 1850 that the weighting of silk became important, primarily to replace the loss in weight on de-gumming and soaping. As will appear later (page 301), whereas the weighting of silk imparts a fullness of handle,

2

it is apt to have certain disadvantages in respect of resistance to light, perspiration, or long storage.

A special method of finishing has also been devised to prevent the loss in weight which normally accompanies degumming and is due to removal of sericin; ecru silk may be steeped overnight in 4 to 5% formaldehyde solution at 20°C. and then rinsed. This process has the effect of "hardening" the sericin and rendering it less soluble in warm dilute alkaline solutions, but it must be noted that the full softness and smoothness and lustre of silk is only developed when the sericin has been removed.

Another feature of silk is the "scroop" or characteristic rustling crackle when rubbed against itself; this is not a natural property of silk, but is imparted by soaking in dilute solutions of formic, acetic, or lactic acid. Dilute sulphuric acid has also been used, but there is always a danger of damage to the fibres. The following concentrations of solution may be regarded as typical for scrooping: formic acid (85%), 10 to 20%; lactic acid (50%), 30 to 40%; and acetic acid (30%), 40%.

Some dyed silks are not sufficiently lustrous, and the "brightening" is often a prelude to the real finishing. About 1 to 5% of olive oil (on the weight of the silk) is boiled to form an emulsion with sodium carbonate and water which is applied at 30°C., followed by treatment with acid which liberates the oil and imparts scroop at the same time.

Silk is not particularly resistant to degradation by light, particularly when it has been weighted, and attempts to overcome this defect have been made by impregnation with 2% thiourea solution.

The natural beauty and charm of silk are such that it requires comparatively little finishing, other than the smoothing and straightening processes which are necessary with all fabrics.

The usual methods of handling are similar to those employed with the lighter and medium-weight cotton and rayon dress goods. The silk fabric, after bleaching and dyeing, is generally dried in a festoon machine or other slack-drying device such as the air-lay machine, and then stentered to width on a frame equipped with a steam box. Where softening preparations are applied, this may be done by a mangle at the start of the stenter, or, alternatively, the cloth may be impregnated with the softener and then finished on the blanket-drying cylinder.

Stiff finishes are occasionally required, and preparations of gum, soluble starch, dextrin, gelatine, or glue have been utilised; they are mostly applied to the back of the fabric in the usual manner, but with some of the lighter constructions, the finishing solution has been sprayed on to the fabric.

Many silks are calendered, and ribbons in particular give moire effects by a simple variation of ordinary calendering (see page 77):

other silks are given a press finish, the finest being merely smoothed by a cold pressing.

Weighted silks and some printed silks may need mechanical softening on the breaker.

A natural lustre machine is also available for silks and rayons (see page 80), and this simulates domestic ironing by heating the back of the fabric with highly polished rollers, while the face passes over felt-covered rollers which preserve any brocade or other woven effects.

PILE FABRICS

Velvets are utilised in three main ways: first, as upholstery fabrics; secondly, as dress materials; and thirdly, as linings for boxes, coverings of shoes, artificial furs, collars, hat trimmings, and many other miscellaneous purposes.

In all cases, it is customary to cut the velvet before the processes of bleaching and dyeing, and although there are many machines for cutting the loops of the woven fabric which provide the pile, yet a very considerable quantity of velvet is still cut by hand.

The chief object in the finishing of all types of velvet is to make the pile stand erect; with dress goods, the pile is usually finished perfectly erect, but many upholstery velvets are finished at about 10° or 20° from the vertical, in order to avoid pressure being applied in use squarely on the tips of the fibres. Miscellaneous velvets may have the pile "laid" at various angles from 45° upwards, according to the purpose for which they are intended.

Many upholstery velvets have a mohair pile or a mohair-worsted mixture, and it is customary to give these a permanent set before wet processing; the fabric may be framed in a cottage steamer and subjected to steam pressure of 5 to 10 lb. per sq. in. for 30 to 60 minutes. This obviates excessive matting of the pile during scouring (if any) and dyeing, which usually take place in rope form. The excess of water may be removed by a centrifuge, but with better qualities of fabric, it is preferable to use a vacuum-slot machine after opening the cloth to its full width.

If the pile is dried in a distorted condition, it is very difficult to finish properly, so the general method is to brush the pile into an erect state immediately before drying. There are various machines for this purpose, but the simplest consists of a stand equipped with two rotating cards of brushes, one of which is made of bristles and the other of stainless steel card-wire about one inch in length. The softer bristles run with the pile and the stiffer card-wire against the pile; the cards revolve in opposite directions at about 500 r.p.m. Before meeting the cards, the fabric is straightened by passing over an expander bar which removes all creases.

A steam-box is often situated under the stand to make the pile plastic and therefore easier to manipulate. This preliminary treatment opens and untangles the pile, before the cloth passes on to a second similar unit, after which the fabric is beaten to complete the erection of the fibres and the opening of the tufts.

Drying usually takes place in a machine which resembles the pin stenter employed for woollen and worsted dress goods, arranged in three to five tiers; feeding is generally by hand.

An alternative machine comprises a beater which precedes the drying and brushing frame. The beater untangles the matted pile, and the fabric then passes into the pin stenter which is equipped with from eight to sixteen rotating cards, the majority of which rotate against the pile. Steam-boxes are kept under the first part of the stenter, but the remainder is enclosed to complete the drying with steam coils.

The dried and brushed fabric is next sheared to obtain a lustrous uniform surface. The shearing machines are usually placed in line with the drying unit to expedite production. Most velvets are sheared to give a pile varying between 0·125 and 0·25 in. in height; a shorter pile gives a fabric which lacks cover and reveals the back of the fabric to an excessive amount. The most regular cropping is obtained by running the cloth into the shearing machine against the pile, as otherwise there is a tendency to lay the pile rather than to cut it. After the first cropping, the fabric is steamed and brushed again, followed by a second cropping.

With upholstery velvets, the slight lay of the pile is given by passing the fabric over a steam-cylinder on which is fitted a curved plate; the distance between plate and cylinder is carefully adjusted to lay the pile slightly, and its angle is set by the action of the steam.

Some mohair upholstery fabrics are mothproofed; this may be done from aqueous solution, after the first brushing and drying. If the solution is applied by a mangle, the pile of the fabric must be laid by a brush rotating with the pile, in order that the pile is not disarranged in an irregular manner when passing through the mangle. Mothproofing agents which are soluble in organic solvents may be applied by spraying.

Some of the cheaper upholstery fabrics receive a special finish to secure the pile more firmly to the back of the fabric. Gum tragacanth or locust-bean paste may be applied to the back by spreading; rubber latex has also been employed for this purpose.

Cotton velvet is dealt with in much the same manner as that previously described, except, of course, with regard to permanent set. Many cotton fabrics are waterproofed by the aluminium-soap method or with emulsions of paraffin wax; these treatments take place after the preliminary brushing and drying.

Some rayon-pile upholstery fabrics are specially brushed by first laying the pile almost flat by running all the cards with the pile; a second brushing treatment follows in which the carding is done from side to side instead of from end to end. Fireproofing and waterproofing mixtures may be applied after the preliminary brushing.

Velvets for dress goods are generally made of silk, rayon, or cotton; they are constructed with a short dense pile whose finishing requires careful attention to detail.

Many of the finer qualities are scoured and dyed on star frames, after which they are vacuum extracted at full width and beaten to free the pile prior to brushing. It is customary to leave about 100% of water in the fabric to facilitate the brushing.

Chiffon velvets are often finished on hand-frames where the carding is also done by hand; the drying is effected by charcoal wagons, which are pushed along under the fabric during the carding.

Where carding is carried out by machine, the brushes must set rather deeply in order to ensure a smooth and even effect; shearing is effected gradually and frequently so as to avoid a ragged appearance.

Softeners may be applied after the preliminary brushing, and the excess liquor removed by vacuum extraction in the usual manner; similarly with the scooping solutions.

Some of the finer velvets require side-brushing to obtain an even and regular cover.

The so-called transparent velvets are often made with a silk back and a rayon pile; the crushing of the pile was a defect in the original constructions, but this may be obviated by utilising the crease-resisting finish which is usually applied after the initial brushing. The transparent velvets are often finished with an erect pile, but occasionally with a slightly laid pile; in all cases the rayon velvets are first wet-brushed with a moisture content of 100% and the brushes revolving with the pile, in order to have a smooth uniform surface for the subsequent operations. The fabric is then treated according to the particular finish required, such as softening, waterproofing, or resin treatment; wax emulsions are sometimes applied to improve the lustre of the pile, although this is commoner with cotton velvets than with rayon. The subsequent drying and brushing operations take place on an evenly arranged pile, followed by shearing and brushing sometimes with side brushes.

The finishing of pile fabrics is capable of many variations and the range of effects is large; some of the more interesting novelties have been described in detail by Hillman (Rayon Textile Monthly, 1936, *17*, 107, 169, 238, 295, 363; 1937, *18*, 94), including cut-out effects.

HOSIERY

The knitted construction lends itself to the manufacture of cheaper fabrics in general than woven cloth; developments in knitting machines and the advent of rayon have resulted in a great output of knitted material for underwear to which knitted fabrics are particularly adaptable on account of their elasticity, porosity, pliability, and readiness to shape themselves on the body.

On the other hand, the ease with which knitted goods may be stretched limit their use as a universal clothing medium, and also brings special problems in connection with finishing processes. The knitted structure is not suited to a great variety of finishes, but this is perhaps not required, for material which has to be worn in close contact with the skin must be soft and supple, and there is no necessity for a wide range of finishes.

It is not proposed to discuss the finishing of knitted goods, but only knitted fabrics; these fall into two main types—tubular material and flat knit. For ease in manipulation, it is customary to sew the two edges of the locknit material together to make a tubular fabric before starting the wet processing.

The general methods of scouring, bleaching, and dyeing are determined by the fibre of which the material is composed, but a great part of knitwear is neither bleached nor dyed, as this is often not required for underwear. The tubular fabric is usually wet-processed on wince machines, taking care to avoid distortion, dried, stretched to width, sometimes raised slightly on the surface, or either calendered or pressed.

Popular knitted goods are made from rayon, wool, or cotton.

Rayon locknit is of special importance to garment manufacturers (or makers-up) for several reasons. First, the locknit material possesses the valuable property of not laddering; secondly, it is knitted flat and is suitable for cutting into various shapes; and thirdly, it has a pleasing and attractive appearance.

The flat material resembles a woven fabric rather than the tubular circular knitted fabric, but nevertheless it is better to process the fabric in tubular form, for otherwise the selvedges curl and form a roll which is difficult to penetrate. Hence, one of the first operations in finishing is to sew the edges together and make a tubular fabric; a special machine unrolls the edges immediately before stitching. The face of the fabric is usually made the inside of the tubular material in order to protect it from damage during processing.

The tubular fabrics are generally scoured on the wince, or on the dolly machine, and each length of material has its ends sewn together to form an endless band; some four to six of these endless bands are treated simultaneously side by side. The nature of the scouring liquor is determined by the type of fibre in the material; a simple soap solution is preferred for acetate and the temperature should be kept below 80°C. unless delustring is required. With regenerated cellulose it is possible to scour at 95°C., which is about the maximum convenient temperature for a wince machine.

Acetate rayon locknit is not particularly troublesome with regard to the development of crease-marks, and is more satisfactory in this respect than Milanese; nevertheless, if held in a creased state in hot water for several minutes the creases tend to persist, particularly if the fabric is under pressure. Hence it is advisable to keep the fabric in open width as far as possible and also to avoid pressure when the fabric is at the bottom of the wince machine; for this reason an elliptical wince is preferred to a circular wince, as the fabric is plaited down so as to be well spaced out, with fewer folds and the minimum of pressure on the bottom layers. In order to avoid damage by friction and chafing, it is customary to make the whole machine of stainless steel, but to wrap the wince with cotton to give the necessary grip on the fabric and draw it round and round during scouring, bleaching, and dyeing, which usually take place in the same machines.

After the bleaching and dyeing processes, the fabric is hydro-extracted and then dried on a brattice drier; the extraction of water must be as thorough as possible, for it is much cheaper to remove the moisture mechanically than by heating. Viscose rayon will retain more water than acetate rayon after hydroextraction, and this point needs attention in the subsequent drying, for most brattice driers only operate at three speeds, and a slightly high water-content means a lower speed of drying and a reduced output.

The tubular locknit material is generally very twisted when it leaves the hydroextractor and should be opened and plaited into laps so that it can be fed on to the brattice evenly and so ensure even drying.

The dried material is actually "inside-out" and must be turned for the dry finishing processes; this is usually done by threading the fabric on to a metal tube of large diameter, and then withdrawing it through the centre. There are no continuous methods for turning tubular fabrics.

An alternative to the brattice drier is a machine specially devised for tubular fabrics, which are piled on a vertical tube through which hot air is blown; the fabric is drawn upwards to the nip of a two-bowl calender which forms a seal forcing the hot air to pass through the fabric and dry it. Creases are prevented by a special stretcher for tubular knit material (see page 66).

For flat goods of knitted construction, a special stenter has been devised with attachments to open the curled selvedges and impale them on the pins of the machine; both length and width may be controlled. Wide material is often finished on the hand-frame and may need support in the centre to avoid stretching by sagging. Many stentered materials have a somewhat firm finish which may be "broken" by mangling between soft rubber rollers.

Tubular knit materials are not finished when dried, but usually require calendering; wool goods are finished on moderately heavy calenders, but lighter machines are available for silk and rayon. The steel bowls of the calender are often covered with an endless blanket, which may be removed if it is wished to finish the fabric in direct contact with the metallic surface. Travelling endless blankets also guide the fabric round the bowls so that it passes between the travelling blanket and the bowl for about 240° of its circumference. The width of the fabric is maintained by the special stretchers devised for tubular knit goods (see page 66). The fabric is steamed just before it passes through the hot calender and the moisture enables it to be set to the required width; jets of steam may be blown into the fabric from the inside or, alternatively, the fabric may pass through a steam-box, according to the type of stretcher employed.

Cotton hosiery may be manipulated in the same general manner as that previously described; the fibres, however, are more robust and may be scoured in the usual way for cotton, and also bleached and dyed. It is important, however, to avoid stretching the material, which is readily distorted by reason of the knitted structure. Although permanent creases are not formed so readily as with rayon, it must be remembered that knitted yarns have been stretched, and if allowed to shrink on to a crease in the hot wet state, then that crease is very difficult to remove. Many knitted cotton fabrics are mercerised without tension in order to produce a firm, close fabric by reason of the shrinkage which takes place; such fabrics are often utilised in the manufacture of gloves, and are given a suède finish by friction against oscillating rollers which may be covered with emery cloth, glass paper, or carborundum.

Many forms of knitwear are raised to improve their softness and porosity; they are generally softened beforehand, to lubricate the fibres. The simplest method is with teazles and this is suitable for coarse loosely-twisted yarns, but a rotary machine consisting of rotating rollers covered with card clothing and arranged axially around a large cylinder is suitable for a large variety of cotton, rayon, and woollen fabrics. Rayon goods require especial care in treatment on account of their tensile strength and fine filaments.

Wool hosiery is manipulated in much the same manner as other knitted fabric, but the finishing operations are modified somewhat on account of the properties of the wool fibre. The tubular material is often scoured in open width and then milled in the pendulum stocks, the shape of which causes the fabric to roll intermittently; for other methods of milling, the goods may be treated in the combined scouring and milling machine. The milling is directed to the production of a closer and more compact fabric, but not to the blinding of the knitted structure by felting.

A great deal of knitted material is never bleached; for example, the men's underwear fabrics are usually "natural colour," but much of the finer materials may be bleached. As one of the great defects of wool goods which are frequently washed, is the ease with which they felt and became matted, it is customary to give an "unshrinkable" or non-felting finish before the bleaching process, if any. The dyeing process then follows where required.

The web of fabric is usually dried by removing the excess of water on a hydroextractor and the remainder on the brattice drying machine; alternatively, the tubular drying machine may be used. The tubular knit material is then turned with the face to the outside and gently brushed and raised to give a soft and woolly effect; a high degree of raising is given to some fabrics. The final treatment is to press the goods in a press of the Hoffmann type or, alternatively, to use the felt calender and take suitable precautions against distorting the knitted fabric.

It will be noted that knitted wool goods are not crabbed or blown, as the knitted structure is too readily distorted.

LACE

The finishing of lace has its own features on account of the ease of distortion which is midway between that of woven and knitted structures. Many lace materials are produced in widths which are three or four times that of woven fabrics, and even the narrow lace fabrics are made side by side, joined together by a linking thread which may readily be withdrawn at a later stage.

After scouring, bleaching, and dyeing, the narrow lace may be finished on the type of stenter which is normally used for cotton fabrics, but running at a lower speed; the wider lace fabrics are generally finished on the old-fashioned hand-frames. These consist of two parallel horizontal rails with end-rails; the distance between the side-rails is controlled by screw-rods, and it is also possible to adjust the distance between the end-rails. Hence the lace fabric may be framed and dried under such conditions that it will not shrink on subsequent laundering.

The fabric is fixed to the side-rails by impaling on pins which are coarser and wider apart than those found on ordinary stenters; the length and width of the hand-frame are then adjusted in accordance with previous experience or after preliminary trials. The lace is then left to dry, and this may take from 10 to 30 minutes, according to the quality of the material and the amount of dressing it may have received. Generally, the hand-frames are arranged in rooms about 150 to 200 yards in length and 40 to 50 yards in width, to accommodate three frames; the whole room is heated by steam or hot-water pipes arranged across the floor, and a gentle current of air is provided by flap fans situated above the frames.

Many types of lace are required with a stiff finish which may be given with starch or gum; an old favourite was a mixture of starch and glue, the proportions of which were varied in accordance with the nature of the goods. Where a very stiff effect was needed, the goods were stretched on the frame and the dressing applied by "slopping" on to the fabric and then spreading evenly but quickly with brushes or long wooden rollers; in both cases, considerable work by hand was necessary to ensure even application and avoid uneven drying. Excess of stiffening was often removed by beating the lace with canes during the drying process.

A moderately stiff effect may be obtained with starch alone, which may be applied from the mangle in the usual manner after which the fabric is spread on the frame by hand.

In all methods of finishing the wide lace, it is usual to wind it from the frame on to a wooden roller, after which it is transferred to a cutting-room, where the pieces are trimmed and adorned with edge-tapes, if necessary, and then passed through a heated calender to flatten the material and increase the lustre. Many nets and lace curtains are folded and pressed in a hot press as a final finishing operation.

PLATE I

Fig. 1. The Foxwell Guider.

Fig. 2. Scrimp Rail (Farmer Norton).

Fig. 3. Revolving Expander (Farmer Norton).

To face page 26.

PLATE II

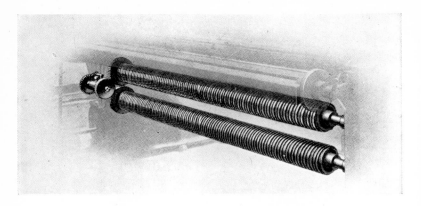

FIG. 4. Scroll Opener (Farmer Norton).

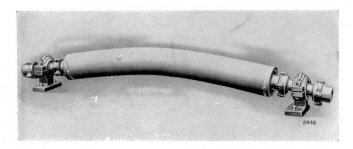

FIG. 5. Curved Rubber Expander (Mather & Platt).

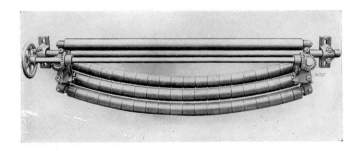

FIG. 6. Mycock Expander (Mather & Platt).

CHAPTER II
FINISHING MACHINES

STRETCHING DEVICES

Accessory stretching machines are used in both dry and wet processes. It is necessary to stretch the cloth for two reasons: first, to free it from creases as it passes through the various finishing machines, and, secondly, to produce the required width. In the first case, the warp "takes care of itself" owing to the straightening produced by feeding the cloth under slight tension; the weft, however, needs special attention which is sometimes only a pair of tension rails with a young operative to see that the fabric is as straight as possible and free from creases, particularly at the selvedges.

Fabric guiders are almost standard fittings, however, and one of the best known is the Foxwell Guider, which operates automatically. A driven rubber roller presses against a flat plate and the fabric passes between them; the inclination of the axis of the roller to the weft of the cloth draws the fabric to the side of the machine. The plates are set to the width of the cloth and two stops are adjusted to the position in which the fabric should enter the machine. Any outward displacement of either stop releases the pressure and frees the cloth, which is then drawn to the other side by the opposite roller; the cloth is thus maintained between the stops. The rollers may be operated by compressed air, electro-magnetically, or by the force from a freely rotating roller in contact with the moving cloth. The Foxwell Guider is illustrated in Fig. 1.

In the Foxwell-Dungler Guider, the rollers are held together by spring-pressure, and the frame carrying them is mounted on a swivel bearing; the angle of the roller axis varies automatically with the position of the fabric, and thus regulates the lateral travel of the selvedges.

Expanders are also employed to free the cloth from creases and to stretch it slightly in the weft direction. In the Mycock type, the expanding device consists of a number of grooved bobbins which interlock and are mounted on a curved shaft. The interlocking of the bobbins is loose enough for them to rotate as a whole when the cloth passes over them and is thus expanded. It is possible to raise alternate bars, increase the tension on the cloth, and hence the lateral stretching. The usual types have either three or five bars; the expander is illustrated in Fig. 6.

The simple curved rubber expander is formed by a rubber sleeve which covers a spring mounted on a curved bar. A later type, shown in Fig. 5, gives maximum flexibility by supporting the sleeve by bobbins with plain rims running in ball-bearings; between each spring is fitted a spiral spring and a number of distance pieces, the whole being supported on a curved bar.

The commonest type of scrimp rail is a simple grooved bar, the ridges of which diverge from the centre. Scrimp rails are also composed of oval metal discs, with fibre washers between them and threaded on to a square-section steel bar. The divergence of the discs straightens the cloth as it runs over the rail under slight tension.

Scroll opening rollers are very efficient in opening cloth, and are driven in pairs in the counter-direction to the cloth, which passes between them. A somewhat similar device in principle is formed by the conical opening rollers which are set diagonally; the cones are pivoted at a central point, and each is fitted with a brake contrivance which causes the left or right cone to be stopped should the cloth run to the side in the direction of that particular cone. This action also causes the two cones to swing sideways from the pivot and make the cloth move back to its central position.

Revolving and spreading expanders consist of floats which move laterally from the centre of the expander to its extremities; they are mounted to form a hollow cylinder with cam wheels at the ends to bring about the lateral movement as the expander rotates. The floats may be made up of grooved brass rails or of felt-covered metal for delicate fabrics.

The above methods of stretching the fabric are mainly accessory devices for attachment to other machines. The Belt Stretching Machine, however, is concerned only with stretching the fabric across its width by tightly nipping the selvedges between the rims of two large diverging pulleys and the belts running over them; the pulleys are adjusted at an angle so that they diverge towards the delivery end. The stretching pulleys are covered on their faces with rubber, and the endless belts may also be rubber-covered, but are sometimes made of canvas. As the stretching pulleys work on swivelling bosses, they may be set to give any required amount of stretch to the fabric. The belt stretcher acts in a positive manner.

The Palmer stretching device utilises pulleys placed normally on their axes instead of eccentrically, but above the pulleys are situated two endless belts which make contact with the upper semi-circumference of the pulleys, but fit diagonally across them; when the cloth passes between the endless belts and the pulleys the diverging movement of the belts stretches the fabric across its width. It may be mentioned that this device was accessory to the felt calender (see page 54), and the complete installation was known as the Palmer machine, but the belt-stretching part is rarely used now, and the term "Palmer" is sometimes applied to the felt calender alone.

Stenters are the main stretching devices in textile finishing and are commonly employed to stretch and dry the fabric at the same time, as described on page 58. Nevertheless, a short clip stenter of 10 to 30 feet in length is sometimes utilised alone to stretch fabrics, and occasionally is situated at the end of a range of drying cylinders in order to produce the required width. These small stretching machines are often fitted with weft-straightening devices, such as those described on page 64. A short stenter may also be situated in front of a set of drying cylinders, to bring the cloth to the required width and straighten the weft before passing to the drums.

WET FINISHING MACHINES

The commoner finishing processes are often divided into two broad categories, wet and dry. The following short survey deals with the machines used for these processes.

The two chief wet-finishing processes for wool fabrics are concerned with permanent set (see page 152), and with the ability of wool to contract and consolidate on milling (see page 164). Cotton fabrics, on the other hand, do not acquire permanent set, nor can they be milled; however, cotton is plastic in the wet state and may be mangled to give a smooth sheer fabric as a foundation for impregnation processes with starch and other common finishing preparations (see page 275).

MACHINES FOR PERMANENT SET

The chief machines for imparting permanent set to wool and worsted cloths are the crabbing and blowing machines; for purposes of convenience the decatising or dry-steaming machine is also included, although dry decatising is not a wet process.

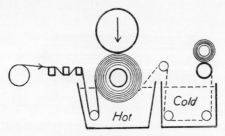

Fig. 7.—Diagram of crabbing.

In the ordinary type of crabbing machine the cloth is arranged to run at full width, free from creases and under suitable tension and pressure, on to a crabbing roller which is immersed in boiling water. The operation of crabbing is repeated twice and sometimes oftener.

to give an even effect throughout the piece and avoid "ending."
The machines generally consist of a roller on which the dry cloth is
wound, an expanding roller, and two or three troughs supplied with
hot and cold water or with steam; each trough contains a crabbing
roller with a weighting roller above. At the delivery end of the
machine is situated a device for winding the cloth from the last
crabbing roller on to a hollow steaming cylinder.

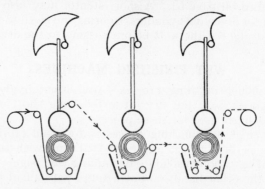

FIG. 8.—Diagram of three-bow crabbing machine.

Machines are available with one, two, or three crabbing rollers;
with the last-mentioned type, cold water is often used to complete
the setting of the fabric, with either slow or rapid cooling. As
previously indicated, the crabbing machine may have a perforated
roller for blowing (see later) incorporated with it.

A machine for winding and crabbing is also available; the fabric
passes over tension rails on to a short tenter chain which stretches
the cloth as it passes over a steam-box, and on to the boiling or
blowing roller. One of the objects of this machine is to obtain an
even tension.

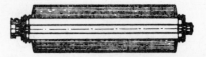

FIG. 9.—Diagram of blowing machine.

The blowing machine consists of a perforated metal cylinder on
which the fabric is wound with a cotton or canvas wrapper at each
end; the wrappers are wider than the cloth. When the wrapper has
been firmly bound at the ends with cord, steam is blown through
the perforated cylinder for several minutes, after which the fabric
is blown dry before re-winding on to a second roller and blowing
again in order to avoid "ending."

The decatising or dry-blowing machine also utilises a perforated cylinder on which the fabric is wound, but interleaved with a wrapper of cotton or linen. Both apron and fabric must be wound under even tension and free from creases, after which *dry* steam is blown through the fabric; when blown dry, the steam is stopped and the cloth cooled by drawing or blowing air through it. The fabric and

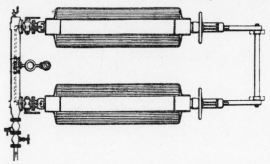

FIG. 10.—Diagram of double-blowing machine.

apron are then re-wound on to a second cylinder and the decatising repeated to obviate "ending." Perforated rollers are available with various diameters, the smaller machines being made with rollers of 6 and 9·5 inches diameter, whereas the more recent decatisers have rollers of 18 and even 24 inches diameter; the latter permit a reduction in the number of layers of cloth through which the steam must be blown and so give a more even effect from end to end.

MILLING MACHINES

The milling of wool and worsted cloths depends on heat, moisture, and intermittent pressure, as discussed on page 164.

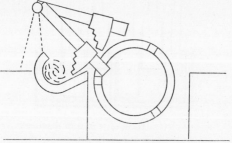

FIG. 11.—Diagram of fulling stocks
(gravity type).

Two main types of machine are available, the fulling stocks and the rotary milling machine, or fulling mill.

The function of the stocks is to reproduce the old treading action when fulling was effected by trampling the wool underfoot. The milling portion of the machine is shaped in the form of a hammer-head which may be raised by a wheel and then allowed to fall, or

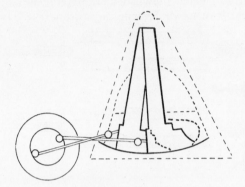

FIG. 12.—Diagram of fulling stocks
(crank-driven).

may be positively driven by cranks. The shape of the stocks is such that as the beaters fall they not only compress the fabric, but also partially turn it and so produce an even effect.

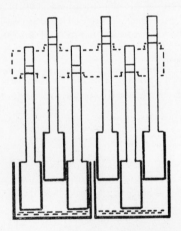

FIG. 13.—Diagram of tom-tom machine.

A special form of stocks is utilised by finishers of knit-goods and popularly known as the "Tom-Tom" machine; the beaters are lifted by cams and allowed to fall into the trough in which the goods are placed. At the same time the trough moves backwards and forwards.

With many finishers of knit-goods, this machine is also known as
the "dolly," but it must not be confused with the rope-scouring
machine commonly used with piece goods; the Tom-Tom machine
may also be used for scouring knit-goods and garments.

Rotary milling machines consist of a large trough with a curved
bottom to enable the fabric to slide easily; the cloth passes through
a mouthpiece and between squeezing rollers, the earthenware
mouthpiece guiding the cloth into the nip of the rollers which feed
it into the spout of the machine. A roller mouthpiece is popular
on many machines. Some of the fulling takes place in the spout,
the lid of which is weighted to vary the extent of the effect. On

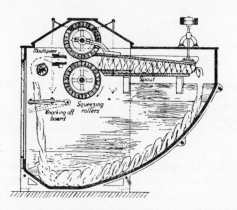

FIG. 14.—Diagram of rotary milling machine.

emerging from the spout, the cloth slides down the curved base of
the machine and through a draftboard to the mouthpiece; the draftboard separates the strands of fabric and is also connected with an
automatic stop, popularly termed the "knocking-off board." The
general method may be seen from Fig. 14, but there are many
variations.

A combined scouring and milling machine is available in which
the operations of scouring, milling, and washing may be carried out
without loss of time in moving the pieces and sewing them together.
This type of machine is illustrated in Fig. 15, from which it will be
seen that there are two top rollers running on a larger roller with
flanges; below these is a trough for catching scouring liquor and
water. These machines are very suitable for fabrics which do not
require much milling, and are often employed for tubular knit
material.

Another machine combines the fulling stocks with the milling
machine; the spout at the back of the rotary milling machine

conducts the fabric into a hopper or fulling stock, the hammers
of which have a vertical motion imparted by a double crank.

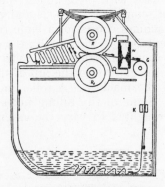

FIG. 15.—Diagram of combined scouring
and milling in milling machine.

The fabric passes over the guide roller (*G*) and between the width
rollers (*W*) to the main squeezing rollers (*R*); it then goes through
the milling box (*M*) into the liquor, after which it passes up
through the "knocking-off" board (*K*). In operation the pressure
on the fabric may be adjusted from the spring (*S*) and the weight
of the lid (*L*).

A full account of various milling machines has been given by
"B.H." (Textile Manufacturer, 1924, *50*, 384, 520; 1925, *51*, 166, 244,
315, and 351); a more recent account of some special machines is due
to Kilburn Scott (J.T.I., 1933, *24*, 247P).

MANGLES AND MANGLE FINISHES

Most piece goods made of cotton or linen are bleached in rope
form, and after the sequence of operations which make up the
bleaching process, the cloth is opened to full width by the scutcher.

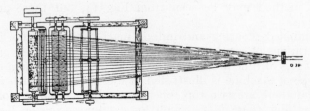

FIG. 16.—Diagram of scutcher showing beater
and scroll openers.

At this stage many types of cloth are dried before passing to the
next process, and in some cases the cloth is passed through a mangle
to remove excessive moisture before drying. The WATER MANGLE

PLATE III

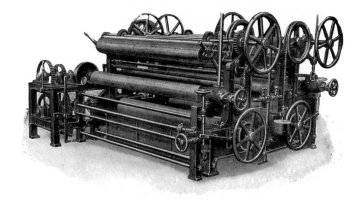

FIG. 17. Combined Crabbing and Steaming Machine.

FIG. 18. Winding and Blowing Machine.

Courtesy of Sellers & Co. (Huddersfield) Ltd.

To face page 34.

PLATE IV

FIG. 19. Fulling stocks (side action).

Courtesy of Sellers & Co. (Huddersfield) Ltd.

PLATE V

FIG. 20. Williams-Peace Combined Scouring and Milling Machine.

Courtesy of J. Mitchell & Sons.

PLATE VI

FIG. 21. Chain Mercerising Machine (Mather & Platt).

FIG. 22. Chainless Mercerising Machine (Farmer Norton).

is used for this purpose alone, but is much more frequently employed as a method of giving the cloth the necessary foundation for subsequent finishes. Cotton and linen cloths are more or less plastic in the wet state, so that heavy mangling closes and rounds the yarns and generally prepares the cloth for the filling mixtures which may be applied. Water-mangling is a form of wet calendering.

Water mangles are commonly made with from three to six bowls, but even eight-bowl mangles are in use; closed or open framing may house the mangle assembly, but open framing has the advantage of permitting each bowl to be removed without disturbing the others.

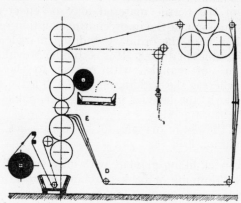

Fig. 23.—Diagram of water mangle
(Farmer Norton).

The mangles are usually equipped with tension rails and an expander at the entering side and either batching tackle or plaiting apparatus at the delivery side. Bowls may be made of cotton, rubber, sycamore, jute, or cocoa fibre and brass; with the three-bowl mangle the metal bowl is almost always the centre bowl. Better results may be obtained from five- or six-bowl mangles, and here it is possible to effect partial drying by heating the metal bowls. For instance, in a six-bowl water mangle of Sir James Farmer Norton Ltd., the arrangement of the bowls from the lowest upwards is brass, cotton, brass (steam-heated), cotton, brass (steam-heated), or cotton, cotton. The metal bowls are geared together to prevent slip and the mangle is equipped with a chasing apparatus for giving a "thready" effect to the cloth.

The cloth passes from the entering batch over the usual tension or stave rails into the water-box and then over the expander to the lowest nip of the mangle. After passing through the various nips, the cloth runs over drying cylinders, where it is partly dried, and then passes under the bottom chasing roller (D), over the scrimp rails (E), and into the second nip of the mangle. Two or three layers of cloth may thus be passed through the mangle and given the special chasing effect, after which the material may be batched or plaited ready for drying. Fig. 23 shows the general system of chasing on the water mangle, which, when followed by drying, may be the sole finishing operation for certain classes of fabric.

IMPREGNATING MANGLES are used for a variety of finishes, but the starch finish still remains the commonest.

The newer resin finishes are best applied with a heavy mangle of the type which is used in the mercerising processes for impregnating the cloth with sodium hydroxide solution; in this manner a thorough impregnation of the textile material may be effected, and at the same time the amount of the impregnating solution retained by the cloth is less than with the ordinary padding mangle and produces subsequent economies in drying. It is becoming prevalent to measure the "expression" of mangles with respect to the impregnating material, and whereas the padding mangle will leave some 100% of liquor on the cloth, the heavier mangles are capable of 60 to 75% expression for cotton goods.

Returning to the use of mangles for starch finishes, there are four methods in common use:

(a) The back-filling mangle, with only one roller or bowl.
(b) The skimming or back-starching mangle, again with one bowl.
(c) The simple two-bowl mangle for ordinary impregnation.
(d) The friction mangle, where the upper bowl runs at a higher speed.

The back-filling process is applied when the fabric has to be treated on one side only, and a number of mangles can be utilised

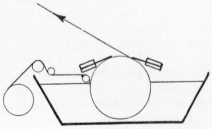

FIG. 24.—Diagram of the "Tommy Dodd"
back-filling machine.

for this purpose. One of the best known is the "Tommy Dodd," in which the cloth lies in close contact with the bowl and is carried through the filling in the trough as the bowl revolves; the upper surface of the bowl is kept clean by a doctor blade so that only one surface of the cloth is filled. A second doctor blade produces an even application of the filling material. The filling preparation is kept well mixed by a mechanically driven agitator. Back-filling mangles of this type are made by most manufacturers of textile finishing machinery, and the bowl may be made of cotton, brass, or sycamore.

For "skimming," mangles are available in which the cloth does not enter the trough, but skims the upper surface of the bowl, which revolves in the starch trough and picks up the filling which it applies

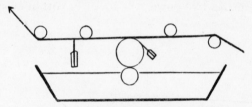

Fig. 25.—Diagram of the "Betty Dodd" back-filling machine.

to the cloth, any excess being removed by a doctor blade, which sometimes has a traversing movement to ensure an even coating. Another doctor blade regulates the thickness of the filling applied to the roller. This type of machine is also known as the "Betty Dodd."

Two-bowl mangles are available for ordinary starching, where the direct-nip feed can be used in which the cloth passes directly between the two rollers, the lower of which revolves in the starch trough and picks up the filling which it applies to the cloth; a similar mangle may be used for slop-padding, where the cloth is fed into the filling in the trough before it goes through the nip of the mangle.

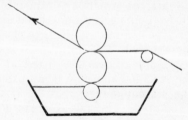

Fig. 26.—Diagram of friction starching mangle with direct-nip feed.

Some cloths necessitate a more compact finish than may be obtained with the usual starching methods, and in these cases it is possible to force the starch into the cloth with the aid of a friction mangle. This is a two-bowl machine in which the large bottom bowl is made of cotton or sycamore and the smaller upper bowl, which runs at a higher speed, is made of brass; spare friction wheels are generally available to give different degrees of friction. Owing to the lower surface speed of the lower bowl, a friction or rubbing effect is set up in addition to the pressure exerted by the mangle, with the result that a very complete filling of the interstices takes place, imparting a full and solid appearance to the cloth.

In view of the various methods of applying the starch fillings, Universal Mangles have been designed by many of the machinery manufacturers and can be used for various finishes. A common type of design comprises two bowls, the lower of cotton or sycamore and

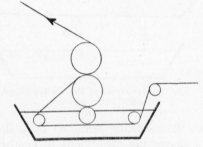

FIG. 27.—Diagram of starching mangle
with simple impregnation.

the upper of brass, complete with cleaning doctor. When both bowls are utilised, the cloth may be given an ordinary starch finish or a friction finish, but when the upper bowl is raised it is possible to use the mangle for back-filling. The direction of the lower bowl may be reversed and a doctor brought into operation.

A combined ordinary and back-starching mangle is made by Messrs. Mather & Platt, in which an adjustable brass starching roller is used; when back-filling is required the upper bowl is raised and the brass roller acts as a feeding roller to the lower bowl, which actually applies the starch to the cloth, any excess being removed by a doctor knife. Guide rollers are fitted at the entering and delivery ends of the machine and may be adjusted so that the bind of the cloth on the starching bowl may be regulated to suit the amount of starch required. The excess of starch is removed by a doctor, and a second doctor knife cleans the starching bowl.

A combined starching and filling mangle is also made by the same manufacturers, and its special feature is the arrangement of the squeezing rollers which run below the level of the filling mixture in the trough. These squeezing rollers are arranged in horizontal fashion, and over them is the mangle system; one of the squeezing rollers is made of brass and the other two of rubber, whereas the mangle consists of the usual brass and wood combination, the brass bowl being in the lower position.

The standard three-bowl mangle may also be used for the application of starch and other finishes; the popular arrangement is for the brass bowl to be the driving bowl which is supported between

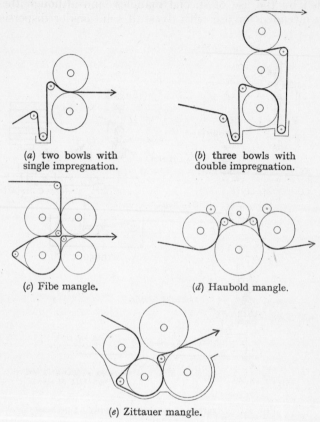

(a) two bowls with single impregnation.

(b) three bowls with double impregnation.

(c) Fibe mangle.

(d) Haubold mangle.

(e) Zittauer mangle.

FIG. 28.—Diagrams of mangling methods.

two cotton, sycamore, or rubber bowls. In addition to the more obvious methods of impregnating the cloth on these mangles, some very ingenious systems have been devised.

In general, the cotton and sycamore bowls are only used on mangles for applying starch and other older types of filling; for many of the newer finishes it is customary and preferable to use the brass and rubber combination. The older mangle is hardly a precision instrument, but some of the newer finishes necessitate a very even and regular impregnation which cannot be given with wood or cotton bowls. With the necessity for careful control of impregnation, it is becoming common to measure the "expression" of a mangle, i.e. the amount of water it leaves in the cloth after impregnation, as previously mentioned.

Within recent years, the impregnation methods have been extended by the use of special mangles, and although these were mainly intended for use with dyestuff solutions or dispersions, yet

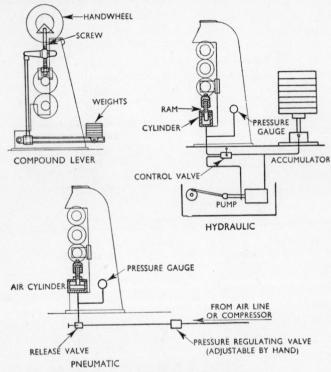

FIG. 29.—Diagram of methods of applying pressure to mangle bowls.

they may sometimes prove of value for impregnating special fabrics with the newer finishing agents. The Fibe machine was designed by Fischer of Czechoslovakia and constructed by Benninger (it is called the Convex machine in the U.S.A.). The liquor is encased by four rollers arranged in two pairs, and air is excluded; the de-aerated cloth receives four squeezings in passing through the machine. Another interesting development also uses four rollers, three of which are arranged horizontally whilst the fourth is situated over the centre bowl to form two troughs through which the cloth is passed.

It may be remarked that mangles with the bowls arranged side by side horizontally instead of vertically are commonly used with knit goods; the bowls form their own trough, the escape of the liquor being prevented by end-plates.

Heavier mangles are used for the mercerising process, and also for some of the newer resin finishes, as previously mentioned. Opinion is somewhat divided on the question of the hydraulic pressure *versus* the system of weights and compound levers as usually found on the lighter mangles; hydraulic mangles seem to give a better and more even expression, and it is also possible to repeat given pressures more easily. On the other hand, the lever system is less complicated and there is no danger of leaking valves and pumps.

Most of the heavy mangles have three bowls, although two-bowl mangles are also found; the advantage of the three-bowl mangle lies in the better impregnation and the possibility of multiple impregnation with one machine—some ingenious methods of arranging the cloth are shown in Fig. 28.

In the three-bowl mangle of Messrs. Mather & Platt, two iron bowls are positively driven and the rubber bowl floats between them and is driven by frictional contact, thus prolonging its life. Jacketed troughs are available to maintain the impregnating solution at the required temperature, and inside the trough may be placed a special suction pipe with a slot to draw the liquor through the fabric passing over it and so ensure a most thorough impregnation. Mercerising mangles are also made by Farmer Norton. The high pressure exerted by these mangles varies from 10 to 25 tons, and a popular length of the bowl is 65 inches.

FINISHING RANGES

With the simple starched or filled cloths, the drying process is carried out on the set of cylinders, arranged in horizontal or vertical fashion, forming the well-known drying machine. Marking of the filled back or peeling of the starch may be obviated by lapping the first few cylinders with thin cloth and threading the material to be dried into the machine in such a manner that the back of the material does not come in contact with the cylinders until sufficiently dry to prevent marking. An alternative method is to arrange for a number of the cylinders to be water-cooled in such a manner that the filled side of the cloth only comes into contact with the cooled cylinders.

A common arrangement is partially to dry the cloth on a cylinder of large diameter, the surface of the cylinder making contact with the unfilled side of the cloth only. A diameter of 7 feet is common for this type of cylinder, which is followed by 12 or 14 cylinders of the normal size, some of these being water-cooled if necessary. Fig. 30 shows a skimming range of Farmer Norton where the drying is effected by one large cylinder of 10 feet 6 inches in diameter, followed by nine smaller cylinders of 22-inch diameter.

It is possible to arrange a set of drying drums in one tier and to have a lower set of wooden winces or drums so that only one surface of the cloth comes into contact with the hot surface; alternatively, guide rollers may be provided, even on a normal set of drums, so

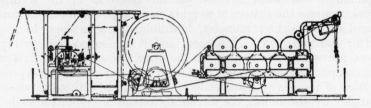

FIG. 30.—Starching and drying range (Farmer Norton).

that only the unstarched side of the cloth comes into contact with the heated cylinders.

Cloth which has been starched on both sides is usually dried on a stenter, or is sometimes partially dried on the stenter and then passed over drying cylinders to complete the process.

Fig. 31 shows a starching, stentering, and drying range.

It is usual to have the mangle and drying apparatus coupled together to form a finishing range in many types of processing, with obvious advantages in running the material through the plant. The use of universal mangles coupled with stenters provides a very flexible arrangement.

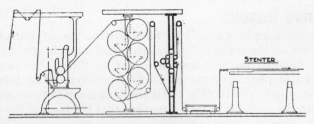

FIG. 31.—Impregnating and drying range (Mather & Platt), with weft straightening device.

Ranges for the application of softeners to the cloth comprise mangle and stenter or drying cylinders, the former being preferable as it gives a softer handle to the goods and finishes them to the correct width. Resin finishes may be applied on a range consisting of mangle, stenter, or drying apparatus, and the final heating device for setting the resin or completing the polymerisation if necessary.

The mercerising process, as outlined on page III, is generally carried out on a range which consists of the mangle and the washing and stretching apparatus, which may comprise a special type of stenter or an arrangement of curved expander rollers.

The most popular type of mercerising range comprises a mangle for impregnating the fabric with caustic soda and a clip stenter for washing and stretching the cloth. Many ranges include two mangles with a set of iron drums between them; these drums are driven by the passage of the cloth and are mounted on ball-bearings. In this manner it is possible to allow a period of time in which penetration into the cloth takes place, and it is sometimes so arranged that a difference in speed between the mangles imparts warp tension and increases the lustre of the fabric. A second function of these drums is to prevent the selvedges turning or rolling during the action of the alkali.

The stenter must be of a robust type as it pulls the shrinking cloth to its original width during the removal of the alkali against the force of the contracting fabric; methods of washing on the counter-current principle enable moderately short stenters to be used, but these vary from 50 to 75 feet in length. The first 20 feet or so is the length during which the fabric is stretched to width, and then washed by a system of sprays or weirs; a special dipping frame, made by Zittau, is equipped with obliquely placed chain-rails, in such a manner that the cloth runs through a long tank filled with recovered wash-water. Washing frames with spurt-pipes are commonly employed, with the pipes above the cloth and suction boxes below; the main part of the wash-liquors pass through the fabric to be collected in troughs and used on the counter-current system. Fresh water is thus sprayed at the delivery end of the stenter and becomes progressively stronger in alkali as it is collected and again sprayed nearer the entering end.

The standard washing system of Mather & Platt operates through a number of weirs, so designed that the wash-liquors flow on to the fabric in an unbroken stream, the width of which corresponds to that of the fabric; the system of weirs, suction boxes, circulation and vacuum pumps, together with piping and troughs, effects considerable economy in the consumption of water and facilitates the recovery of alkali at a reasonably high concentration. The troughs under the stenters are sometimes built of concrete, but cast iron is preferable.

Some mercerising ranges include a recuperator, whose function is to remove the residual alkali from the fabric after it has left the stenter. This machine consists of a cast-iron chamber containing two rows of rollers, the top row being driven. Wash-water is fed into the chamber at the delivery end and forms a water-seal; there is another seal at the entrance, and in this way it is possible to exclude all air from the chamber by the admission of low-pressure steam, which plays on to the fabric and removes the residual alkali in a remarkably efficient manner by a type of steam-washing. The condensed liquor is removed by the counter-current wash-water flowing through the bottom of the chamber, and this liquor forms the supply for the washing apparatus on the previous section of the mercerising range.

Chainless mercerising ranges are also used to some extent, and in these, as the name implies, there is no stenter frame. The stretching and washing device consists of a series of curved rollers; the warp tension and the curvature of the rollers are responsible for increasing the width of the fabric. In the Farmer Nórton system, the warp tension is controlled by a hydraulic compensator, and in the trough of curved expanders these are so constructed that the bobbins at the extremities have a larger diameter than those in the middle; consequently there is no distortion of the weft as the cloth moves forward. The first set of expanders is situated in front of the washing compartment and each expander has a covering of rubber; the expanders in the washing compartment are made of cast iron. The general arrangement is to have six or eight dry expanders, followed by nine iron expanders running under water in the washing compartment which is divided into five different parts arranged for the counter-current system.

A chainless padless machine has aroused some interest in Germany and Switzerland; the fabric is maintained under tension by a series of rollers throughout the whole of the impregnating and washing processes. It is of some interest to note that in any of the chainless developments it is possible to mercerise two and even three fabrics superimposed.

An account of mercerising machines of various types has been given by Marsh (Mercerising, Chapman & Hall, London, 1941).

COMPENSATORS

Where the fabric is passed over two machines running in tandem, it is necessary to ensure that the speed of the fabric is the same on the two machines. The simplest synchronising device is a "compensator" in the form of a rising and falling counterbalanced roller which lies in a loop of the fabric keeping it at constant tension; hand regulation of the machines is often sufficient to maintain the position of this roller within the required limits.

A more modern arrangement for high-speed machines enables the compensator to regulate the speed by means of its travel. This may be achieved in two ways: first, by coupling the compensator shaft to a face-plate rheostat for controlling the motor speed; or, secondly, by a delicately balanced roller coupled to a contact switch which operates the control gear of a small pilot-motor which changes the speed of the machine.

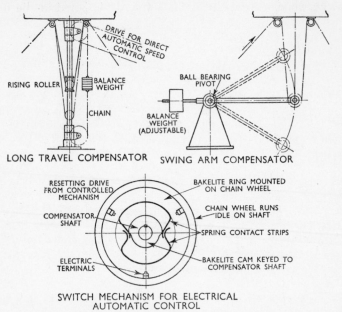

LONG TRAVEL COMPENSATOR   SWING ARM COMPENSATOR

SWITCH MECHANISM FOR ELECTRICAL AUTOMATIC CONTROL

Fig. 32.—Diagrams of compensator arrangements.

Two chief types of compensator are those in which the roller rises or falls vertically on its long supporting columns, and the alternative swinging arm support in which the arms carrying the roller are mounted on a ball-bearing pivot.

WASHING MACHINES

The scouring machines for woollen and worsted fabrics may also be utilised for washing; in their simplest form they may be represented by the "dolly," which is a large trough, whose section is quadrant-shaped, above which is placed a pair of rollers to squeeze the fabric as it passes round and round in an endless band. Below the rollers is often situated a smaller trough with its own outlet, so that it may either discharge separately or into the main trough. Accessory devices, such as guide-rails, are part of the machine; it is possible to release the top roller and wash the fabric without pressure. Open-width washing is conducted on a different machine, but on a similar basis.

Rope-washing machines are also available for cotton and linen cloths; they are of two main types in which the rope may be tight as it passes through a shallow box, or the rope may be slack and pass through a deep trough. In both cases, the machine has a pair of heavy wooden bowls into which the fabric is fed in the form of

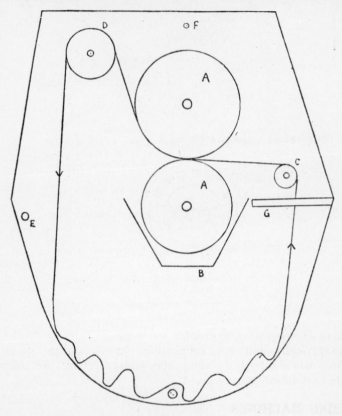

FIG. 33.—Diagram of "dolly" machine for scouring and washing in rope-form.

A indicates the squeeze-rollers, *B* the trough or sud-box, *C* and *D* the guide-rollers, *E* and *F* the spurt-pipes, and *G* the draft-board.

two ropes, one at each end; guide rollers cause the cloth to pass through the trough and a peg-rail prevents entanglement. The two ropes leave the centre of the machine together, and sometimes an auxiliary roller situated above the two bowls gives an additional squeeze to the cloth on leaving. It is also possible to arrange the run of the fabric with a single piece running through from one side of the machine to the other, spirally. Automatic stop motions are usually provided should the ropes foul one another, and many of these machines have a sliding wince to adjust the tension on the fabric.

One of the commonest types of open-width washing machines merely consists of a series of compartments, each of which is fitted

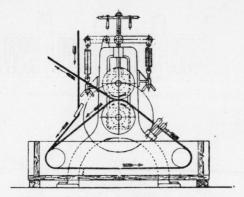

Fig. 34.—Diagram of rope-washing machine (Mather & Platt).

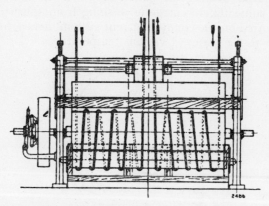

Fig. 35.—Diagram of rope-washing machine (Mather & Platt).

with a squeezing device and a series of guide rollers. If necessary, spurt-pipes may be fitted to the nips or squeeze-rollers. In a special machine made by Mather & Platt, beaters are placed at the surface of the liquor, and between, but not touching the vertical laps of cloth; the liquor is thrown energetically on both sides of the fabric and exerts a thorough cleansing action.

A ripple washing machine, made by Mather & Platt, is very suitable for delicate fabrics. The cloth slides down an inclined plane

of glass on to a travelling apron of phosphor-bronze wire gauze
which moves more slowly than the speed at which the cloth is
delivered; this produces small folds or ripples of fabric on the

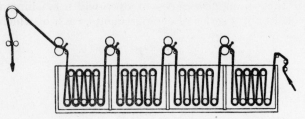

FIG. 36.—Diagram of full-width washing machine.

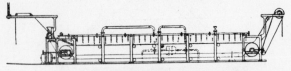

FIG. 37.—Diagram of ripple washing machine
(Mather & Platt).

travelling apron. During the period in which the fabric is on the
apron, it is subjected to energetic washing from spurt-pipes which
may be operated on the counter-current system; hence, for example,
it is possible to use water at various temperatures.

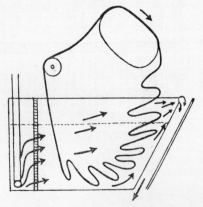

FIG. 38.—Diagram of use of wince machine
for washing by overflow.

The wince or winch machine is very versatile in its uses. It
generally consists of a driven wince extending across the full width
of a vat equipped with a perforated partition for steam-pipes; the
vat may be rectangular, V-shaped, or have a section in the form of

a quadrant enabling the fabric to slide. The wince itself may be circular or elliptical in shape, and the latter is often preferred on account of the plaiting motion. When used for full-width working, the machine may be fitted with a guide roller or bar at the front, and this may be replaced with a peg-rail for treating cloths in rope form. Some wince machines are totally enclosed.

DRYING TEXTILE FABRICS

The drying of textile fabrics usually takes place in two stages: (*a*) the mechanical removal of excess water, and (*b*) drying by evaporation.

The excess of water may be removed by mangling under more or less heavy pressure, or by hydroextraction, or by suction.

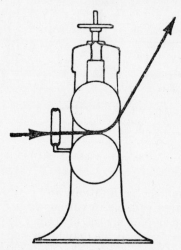

Fig. 39.—Diagram of mangle for cloth in rope-form.

Where the fabric is in rope form, a small two-bowl mangle or squeezer is commonly used. This is about 15 to 18 inches in width and of robust construction; two ropes of cloth generally pass through the nip of the machine before going to the scutcher, which is an apparatus for opening the cloth before drying. The top bowl of the mangle may be made of wood, compressed cotton, compressed coco-nut fibre, or of rubber; the bottom bowl, which is driven, is usually made of brass. Pressure may be applied by compound levers and weights or by springs.

Where the fabric is in open width, larger mangles are used, and an account of these is given on page 34. It is obviously important that the open-width fabric should be free from creases or the cloth may be marked, if not cut, by the heavy pressure exerted; hence expanders are employed to obviate this possibility.

Hydroextraction may be carried out in the common basket form of centrifuge which consists essentially of a perforated cage of copper or galvanised iron mounted on a central spindle and contained in a steel casing. The wet fabric is placed in the cage, which is then caused to rotate at a high speed, developing centrifugal pressure which forces the cloth to the inner wall of the cage; the excess of

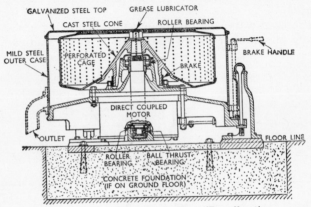

FIG. 40.—Diagram of centrifuge (Broadbent).

water passes through the perforations and is drained away. Centrifuges of this type are available in various sizes from 36 to 72 inches in diameter and developing speeds of from 1,000 to 600 revolutions per minute respectively; the drive may be by belt, friction, or directly by electric motor. Depending on the size of the machine and the type of fabric, the centrifugal action may require from 2 to 10 minutes to remove the excess of water; about 50 to 60% of water remains in the goods, estimated on the weight of the dry material.

With some goods, particularly smooth fabrics and rayons, there is a danger of the perforations of the cage marking the outer layers of the fabric where they are forced against the walls by centrifugal force; this may be obviated to some extent by lining the inside with a loose wrapper of cheap cotton cloth.

Centrifugal machines are also available where the cloth is wound at full width on a perforated cylinder which is rotated at high speeds.

The above machines extract water from the cloth in a discontinuous manner, but continuous extractors may be used where the fabric is treated at full width and the water removed by a vacuum pump. These machines consist fundamentally of a cylinder with a narrow slot across the top, and the cloth passes over the slot, water being sucked out of it by a vacuum pump which is connected with the cylinder. The length of the slot is adjusted according to the width of the cloth, and water is extracted very evenly with the minimum of disturbance to the face of the cloth. The machine is satisfactory for heavy fabrics, but with lighter fabrics it is advisable to place a heavy felt over the fabric as it passes the slot, and so

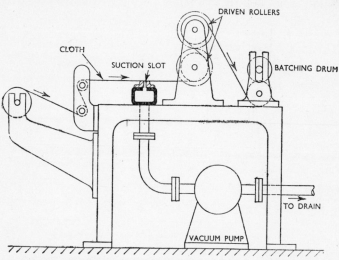

FIG. 41.—Diagram of machine for hydroextraction by suction (Dalglish).

create a better vacuum. The suction extractor is very suitable for fabrics which have to be manipulated at full width, but may not be subjected to the tension and pressure of a mangle.

When the three mechanical methods of removing excess water are compared, it is found that the mangle is the cheapest, and the suction extractor the most expensive. The centrifuge is useful on account of its versatility, but the output is low.

It is generally advisable to remove as much water as possible by mechanical means, not only on account of cost, but also because, as these processes reach their limit of efficiency, the residual water is evenly distributed, and this is a great aid to the subsequent drying operations.

DRYING

The two general methods of drying textiles are by constant temperatures, as in cylinder drying, or by hot-air drying, in which the heat content of the air in the immediate vicinity remains constant but the temperature falls as moisture is absorbed, leaving the fabric at a constant temperature as long as water is actually present.

The three available methods of heat transfer are by conduction, convection, and radiation. Conduction is commonly used in the cylinder-drying machines, or "cans," where the fabric is heated by direct contact with a metallic surface. The most frequent method of drying textiles, however, is by convection currents as employed in the numerous hot-air machines. Radiation methods have been

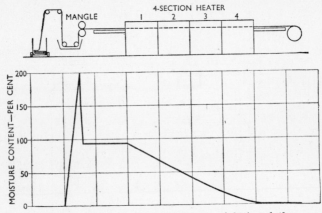

FIG. 42.—Diagram of typical process of drying cloth.

almost abandoned except for a few special purposes; recent developments in the U.S.A. indicate an interest in infra-red radiations for drying. (Many stenters of the old-fashioned type are still in useful existence and some of them rely on radiation from steam-pipes; these are often encountered in wool-finishing plants.)

CYLINDERS

The commonest form of drying machine is the set of steam-heated revolving cylinders or drums around which the cloth passes, giving up its moisture as it moves forward. Steam, under pressure of 5 to 40 lb. per square inch, is passed into the cylinders through the hollow framework of the machine, a special bearing known as a doll-head, and the end nozzle of the cylinder. As the water is evaporated from the wet cloth, the steam gives up its latent heat, and water condenses inside the cylinder and is removed by an ingenious system of collectors or "buckets," which deliver the condensed water to the opposite nozzle, where it drains through the hollow framework on the water side of the machine, complete with steam-traps and other devices.

The cylinders are usually made of copper, tinned copper, or tinned iron to suit various requirements, but for certain purposes stainless-steel cylinders may be preferred. The set of drums may be arranged vertically, horizontally, or in a combined vertical and horizontal unit comprising from 6 to 30 or more cylinders; the horizontal arrangement is generally in two tiers.

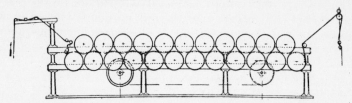

Fig. 43.—Horizontal range of drying cylinders (Mather & Platt).

Although the use of cans is the cheapest method of drying cloth on a large scale, it has certain disadvantages; there is no control of width and the fabric is stretched lengthwise; further, the firm contact with the metallic surface is apt to impart a harsh papery finish which is not generally acceptable. It is possible, however, to effect a partial drying on cylinders and then complete the process on a

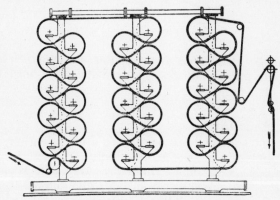

Fig. 44.—Vertical range of drying cylinders (Mather & Platt).

stenter, with control of width and the production of a softer finish; alternatively, the cloth may be brought to width on a short stenter (see page 58) and then dried on cylinders.

Electrically-heated cylinders were introduced in 1928, and comprise a stationary inner cylinder, mounted on a hollow shaft and carrying robust heating elements, and a thin outer shell mounted on ball-bearings and moving freely around the stationary cylinder.

A special method of cylinder drying enables the drum to be used as a valuable drying and finishing machine; this is seen in the blanket-drying machine or felt calender, sometimes called the Palmer machine. The main cylinder is generally 6 to 8 feet in diameter, but larger types are available; around the greater part of the cylinder passes an endless felt blanket. The fabric is fed between the blanket and the cylinder, and is kept against its hot surface by the pressure of the blanket. In this manner there is no undue tension or warp extension; indeed, a modification of this machine brings about a contraction warp-way, as described on page 248.

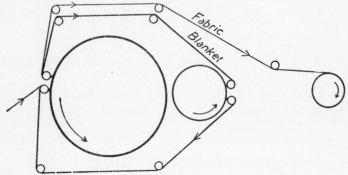

FIG. 45.—Diagram of blanket-drying machine or Palmer.

The Palmer is also known as the blanket-finishing machine, for in addition to drying the fabric, it gives an attractive finish characterised by a soft handle and a smooth lustrous surface.

HOT AIR MACHINES

Many machines have been devised to utilise a current of hot air to absorb and remove water from textile fabrics; probably the earliest attempts were some form of the old hanging-room in which the wet fabric was suspended from poles and allowed to dry in the warm air. Air movements were gradually increased with improved output, and the air-stream was heated by passing over steam-heated metallic surfaces on account of the convenience and cheapness of steam as a source of heat.

Increased output was obtained in the hot-flue type of drier built of panels and framework to form a heated enclosure through which the cloth was drawn over a series of rollers at the top and bottom of the machine. Many of the top rollers are driven and the bottom rollers act as guide rollers; the rollers are placed only short distances apart to prevent creasing of the cloth, including turning of the selvedges. A slipping clutch on the driven rollers allows for adjustment of the fabric throughout its passage. In the later types of hot-flue driers, the drying is effected in two stages: first, by heat radiated from steam-chests between the laps of cloth and also by hot air; and secondly, by a final stage of hot air supplied by fan and multitubular heater, and discharged through vents between the laps of the supported fabric.

Hanging driers were later developed consisting of an insulated metal casing inside which a series of poles moved forward slowly on a pair of conveyor chains; the wet cloth was fed into the entering end by rollers with a device causing the fabric to fall over the moving

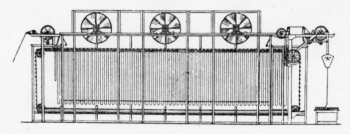

FIG. 46.—The Hurricane Loop Drier.

poles in loops, the length of which could be varied. Hot air was circulated through the casing of the machine, either vertically or horizontally, but at comparatively low velocity to avoid disarrangement of the loops. This type of Festoon Drier has been improved in many respects; some of the later types adopt a counter-flow system of air-circulation whereby the wet cloth at the entry encounters the hottest air, but the dry fabric near the exit meets cooler air.

The heating coils or gilled tubes are generally separated from the chamber itself by open partitions, to permit re-circulation; a small amount of moisture-laden air is continually withdrawn and a corresponding amount of fresh air admitted. These machines were highly developed in the U.S.A. in the form of Proctor driers and Hurricane driers.

Given some support for the fabric, it is possible to use higher air velocities and obtain a greater output; numerous machines of the creeper type are available, and a typical model utilises several layers of travelling lattice or netting on which the cloth would rest while a transverse air-stream blows on it. The well-known brattice driers illustrate this principle, but the support for the fabric is insufficient to allow a high air velocity to be used.

The Multipass Airlay Drier, however, ensures a high output and gentle manipulation. The fabric rests on the flat cork faces of poles which are carried up and down, almost vertically, by a pair of conveyor chains. Fine jets of warm air are blown from slots on to one side of the cloth and thus hold it against the cork faces as well

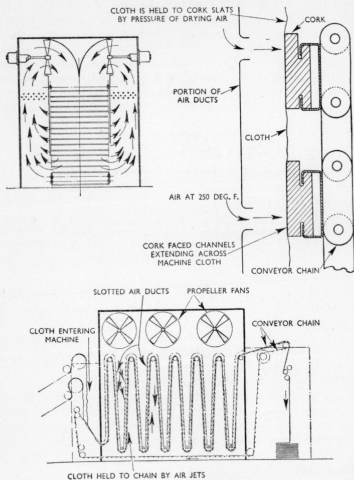

FIG. 47.—Diagrams of Air-lay Drier.

is drying it. In this manner, a great proportion of the hot air comes into intimate contact with the fabric and ensures a more efficient heat transfer.

The Buti or Weisbach drier is somewhat similar in principle. The machine consists essentially of an outer casing in which is situated a drum of large diameter and covered by a blanket or felt supported on a perforated steel shell. The cloth to be dried is fed into the casing and falls against the blanket on the drum; hot air is blown into the casing and extracted from the inside of the revolving drum after passing through the cloth and the blanket. The air pressure

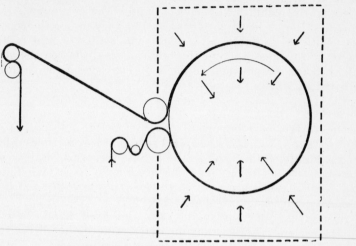

FIG. 48.—Diagram of Buti drying machine.

keeps the fabric against the blanket which supports it against any practicable air-pressure; at the same time natural shrinkage takes place, particularly if the fabric is entered at a greater speed than

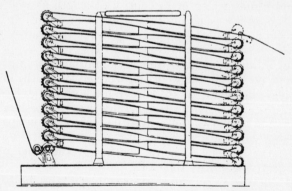

FIG. 49.—The Cell Drier (S. Walker & Sons).

that of the drum itself. These machines, like the Airlay drier, give excellent results in the drying and finishing of light and delicate fabrics, particularly crêpes, as it is possible to bring about warp-shrinkage during drying.

Mention may be made of the Cell drier which was put forward as an alternative to cylinders. This type of drying machine utilises radiation to a large extent. A series of steam-heated cells of a special alloy are arranged one above the other in two tiers, both of which are slightly inclined to the horizontal. The rectangular cells are 5 inches deep, 4 feet 6 inches wide, and vary in length according to the width of the fabric for drying. The source of heat is steam at 25 to 30 lb. pressure, and the fabric passes between the cells at a slight distance from their surfaces; the passage of the cloth may be assisted by rollers.

Stenters

One of the most important pieces of textile finishing machinery is the stenter, which is also called tenter; it is sometimes referred to as the stenter-frame, and in the U.S.A. the word "frame" alone is used. The chief function of the machine is to stretch the fabric, and some stenters are devoted to this purpose alone, but the great majority combine stretching and drying.

The oldest form of stenter was the fixed hand-frame, which comprised two parallel rails on which were mounted rows of pins to hold the cloth; when the fabric had been impaled on the pins by hand the rails were caused to move apart by cross-rails, so that the cloth dried in the stretched state, free from creases, and, further, some control over the final dimensions was realised. This system is still used for lace and net fabrics where widths of 400 inches may be encountered; cloths such as the crêpe georgette are also often dried on the hand-frame, which gives control of length as well as width. The hand-frames are generally placed in warm rooms, and a gentle current of air is provided by large flaps over the frames; narrower hand-frames are sometimes arranged in tiers.

The first continuous stenters were also multilayer drying machines, and this type persists in the wool and worsted trade, the first tentering machine being made in 1854 by Whiteley of Huddersfield; the single layer or Scotch stenter is generally used for cotton, silk, and rayon, although some two-tier or return stenters are in operation for silk and rayon fabrics.

Steam-heating in one form or another is the chief method of heating the air which dries the cloth, although a carriage of glowing charcoal is still used in certain works which specialise in the finishing of velvets, particularly on hand-frames; partial drying with gas-burners is used on some stenters for silk and rayon.

Most continuous stenters are limited to about 70 inches in width, but special types are available for goods up to 100 inches wide.

The pin-rails of the hand-frame are replaced by moving pin-chains in suitable guides; originally the fabric was fed into the machine by hand, the first few yards of rails diverging until the required width was obtained, after which the chains run parallel.

An alternative to the pin stenter is the clip machine, where the selvedges of the cloth are gripped by spring clips; the invention of an automatic or self-feeding clip gave a great impetus to the growth of automatic clip stenters which are so widely used for cotton and linen fabrics. This type of machine has a higher speed than the pin stenter, and is generally made with flat chain-rails, the chains being

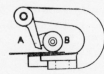 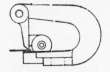 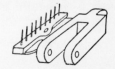

FIG. 50.—Diagram of automatic clip (Mather and Platt). (*A* is the tongue and *B* the pawl.)

FIG. 51.—Diagram of a link in the pin-chain.

returned in a horizontal plane. The chain-rails which carry the chain of clips are adjusted to width by screws, which are operated together by a shaft which passes along the stenter, but the two sections of rail at the entering end are separately adjustable, being set narrower at the entry, but diverging as they join the longer rails where the fabric is brought to its full width.

Some clip stenters of the single layer type are arranged as "jigging" stenters, that is, the cross-rails are caused to oscillate about their vertical centre support and carry the chain-rail with them; this gives the cloth a diagonal or "to-and-fro" movement which helps to

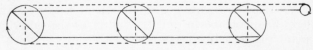

FIG. 52.—Diagram of oscillating motion for jigging.

straighten weft threads, break any temporary adhesions at the intersections of warp and weft, and so produce a softer effect sometimes known as the elastic finish. The jigging motion is generally provided by a crank disc and connecting rod; the stroke is often variable up to 24 inches and the speed up to 30 strokes per minute.

Automatic clip stenters for cotton goods may vary in length from 60 to 120 feet; a popular type is 90 feet long, and may give an output of 140 yards per minute with certain fabrics.

The clip stenter, however, is not suitable for many of the finer qualities of silk and rayon, so that there has been a return to the pin stenter with its modern improvements, such as the overfeed device for reducing potential warp shrinkage (see page 244).

The chains of the pin stenter return in a vertical plane, and this lends itself to a lighter construction and simpler driving mechanism. The adjustment of width is similar to that of the clip stenter, but some modern machines have a special tapering main-frame to allow for weft shrinkage during drying.

Wool tenters are generally of the multilayer type, on account of the greater amount of heat necessary for drying the thicker material. A modern tenter may comprise as many as ten layers, the fabric being fed into the top layer of the machine up an incline; the hottest air is generally in the top layers and the temperature gradually decreases towards the bottom layer, so that the cloth may be

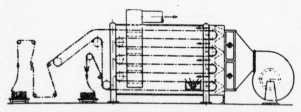

FIG. 53.—Diagram of Multilayer stenter.

conditioned by the incoming fresh air. The multilayer tenters may hold from 55 to 150 yards of fabric at one time.

All modern stenters have some automatic method of feeding the fabric to the pins or clips, and these methods fall into two main types: first, by moving the cloth selvedge in line with the rails; or, secondly, by moving the rails to follow the position of the selvedges. The first method is commonly used with clip stenters where no high degree of accuracy is essential; a small pair of rollers is situated at each side of the machine to pull the fabric to the sides, and at a certain point the selvedge meets a feeler-mechanism which releases the grip of the rollers. Devices of this type may be operated mechanically (Durrant), electrically (Wood), or by compressed air (Foxwell). Most pin stenters utilise rail-guiding rather than cloth-guiding; a popular type employs a reversible electric motor on each rail, driving a screw through reduction gearing. A light cloth-feeler operates between two electric contacts which in turn close the coil circuit of one or other of a pair of reversing contactor switches controlling the motor. The inertia of the moving parts demands a lightness which is accompanied by a lack of robustness; hence a reciprocating rail-guider has been developed where the rail is actuated by a piston in a cylinder, the motive power being compressed air or a liquid. The all-pneumatic type has been developed by Mather & Platt, and the combined pneumatic and hydraulic type by John Dalglish and Sons.

Practically all modern stenters remove the moisture from the fabric by hot air. Multilayer machines originally relied on heat from steam coils which were placed between the tiers or layers of fabric, with the cloth passing over and under. The next step was to circulate the air and in many types, although the fabric still travels around the steam-pipes, the drying chamber is divided into compartments by partial floors which are fitted with fans. Air is circulated from the two bottom layers into the next two, and distributed warp-way;

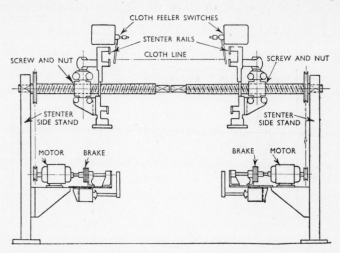

Fig. 54.—Diagram of rail-guider with two motors.

in turn, the next fan and distributing boxes convey the hot air to succeeding layers.

With single-layer stenters, the standard method of heating for many years was by streams of hot air directed on to the cloth by branches or "puffer-pipes," which projected from a trunking below and often above the frame. The necessary hot air was produced by a multitubular heater supplied with low-pressure steam, and one blowing fan; an alternative method was to use one or more battery-type heaters supplied with high-pressure steam, each with its own blowing fan. On leaving the heater or heaters, the air is distributed by sheet-iron trunking and directed on to the fabric by swivel nozzles. Many pin stenters relied on convection and radiation from steam-pipes under the fabric. Now, as the rate of removal of the moisture from the fabric increases with the velocity of the air-stream, attempts were made to make air-streams impinge on and along the surface of the fabric from both sides, but at high velocity the old puffer-pipe gave an unbalanced effect. Further, the return of the pin stenter made it essential to balance the high-velocity air-streams. The Krantz and Jahr cross-current systems of air-heating rely on the circulation of air through a heater, across the fabric, both above and below, at right angles to the length of the stenter, and back to the fans. The air velocity at the surface of the cloth is increased by baffles, and the whole machine is enclosed by insulated panels.

The actual heating of the air is done by gilled-tube radiators, with steam in the tubes; air is blown over the tubes by a fan or by several fans, and it is possible to have the stenter chamber served by

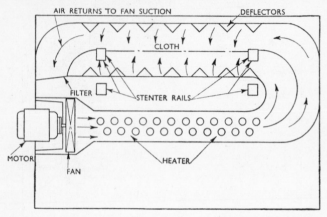

FIG. 55.—Krantz system of air-circulation.

several fans blowing air at different temperatures, usually highest at the entering end.

One of the difficulties in drying textile fabrics by heated air is that the cloth becomes surrounded by a sheath of warm but stagnant air which is apt to form a barrier to the absorption of more heat. This layer may be dissipated by the method developed by Spooner, in which the hot air is subdivided into thin streams by nozzles of a truncated venturi type which convert the static pressure into velocity; the air-streams impinging on the cloth create sufficient turbulence to destroy the boundary layer and permit warm, dry air to replace it. The air is caused to impinge transversely on the fabric at high velocity by pressure chambers situated above and below the cloth with the nozzles or slits stretching across the whole width. An interesting feature of the high evaporative effect, is that the fabric itself is kept cool by the evaporation of the water with a beneficial action on handle and finish. This point is not always understood, and it may perhaps be emphasised that when cloths are wet, the evaporation of water depends more on the difference between dry- and wet-bulb temperatures than on the actual temperature; the wet-bulb reading gives the temperature of the wet cloth. Now the drying process does not proceed at a uniform rate, for the first 75% of the moisture may be removed in 20 to 25% of the total drying time, but when the moisture content falls to the neighbourhood of 30%, the temperature of the fabric will rise and approach the dry-bulb temperature of the surrounding air. At this stage, the temperature must be lowered to a point where there is no danger of injury to the textile material. Considerations of this type are responsible for many drying machines being divided into compartments or zones, which enable lower temperatures to be used as the cloth becomes dry. It is also important to avoid sudden

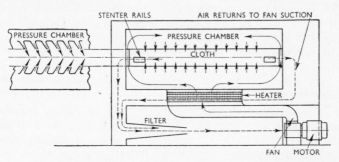

Fig. 55A.—Diagram of Spooner method of air-circulation.

changes during the drying process, and many machines arrange for a slow evaporation by controlling the humidity of the hot air; this may be done by the counterflow system of drying where the wet fabric at the entry encounters hot humid air which has already passed through the rest of the stenter. Intelligent use of these principles enables high temperatures and high humidities to be employed at the entering end of the machine, and to increase the speed of drying without surface baking, which so easily results from high temperatures without controlled humidity.

The number of drying processes to which fabrics are subjected during their bleaching, colouring and finishing is kept to a minimum not only because of expense, but because most types of drying reduce the absorptive capacity of the textile material. It is well known, for example, that the moisture regain of textiles at any relative humidity depends on whether the textile material has reached equilibrium by absorption or by desorption; the moisture content of the fabric also influences many of its physical properties. Unfortunately when attempts are made to dry the fabrics by desorption to the normal regain, utilising machines which operate at a constant speed for the particular cloth, it is not possible to cope with variations; hence the damp spots cause irregularities in dyeing and printing, because part of the cloth has been dried and other parts have been over-dried. The general practice, therefore, is to produce a uniform material by over-drying all of it, and then conditioning the fabric by absorption. In point of fact, most cloth is over-dried because of the considerable margin of safety which is allowed to produce dryness; this results in a deterioration in quality, a reduced absorptive capacity, and a low output.

However, an automatic moisture recorder has recently been developed to give a continuous indication of the moisture content of the fabric and also to control the speed of the stenter so that the moisture content is kept substantially constant. In these circumstances, the cloth is not over-dried and a pleasant handle is assured. The method has been described by Laurie and Dalglish in B.P. 563,480 and 567,259; it makes use of the resistance principle.

With regard to the actual drive of the stenter, most modern machines are electrically driven and fitted with push-button control.

In very many fabrics, it is necessary to have the weft at right angles to the warp; this can be corrected by mounting the fabric in a roll on a swivelling stand and making the necessary adjustments by hand. There are, however, two mechanical devices for straightening the fabric, one of which is to use a series of canting rollers so arranged as to lengthen the path of that selvedge which requires retarding to bring it at right angles to the warp; the second method is to mount a differential gear on the vertical driving shaft of the stenter, and retard or advance the speed of one of the chains, as required. A somewhat elaborate system with photo-electric cells has been devised by the G.E.C.

Some stenters are fitted with steam-boxes at the entering ends, so that fabrics which have been dried by festoon driers, for example, may be damped just sufficiently to enable the stenter to bring them to the required width.

As previously mentioned, it is possible to have the stenter operating in conjunction with the drying cylinders, either with a partial drying on cylinders beforehand, or, as with some clip machines, the cylinders may follow the stenter and dry the selvedges.

At the delivery end of the stenter, the fabric is generally plaited on to tables or into wagons; the short type of stenter used for stretching without heating may be fitted with a drum-batcher, but the fabrics on which it operates should be able to withstand tension and somewhat rough handling. Other methods of batching, of course, may be used with even fairly delicate fabrics.

KNIT GOODS

Although knit goods are made in tubular form and in the flat state, most of the latter are converted to tubular form by stitching the selvedges before wet-processing. When ready for drying and finishing, the excess of water may be removed on the centrifuge, and the drying completed on the brattice machine, the stenter or a special tubular drier.

The brattice machine generally takes the form of a rectangular chamber through which warm air is circulated; the brattices are preferably made of stainless steel strips which form long horizontal loops on which the cloth is carried, falling on to the lower lattice at the end of each loop, and thus by a circuitous route traversing the

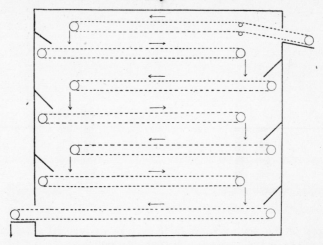

FIG. 56.—Diagram of brattice drying machine.

length of the chamber several times as it falls from tier to tier until it finally emerges in the dry state.

The dried material is actually "inside-out," and must be turned for the dry finishing process; this is usually done by threading the fabric on to a metal tube of large diameter and then withdrawing it outwards through the centre.

An alternative to the brattice drier is the tubular drier, where the cloth is turned with its face side out, and then piled around a vertical tube through which hot air is blown upwards. Above the tube is a special stretching device and a two-bowl calender. A cartridge-loading mechanism enables the drying to approximate to continuous treatment. Two cartridges are mounted opposite one another on a turntable, with one cartridge under the drying tube; the latter is a continuation of the tubular centre of the cartridge, and the warm air is supplied from below. The drying tube is a steel cylinder with slots and perforations to direct the warm air upwards and at an angle to the fabric as it is drawn to the nip of a felt calender which forms a sort of seal, forcing the warm air through the cloth. The drying head consists of a steel frame on which are mounted an adjustable stretcher and rings; the internal stretcher may be attached

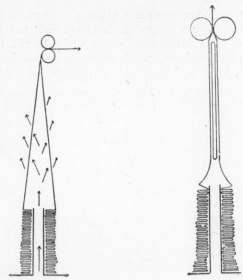

FIG. 57.—Diagrams of drying machines for tubular fabrics.

to the top of the drying tube, or it may be suspended vertically and kept in position by fabric feeding-wheels, which press lightly on the outside of the tubular cloth. The rings which are attached to the drying head are supplied in various diameters, so that a wide range

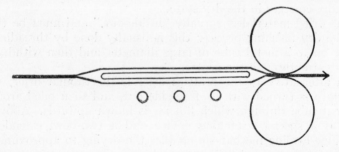

FIG. 58.—Diagram of steaming and drying tubular-knit fabrics.

of fabrics can be handled; the bottom ring applies tension to adjust the length of the fabric, the width being adjusted by the upper rings. Drying the fabric in a circular form evenly distends the loops and eliminates bowing and distortion.

PLATE VII

Fig. 59. Drying Cylinder showing buckets (Mather & Platt).

Fig. 60. The Charlesworth-Whiteley Tentering Machine
(10 layer, 4 bay).

Courtesy of Wm. Whiteley & Sons.

PLATE VIII

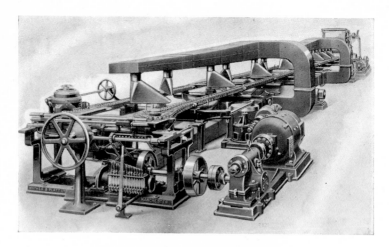

FIG. 61. Mather and Platt clip-stenter showing trunking
and air-ducts.

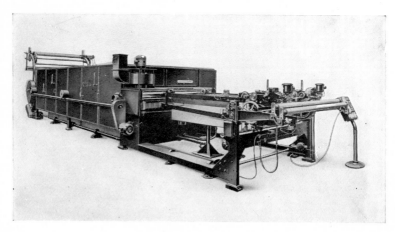

FIG. 62. Mills and Platts Pin Stenter.

Courtesy of Mather & Platt.

To face page 67.

A special type of stenter has been devised for drying and finishing lock-knit material in open width; spiral rollers open the curled selvedges which are impaled on the pins by rotating brushes. Feeding devices on each side of the machine act in accordance with the variations in width, and the length is also controlled by varying the rate of feed into the stenter.

As previously mentioned, many tubular knit goods are finished on a felt calender, with a stretcher to maintain the correct width. These calenders may be fitted with steaming devices to damp the dry cloth; with the floating stretcher, a steam-box is generally used, but with a fixed stretcher, jets of steam may be blown into the fabric from the inside. Steaming enables the wales of the knitted structure to be set and the width fixed.

INFRA-RED DRYING

As previously mentioned, considerable attention has been given to the possibility of drying with infra-red rays, particularly in the U.S.A. Lamps of the 500- or 1,000-watt type, complete with reflectors, are arranged in banks and the rays directed on to the surface of the fabric; as accessory drying devices, they may result in increased output of the order of 15 to 25%.

Another type of installation uses gas-fired radiant heat generators with a special refractory surface which becomes incandescent and emits infra-red rays. Advantages claimed for this type of heat include high temperatures, low transfer loss, high efficiency, and good penetrating powers. The gas-burning units are stated to be less expensive and more compact than a battery of lamps. Under the conditions of operation it seems probable that the installation operates by 50% radiant heat and 50% convection heat.

The subject has been discussed in the *Textile World* (1943, *93*, 56).

In view of the rather extravagant claims for infra-red drying, which have been made in certain quarters, attention should be drawn to the difference in efficiency between infra-red *heating* and infra-red drying.

DRY FINISHING MACHINES

It is somewhat of a paradox that the first machines to be discussed under the heading of "dry-finishing" are those which impart a certain amount of moisture to the fabric; this is because most textile fabrics can be plasticised by the presence of water vapour, and unless they are so plasticised, most dry mechanical finishes are relatively ineffective.

CONDITIONING AND DAMPING

As the physical properties of all textile materials vary to a very large extent with the moisture of condition, it is very important that this should receive attention before the fabric is subjected to any mechanical operation which depends on pressure, friction, and other forms of more or less slight deformation of the material for its effect.

It is possible to allow fabrics to lie for some time in a humid conditioning-room, or more quickly, to spray water directly on to the cloth or to blow steam through the fabric. The first method is apt to give uneven results and is slow, whereas the second deposits water on the surface of the material to a greater extent than in the interior.

The Sjøstrøm Conditioning Machine is capable of giving textile fabrics their moisture of condition in a very efficient manner. It

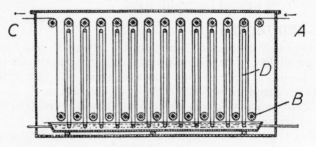

FIG. 63.—Diagram of the Sjøstrøm conditioning machine.

consists essentially of a closed chamber apart from the entrance and exit for the cloth; from side to side within the chamber extends a series of driving rollers at the top and guide rollers at the bottom. All the top rollers are driven so that there is no uneven tension applied to the fabric. Trays are situated in the bottom of the chamber and supplied with running water, into which the lower parts of endless aprons are dipped; these aprons are located in each space between the fabric guiding rollers, and so bring water into close proximity with the cloth without actual contact. This arrangement exposes a cool, continuous, wet surface close to the fabric, which on passing into the machine immediately starts to absorb water vapour supplied by evaporation from the aprons. There is no possibility of the fabric becoming excessively wet because the humidity of the atmosphere in the machine is less than 100%, and there is no spray or other excess of water in the air. The passage of the cloth through the machine may vary from 30 seconds to 2 minutes, and it is particularly useful where cloths have been previously subjected to some hot process as the cooling effect is considerable.

A diagram of this machine may be seen in Fig. 63; the fabric enters at A, passes partly round the top driving roller, down to the guide roller *B*, and so on through the machine to the exit *C*. The aprons or conveyors for the water are seen at *D*.

In addition to preparing the cloth for finishing operations, the conditioning machine is also useful in restoring the moisture content of the goods before making-up, and hence improving the handle and appearance.

Brush Damping Machines are made by most manufacturers of textile finishing machinery. Essentially, the machine is an arrangement whereby a brush, revolving at high speed in contact with water in a trough, sprinkles water on to the fabric which passes

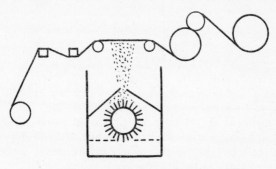

FIG. 64.—Diagram of the brush damping machine.

above it. The brush is generally made of fibres, bristles, or of copper spikes; some regulation of the damping of the cloth may be achieved by adjusting the level of the water in the trough by an overflow pipe. Further regulation is effected by adjusting the opening at the top of the box through the use of hinged lids. If only slight damping is required, the arrangement may be modified by the addition of a wooden furnishing roller, which runs in the water in the trough and acts as a feeding roller for the brush.

The cloth passes over the usual tension rails, scrimp rail, and guide roller to the position above the water-trough; it then passes round the draw drum and over a pressing roller, which forms a nip, to the batching apparatus or plaiting device.

The Spray Damping Machine is generally regarded as an improvement on the brush damping machine, as it conditions the cloth more uniformly. Water is atomised by discharging it under considerable pressure on to an inclined disc, the resulting very fine spray being delivered on to the cloth passing at a suitable distance above the feed-pipe. The necessary nozzles, the number of which varies according to the width of the machine, are attached to a common feed-pipe, which is supplied with water under pressure from a three-throw pump. The feed-pipe and nozzles are enclosed in a wooden box fitted with an adjustable hinged lid which permits the amount of damping to be controlled by hand. An automatic device is provided whereby the sprays are shut off immediately the machine stops, so that there is no risk of over-damping the fabric if the machine should be stopped suddenly. Fig. 69 shows a good example

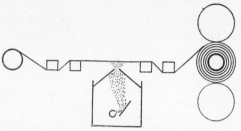

FIG. 65.—Diagram of the spray damping machine.

of the spray damping machine; portions of the trough have been removed to exhibit the spray-pipe and nozzle.

Another type of spray may be produced by blowing air under pressure across fine water-jets, the amount of damping of the cloth being regulated by the height of a constant-level water reservoir which supplies the jets by gravity feed.

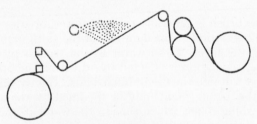

FIG. 66.—Diagram of a spray damping machine for wool goods.

A novel method of conditioning fabrics has been devised in the "Fridg" system of Sellers & Co., of Huddersfield. One of the difficulties in the normal method of conditioning fabrics in the air arises from the fact that a considerable amount of heat is given up by the textile material as it absorbs moisture; the temperature of the immediately surrounding air is thereby raised and its relative humidity reduced so that it is less able to impart its moisture to the fabric. This cushion of air acts as a barrier to cooler air or to water vapour which normally diffuses into the cloth. Now the "Fridg" method reduces the temperature of the cloth to a minimum, with the result that conditioning is greatly accelerated. The fabric passes through a side-slit into a chamber supplied with cooled air drawn from the atmosphere by a fan and passed through cooled gilled tubes. Excess of air is blown on to the fabric just as it enters the cooling box, and further supplies of cooled air from a second cooling system are blown on to both sides of the fabric in the cooling box. The cooling apparatus operates on the system of the compression and expansion of gases, such as ammonia or carbon dioxide, and utilises a compressor and gilled coils. If extra moisture is required in the cold air, a washed-air device may be incorporated in the intake pipes of the fan and an adjustable amount of haze created in the cold chamber; generally, however, the air is nearly saturated by the cooling alone without the addition of moisture. The actual temperature realised is slightly above the freezing-point of water where conditions tend to be uniform, as air with any given moisture content increases in relative humidity as it is cooled.

Conditioning stenters are very useful for conditioning cloth after leaving the drying apparatus and setting it to width before further finishing operations such as calendering. The conditioning stenter is also useful for crêpes and other goods which have been dried in the slack state to realise their particular finish, but need stretching to width before making-up. Two methods are commonly employed for conditioning the dry cloth; in the first of these, the fabric passes over boxes containing perforated steam-pipes covered with gauze and placed some feet along the stenter at the entering end, but prior to the point at which the rails start to diverge. In the second method, the cloth runs over rollers and through a steaming box or chest which is situated in front of the stenter; in this manner the fabric receives a thorough damping before reaching the stenter, but at the same time any steam escaping from the box is kept away from the stenter machine.

MANGLING

The mangle finish is still used for certain fabrics and, as its name implies, it consists in a prolonged period of mangling; whereas calendering, in general, consists in a momentary application of pressure to the fabric as it passes between the bowls of the machine, mangling, on the other hand, involves first rolling the cloth on to a "pin," which is then placed between the stones of the stone mangle or the bowls of the hydraulic mangle, where it is subjected to continuous and heavy pressure. During the course of the mangling process, which may occupy from 10 to 20 minutes, the direction of rotation of the pin may be changed from time to time.

This type of finish is usually limited to heavy fabrics of jute or linen, but where the lighter cellulose materials are finished in this manner, it is customary to protect the fabric on the "pin" by a cloth cover, which prevents damage, particularly at the ends, and also keeps the material clean. The goods are generally damped and then calendered before beaming; in this manner the yarns are somewhat flattened before mangling and possibilities of cutting are reduced, for it must be realised that in the mangling process, the pressure is applied to the whole piece at once through the layers of cloth wound on the iron "pin."

The stone mangle is a very old and cumbersome appliance which comprises two large flat stones between which the two beams of cloth are placed; the lower and heavier stone is fixed, but the upper stone is moved backwards and forwards by a crank arrangement.

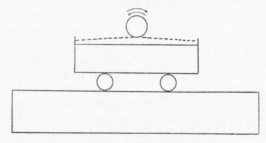

FIG. 67.—Diagram of the stone mangle.

The weight of the upper stone, with box and ballast, may amount to 50 tons.

The rolls of fabric must be maintained at right angles to the run of the machine or they will be damaged. From time to time the rotation of the rolls is reversed by withdrawing a roll of fabric and turning it round before re-inserting it between the stones; it is also customary with some cloths to re-wind them on a fresh pin so that the interior of the roll is brought to the surface for a second period of mangling.

With the special hydraulic mangle, the pin of cloth may be placed between two heavy bowls and mangled for the necessary length of time; most mangles are fitted with a reversing gear to alter the direction of rotation of the bowls as required. The top bowl may be raised for removing the finished piece and inserting a fresh roll of cloth; the change may be effected by sliding the pins horizontally, or revolving plates may be fitted with three mangle pins set at angles of 120°, thus enabling one pin to be wound with cloth and another unwound during the mangling of the third roll of fabric. At the end of each run, the plate is moved one-third of a revolution to fit a new pin and bring the finished piece to the unwinding position.

This type of mangle finish gives a full, soft and mellow effect; a similar principle or method has been utilised for softening or breaking stiff finishes, as described on page 82. The same idea is also used for "chesting," as outlined on page 75, as an alternative to beetling.

CALENDERS

The use of the calender is an important branch of the finishing of cotton, linen, rayon, and silk material. With some cotton cloths it may be used as a preliminary to the starch or filled finish, as it has the effect of closing the threads and flattening the goods; alternatively, there is a lustre and feel which come from the calender, and these, in conjunction with the closing of the yarns already mentioned, impart the final finish to many textile materials.

Prior to calendering, it is often customary to stretch the conditioned fabric to bring it to the required width, and remove crinkles and creases, before passing through the heavy nip of the calender. The Belt Stretcher (see Fig. 70 and page 28) is used for this purpose.

Fundamentally, the calender consists of a series of heavy rollers or bowls, mounted vertically in a robust frame.

The chief essentials in calendering are the moisture present in the cloth at the moment of calendering, the composition, number, and arrangement of the bowls, together with their pressure and temperature. The bowls may be made of metal or of compressed material such as cotton or paper; the degree of hardness depends on the particular finish for which the bowl is intended. The metal bowls are usually made of chilled iron with a hard, highly-polished surface; these bowls are generally hollow, so that they may be heated, but very often the bottom bowls are made of close-grained cast iron.

Different combinations of bowls are capable of imparting different finishes to the fabric, but in general, the metal bowls are never in contact with one another.

Although both closed and open frames may be used as supports for the bowls, the latter is almost universally adopted owing to its greater convenience when it is necessary to remove any particular bowl. Pressure may be applied by compound levers and weights, or hydraulic pressure may be used as an alternative. "Dead set" may be utilised on some calenders if required.

Calenders are made in many different forms, with from two to eleven bowls, and may be adapted to perform various finishing operations; some of the larger calenders are fitted with the necessary devices for utilising only a certain number of the available bowls.

In most cases, all metal bowls are geared together in order to prevent slip.

Where it is necessary to heat the metal bowls, this may be done with steam or gas, the latter being preferred for high temperatures.

Swizzing finishes are obtained merely by passing the cloth, suitably conditioned, through the nips of the calender in which the surface speed of all the bowls is the same; the cloth is then batched or plaited as required. A smooth appearance is thus obtained according to the number and composition of the bowls.

Friction calendering, however, gives a higher gloss and a greater closing of the yarns; it is produced by bringing the cloth into contact with a heated, polished, chilled-iron bowl which is travelling at a faster speed than the cloth itself. Three-bowl heavy friction calenders are suitable for the finishing of highly-glazed linings, prints, bookcloth, and tracing cloth. The bottom bowl is usually made of close-grained cast iron, the middle bowl of cotton, and is of greater

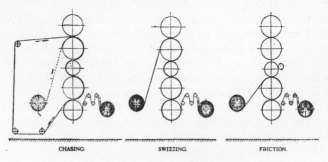

CHASING.   SWIZZING.   FRICTION.

Fig. 68.—Diagram of methods of using the calender
(Farmer Norton).

diameter than the others to allow for wear; the top or glazing bowl is made of highly-polished chilled iron and is heated by steam or gas. An arrangement of spur-wheels enables the top bowl to produce a surface speed 1·5 to 2 times that of the lower bowls, although for some book-cloths the friction ratio may be increased to 3·5 to 1. The cloth is passed into the bottom nip and round the middle bowl, which is revolving at the same surface speed as the bottom bowl; the top bowl, with its higher surface speed, produces the friction effect by polishing the cloth. For light friction effects it is sometimes sufficient to use a calender with two cotton bowls and a centre steel bowl, the bottom two bowls being geared together so as to give slight friction; this gives a slightly higher polish than that obtained by swizzing alone.

A special four-bowl double friction calender is made by Mather and Platt; the cloth is subjected to friction twice during one passage through the calender, which comprises a bottom bowl of close-grained cast iron which is steam-heated, a cotton bowl, a steam-heated chilled-iron bowl, and a cotton bowl.

Chasing finishes are obtained with all the bowls running at the same surface speed; the cloth is passed through the nips of the calender, over external rollers and back into the bottom nip of

PLATE IX

Fig. 69. Spray Damping Machine.

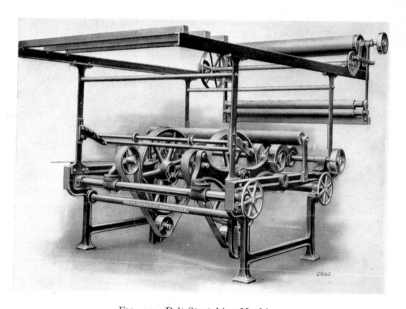

Fig. 70. Belt Stretching Machine.

Courtesy of Mather & Platt.

To face page 74.

PLATE X

FIG. 71. Three-bowl Calender.

FIG. 72. Seven-bowl Calender.

Courtesy of Mather & Platt.

PLATE XI

FIG. 73. Five-bowl Universal Calender
with chesting arrangement.

FIG. 74. Two-bowl Schreiner Calender.

Courtesy of Mather & Platt.

PLATE XII

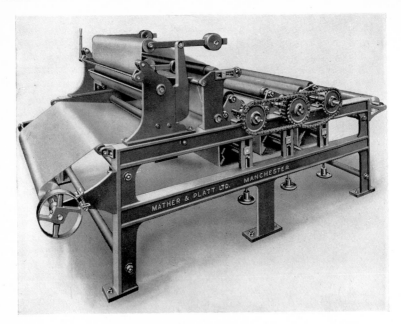

FIG. 75. Tampon Machine.

FIG. 76. The "Palmer" Machine.

Courtesy of Mather & Platt.

To face page 75.

the calender again. In this way the cloth may be led through the calender several times, one layer of cloth lying over another in multiple fashion. The operation of chasing produces the effect of rounding the yarns to give a "thready" or linen appearance, together with a soft handle and a slight amount of watermarking.

Calenders with more than three bowls are usually so designed to give friction, chasing, and swizzing finishes if required; they are sometimes termed Universal Calenders, and generally comprise four, five, or seven bowls. Fig. 72 shows a seven-bowl calender and Fig. 68 an arrangement for various calendering operations. In a calender of this type, the usual arrangement of bowls passing from bottom to top is close-grained iron, cotton, polished chilled iron (the driving bowl), cotton, polished chilled iron.

Calenders may be used to simulate the beetle finish, and for this purpose the metal bowls are not utilised, but the calender is fitted with soft nips throughout; the bottom bowl is usually compressed paper and the remainder compressed cotton.

The chesting calender is made with five bowls and is mainly used for linen finishes. A popular arrangement of the bowls, passing from bottom to top, is cast iron, cotton, heated iron, cotton and iron. In addition to the weight of the bowls, pressure is applied by long horizontal levers which act on the bearings of the top bowl; connected to these levers are vertical rods with rack-teeth gearing with pinions on a horizontal shaft. A pulley is keyed to the pinion shaft and attached to the pulley is a chain to which weights may be fixed to produce the necessary pressure. From Fig. 73 it will be seen that this machine may be used for ordinary calendering, but in addition the cloth may be passed through the nips and then wound round the top or second bowl—the batch may then be rolled or mangled until the required finish is obtained. This operation is termed "chesting," and pressure is maintained by the rack lever mechanism. A very "thready" finish is obtained in this manner.

A wooden board or "chesting knife" presses against the full width of the chesting bowl and ensures that the first end of the cloth passes round this bowl. The direction of rotation of the bowl may be alternated from time to time, for if the roll was revolved in the same direction continuously, the cloth would stretch and there would be a tendency for it to tear. After chesting for the required time, the top levers are raised by the rack-gear mechanism and the chesting bowl is allowed to revolve freely and the cloth may be unrolled. This method of finishing is similar in principle to that described on page 72.

Some calenders have been designed specially for the finishing of silk and rayon goods; one of these consists of three bowls, the top two being of cotton, whilst the bottom bowl is made of chilled iron and is steam-heated. The fabric is actually passed between the two cotton bowls, and the bottom bowl acts as a bed-bowl, but also keeps a smooth and polished face on the cotton bowl. Calenders of this type are used as an alternative to the slow process of hot-pressing. For many of these calenders, the bowls are constructed so as to have some resilience; the actual composition is often soft-pressed woollen paper, but some special bowls have been constructed and are often described as "elastic" bowls. A common method is to cover the central shaft with a serpentine band, standing on edge, with the weft worked in a step-shape and the warp setting decreasing radially outwards; the operative portion is thus formed by radial weft threads. Bowls of this type are not easy to produce. An alternative method (B.P. 431,815) is to use a curved plaited band of uniform density throughout, wound edgewise on the shaft; the uniformity of density is achieved by dividing the plaited band into sections and inserting a larger number of threads in the outer part than the inner. The covering is then axially compressed about the axle to make a large majority of the threads extend radially. Some elastic bowls have also been built from knitted fabrics.

Schreiner

The "silk-finish" is obtained by a special form of calender, and is an attempt to give to certain cotton goods the beautiful lustre associated with real silk; the first attempt to emboss fine lines on cotton was described in B.P. 170 of 1860 by Appleby, but the real success was due to Schreiner about 1895. If cotton is subjected to slight pressure, a low degree of lustre is obtained, whereas if the pressure is great, the numerous small surfaces are merged and give no satisfactory lustre, but only a specular reflection, as in a mirror. Schreiner argued that in order to obtain a silky lustre it is necessary to produce on the fabric a very large number of small reflecting surfaces distributed in several planes. Engravings of 125 to 500 lines per inch were made on various metallic calender bowls and applied to different fabrics.

The production of lustre by the Schreiner finish is therefore a method of embossing, and the lines must be engraved so as to form a slight angle with the weft or warp; in weft sateens, for instance, it is usual to engrave the lines at an angle of about 20° to the weft in the direction of the twist of the yarn. Plain cloths may also be improved by schreinering, but in this case the engraving is much coarser and averages about 150 to 200 lines per inch.

The usual Schreiner calender is built with two bowls in an open frame; the upper bowl is made from special quality close-grained steel of high carbon content and engraved with the necessary number of lines. The bowl is heated by gas to the necessary temperature, usually of the order of 150°C., or even higher. As the cloth passes between the bowls, it is subjected to pressures of 100 tons or more, provided by hydraulic rams under the bearings of the bottom bowl, which is generally driven by silent chains; an adjustable friction plate is provided to prevent skidding when pressure is applied and so obviate damage to the bowls. In some cases, the lower bowl is provided with a skewing arrangement, enabling it to be set at an angle, and in this manner an enhanced brilliance may be given to the cloth. In some of the latest types of Schreiner calenders, a special relief valve enables the stitchings to be passed through the machine without damage and without loss of schreinering.

Where a large output is required, a three-bowl Schreiner calender may be used; the engraved bowl is placed in the middle, and the cloths are passed through the upper and lower nips simultaneously. Machines of this type are employed for low-quality fabrics where the highest type of schreiner finish is not required.

The "spun-glass" finish is logically in the same class as schreinering, and is another example of the silk finish. The engraved lines are usually wider than the schreiner line and run at right angles to the horizontal axis of the steel bowl, which is made to run at a slightly greater surface speed than the lower bowl. This difference produces a slight friction effect, which, combined with that of schreinering, produces a very attractive lustrous finish.

The actual details of schreinering depend to a large extent on the type of cloth, and in general the material must be well singed, mercerised, and dyed before treatment. Immediately before the actual schreinering process, the cloth is sheared to remove any projecting fibres which may have appeared subsequent to singeing. A light finish, usually of vegetable gum, is applied to the back of the cloth, which may be passed through an ordinary calender before going through the Schreiner. The moisture in the cloth must be carefully controlled, and it is common practice to damp the material before schreinering. The details of speed and temperature vary, but temperatures of 150°C. or more are common, and the speed generally varies from 15 to 30 yards per minute. As a large amount of schreinering is done on goods previously dyed with aniline black, considerable care and experience are necessary to avoid tendering the material.

The "silk finish" produced by schreinering is not fast to washing as the impression of the fine lines is disturbed and destroyed when the fibres are swollen with water. Most schreinered material is used for linings which are not washed, but even here the effect is not "spot proof," although many unsuccessful attempts have been made to produce a permanent schreiner effect.

The moire finish is related to schreinering and is generally applied to cloths in which the warp has yarn of harder twist than the weft. The moire effect resembles watermarking and is a sort of local embossing due to the self-compression of the yarns producing an optical effect. The original form of treatment involved running two layers of fabric through a plain calender in such a manner that each fabric made an impression on the other; it is now possible to produce this effect on a single fabric by a suitable calender bowl. The steel bowl is engraved with a plain line, either horizontal or diagonal, according to the design required. The cloth is moved sideways to and fro as it passes through the nip, and the irregular crossing of the warp by the engraved line or pattern produces the watermark effect. (See Am. Dyes. Rep., 1947, 36, 150.)

The moire antique finish may be produced on a three-bowl calender. Two pieces of cloth are passed twice through the calender, face to face, so that the back of each piece comes into contact with the hot steel bowl. The super-imposition of the warps of the two pieces pressed together produces the finish; it is necessary to pass the cloths through the machine twice, so that the gloss on the back of both pieces is the same.

Embossing Calenders

The older types of embossing calender were designed to reproduce certain effects for bookcloth, imitation leather, and so forth. They were generally made with two or three bowls.

In the two-bowl machine, the heated and engraved metal bowl was used in conjunction with a paper or cotton bowl of twice the diameter of the metal bowl. In the three-bowl machine, the engraved metal bowl is generally mounted on a steel mandrel which is placed between two cotton or paper bowls whose diameter is about three times that of the metal bowl.

More recently a much lighter embossing calender has been devised for assisting in the finishing of crêpes. Good specimens of "pebble" from real silk crêpes were photographed and then engraved on metal bowls; these patterns may be transferred, by embossing, to rayon crêpes in the loom state and so pre-form the pattern into which the fabric is induced to set in the later operations of crêping, as discussed on page 94. The upper bowl is usually engraved with the pattern which becomes impressed on the lower paper-on-steel shell; moisture, heat, and pressure impart the pebble or crêpe pattern to the fabric as it passes between the bowls.

THE BEETLE MACHINE

Beetling is applied to linen fabrics and to certain qualities of cotton. The usual type of machine comprises a very heavy frame, supporting about forty hardwood faller stamps which are operated by cams attached to a horizontal shaft known as the "wiper beam"; the cams lift the fallers in sequence and allow them to fall on to the roll of fabric which is wound on a robust iron shaft immediately beneath. The fabric is thus subjected to the hammering action of the fallers, and the beam is slowly revolved during this treatment, and also moved to and fro longitudinally so as to distribute the hammering evenly. The machine generally takes a beam about 14 feet in length, and is capable of dealing with two, three, or four pieces of cloth according to the width of the material. During the

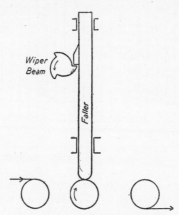

FIG. 77.—Diagram of beetling machine.

beetling process, a second beam at the side of the machine is either being wound with fresh fabric, or is being stripped of the treated cloth. When the beetling is complete, the cloth is generally re-wound so as to bring the outer layers to the inside; the process of beetling is then repeated in order to ensure an even finish throughout.

A high-speed beetling machine has been devised by Messrs. Mather and Platt, and utilises metallic hammers suspended on belts tightly stretched round "C" springs. Four sizes of machines are available with 18, 21, 24, or 28 hammers, which are free to oscillate vertically and thus give perfectly elastic blows. The crank-shaft which runs at 400 r.p.m., can be raised or lowered bodily, and so give a lighter or heavier blow to the cloth, as required.

A new type of all-metal beetling engine has been devised by Frazer and Haughton (B.P. 284,514) in which the vertical faller of the old machines is replaced by a double-ended hammer operated by two camshafts. Two beams of cloth, one on each side of the row of hammers, are beetled at once; the hammer falls by gravity to one side and is then lifted by the opposite cam just over the dead centre, to fall on the opposite beam. The rate of beetling is about sixty complete cycles per minute, and is limited by the fall of the hammer under gravity, as in the old machines; however, whereas beetle finishes took from 12 to 40 hours on the old machines, this has been reduced to 6 hours on the new type. The blow is heavier than with the older wooden faller beetle, but there is no bounce and secondary hammering. One defect of very prolonged beetling on the older machines is the distortion and cracking of fibres at their most

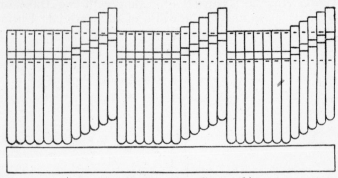

FIG. 78.—Diagram of beetling machine.

exposed points where weft yarns bend under the warp, as shown by Searle (J.T.I., 1924, *15*, 382). An interesting account of this new machine has been given by Butterworth (J.T.I., 1933, *24*, 209P).

TAMPONING MACHINE

Many fabrics with a lustrous face, such as satins, suffer from "cracking" or displacement of the threads during manipulation in bleaching, dyeing, and finishing. A tamponing machine has been devised by Messrs. Mather & Platt to correct this defect; the fabric is softened with a suitable oily solution or emulsion, and then gently beaten with small felt-covered mallets as it passes forward through the machine. Although the principle is somewhat similar to beetling, the machine is much more delicate in its action on the silk and rayon fabrics.

NATURAL LUSTRE MACHINE

This machine is suited to the finishing of silk, rayon, and cotton goods with a woven pattern, accentuated during the treatment, which simulates the domestic practice of ironing the back of a fabric whose face is in contact with the ironing blanket.

The fabric passes over an expander roller to a steam-heated cylinder covered with felt, and is damped *en route*; the fabric then passes over felt-covered calender rolls, above which are highly-polished steam-heated iron rollers resting on the felt-covered rollers with their own weight. A slight drag is given to the fabric between each set of rollers to imitate the stretching action of domestic ironing, and thus impart a "natural lustre." When the fabric leaves the polishing rollers, it passes round a polished steam-heated cylinder, which drives the moisture through the fabric and helps to raise the woven pattern which has been partly flattened during the calendering process.

SOFTENING OR BREAKING MACHINES

Cloths which have been dried on steam-heated cylinders are apt to have a crisp feel which is not desirable; to a greater extent, a boardy handle results from many of the printing operations and other processes where starches, gums, and thickening materials have been used. Many calender finishes impart a papery feel. As it is

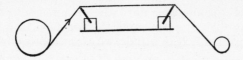

FIG. 79.—Diagram of doctor breaker.

often necessary to break down this stiffness, the mechanical devices for this purpose have come to be known as breaking machines.

The simplest method is by flexing the cloth, and this may be done by drawing it, under tension, over a knife-edge provided by a doctor knife or scraper; the degree of "breaking" may be varied according to the angle formed between the knife and the cloth.

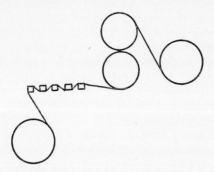

FIG. 80.—Diagram of Canroy machine.

The Canroy machine may also be used for softening fabrics, and in its simplest form consists of a series of tension rails, which impart a flexing action to the fabric, and a light two-bowl calender which further softens the material. Canroys are used for a variety of

6

purposes and are fundamentally machines for winding cloth on to
a batch-roller, and so may be used merely for winding, for inspection
of cloth, for brushing, and for many other purposes.

The use of rollers or bowls forms the basis of a softening machine
produced by Mather & Platt, which combines a damping device
with the breaking mangle. The fabric passes through a spray
damping machine, over a number of tension rails which exert some
breaking action, and is finally batched on a roller running between
two cotton bowls in the breaking mangle. As the batch increases in
diameter, the top bowl and racks rise and cause the brake-pulley
attached to the pinion shaft to slip, thus putting pressure on the
batch; the pressure may be regulated according to requirements by
adjusting the brake. When the full diameter of the batch has been
reached, pins are placed in the holes provided in the racks, and the
mangling of the cloth continued under the pressure of the levers
and weights of the mangle, until the required effect is reached;
the machine is then stopped, and the top bowl raised to release
the batch of cloth which is withdrawn from the machine (compare
page 75).

The Stud- or Button-breaking machine acts on a different principle. It consists of a series of hardwood rollers, usually seventeen,
which are studded with special nails having large cup heads; the
rollers are arranged in two rows. The lower row of rollers is carried
on a carriage with an adjusting arrangement to regulate the relative
positions of upper and lower rollers, and also to permit the lower
row of rollers to be dropped clear of the upper row for ease in passing
the cloth between them before operating the machine. According
to the positions of the rows of rollers it is possible to produce a very
slight binding effect or a much greater action; this in turn decides
the break-action on the cloth. The rollers are not driven, but the
cloth runs between the two rows, describing a sinuous path which
flexes the material in the warp direction to a high degree, while the
buttons or studs exert a finer flexing action at the same time. Having
passed through the machine once, the cloth may be passed in the
reverse direction and then backwards and forwards until the required
softening has been attained.

The Scroll or Spiral breaker exerts a similar effect and consists
of a number of polished steel scrolls which are driven in this case.
The machine generally runs at about 45 yards per minute, and is
fitted with a return or reversing motion, so that the cloth may be
treated until the correct handle has been reached. The flexing action
is rather more vigorous in the weft direction with this machine than
on the button-breaker. The severity of the action can be regulated
so that the machine is capable of treating light cloths as well as
heavier fabrics.

An interesting machine for breaking down stiff and papery finishes is formed by two corrugated bowls with the corrugations at right angles to the long axis of the bowl; thick rubber sleeves cover the bowls and are maintained at tension by passing over subsidiary rollers of small diameter. The cloth passes into the nip, where it is rapidly flexed by the corrugations and subjected to the breaking action. This is an old-fashioned machine, rarely seen in England, but very popular in France, where it is often used for both silks and rayons.

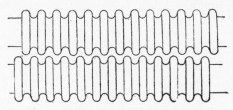

FIG. 81.—Diagram of Corrugated Bowls for Softening or Breaking.

The jig stenter, of course, also exerts a breaking effect, as described on page 59.

A special type of softening machine was made by Gessner for producing a wool finish on cotton; the fabric was passed between sixteen pairs of rollers covered with fine card clothing and driven at the same speed as the fabric up to 100 yards per minute. The full effect was only realised after numerous passages through the machine; it is perhaps necessary to point out that the action of the card clothing was not to raise the material.

RAISING MACHINES

The process of raising consists of lifting from the body of the fabric a layer of fibres which stand out from the surface; in many cases, a specially prepared surface results from milling or even from particular woven structures. The formation of pile or cover on a fabric results in a "lofty" handle, and may also subdue the weave or pattern of the cloth in addition to blending the various colours. In some sequence of processes, the raising operation may be a preliminary to milling so as to produce a heavier surface matting of the fibres.

Raising machines are of two types—teasel machines and card-wire machines. As the output of the card-wire machine is higher than that of the teasel type, it is customary to start raising on the wire machine and complete it with teasels; there are certain finishes which can only be produced with teasels.

Both types of raising may be done with the fabric in the wet or dry state, but moist raising is probably most widely adopted, for wool if not for cotton.

Teasels are obtained from a species of the thistle plant specially cultivated for the purpose; some teasels are 2 inches long, but the average type is 1·5 to 1·75 inches in length for commercial use. King teasels are 4 inches long. The teasels are prepared with steam or hot water and then set into frames or iron slats as tightly as possible to form one or two rows. The slats or frames are placed on a drum which rotates, and the fabric is brought into careful contact with

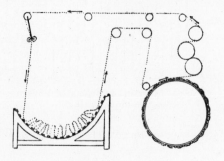

Fig. 82.—Diagram of teasel raising machine.

the teasel-filled slats; raising must take place very gradually, and the fibres are really untangled and lifted instead of being torn from the surface of the fabric; the process usually starts with old teasels whose points have been worn and softened. New and sharper teasels may be used when some surface or pile has been developed. In the course of the process the teasels become filled with wool fibres and also become damp, when they are removed for drying and brushing. An extension of the moist teaselling process is the wet raising where the cloth is actually saturated with water during the raising treatment; this effect is not strictly raising, but lays the raised pile in one direction on the surface of the cloth.

In the moist and wet processes, the swollen fibres are less rigid, and this assists raising; dry raising is very suitable for fabrics which have not been milled and a more spongy effect is produced.

The rotation of the cylinder of the machine is in the same direction as the fabric, but at a higher surface speed; the usual type of machine is single-cylinder with arrangements for reversing the direction of run after one passage of the fabric. Several treatments with increasing contact are usually necessary for the required result. Machines are also available with two cylinders and a return mechanism whereby continuous raising of a number of pieces in one length may be effected; obviously the number of "runs" depends on the nature of the material and the effect required.

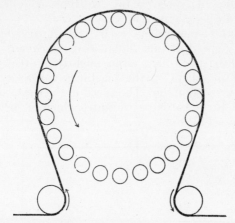

FIG. 83.—Diagram of card-wire raising machine.

Card-wire raising machines are usually constructed on the basis of a cylinder around which are mounted small rollers covered with the wire filleting. Two main types of machine are available: single

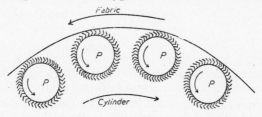

FIG. 84.—Single action raising.

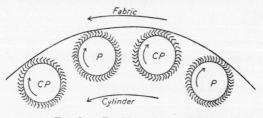

FIG. 85.—Double action raising.

and double acting. In the single-acting machine, the pile or cover is raised in only one direction as the wire-covered rollers rotate in the opposite direction to that of the cylinder. The double-acting machine has two sets of rollers termed pile and counter-pile rollers, which rotate at the same speed and also in the same direction; the points of the card-wire are set in opposite direction to each other, and by adjusting the speed of the two types of roller, more or less raising effect can be produced.

Pile and counter-pile rollers each have separate gear-boxes, so that the rotary speed of pile rollers may be caused to differ from that of the counter-pile rollers either slightly or greatly, as required.

The number of rollers on the machines varies according to the type, but thirty are common. The speed of the wire-raising machines varies from 12 to 15 yards per minute, which is 20 to 30% higher than that of teasel-raising.

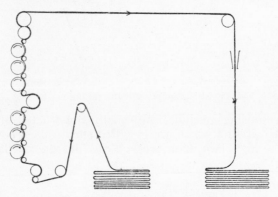

FIG. 86.—Diagram of sueding machine.

Very different effects are created by the single- and double-acting machines; in the former the pile is laid like a fleece, whereas in the latter the pile is raised to stand erect. The teasel-raising gig imparts a brushing and polishing action which is not realised with the Moser or card-wire machine. The severity of the action also differs in the two machines.

A very mild form of raising may be produced on cotton or wool goods by the sueding machine shown in Fig. 86. A series of rollers is covered with an abrasive surface such as sandpaper or emery cloth, and the fabric to be sueded is brought into varying degrees of contact with the abrasive surface by use of guide rollers.

BRUSHING MACHINES

The brushing process is intended to make the cloth level and clean; it removes loose fibres and foreign matter which may have become entangled with the pile, and also can be used to raise the tips of the fibres before shearing. Brushing may also follow shearing to remove any loose-cut fibres.

The brushing treatment is often combined with steaming to remove press glaze; alternatively, brushing may be employed to lay the pile in one direction where it is fixed by the action of steam. The usual type of machine comprises two brush cylinders, the bristles

FIG. 87.—Diagram of steaming and brushing machine.

being of different quality to suit various types of work; arrangements can be made whereby the fabric strikes each brush twice. The amount of contact may be varied by a simple cam device, or by lifting the fabric on rollers.

SHEARING MACHINES

The shearing process is also referred to as cutting and cropping. Fundamentally, the simplest machine operates in the same way as a lawn-mower, with revolving knives and an adjustable bedplate; very accurate setting is possible. The general purpose of shearing is to trim and level the surface pile produced by raising and to remove

FIG. 88.—Illustration of the principle of shearing or cropping.

surface fibres in clear-finished goods; obviously this is not done with fleecy finishes as for blankets, but for woollens and worsteds, shearing is rarely omitted. Striped patterns may be produced by a shearing machine with an indented bedplate.

Drastic shearing may take place on fabrics such as gaberdines and serges, which require a clear-cut finish, fairly severe shearing on suèdes, and a light cropping on velours. The amount of shearing depends on the length of the pile, and for pattern effects it is essential to have some pile to cut.

The cutting is done gradually, for if the machine is incorrectly adjusted in the early stages of cropping, the fabric will be torn.

Multiple cropping and shearing machines are produced with up to five cylinders, but for fine worsted and woollen fabrics three- or four-cylinder machines are commonly used. The process is continuous and speeds of 8 to 20 yards per minute are obtained.

NAPPING MACHINES

Napped effects are often produced on costume cloths and over-coatings; it is obviously essential to have enough pile or surface hairs with which to "nap." The process follows raising and cutting whereby the required initial level fibrous surface is formed on which to work. The fabric is drawn forward at about 4 yards per minute on to a stationary plush-covered table, above which is situated a swinging table covered with glass-paper or a rubber pad, which comes in contact with the fabric and rubs the nap in a certain way, as controlled by eccentric cams, which are set to produce different effects. For instance, a bead effect is created by the upper table moving at high speed with a short circular motion; the size of the bead is determined by the length of the pile. Wave effects are produced by a reciprocating motion in the opposite direction to the wave; the size of the wave is determined by the length of the stroke. Wave effects may be produced in warp or weft direction, or diagonally from right to left or left to right.

The napping process is discontinuous, the cloth being treated in portions from 2 to 4 feet in length.

PRESSING MACHINES

The pressing of woollen and worsted material is applied to all the clear-cut finishes, in order to make them firm, solid, and smooth; to a less degree the press finish is given to ordinary woollens and also to some rayons, silks, and cottons. In general, however, the press-finish for worsted may be regarded as the counterpart to calendering in the cotton and linen trade, and here again it is essential that the goods should be properly conditioned beforehand.

In the hydraulic or vertical press, the entire piece is pressed at one time, folded with electrically-heated press-papers between the folds. (The older method was to use iron plates heated by steam.) The press-papers are made of glazed cardboard with a resistance-metal lining and projecting tabs; the papers are inserted by hand as the fabric is plaited or cuttled mechanically. The pile of papered fabric is then transferred to the press and the tabs connected by

PLATE XIII

FIG. 89. Stud Breaking Machine.

Courtesy of Mather & Platt.

FIG. 90. Scroll Breaking Machine.

Courtesy of Whitehead & Poole.

To face page 88.

PLATE XIV

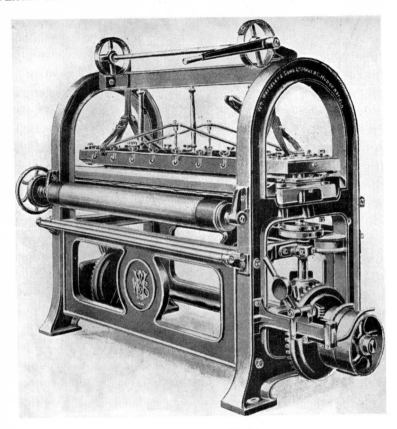

FIG. 91. Napping Machine.

Courtesy of Wm. Whiteley & Sons.

FIG. 92. Rotary Hydraulic Press.

Courtesy of Arthur Heaton & Co.

clips to the electric supply; pressure is applied, amounting to about 450 to 500 lb. per square inch. The time of heating varies greatly with the nature of the fabric, and may be as little as 10 minutes, or as long as 3 hours. The fabric is then refolded so that the overlapping edges at the first pressing are placed in the middle, and the pressing process is repeated.

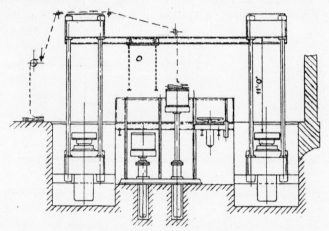

FIG. 93.—Diagram showing the arrangement of presses and lifts.

A typical arrangement of presses and lifts is seen from Fig. 93 (Arthur Heaton and Co.), and the method of papering and de-papering is shown in Fig. 94. The pieces to be pressed are drawn from the pile A and transferred to the lift table D, and at the same time, the press papers are inserted from the lifts E and F. When

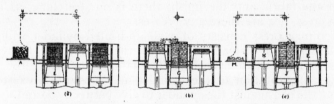

FIG. 94.—Diagrams showing papering, turning, and de-papering.

loaded, the level of the lift is adjusted and the pile of pieces is transferred to the press by an overhead railway O'. After the first pressing operation, the load of pieces is transferred to the lift G, and moved to the lift H by sliding the papers across, ensuring that the unpressed portion now comes in the middle of the paper. After the final pressing, the pieces are de-papered as shown in Fig. 94c.

An automatic flat press has also been designed consisting of a fixed top plate, an intermediate plate, and a rising plate, all of which are heated. A ram below the rising plate produces the pressure. The fabric is passed between the two movable plates by guide rollers, and passes to and fro about five times so that five thicknesses may be pressed at one time. When the rollers and fabric are at rest, pressure is applied, and after a given time, the pressure is released and the plates fall apart; a system of cams and levers causes the

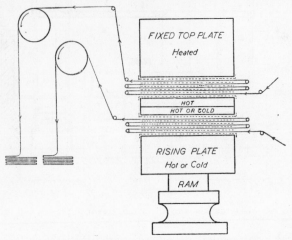

FIG. 95.—Diagram of continuous flat press
(Hattersley Pickard).

rollers to revolve and draw more cloth forward, stop, and be subjected to pressure by the rising plate. The cycle may be repeated four times per minute. The temperature and pressure may be varied to suit the fabric and the finish; there is no stretching, as in the rotary press, nor are there any creases.

The rotary press consists of a steam-heated cylinder which fits into the hollow of a steam-heated bed; the diameter of the cylinder may vary from 15 to 24 inches. The fabric is carried through the press by the rotation of the cylinder and pressure is exerted by pressing the bed against the cylinder to give between 500 and 1,000 lb. per square inch. This is a continuous process and the average output is 5 to 10 yards per minute. Rotary presses are also available with two beds or dishes, situated above and below the roller, so that the fabric is pressed twice as it passes through the machine; if necessary, the press may be provided with an apron or endless felt blanket to ensure a light pressing only. The rotary press is not used for the highest qualities of fabric, on account of the stretch which is given to the cloth.

As previously mentioned (page 16), pressed fabrics are sometimes found to have excessive lustre and a papery handle which may be removed by gentle steaming. This must not be confused with dry decatising, where the fabric is steamed in a roll. The steaming which takes place after pressing is open steaming by passing the fabric repeatedly over a slot in a cylinder from which steam is allowed to rise.

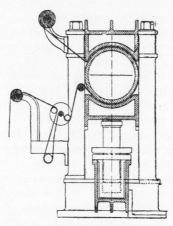

Fig. 96.—Diagram of rotary press.

PLAITING MACHINES

The finished fabric may be plaited and measured on a machine designed for this process. The commonest type plaits the fabric into folds of uniform length by means of a knife-carrier, which spreads the folded fabric on to a convex table which may accommodate the cloth to a depth of 18 inches. At the end of each stroke the folded edge of the cloth is gripped by wooden rails to ensure regularity of plaits. The length of the plait is usually 36 inches, but may be varied if required.

Creasing and plaiting machines are also available; this term corresponds to rigging and cuttling in the woollen and worsted trade. In both cases, however, the machine receives the fabric at full width, and rigs or creases it exactly up the centre and then folds or cuttles it around two "swords" from which it is withdrawn when the required length is reached. Measuring devices are attached to these machines.

Many delicate materials are not creased and lapped, but wound on shells of circular cross-section to avoid creasing and distortion; some pile fabrics are wound on spider-frames and marketed in this form.

CHAPTER III

CRÊPING

It is well known that yarns of even moderately high twist exhibit a great tendency to untwist when freed from restraint; if, however, a highly-twisted yarn is prevented from completely untwisting by being held at both ends, and the ends are allowed to approach, or the tension released, then a series of small loops is formed. This phenomenon of "snarling" is commonplace with many household yarns, and is due to the relaxation of twist.

If twisted yarns are held in the twisted state and wetted, then the fibres swell and there is a much greater tendency to untwist as the swelling is lateral and not longitudinal. Hence, it is possible to construct material in which the torsional energy remains latent until wetted. With suitable fabrics, the swelling of the fibres produces a contraction in width, but as the weft yarns are held at the selvedges they cannot untwist completely, so the energy is utilised in the tendency to snarl or form loops. On account of adjacent yarns and the interlacing of warp and weft, it is not possible for complete loops to form, but rather half-loops which buckle or distort the yarn and produce a disturbance of the surface of the fabric to give a broken appearance termed crêpe or pebble.

Fundamentally, therefore, crêping is due to the contraction in length of high-twist yarn and the tendency to untwist on wetting, and is based on the swelling properties of the fibres. On this account, those fibres which undergo considerable swelling in water are preferred for making crêpe yarns and fabrics, provided, of course, that they are cheap and otherwise satisfactory. The great swelling of regenerated cellulose in water has been an important factor in its use for crêpes in preference to the more expensive silk; rayon swells about 100% in volume in passing from the absolutely dry to the wet state.

Some comparisons of the swelling properties of various textile fibres have appeared in the textile literature, but it is not always clear whether they refer to increase in diameter or increase in area of cross-section; further, sometimes the swelling is estimated on the unswollen fibre in the dry state, and sometimes in the conditioned state. The following data refer to increases in area of cross-section of fibres (assuming a circular cross-section) in passing from the conditioned state at approximately 65% R.H. to the swollen state in liquid water.

PLATE XV

FIG. 97. Plaiting Machine.

Courtesy of Mather & Platt.

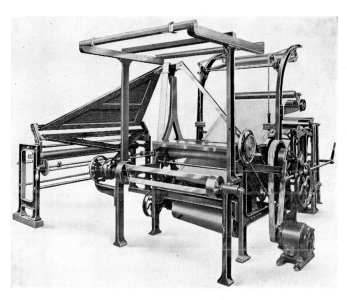

FIG. 98. Creasing and Plaiting Machine.

Courtesy of Wm. Whiteley & Sons, Ltd.

To face page 92.

PLATE XVI

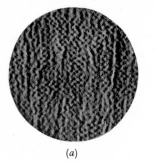

(a)   (b)

Uneven pebble with cracked effects.

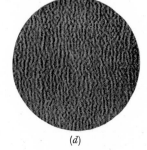

(c)   (d)

Fabrics crêped without embossing.

(e)   (f)

Fabrics embossed before crêping.

FIG. 99. Crêpe effects produced under various conditions on fabrics with acetate warp and crêpe viscose weft, (a), (c) and (e) with 40 filaments; (b), (d) and (f) with 60 filaments.

Courtesy of C. P. Atkinson.

INCREASE IN CROSS-SECTIONAL AREA

Silk	.	.	.	.	.	46%
Wool	.	.	.	.	.	35%
Cotton	.	.	.	.	.	30%
Viscose	.	.	.	.	.	35–60%
Acetate	.	.	.	.	.	6– 9%

It will be seen, therefore, that acetate rayon will require special consideration if it is to be used in the production of crêpes.

RAYON

For most fabrics, the yarns are specially prepared by soaking in a solution of a fixative such as gelatin and a lubricant such as an emulsified vegetable oil, followed by drying and twisting; the number of turns per inch generally varies from 40 to 60. The "twist" is then set by steaming, and the yarns are conditioned before weaving.

A good crêpe fabric must have these highly-twisted yarns suitably distributed throughout the structure to secure uniformity of pebble or a regular irregularity of the surface of the finished cloth. The great majority of crêpe fabrics are constructed with the crêpe yarn in either warp or weft, but georgettes have crêpe yarn in both warp and weft. A popular construction is to have a plain warp and a crêpe weft; the weft is generally built up of two threads with the twist in one direction followed by two threads with the twist in the reverse direction. (Yarns of different direction of twist are tinted with different colours to facilitate recognition; the colours are of such a type as to be readily removed in wet processing.) Canton crêpe, crêpe marocain, and crêpe-de-Chine are generally constructed in this manner, although some of the finer qualities of crêpe are woven with alternating twist in every weft yarn instead of each pair of yarns.

The wetting of the fabric causes the pairs of yarns to tend to untwist in opposite directions, but as their ends are fixed at the selvedges, the fabric shrinks in width, permitting a limited snarling or crêpe effect. It is obvious that some movement of the yarns must be permitted, and as this is restricted to some extent by the yarns of normal twist, these should not be closely arranged in the fabric, nor should they be too coarse. Freedom of movement is also assisted by having the yarn of normal twist composed of fibres whose swelling capacity in water is low; a very popular type of crêpe is therefore made from an acetate rayon warp and a viscose crêpe weft.

The peculiar properties of acetate rayon in another direction have also been utilised in this common crêpe construction. Even when crêping of fabrics is carried out slowly and carefully, difficulties were apt to occur on account of uneven crêping; the uneven movement of the crêpe yarns sometimes displaced the warp yarns laterally, spacing them apart in some places and grouping them together in others, with the production of thick and thin places. A successful attempt was made to overcome this irregular crêping by embossing or moulding the fabric in such a manner that a pattern was formed into which the contracting yarns would be directed. It is believed that the crêpe embossing calender originated in the photographic reproduction of silk crêpe patterns of high quality on embossing cylinders from which they may be transferred by heat and pressure to the crêpe fabric before it receives any wet treatment. The embossing process is sometimes termed pre-crêping, but it must not be assumed that the crêping action is effected by embossing, which only forms the pattern or channels into which the fabric will settle; as the pattern is even and uniform, the final result is much better. The thermoplastic nature of acetate rayon enables the embossing process to be very effective.

The usual procedure is to steam the fabric and then emboss it at a temperature of 120° to 130°C. Before the piece of fabric runs through the embossing calender, care should be taken to ensure that it is free from wrinkles, bias, or turned selvedges. The amount of tension applied should be just adequate for the smooth running of the cloth, as any excess is apt to cause a cutting of the weft.

Considerable care and experience are necessary for the successful operation of the embossing process; otherwise the fine filaments will be frayed, and this defect does not usually become apparent until the final stentering operation. According to Atkinson (J.S.D.C., 1942, 58, 89), the extent and depth of cuts in the highly twisted weft are proportional to the temperature and pressure applied between the bowls of the calender. This is shown by the results in the following table, which refer to comparative strength tests on 3-inch strips of fabric across the weft and covering about 220 picks; readings were taken of the load when the fabric began to tear and when the rupture ceased.

EFFECT OF EMBOSSING ACETATE-WARP VISCOSE-CRÊPE-WEFT FABRIC

Temperature °C.	Tension lb.	Pressure lb./sq. in.	Initial break lb.	Final break lb.
Untreated	—	—	38	42
30	7	400	25	35
		550	22	32
		700	18	22
		850	13	16
		1,000	16	20
		1,150	8	11

Temperature °C.	Tension lb.	Pressure lb./sq. in.	Initial break lb.	Final break lb.
50	7	400	22	28
		550	14	20
		700	14	17·5
		850	14	15
		1,000	12	12
		1,150	10	10
50	13·5	400	18	20
		550	12	20
		700	11	13
		850	10	10
		1,000	10	10
		1,150	6	6

The tension of 7 lb. may be regarded as normal.

These results demonstrate that any form of embossing, even with minimum pressure, has a deleterious effect on the tenacity and extensibility of the fabric, although it would be possible to reach 550 to 700 lb. per square inch at 30°C. without perceptible reduction in strength. Higher temperatures seem to induce tendering, but these are often necessary for a more permanent effect; pressure of 550 lb. per square inch should not be exceeded in such cases.

Because of the thermoplastic nature of the acetate warp, the pre-embossing treatment is at its best on goods containing acetate rayon; under suitable conditions of temperature and pressure the embossed pattern persists for some time, but for the best results the goods should be crêped within 24 hours of embossing. In addition to forming a matrix into which the contracting yarns are directed, the pre-embossing treatment serves to correct uneven tensions in all the rayon yarns and also to correct uneven sizing which may cause uneven contraction. Hence it has become customary to pre-emboss most crêpes, including the all-viscose types, as a more regular effect is obtained. With the latter type of fabric, the effect of embossing is much less effective than where acetate rayon is present and it is necessary to crêpe as soon as possible after embossing. The best viscose crêpes do not require embossing and do not benefit, for a properly prepared and constructed fabric "finishes itself" so that excessive work in finishing is only necessary to cover variations and deficiencies. Cuprammonium rayon does not respond to pre-embossing at all well, but there seems to be a general tendency to emboss almost all crêpes as a precautionary measure.

For the production of the crêpe effect it is not sufficient merely to wet the fabric; a certain amount of pebble will be produced in this manner, but the full crêpe appearance demands a very thorough saturation with water. It might be thought that the crêping action could be effected at the same time as the scour, and whilst this might be possible in theory, actual practice has shown that it is better to have a crêping bath which is quite separate from the scouring or boiling process. When the grey cloth is plunged suddenly into a boiling soap solution, the fabric structure is loosened and more scope is given to the action of the crêpe yarns, with the result that the pebble is somewhat coarse in character as well as uneven. The modern tendency is towards a slow crêping action which produces a much finer pebble and a more even effect. One of the older methods of handling crêpes was to treat them in concentric form on special

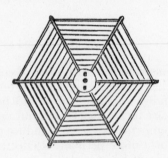

FIG. 100.—Diagram of the star frame
for crêping.

star-shaped frames with small hooks securing the selvedges; these frames were lowered into the vessels which contained the necessary liquors for scouring and dyeing. This somewhat tedious process was necessitated by the fact that unless handled in open width, crêpes were apt to develop creases or other irregularities which became set and were impossible to remove without spoiling the appearance of the fabric. Some large part of these defects, such as crows'-feet marks, was due to the fact that local irregularities in respect of pressure or firmness prevented a uniform crêping. When crêpes are sufficiently steeped in open width and free from creases they may be handled subsequently in rope form; this method revolutionised crêping technique.

A useful account of crêpe finishing has been given by Pickering (Dyer, 1944, *91*, 34); all crêpes should be received on wooden pegs or cardboard tubes, for plait-marks will almost certainly show themselves in the finished goods. Many faults which appear after dyeing are most difficult to remedy; they are largely obviated by efficient oversight in the grey-room and by careful crêping.

Crêping was based on the methods adopted for real silk, and the following manipulative processes may be considered:

(*a*) Treatment on star-frames.
(*b*) Treatment in book-fold form.
(*c*) Treatment in the loop or reeled form.
(*d*) Continuous crêping.

It should also be appreciated that the speed of crêping has an enormous effect on the finished fabric; some crêpes contain a high degree of pebble, whereas the flat crêpes with little pebble may show very little surface difference from ordinary fabrics, but on handling they exhibit the peculiar extension and elastic properties associated with crêpes. Flat crêpes are produced by a slow and regular relaxation of the twist in the yarns; even with this slow and natural contraction, shrinkages of at least 12·5% are required for the typical effect.

The coarse or fine nature of the crêpe is influenced by a number of factors, including yarn and fabric structure as well as the finishing treatment. Coarse pebble results from a yarn of high twist made with a few coarse filaments and a soft size; the crêping treatment should be in solutions of high concentrations and high temperatures. For fine crêpes, on the other hand, the yarn should have a relatively low twist and consist of numerous fine filaments and a hard size; the shrinkage in finishing should take place in solutions of low concentration and at a relatively low temperature. It may be remarked that suggestions have been made to control the crêping during finishing by the addition to the crêping bath of solutions which repress the swelling, as for example, 5% of common salt or 10% of glycerol.

Crêping is an initial finishing process; that is to say, it takes place before bleaching or dyeing, and is the first stage in the treatment of the woven cloth for the consumer.

As it is customary to bleach and dye after crêping, it will be realised that these processes involve further wet treatments in which more crêping is apt to occur if the goods are not already fully crêped; bleaching and dyeing generally take place in rope form or sometimes in semi-open width, so that any crêping at this stage would involve the production of permanent creases and other marks on account of the differences in tension and pressure in various parts of the fabric. Hence it is essential to realise the importance of complete and thorough crêping before the fabric is allowed to form a rope.

The general procedure, therefore, is to give a crêping treatment in open width, followed by a scour, in which any residual strains are also removed; as previously mentioned, it is often advantageous with acetate warp and viscose crêpe weft fabrics to emboss a pattern on which the crêpe is induced to form.

The manipulation of the fabric during crêping may take place in

7

discontinuous or continuous manner; the discontinuous methods are founded on the old treatments for crêpes of real silk and involve forming the fabric at full width into a reel or plaiting it into book-fold. The cloth is then treated in loops or in folds at full width and without tension; this method is slow and demands personal attention, but gives excellent results.

With the popular acetate warp, viscose crêpe weft material, a common sequence of operations is as follows:

(*1*) Stenter to remove wrinkles.
(*2*) Emboss.
(*3*) Crêpe by one of the following methods:
    (*a*) book-fold—suspend on strings from a selvedge.
    (*b*) loop—suspend on strings from a selvedge.
    (*c*) loop—suspend on poles.
    (*d*) continuous crêping.
(*4*) Scour, generally in rope or semi-open form.
(*5*) Bleach and dye.
(*6*) Hydroextract.
(*7*) Dry loose in a festoon machine.
(*8*) Soften and stenter to width, or use Palmer machine.
(*9*) Calender or decatise.

Crêping is usually effected by stringing the pieces and gradually raising the temperature, starting from cold water. A fuller crêpe with more "pebble" can be obtained at a higher temperature, but creasing and cracking are apt to occur, particularly in cloths with acetate warp and viscose weft and of low quality. The crêping process is determined to some extent by the type of fabric, but in general, an increased pebble is obtained by the cold-to-hot method, followed by slack drying on a brattice or festoon drier.

With many fabrics containing acetate rayon, it is customary to delustre and crêpe in one operation; the general methods of reducing the lustre of acetate rayon are described on page 319.

A special type of semi-delustred acetate yarn called Opaceta was marketed by Courtaulds, and this retains its dullness even after ironing; it should not be delustred with phenol. If further delustring is required it may be achieved by treating in soap solutions at temperatures between 80° and 100°C., the maximum effect being obtained at 100°C.

For crêping fabrics containing Opaceta, a flat crêpe and soft handle may be obtained by starting in cold water and raising the temperature; for a semi-delustred effect the temperature may be raised to, but not above, 80°C. If a large pin-head effect is required, crêping should be started at a higher temperature, the dullest results being obtained at 100°C.

In a typical treatment of crêpes, the fabric may be reeled or plaited into book-form with laps of 36 to 44 inches; the book of fabric is then sewn with loops of twine through the selvedge on one side only of the book. The loops are about 10 inches long. The fabric is suspended from a horizontal pole which passes through the loops, so that the weft hangs vertically in the soap bath into which the fabric is lowered so that it is completely immersed. In this manner, the liquor is able freely to circulate between the folds of the cloth, which is free from creases during the crêping action. The

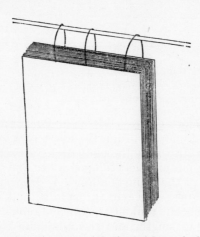

FIG. 101.—Diagram of the book-fold method of arranging cloth for crêping.

temperature of the soap solution is often about 75° to 80°C., but it is preferable to start with a warm solution and gradually raise the temperature.

The use of soap instead of water may be attributed to two factors: first, the soap solution is a good wetting agent; and, secondly, it acts as a lubricant and assists the movement of yarns, which slide over one another during the crêping. Where the fabric contains cellulose acetate rayon, the temperature should not exceed 85°C., or some delustring may result; in actual fact, advantage is often taken of the crêping treatment to produce a subdued lustre on acetate rayon at the same time, by raising the temperature and adding a little phenol to the soap solution (see page 320).

An alternative to the book-fold method of handling crêpes is to treat the reeled fabric in hank-form without stringing; the cloth is suspended from pairs of half-round sticks and turned by a similar method to that used in the dyeing of yarn in hank-form. In this case, however, the warp hangs vertically.

The fabric may be wound on a collapsible reel, and the selvedges at the end are stitched to the selvedges of the fold beneath. The reel is then collapsed and the fabric is withdrawn on two smooth sticks, one of which acts as a support for the cloth and the other is used for turning it every 10 to 15 minutes.

The manipulation of the fabric in book-fold or reel is obviously discontinuous, but methods of continuous crêping have been devised. The continuous method is definitely preferred in the U.S.A., but the book-fold method is more common in England.

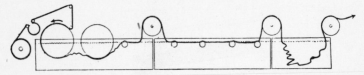

FIG. 102.—Diagram of the trough system of continuous crêping.

A simple continuous process consists in passing the fabric, in open width, around and under a drum, the lower part of which dips into the crêping liquor; this wets the cloth and starts the crêping action evenly, whilst the fabric is held in open width and free from creases. At the underside of the drum the fabric is drawn away, and either floats or is carried on a conveyor through the bulk of the liquor and still in open width. The tank or trough containing the solution may be 12 to 18 feet in length, and the minimum time of treatment should be about 10 minutes.

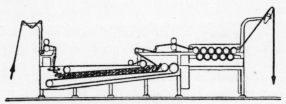

FIG. 103.—Diagram of the lattice system of continuous crêping.

This method is not very suitable for heavy fabrics; the difficulties of avoiding creases and the fact that crêping is apt to take place somewhat rapidly also contribute to a preference for crêping in book or folded form.

A commonly used crêping liquor which seems satisfactory for a variety of fabrics is 1% of a good oil soap, 0·25% soda ash, and 0·1% of a sulphated fatty alcohol or other good wetting agent. The solution should give uniform and instantaneous wetting, whereby the size softens and the yarns swell to cause weft shrinkage and crêping; complete removal of the size generally takes place in the subsequent scour.

Fabrics composed entirely of regenerated cellulose are sometimes passed through a crêping bath of sodium hydroxide solution, which produces a great increase in diameter. This preliminary treatment with alkali at 25° to 30°C. gives a slightly more regular and a finer crêpe than that produced by the action of hot soap, but the cloth is a little harder. The optimum concentration of sodium hydroxide varies according to the particular fabric, but is easily determined by testing strips, 10 inches in length, in solutions of 2°, 4°, 6°, and 8°Tw.NaOH.

It is necessary to maintain a strict control of the alkali process in order to avoid tendering, but maximum contraction may readily be obtained in this manner. Such a treatment may be found satisfactory with goods of the crêpe-romaine type which often contain spun rayon crêpe yarns. Experience has shown that it is not easy to secure full crêping with this type of fabric, even in open width, by ordinary methods, and that further shrinkage takes place in rope form, causing crease marks, possibly on account of mechanical agitation, which is known to promote shrinkage. The alkali should be removed by rinsing before passing to the scouring process.

Excellent crêpe fabrics are also made with real silk crêpe wefts, and these are generally treated in book-fold or loop form by stringing and suspending from one selvedge; the strings at the lower selvedge may be used to prevent the pieces from ballooning in the crêping bath. Where real silk is crêped, the amount of soap in the bath may be increased to about 2%. The usual procedure is to wet out the pieces in the cold and gradually raise the temperature by a closed heating coil under the false bottom of the vessel; some finishers believe in raising the temperature to slightly above that which will be used in any subsequent process in order to avoid cracking during scouring or dyeing. The time taken to raise the temperature to the maximum may be 1 to 2 hours for goods containing rayon and 3 to 4 hours for real silk fabrics. Where fabrics contain acetate rayon, they must not be permitted to remain too long in the soap solution even at 80°C., as saponification is apt to occur after 4 hours; if delustring is required, however, then other methods are adopted.

The subsequent scouring bath is really to complete the removal of size. With acetate warps, and gelatine sized wefts, a bath containing 0·15% soap and 0·1% ammonia, together with a little solvent, has been recommended by Atkinson (J.S.D.C., 1942, 58, 89); with oil-sized wefts, it is advisable to use 0·15 to 0·25% soap flakes, and 0·1% sodium perborate at 60° to 70°C. for 20 minutes, adding the perborate gradually, followed by a further 0·1% added in a similar manner over a period of 20 to 30 minutes.

When a substantial degree of crêping has occurred, the fabric may be scoured and washed in semi-open width or even in rope form. These processes are generally effected on elliptical wince machines with numerous compartments. A typical hot scouring liquor consists of 0·5% soap, 0·25% sulphated fatty alcohol, and 0·25% tribasic sodium phosphate; it is common to have two compartments for the scouring liquor, the first operating at about 85° to 95°C. and the second at 70° to 85°C., but the higher temperatures in this series should not be used with cellulose acetate rayon unless some delustring is required. Rinsing generally takes place in three stages: first, at a temperature of 70° to 85°C.; secondly, at 40° to 60°C; and, finally, in cold water. It is important to avoid a rapid chilling of the hot fabric, if the finest and most regular crêpe effect is to be obtained.

The fabric may then be hydroextracted on the centrifuge and opened by hand; the centrifugal force is apt to mark the more susceptible crêpes and every care should be taken by such means as careful packing, if necessary in bags, and slow braking at the end of the process. Many crêpes, however, are opened by hand as they pass over the large reel of the elliptical wince, and the water removed by suction on the full-width hydroextractor, which is less prone to disturb the surface of the cloth in its wet and swollen state.

It is most essential to pay strict attention to the method of drying if a satisfactory handle is to be achieved. The goods are best dried in a current of warm air in some form of loop or festoon drier, taking care to avoid warp extension during the feeding of the fabric into the machine; drum driers of the Bouthion or Weisbach type may also be used, but with a slightly lower production. Machines of this type allow the fabric to dry and shrink naturally at the same time.

The temperature of drying should be uniform and preferably not in excess of 85°C.; indeed, the best handle from the standpoint of mellowness is often obtained at 60°C.

The pieces may then be finished on a stenter which adjusts the width and straightens the weft; it seems preferable to roll the fabric on to a shell after leaving the drying stove, as this gives better control when feeding in to the stenter, particularly when the shell is mounted on a swinging stand to enable the weft to be straightened. The usual method of stentering is on the open frame with a steam-box to moisten the fabric as it approaches its maximum width; with some crêpes, the stentering is effected gradually, bringing the pieces to the required width by passing down the stenter two or three times. Care must be taken in stentering to obtain the best effect; a temperature of 60°C. again gives the best handle, but even drying is also essential and some stenters are fitted with a steam coil below the chain race running the whole length of the machine to warm the clips, prevent condensation, and dry the selvedges. With crêpe georgettes, it is often customary to finish the goods on the hand-frames, in order to obtain the necessary dimensions in the finished fabric, as a careful control of warp shrinkage is essential.

In England, and also in continental Europe, many crêpes, particularly of lower quality, are softened in the dyebath, opened and batched at the suction extractor, and finally dried on a Krantz stenter. Pin stenters are nearly always used for the final drying, even if the goods are dried in the loose state after dyeing.

The stentering process must not destroy the crêpe, but merely free the fabric from wrinkles, straighten it, and adjust the width. Considerable shrinkage occurs during crêping; for example, a fabric may be 42 inches wide in the grey state, shrink to between 28 and 30 inches on crêping, and finish at 36 inches in width. Warp shrinkage is often 10 to 15%.

It must be remembered that, when properly crêped, the fabric has natural dimensions and every attempt should be made to adhere or approximate to these during the final finishing processes. The latest types of overfeed pin stenters with balanced airflow and thermostatic control are capable of giving satisfactory results in respect of handle and of rate of drying.

An alternative method of drying is on the blanket-finishing machine of the Palmer type; the fabric may be brought to width on the belt stretcher, or on the short stenter with which some Palmers are equipped. The pressure of steam in the cylinder should not exceed 5 lb. per square inch or some glazing may occur; the pressure of the blanket should also be at a minimum.

Where softeners are applied, with novelty crêpes and fancy weaves, this is better done in the final rinse after bleaching or dyeing; with ordinary crêpe fabrics, however, the use of a mangle is preferable on account of penetration. The application of the softener may then take place immediately before stentering. Some crêpes are stiffened with a little dextrin, gum, or resin.

For certain fabrics, a calendering operation may be necessary to improve the draping properties, rearrange the pebble, or slightly to dull the general effect; a three-bowl calender with soft bowls at the top and bottom is generally utilised at room temperatures and at low pressures.

With crêpes containing acetate rayon, wool, or real silk, it is often customary to give a decatising treatment; this may also be employed with viscose crêpes which would be flattened by the calender. Decatising removes harshness, excessive lustre, cracks, and non-uniformity of pebble; under the action of steam the fabric becomes plastic and mouldable so that it is possible to rearrange the pebble to some extent.

SILK

The finishing of real silk crêpes is broadly similar to that already described for rayons; indeed, as previously stated, the finishing of rayon crêpes is based on the old methods of manipulating silk crêpes.

The modern method seems to start with a soaking treatment at about 80°C. in soft water containing either 10 lb. of borax or 1 gallon of ammonia (d 1·25) per 1,000 gallons; this treatment removes the tints which are commonly employed to distinguish yarns of different twist, and also removes the throwing oils present in the silk. The pre-soaking results in the formation of a finer and more regular crêpe than that formed by immersing the silk directly into the boil-off solution.

Crêping continues in the usual boil-off process for treating silk in a solution containing about 1·5% of soap; it is wise to control the alkalinity of the soap solution by using caustic soda in addition. A bath at pH 10 to 10·2 will boil-off or scour the usual crêpes in between 2 and 2·5 hours.

An improvement on the usual method of manipulating the fabric in skein form has been described by Le Brun (Text. World, 1935, *85*, 2257); the use of bent rods enables the entire piece of silk fabric to be immersed during the whole treatment.

When boiling and crêping are complete, the soap must be removed by rinsing, and where hard water is a difficulty, the use of sodium hexametaphosphate is an advantage.

WOOL

Two general methods are available for the production of wool crêpes. The first is due to the relaxation of twist, and is that which is commonly employed; the second method depends on the effect of reagents which are capable of causing breakdown of the disulphide bonds and resulting in super-contraction.

Where wool crêpes are produced by the use of hard-twisted yarns, it is important to bring about the distortion of the fabric before the torsional forces are absorbed by the relaxation of the fibres. As is well known, wool is attacked by boiling water with breakdown of disulphide bonds, so that the full effect cannot be realised on account of the rapid decay of stress. According to Strmac (see Speakman, J.T.I., 1941, *32*, 83) the optimum temperature for developing wool crêpes is about 42°C. at pH 5 to 6. As the decay of stress in deformed fibres is greatest in alkaline media and least in acid media, according to Speakman and Shah (J.S.D.C., 1941, *57*, 108), acid conditions are particularly suitable for crêping processes, and, in actual fact, many crêping treatments take place in strongly acid solutions and at temperatures as high as 80°C. 1% H_2SO_4 appears to be a suitable concentration.

With wool crêpes, the relaxation of twist and the formation of pebble may take place during the crabbing process.

Here again it is possible to use other methods; for example, fabrics may be woven in which the warp is comprised of yarns which have been given permanent set, together with those which have not been so treated. During the scouring process, the untreated yarns contract and carry the treated yarns with them to give a cockled effect.

A variation of this idea has been developed by Bliss of the Wool Industries Research Association and patented in B.P. 190,881. The process depends on the fact that it is possible to stretch wool hairs even up to 100% of their original length, but when placed in water again they contract to their original length. It does not appear possible to stretch yarns to 100%, but nevertheless, they may be stretched to a considerable extent in the moist state and then dried. When woven into fabrics and then wetted, the yarns contract and may be used for crêpe effects. (It may be stated that Bliss also describes the production of yarns of fine count by stretching and then setting them in the stretched state by the prolonged application of heat, such as steam or hot water.)

Other treatments rely on chemical crêping; the fabric may be printed with a paste containing hypochlorite and then passed through an acid bath, when chlorine is liberated. A thorough rinse completes the preparatory process. When the fabric is milled, however, the treated portions will contract less than the remainder and so create a crêpon effect.

An alternative process is to print the pieces of wool, usually in a striped pattern, with suitably thickened sulphuric acid; the goods are then passed through a weak bath of sodium or calcium hypochlorite, rinsed, and milled in soap solution. The chlorinated portions of the fabric do not shrink and so permanent crimp effects are obtained. This type of process is usually restricted to lightweight fabrics.

It is also possible to use mixed yarns, some normal and others non-felting, for the production of crêpe effects on milling.

It is well known that when wool is treated with hot solutions of sodium bisulphite, considerable contraction takes place, accompanied by swelling; this effect could be used for the production of crêpes, as suggested by Elsaesser in D.R.P. 233,210. The use of solutions of calcium thiocyanate has been described by Justin-Mueller (Rev. Gén. Mat. Col., 1937, 41, 419). Both of these reagents, however, attack the disulphide bonds of the keratin so that their action is accompanied by damage to the fibre.

The chemistry of the bisulphite reaction on wool is as follows:

$$R-S-S-R + NaHSO_3 \longrightarrow R-SH + R-S-SO_3Na$$

(see also Phillips and Elsworth, Biochem. J., 1938, *32*, 837). The reaction with thiocyanate, on the other hand, appears to depend on the formation of calcium hydrosulphide, which reduces the disulphide bonds to cysteine side-chains.

The use of acidified solutions of calcium thiocyanate seems to have been first suggested by Favre (Bull. Soc. Ind., Mulhouse, 1921, *87*, 65; 1925, *91*, 615). A greater shrinkage is obtained with the thiocyanate than with sulphuric acid; a recommended treatment is to use a crêping bath containing 20 g. of calcium thiocyanate and 6 g. of sulphuric acid (*d* 1·82) per litre. The temperature of the bath should be raised to 75°C. over a period of 15 to 20 minutes and maintained at that temperature for an hour.

Siefert (Z. angew. Chem., 1899, *69*, 86) was the first to investigate the action of thiocyanates on wool generally. For crêping wool, either calcium or barium thiocyanate may be used, followed by steaming; the yarn is apt to be tender during the steaming operation, and this remark applies to the use of sodium bisulphite also. Siefert described the use of concentrated solutions of various salts, such as calcium chloride, zinc chloride, or zinc sulphate for producing high shrinkages with wool; warm zinc chloride solutions may be used, or a solution of zinc sulphate containing 500 g. per litre may be employed at the boiling-point.

Barr and Speakman (J.T.I., 1944, *35*, 77) have drawn attention to the crêping action of phenol, which had previously been shown to swell and dissolve wool by Herzog and Krahn (Z. physiol. Chem., 1924, *134*, 290). Considerable shrinkage takes place when wool is treated for 15 minutes with phenol hydrate ($2C_6H_5OH.H_2O$) at temperatures up to 90°C. When the treated material is washed in running water, it tends to revert to its original dimensions, but the primary shrinkage can be rendered permanent by steaming at 102°C. for 10 minutes. The action of steam enhances the shrinkage and brings about some permanent set.

Examination of a series of phenols showed that the dissociation constant should not exceed 1×10^{-9} at 25°C. or the setting action will be inhibited by the acidity. These data may be applied to the production of pattern effects by printing with phenol and steaming.

COTTON

The production of cotton crêpes follows the two main lines suggested previously; there are two alternatives, first, to use fabrics containing yarns of high twist, when the crêpe depends on the relaxation of twist, and, secondly, to use chemical reagents which exert a strong swelling action on the cotton.

The former method does not necessitate further description.

It is possible to produce crêpe effects of a certain type without the use of highly twisted yarns in the fabric; no characteristic pebble effect is obtained, but there is the peculiar crispness and elasticity associated with the crêpe structure. These crêpes are generally produced by chemical means, rather than the purely physical mechanism of untwisting and swelling, but they rely on swelling agents for their efficiency, that is, solutions of reagents which exert a great swelling action on the particular fibre.

One of the best-known illustrations of this type of crêping is by means of caustic soda solutions on cotton, as in mercerising, but without tension; other swelling agents may also be used, as for example, sulphuric acid, zinc chloride, etc. (see page 111). This method is mainly used for pattern effects by printing in the well-known crimp or crêpon style. The cotton cloth is generally printed in a striped pattern which occupies about 50% of the surface of the fabric; the thickened solution of caustic soda corresponds to NaOH of 50° to 60°Tw. On immersing in water, the cloth shrinks in the printed portions and causes the remainder to crumple with it, thus giving a "cockled" effect. An alternative method is to print the fabric with a resist, which may be applied in any type of pattern, and then treat the whole fabric with caustic soda solution of mercerising strength. Suitable recipes for this method of printing may be found in Textile Printing by Knecht and Fothergill (Griffin, London, 1936, page 848).

Crêping by chemical means is commonly utilised for the production of seersucker, plissé, blister, and crinkle crêpes.

It is also possible to produce crêpe effects by treatment of fabrics containing more than one type of fibre; for instance, a cloth with cotton and silk, or cotton and acetate rayon, may be treated with caustic soda solution which causes shrinkage of the cotton, but not of the silk or acetate rayon. The treatment by padding should be carried out as quickly as possible and the washing operation should be conducted with cold water.

Fabrics with cotton warps and wool wefts may also be mercerised without tension to give crêpe effects; the goods should be washed quickly with cold water in order to avoid attack by the alkali on the wool. Where mixtures of cotton and wool are mercerised to give crêpe effects, the concentration of sodium hydroxide solution should be 22° or 50°Tw.; the use of concentrations around 35°Tw. should be avoided because of their more rapid attack on wool.

ACETATE RAYON

The fact that acetate rayon only swells to a very slight extent when immersed in water has limited its use in crêpe fabrics where shrinkage of the acetate is required; it is most useful, however, where crêpe effects by differential shrinkage are wanted.

In order to produce crêpe effects with acetate rayon, it is necessary to give the yarns much higher twist than required for viscose rayon; often such high twist is accompanied by a reduction in breaking load and also in extension at break, so methods have been sought to obviate these defects. Two general methods are to treat the yarn with volatile swelling agents or with a colloidal substance capable of forming an elastic coating on drying; there are also certain specific methods of treating acetate rayon to improve its crêping power, and induce a potential shrinkage of at least 10 to 15%.

B.P. 351,999 and 352,000 by Dreyfus and Dickie of British Celanese suggest treating the threads with a swelling agent before or after twisting, or, alternatively, treating with a swelling agent and then with a solution enabling the swelling agent to exert its full effect, i.e. with water.

Suitable shrinking agents are the thiocyanates of ammonium, calcium and other metals, zinc chloride, acetic, formic or lactic acids, methyl alcohol, ethyl alcohol, diacetone alcohol, acetone, methyl ethyl ketone, various ethers of ethylene glycol, glycol mono-acetate, methyl acetate, ethyl lactate, diethyl tartrate, aniline, phenols, and the mono-, di-, and triacetins.

Crêping power may be imparted to yarns of acetate rayon by conducting the twisting of the yarn in two stages with intermediate wetting, as described in B.P. 386,344 of Dickie and Moncrieff; another method outlined in B.P. 386,374 is to give an intermediate treatment with vapours which exert a softening action. The insertion of the final twist when the yarn has been softened with organic liquids or vapours or with aqueous solutions is claimed by Dreyfus in B.P. 441,573.

Highly twisted crêpe yarns may also be obtained by twisting the threads in a single stage and steaming them during the insertion of the twist under conditions such that moisture is present (B.P. 437,019). Other processes by Dreyfus and his collaborators include stretching the yarns beyond the elastic limit in hot water or steam and then inserting the twist (B.P. 438,588 and 9); treatment with hot water in the final twisting operation is discussed in B.P. 438,654. Stretching beyond the elastic limit in presence of an organic softening agent and then imparting a high degree of twist is the subject of B.P. 437,943 by Dreyfus, Moncrieff, Menzer, and Eccles.

Another interesting method of inducing crêping power is to shrink the acetate yarn until it has sufficient twist to give crêpe effects; the twist before shrinkage may be 20 to 30% lower than the final twist, according to B.P. 457,933 of Dreyfus.

Reference has been made to the production of crêpe yarns by coating the acetate rayon with a material capable of swelling, drying the treated yarn, and then inserting the necessary twist; suitable coatings suggested by Dickie in B.P. 348,589 are casein, egg albumen, rubber latex, and alginate. The crêpe fabric is formed by treatment with water or other aqueous liquid which swells the coating deposit. Inorganic substances may also be used to increase the bulk of the acetate material and therefore its crêping power, according to B.P. 378,910 of Dreyfus, Dickie, and Moncrieff. Some earlier processes of Dreyfus, B.P. 224,642 and 226,256, describe treatment of the yarn prior to twisting; solutions of gum, gelatin, starch, or glucose may be applied, after which the acetate yarn is twisted, woven into a suitable fabric, and crêped in the usual manner.

Ewing of British Celanese has suggested the application of formaldehyde in the crêping of acetate fabrics containing yarn of high twist. B.P. 519,986 states that the formaldehyde may be applied to the fabric by padding, followed by drying slowly; scouring in a solution of 1 to 2·5% soap for a few minutes at 90° to 100°C. completes the operation. The application of formaldehyde in this manner makes possible the use of less highly twisted weft than is otherwise required for pebble effects, and also brings about a considerable reduction in the duration of the scouring treatment. Urquhart and Marsden of the British Cotton Industry Research Association have suggested the use of vapours of acetaldehyde or crotonaldehyde to produce better crêpe effects with cellulose acetate rayons; according to B.P. 545,422, these vapours should be applied before the scouring or crêping bath.

Chemical crêping, as distinct from the relaxation of twist, has also been suggested for acetate rayon fabrics. Cockled or puckered effects may be produced by printing the fabric with a suitable resist and then treating with nitric acid of 38°Tw. for 30 to 60 seconds, according to B.P. 413,150 of British Celanese; other suitable reagents are zinc chloride and the metallic thiocyanates. The reagents must be removed by a suitable washing process after they have exerted their local shrinking action.

Dreyfus and Dickie, in B.P. 408,654, claim the treatment of acetate rayon with solvents such as 35 to 55% acetone or 38 to 43% dioxan, both of which in aqueous solution produce considerable shrinkage of the acetate. Sowter and Perry, on the other hand, suggest the use of latent solvents in conjunction with water or with water and a compound with an alcoholic hydroxyl group, suitable latent solvents, described in B.P. 534,775, are methylene chloride, ethylene chloride, and ethyl acetate.

Crêping, which is partly chemical and partly physical may be realised by the methods of B.P. 380,505 of Dreyfus; acetate yarns are first shrunk at spaced intervals by application of a shrinking agent and an alcohol suitably diluted with benzene or carbon tetrachloride, followed by doubling with a yarn of cotton or of viscose rayon. The mixed threads are then treated with an agent which will shrink the remaining portion of the locally-treated yarns and so produce cockled effects; suitable shrinking agents are ethyl acetate, methyl chloride, tetrachlorethane, chloroform, dichlorethylene, methylene chloride, and ethylene chloride.

NYLON

Nylon also swells to a very limited extent when immersed in water and this property restricts its use in crêpe fabrics of the conventional type.

According to B.P. 553,442 of British Nylon Spinners, considerable shrinkage may be induced when nylon filaments or fabrics are immersed in warm phenol solutions of at least 2·5% concentration. Mixed fibres and fabrics so treated exhibit novel crêpe effects. A modification of this process (B.P. 562,555) depends upon a pretreatment of the nylon with formaldehyde before the actual shrinkage in phenol or formic acid solution.

It is, of course, known that crêpe-like effects can be produced in fabrics woven from nylon threads which have been cold-drawn to different extents and subsequently shrunk in the scouring operation.

CHAPTER IV
DISPERSION PROCESSES

FOR many years the dispersion processes produced the only permanent finishes for vegetable fibres, and they still remain of great importance. The common chemicals used in these finishes are sulphuric acid and sodium hydroxide, both of which are quite cheap; moreover, they are used in moderately concentrated forms and, having fulfilled their function as finishing agents, they find numerous applications, in the diluted state, in the ordinary processes of bleaching and dyeing.

These dispersion processes were originated by John Mercer about 1844, and were due to his preoccupation with substances which are capable of chemical combination with water and forming hydrates. He considered the possibility of a partial separation of different hydrates by slow fractional filtration, and in the course of his investigations, solutions of sodium hydroxide were filtered through cotton. With 63°Tw. NaOH solutions the fabric was changed considerably, becoming thicker, fuller, and more transparent. This was the origin of the mercerising process.

Mercer also examined the effects of certain concentrations of sulphuric acid at room temperatures and of concentrated solutions of zinc chloride at higher temperatures; hence, all three types of dispersing agents for cellulose were found by 1850.

MERCERISING

The commonest dispersion process for cotton is the mercerising process, effected by treating the material with sodium hydroxide solutions of 55° to 65°Tw. concentration at room temperatures, followed by washing.

The mercerising process of Mercer, where no tension was applied, exhibited the following interesting points:

(a) Shrinkage.
(b) Increase in tensile strength.
(c) Increased extension at break.
(d) Increased hygroscopicity.
(e) Increased affinity for dyes.
(f) Preferential absorption of NaOH during the process.
(g) Increased reaction at lower temperatures.

The silk-like lustre now commonly associated with mercerising is produced by tension; it was discovered by Horace Lowe in 1890, and was not known in Mercer's lifetime. Although the original mercerised product was often termed "fulled cotton," Mercer regarded the increased affinity for dyes as the most important technical aspect.

The lustre of cotton mercerised with tension is mainly due to increased surface smoothness and is intimately associated with the shape of the cross-sections of the hairs. Cotton hairs mercerised under tension are more nearly circular in cross-section than hairs mercerised without tension; Adderley (J.T.I., 1924, *15*, 195) was able to correlate lustre values with the shape of the cross-section of the cotton hair, and show that a good index was obtained by the ratio of the two axes of the hair. Hence, the cause of the improved lustre of

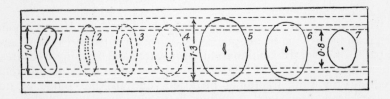

FIG. 104.—Changes in section of cotton hair during mercerising. (Stages *1* to *5* show progressive swelling in alkali; stage *6* shows that shrinkage starts on transfer to water, and is complete on drying as seen in stage 7.)

mercerised cotton is mainly due to the production of a cylindrical form.

Another characteristic feature of the mercerising process is the untwisting of the cotton hair by removal of the convolutions which normally exist in the native material. This deconvolution is an important contribution to lustre as the fibre tends to become cylindrical—the smooth rod of the early investigators.

An estimate of mercerising efficiency is based on deconvolution, and depends on cutting a number of 2-mm. fragments of cotton hairs and counting the proportion free from convolution; the result expressed as a percentage is called the Deconvolution Count. It has been found that if the figure is over 20, then it may be assumed that the fabric is mercerised; naturally the deconvolution depends to some extent on the constraint imposed during the process, so that goods mercerised without tension give better deconvolution counts than when mercerised under tension, and also hairs give better results than yarns, and yarns than fabrics.

Careful investigations by numerous workers revealed that the greatest swelling action of sodium hydroxide on cotton hairs took place in 15% solutions; such solutions are of only moderate concentration, but correspond to the full hydration of the alkali ion. This point was confirmed by examining the swelling action of LiOH, NaOH, KOH, RbOH, and CsOH, when it was found that the maximum swelling concentration depended on the degree of hydration of the alkali ion.

Although it had been established that 15% NaOH solutions (34° Tw.) give maximum swelling, yet commercial mercerising utilised

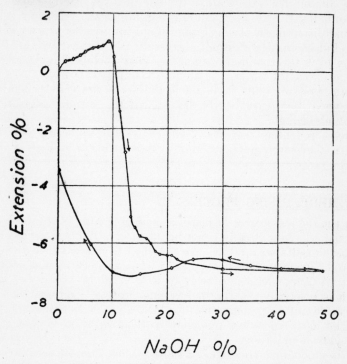

Fig. 105.—Changes in length of cotton hairs treated with a series of solutions of NaOH.

higher concentrations; this was not because of better results, but because of the preferential absorption of NaOH during the mercerising process.

Hence, in order to maintain a concentration necessary for efficient mercerising on a continuous basis, it is necessary to use concentrations which will allow for this preferential absorption. This particular phenomenon has aroused great interest, and as the absorption of NaOH was constant between certain concentrations, it was assumed that a definite compound was formed; later work showed that the water absorption played a large part and fell rapidly after reaching a maximum, thus causing the alkali absorption to appear constant.

8

Two views have been put forward to account for the swelling of cellulose in alkaline solutions of moderate concentration. The first has already been indicated, and takes into account molecular attraction with associated hydration; the second is based on the assumption that cellulose behaves as a weak monobasic acid and forms a sodium salt to an extent increasing with the concentration of the alkali. The excess alkali diffuses into the cellulose according to Donnan's theory of membrane equilibrium, and the resulting unequal distribution of ions brings about an osmosis which distends the cellulose until the osmotic pressure is balanced by the forces arising from the cohesion of the gel. When the alkali is replaced by a large excess of water, the sodium cellulosate is hydrolysed, the osmotic pressure falls, and the cellulose is recovered chemically unchanged, but permanently distorted if the osmotic pressure has been high enough.

These, and other features of the mercerising process, have been discussed in some detail by Marsh (Mercerising, Chapman & Hall, London, 1941).

THE MERCERISING PROCESS

As the highest degree of lustre after mercerising is obtained from material which is already constructed to give the maximum lustre, the best results with fabrics are obtained from weaves of the satin or sateen type in which there is a characteristic arrangement of floats. A preponderance of warp or weft yarn also produces a fabric which is responsive to the mercerising process. Combed yarns are preferable in fabrics mercerised for lustre, but soft-spun singles may be used as there is less tendency to disintegration in fabric than with yarn-mercerising.

It is customary to singe all cloths which are to be mercerised and so remove any loose projecting hairs, which otherwise would shrink and produce a fuzzy surface, detracting from the lustre of the body of the material which had been mercerised under tension. Nearly all woven fabrics are de-sized before mercerising, for otherwise the heat of reaction would necessitate cooling, and the alkali would also become contaminated more quickly than in absence of size.

Opinion is somewhat divided on the question of mercerising before or after bleaching; sometimes the matter is decided by the fabric itself, for with cloths of low tensile strength it may be advisable to mercerise in the grey state so that the strength of the material is increased at the earliest possible moment and so facilitate later manipulation.

Where goods are mercerised in the grey state, it is not generally necessary completely to remove the alkali by washing or acidification, for the cloth, saturated with the residual alkali, may go forward to the kiers where the alkali will be utilised in the scouring process; it may be remarked that a milder scour is required for goods which have been mercerised in the grey state, owing to the removal of some of the cotton wax. It also often happens that a softer handle is obtained on fabrics mercerised in the grey state compared with those treated after bleaching. A fundamental argument against mercerising in the grey state is the difficulty of rapid and even penetration by the caustic soda solution during the 30 to 50 seconds interval between impregnation and washing. The use of special wetting agents for mercerising has helped to overcome this difficulty, but even under the best conditions, high-speed mercerising is apt to be incomplete. A further consideration is that of cost, and where grey mercerising is undertaken, the recovery of the caustic soda is more difficult and expensive.

Reference has been made to the use of wetting agents for mercerising; phenolic compounds, such as cresylic acid, form the basis of most of the commercial preparations, but their wetting powers may be increased by the addition of solvents such as cyclohexanol. The amount of wetting agent rarely exceeds 2%, and in actual fact, about 0·5 to 1% is often adequate. In order to assist wetting, it was sometimes usual to give the cotton goods a preliminary boil in water or dilute alkali, and then mercerise them in the wet state; this procedure not only dilutes the alkali, but also entails a risk of uneven mercerising. The goods must be evenly expressed before mercerising, and all danger of local drying must be avoided.

Bleached or half-bleached material is usually mercerised in the dry state so that the danger of irregularities is obviated; the pure, clean, dry fabric gives more uniform and satisfactory results, and the subsequent dyeing is invariably better.

The usual process of mercerisation utilises caustic soda solution of 55° to 65°Tw. at room temperatures, and care should be taken to ensure that the contact with the alkali is sufficiently long to swell the cotton hairs and cause them to assume a cylindrical shape; owing to the high viscosity of the solution, the chief difficulty is that of poor penetration. When the external hairs of the yarn commence to swell, some constraint is placed on their neighbours, and owing to the limitations of yarn and cloth structure, the possibility of free swelling is considerably restricted. An absorbent material and a good wetting agent assist penetration, but the high pressures exerted by modern mercerising mangles also help; the latest developments in the way of chainless padless machines appear to rely solely on the absorbency of the goods and the wetting powers of the liquor.

The commonest method of mercerising cloth is by a process of shrinkage, followed by stretching during the washing stage. It is usual to employ two mangles for impregnating, although one mangle is often adequate for light fabrics such as lawns and handkerchief cloths. Where two mangles are utilised, a counter-current system may be adopted whereby the first impregnation is with 30°Tw. NaOH, whose lower viscosity assists wetting, before passing to the later compartments to meet alkali of 55° to 65°Tw. and of higher viscosity.

A set of iron drums between the mangles offers a support to the impregnated fabric, prevents rolling selvedges, and permits time for the alkali to react with the cotton. The use of two mangles and a set of cylinders enables certain variations in treatment to be accomplished; for instance, the second mangle may run faster than the first and so produce warp tension, or it may run slower and allow the fabric to shrink somewhat and absorb the alkali better at the second impregnation.

During the process of impregnation, the fabric shrinks, and it is necessary to pull it out again during the removal of the alkali; it is usual to mercerise to grey width in order to produce maximum lustre. The stretching and washing process may take place on a stenter or by means of curved rotating rollers, as described on page 44. The stenter-washing is commoner, and it is usual to start stretching the fabric whilst still wet with the alkali, bringing it to the required width in the first 15 to 20 feet of the stenter and then starting the washing, which may be with sprays, spurt-pipes, or weirs. If the washing is uneven, then the mercerising will be uneven, and the subsequent dyeing will also be uneven. During the passage through the washing portion of the stenter, it is essential that sufficient alkali should be removed from the goods to prevent subsequent shrinkage; this means that the concentration must be reduced to 15°Tw. NaOH (10°Tw. NaOH in the external liquor) before the goods reach the end of the stenter. The actual concentration is determined by the efficiency of the counter-current system of washing. If the fabric leaves the stenter whilst containing alkali of mercerising strength, it is possible to remove this later, without tension, and then stretch the cloth to the desired width; but it will shrink on the first wash. The dimensions of the fabric are more or less fixed at those where the alkali concentration is reduced to below 15° Tw. NaOH. A thorough washing with water completes the process.

Early investigations on the effect of the temperature of the alkali during the mercerising process revealed that the action increases as the temperature falls, so that it is possible to use more dilute alkali which has little effect at room temperatures, but at lower temperatures becomes capable of mercerising cotton. In other words, the same action is seen with alkali of the usual concentration at room temperatures and with more dilute alkali at a lower temperature.

Special effects, however, can be obtained by the use of alkali of the usual concentrations, but at temperatures below 0°C. These methods of mercerising have been investigated and extensively developed by Heberlein; for instance, according to B.P. 108,671, if cotton fabric is impregnated with NaOH solutions of 52°Tw. at a temperature of −10°C. for 1 minute, it acquires a transparent appearance which is not removed even by washing. This effect may be enhanced by a subsequent treatment with sulphuric acid of at least 108°Tw. (see page 121). The concentration of the alkali, the temperature, and the duration of treatment may be varied according to the quality of the material and the desired effect.

B.P. 191,203 discloses that the transparent appearance obtained by the action of cold alkali may be further improved if the material is mercerised in the usual manner, either before or after treatment with the cold alkali. In this way it is possible to achieve a transparent and lustrous effect.

Many variations are possible, some of which are:

(a) Normal mercerisation—cold lye.
(b) Cold lye—normal mercerisation.
(c) Normal mercerisation—cold lye—normal mercerisation.
(d) Cold lye—normal mercerisation—cold lye.

These processes form the basis of the well-known Swiss finish and are mainly applied to cloths such as voiles and organdies, although similar effects may be obtained by the methods of B.P. 200,881 (see page 127).

It must be realised that the peculiar transparent appearance from the use of NaOH at −10°C. is determined to some extent by the construction of the yarn and fabric. According to B.P. 192,227, as the yarns become coarser the transparency disappears until it is replaced by a linen-like effect which is also fast to washing. It is not possible to draw a sharp line of demarcation between the transparent and linen-like effects, but, in general, yarns of 80s counts and finer show transparency, whereas the coarser yarns exhibit the linen appearance when mercerised in this particular manner. This is qualified to some extent by the type of cotton and the construction of the fabric. All these special treatments with low temperatures of 0° to −10°C. apply to concentrations of NaOH of 50° to 60°Tw.

Another interesting process of Heberlein (U.S.P. 1,717,315) does not use such low temperatures nor such high concentrations of alkali; 23°Tw. NaOH at 2° to 6°C., but not above 8°C., is stated to give a stiff effect which is useful for low-quality cotton voiles and loosely twisted material. The firmness and crispness are fast to washing.

The properties of the mercerised product have been examined in considerable detail by various workers. The increased chemical reactivity, but without new chemical properties, has been estimated by oxidation with alkaline hypobromite solutions, when it was found that most commercially mercerised fabrics fell within a reactivity ratio range of 1·22 to 1·63, whereas the unmercerised material gave ratios between 0·95 and 1·12.

The increased absorptive capacity of mercerised cotton is well known; the ratio of the moisture content of mercerised cotton to scoured cotton at any humidity is independent of that humidity,

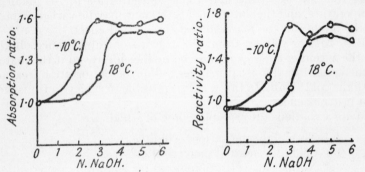

FIG. 106.—Absorption and reactivity ratios of cotton treated with NaOH at −10°C. and at 18°C.

being 1·57 for absorption and 1·46 for desorption, when the cotton was mercerised without tension. Commercially mercerised fabrics generally show an absorption ratio of 1·2.

The increased absorption of dyestuffs is a noteworthy feature of the mercerised product, being greatest when the material has been mercerised without tension; no matter whether the cotton is mercerised with tension or no, the drying of the material after mercerising brings about a decreased affinity for dyes compared with that possessed in the wet state, and this decrease is greater the higher the temperature of drying.

The absorption of dilute alkali by the mercerised material has also aroused interest, and may be used as a test of mercerising efficiency, but here again the product mercerised without tension gives higher results than that treated under tension. As most fabrics are mercerised for increased lustre, these tests are of limited value, for the full lustre only results from mercerising under tension.

Lustre is only a superficial property which may also be produced by mechanical means, but good mercerising is a deep-seated phenomenon. The measurement of lustre cannot be regarded as an absolute test of mercerising efficiency; the various methods of estimating lustre have been given by Marsh (Mercerising, Chapman & Hall, London, 1941). A good estimate of mercerising efficiency may be had by examination of cross-sections of the mercerised product under the microscope; a peculiar compactness of the rounded fibres is characteristic of cotton which has been properly mercerised under tension.

During the mercerising process, the native cellulose changes to the hydrate or dispersed cellulose, as revealed by X-ray photographs; hence the degree of mercerising may be estimated by the extent to which the conversion to the dispersed form has been effected, and the amount of tension applied during the process is revealed by the degree of orientation.

The X-ray photographs also show that as a result of the mercerising process the planes of the molecular chains have been moved apart and the chains of glucose residues have also been given a slight twist; this results in the hydroxyl groups being more accessible than in native cellulose and so accounts for the increased reactivity and absorptive capacity of the mercerised product.

Before leaving this subject, it may be remarked that it is not possible, in the same product, to have maximum lustre and maximum absorptive capacity.

Rayon

The mercerisation of rayon may appear to be completely unnecessary on first thoughts, for it already possesses a high degree of lustre; indeed, there are numerous processes for reducing the lustre of rayon which is sometimes thought to be excessive (see page 308).

Many textile materials, however, consist of mixtures of cotton and rayon, and it is often necessary to mercerise the material either to improve the lustre of the cotton or to bring its affinity for dyes closer to that of the rayon.

It may be mentioned that acetate rayon withstands the action of caustic soda of mercerising strength, provided the temperature does not exceed 15°C., so that all that is necessary is to conduct the mercerising process as rapidly as possible and wash with cold water instead of hot water so as to avoid hydrolysis of the cellulose acetate.

Actually, regenerated cellulose also withstands the action of caustic soda of mercerising strength, but the difficulty arises when the alkali has to be removed, for in washing with water, the alkali becomes diluted, and at a concentration of 9% the swelling of the rayon is so pronounced that it loses its form and becomes disintegrated. Prolonged immersion brings about dissolution. One of the earliest suggestions for obviating this difficulty was made in B.P. 295,062 of the Bleachers' Association, and relies on rapid removal of the alkali with water at temperatures over 50°C.; even when the alkali on the rayon passes through the dangerous concentrations there is less risk, for the rayon is less soluble in hot alkali than in cold alkali.

It has also been suggested to add solutions of various salts to the mercerising liquor and so depress the swelling of the cellulose; this method is not very reliable and suffers from the further drawback that the lustre of the cotton is adversely affected by the presence of salt. The addition of common salt to the extent of 40 g. per litre to 20°Tw. NaOH solutions reduces the swelling of the rayon by 30%.

An alternative suggestion in B.P. 323,307, by Marshall, is to employ protective agents in the wash-waters; suitable substances are the chlorides, sulphates, and nitrates of sodium and potassium, and also certain organic compounds such as sucrose, glycerin and sucrose. Common salt is the most convenient, and solutions of 8% concentration at 45°C. give good results and do not interfere with the lustre of the cotton, nor with the handle of the rayon. B.P. 363,883, also by Marshall, covers the use of carbonates and bicarbonates in a similar manner. These processes make use of the osmotic theory of swelling; the viscose in alkaline liquors absorbs some NaOH which attracts water by osmosis during washing, but this cannot occur when washing in salt solutions or the salt solution would become more concentrated, and this is in opposition to the natural tendency to dilution.

One of the peculiar differences between solutions of sodium hydroxide and potassium hydroxide is that rayon does not dissolve in the latter; this fact has been utilised in mercerising, as outlined in B.P. 295,488 by Hall.

Rayon may be treated in KOH solutions of 55° to 60°Tw. without deleterious effect, provided the temperature is maintained above 15°C.; concentrations of KOH of this order are also capable of mercerising cotton. The time of treatment should be as short as possible, and the mercerising, stretching, and washing should only occupy about 90 seconds. The low degree of swelling of rayon in solutions of KOH is accompanied by less extensibility with less possibility of damage by shearing forces in the swollen state, as compared with solutions of NaOH.

For mixtures of cotton and spun rayon it is almost essential to make use of a mercerising process which will bring about an improvement in the lustre and dyeing properties of the cotton without adverse effect on the rayon. The use of KOH alone is expensive, and great attention has been devoted to the mixtures of NaOH and KOH, particularly in Germany. The composition of the mixture requires some care, and the proportions of the two alkalis should vary with the proportions of the two fibres. For example, a mixed material with 70% cotton and 30% rayon may be mercerised in a mixture of 70 parts by volume of 52°Tw. NaOH and 30 parts by volume of 52°Tw. KOH. Whatever mixtures are used, it is important that they should exercise the mercerising effect on cotton equivalent to that of 52°Tw. NaOH solution. This is possible with mixtures within the range of 70 to 80 parts by volume of NaOH and 30 to 20 parts by volume of KOH solutions.

PARCHMENTISING

The original specification of Mercer—B.P. 13,296 of 1850—mentioned three swelling agents for cotton or flax; these were caustic soda of 60°Tw., sulphuric acid of 105°Tw., and zinc chloride solution of 145°Tw. at 65° to 70°C. The acid and alkali were utilised at room temperatures.

The action of sulphuric acid of various concentrations is characterised by three stages of reaction; the first effect occurs with H_2SO_4 of 110°Tw., when a soft result is obtained resembling a fine wool; the second effect is obtained with 114°Tw. acid, when considerable contraction takes place and the cloth becomes stiff, whereas the third effect is produced with sulphuric acid of 116° to 125°Tw., when the fabric becomes stiff and semi-transparent. The treatment of cotton with sulphuric acid was also investigated by Blondell (Bull. Soc. Ind., Rouen, 1882, *10*, 438, 471), who observed that swelling and shrinkage occurred with acid of 91° to 106°Tw. (45° to 50°Bé), but that vigorous parchmentising only took place with acid of 116° to 123°Tw. (53° to 55°Bé).

It is now well known that sulphuric acid of 110°Tw., and above, has a completely different action from concentrations below 110°Tw. Although the more concentrated acid imparts a parchment-like effect in a few seconds, yet H_2SO_4 of 106°Tw. never produces the transparent and slightly stiff finish even after several minutes, nor does the prolonged action reduce the tensile strength of the material, in contradistinction to the action of the stronger acid.

According to the nature of the acid treatment, so must the later finishing of the treated fabric be carried out. The acid finishes fall into two main types: first, those in which the fibres move freely; and, secondly, those in which the fibres have been caused to cohere by more drastic treatment. The organdie finish belongs to the first class, and with many of the higher quality products, a series of treatments is given rather than an attempt to reach the required stiffness in one operation; in between the treatments the fabric is dried at as low a temperature as is practicable, on a jigging stenter.

The action of sulphuric acid on cotton has received great attention from the Swiss firm of Heberlein. B.P. 12,559 of 1914 was the first of a long series of patents dealing with the acid finishes on which this company has specialised, and was based on the observation that the action of H_2SO_4 of less than 110°Tw. is much more intensive if the cotton has previously been mercerised. Apparently the effect of mercerising and bleaching is to render the cotton more susceptible to treatment, so that when subjected to the action of 103° to 110°Tw. H_2SO_4, the mercerising lustre disappears, and instead of the transparency obtained at the higher concentrations, the fabric assumes a fine, light, and crêpe-like nature appearing fuller, softer, and more wool-like. The best effect is obtained with sulphuric acid of 104·5° to 107·5°Tw. (49·5° to 50·5°Bé); washing and neutralising complete the process. Pattern effects may be produced by the local application of a resist before treatment with acid. The time of reaction is determined to some extent by the type of fabric under treatment, but is usually a matter of minutes. Where sulphuric acid of 107·5° to 109°Tw. (50·5° to 51°Bé) is used on unmercerised cloth a transparent and parchment-like effect is obtained in a few seconds, but on mercerised cloth the reaction takes a longer time and may require a few minutes.

B.P. 13,129 of 1914 is concerned with the production of parchmentising effects whereby the fabric becomes thinner, finer, and more transparent. These normally occur when cotton fabric is treated with sulphuric acid of 119° or 120°Tw., for a few seconds, but when mercerised cloth is treated, parchmentising effects can be obtained with sulphuric acid whose concentration exceeds 108°Tw. Pattern effects may be obtained by the local application of a resist before treatment with acid, and the pattern may be accentuated by subsequent dyeing as the effect of the acid is to impart a greater affinity for many dyestuffs.

It must be understood, of course, that with all these acid treatments the fabric is processed at room temperatures and washed free from all traces of acid at the end of the allotted time.

With the weaker or crêping acid, the most attractive effects are realised on lightweight cloths containing fine cotton yarns; muslins, voiles, lawns, and similar fabrics shrink during the treatment and give characteristic effects, which are soft and elastic in nature. Stronger acid gives the parchmentising effect which, on the above type of cloth, produces the organdie finish. The introduction of a resist applied locally enables valuable pattern effects to be formed, and these resists may be purely mechanical, as in embossing, where the compressed areas of the fabric respond less quickly to the action of the acid than the uncompressed parts.

The use of a heavy calender, sometimes a heated calender, is capable of giving translucent effects when applied to the acid-treated fabric, either after washing free from acid or after washing and drying. Some tracing cloths are produced by these means.

These calendering effects appear to rely on the plastic nature of the swollen material, and have also been utilised in the Simili process, where fabrics of short staple cotton are swollen by sodium hydroxide solutions, washed, and calendered in a machine with heated rollers and a skew-bowl to impart a high degree of lustre.

From the work on the effect of sulphuric acid on cotton, it is clear that the action of acid is more intense if the cotton has previously been mercerised; on the other hand, acid-treated cotton behaves differently to mercerising from cotton which has not been treated. More extensive developments of this principle have been outlined by Heberlein in B.P. 100,483; novel effects may be obtained by causing H_2SO_4 of over 100°Tw. and NaOH of over 23°Tw. to act on the fabric several times alternately. Repeated treatments of cotton with sulphuric acid or with caustic soda alone have no effect further than the first; that is to say, the second treatment with the same reagent is without effect. Alternate treatments with acid and alkali, however, give novel effects, when one or other of the two reagents is allowed to react at least twice with the intermediate action of the other reagent. In between the treatments, the goods must be well washed and subsequently dried. Variations in the effect may be produced by permitting more or less shrinkage during the treatments; pattern effects may also result by the use of suitable resists. The sulphuric acid may be replaced by phosphoric acid (123° to 130°Tw.), hydrochloric acid of 38°Tw. at 0°C., nitric acid of 85° to 94°Tw., or zinc chloride solution (169°Tw.) at 60° to 70°C.; the acids, of course, are applied at room temperatures, or less.

Some special effects, however, may be realised by the use of acid and alkali at low temperatures.

The influence of temperature on the mercerisation process has been discussed on page 117.

It was found by Heberlein that special effects resulted from the treatment of cotton with caustic alkali cooled below 0°C.; the transparent effect is quite different from that obtained by ordinary mercerising. In B.P. 108,671 it is stated that when a cotton fabric is impregnated for 1 minute with 52°Tw. NaOH solution at − 10°C. it acquires a transparent effect which is not removed by washing. The concentration, temperature, and time of action may be varied according to the quality of the fabric and the required effect. Enhanced transparency is obtained by subjecting the fabric which has been mercerised at low temperatures to the action of H_2SO_4 of over 107·5°Tw. concentration, and the acid, too, may be applied at a temperature below 0°C. whereby its action may be prolonged. Alternatively, the fabric may be treated with sulphuric acid of over 107·5°Tw. first, and then with caustic soda of mercerising strength, say 50°Tw., but cooled below 0°C. The combined process may be utilised to produce pattern effects by the application of local resists. The cold alkali may also be employed in the sense of B.P. 100,483 (see page 123), whereby alternate treatments with acid and alkali are so arranged that a treatment with one reagent takes place between two treatments with the other, each reagent being removed by washing after application.

It is also possible to combine the sequence of processes described in B.P. 191,203 (see page 117) with an acid treatment before or after the mercerising sequence; sulphuric acid of 108°Tw. or more is suitable in this respect.

The production of wool-like effects, as discussed above, is outlined in U.S.P. 1,414,872 and 1,439,513; the latter refers to the treatment of fabric, first with sulphuric acid of 103° to 109°Tw., followed by washing and mercerising without tension. Transparent effects from the use of mercerising concentrations of caustic soda, but applied at temperatures below 0°C., are described in U.S.P. 1,265,082; other specifications for transparent effects on fine cotton goods are U.S.P. 1,144,655, 1,201,961, and 1,288,885.

As previously mentioned in B.P. 12,559 of 1914 (see page 121), when mercerised cotton is treated with sulphuric acid of 103° to 110°Tw., the lustre disappears and the fabric acquires a fine crêpe nature, appearing thicker, fuller, and more wool-like; the best action is obtained with 105° to 108°Tw. sulphuric acid. When stronger acid is used, according to B.P. 13,129 of 1914, the cotton fabric becomes transparent and gives an organdie effect; sulphuric acid of 108° to 120°Tw. is employed for this finish. B.P. 213,353 of the Calico Printers' Association discloses the fact that linen-like effects may be obtained by treatment, either before or after mercerising, with sulphuric acid of 106° to 113°Tw., but also for a shorter period of time than was necessary by the previous processes. The times of treatment vary from 4 to 8 seconds. When mercerised lawn from Egyptian cotton is treated with 105°Tw. H_2SO_4 for 20 minutes at 3°C., it acquires a fine wool-like appearance, being softer and fuller than the original material. A similar lawn treated with 111·5°Tw. H_2SO_4 for 6 seconds at 10°C. becomes fuller and stiffer, resembling a fine linen fabric. A third sample of the same mercerised lawn was treated for 7 seconds at 9°C. with 120°Tw. H_2SO_4, and became materially stiffer and very transparent, giving the appearance of a high-grade organdie. The process of the C.P.A. appears to be restricted to the use of sulphuric acid of 106° to 113°Tw.

Most of the processes outlined above were applied to lightweight fabrics of moderately fine construction, and gave a beautiful transparent result, which formed the basis of Heberlein's "Opal" finish. The permanent transparent effect, however, was not obtained on coarser fabrics; although the chemical action on the cotton fibres in coarse and fine yarns is the same, the finish as a whole is quite different, for as the yarns used become coarser the transparency disappears and gives place to a linen-like effect. It is not possible to draw a very sharp line of demarcation between the transparent effect and the linen-like finish, but yarns of 80s count and above give the transparent effect, whereas those below 80s exhibit the typical linen finish; the quality of the cotton and the nature of the cloth are subsidiary factors.

Variations in the effect may be produced according to the amount of shrinkage which may be permitted during the cold mercerising; enhanced results come from following the mercerising with a treatment in sulphuric acid of more than 108°Tw., or by treatment with acid, followed by mercerising.

The linen-like effect on medium and coarse yarns is described in B.P. 192,227 and U.S.P. 1,439,519, and forms the basis of the "Hecowa" finish. Where fabrics containing yarns of less than 80s count are used, the effect may be produced in greater or less degree from cold caustic soda solution, alone or followed by H_2SO_4 of over 108°Tw.; the order of treatment may be reversed, and repeated treatments may be given with the alternations described on page 121.

Linen-like effects may also be produced on cotton fabrics containing yarns of less than 60s count, by subjecting them to the action of sulphuric acid between 103° and 106°Tw. at a temperature between 0° and 5°C. for at least 4 minutes, followed by washing and mercerising under tension with NaOH solutions above 23°Tw. at ordinary temperatures. This process is due to Matt (B.P. 244,485).

From the foregoing account of the effect of sulphuric acid on cotton, it would appear that the question of concentration is rather critical in determining crêping or parchmentising action. Some interesting and additional data have been provided by Birtwell, Clibbens, Geake, and Ridge (J.T.I., 1930, 21, 85) in connection with their work on reactivity ratios of mercerised cotton (see page 118). A parchmentised cloth gave a figure of 1·6, which is greater than the average from commercial mercerising (1·45), a transparent organdie gave 2·07, which is well outside the mercerisation range, and a linen finish from sulphuric acid gave 1·23.

The swelling of cotton in sulphuric acid, unlike that in caustic alkalis, does not reach a limit short of complete dissolution, so that the time of treatment must be short in order to avoid damage; the swelling is greater, so that the reactivity ratio is apt to be greater also. For concentrations of acid up to 64% (110°Tw.), the effect on the reactivity ratio of the treated cotton is small, but between 64 and 69% H_2SO_4 (110° to 120°Tw.) there is an extremely rapid increase in reactivity with increasing concentration. The action is very sensitive to small changes in concentration.

EFFECT OF SULPHURIC ACID; 15 SECONDS AT 20°C. ON
BLEACHED MUSLIN

H_2SO_4 % by weight	Reactivity ratio	Absorption ratio
0	1·03	1·00
62·5 (106°Tw.) . . .	0·97	1·10
64·0 (110°Tw.) . . .	0·97	1·20
66·0 (114°Tw.) . . .	1·57	1·41
68·7 (120·5°Tw.) . . .	1·92	1·66

The influence of temperature on the action of the acid is striking and unexpected. With H_2SO_4 of 62·5% concentration both absorption and reactivity ratios are increased by reduction in the temperature

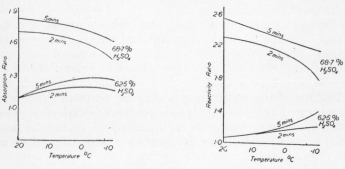

FIG. 107.—The effect of temperature on the treatment of cotton with sulphuric acid.

of the acid (as with NaOH), but with 68·7% (120·5°Tw.) H_2SO_4 the ratios fall as the temperature of the acid falls. The results are illustrated in Fig. 107.

Controlled Dispersion

In working any process which depends for its effect on the treatment of cotton with strong sulphuric acid, it is important to adjust the concentration of the acid very accurately; further, it is necessary to interrupt the reaction suddenly at the end of an exact period, for otherwise there will be considerable degradation of the cellulose, as shown by a diminution in tensile strength and an undesired hardness.

Heberlein, in B.P. 196,298, discloses that salts of heterocyclic bases, particularly those of pyridine, are capable of stabilising or controlling the swelling action of sulphuric acid when added to it; the swelling action may therefore be accomplished without risk to the fabric or yarn. It is possible, by this means, to prolong the duration of action fifty-fold without injury. For example, one part of pyridine and 4 parts of sulphuric acid (169°Tw.) produce a soft transparent effect on previously bleached and mercerised muslin in about 4 minutes. Again, a wool-like effect may be obtained by treating a mercerised cotton fabric for 5 minutes, with a mixture of 1 part of pyridine and 9 parts of sulphuric acid of 129°Tw. The two above examples relate to an improvement in the treatment of mercerised cotton with sulphuric acid, as outlined in B.P. 192,227, but it is also possible to obtain linen-like effects on cotton by treatment with the mixture of acid and base alone.

Glycerin has also been used to restrain the action of strong sulphuric acid on cotton (B.F. 519,745).

According to Textil Werk, Horn, the well-known treatment of cotton fabrics with sulphuric acid of suitable strength to obtain transparent effects also renders the material unpleasantly stiff. This may be obviated by the methods of B.P. 195,620, which comprise the addition of ammonium salts to the sulphuric acid solution; for example, a solution containing 69% sulphuric acid, 5% neutral ammonium sulphate, and 26% water may be applied at 10° to 18°C. or 5 to 10 seconds.

Another method of controlling or restraining the action of sulphuric acid on cotton has been described by Barrett and Foulds in B.P. 200,881. It appears that formaldehyde modifies the action of sulphuric acid of over 110°Tw. on cellulose yarns and fabrics; even 0·5 to 1% of 40% formaldehyde solution renders the action slower, and enables the time of treatment to be extended without damage. Crêping may be carried out with acid of 90°Tw. and upwards if formaldehyde is added.

Formaldehyde modifies the action of the stronger acid in a remarkable manner; with a light cloth, an exposure of 20 seconds to 140°Tw. (77%) H_2SO_4, is too long and a tendered fabric results, but with 0·5% of formaldehyde a good result is obtained in 20 seconds. Light cloths treated for short periods are much softer than those subjected to the usual parchmentising practice, but retain the peculiar transparency, and show characteristic effects on embossing or calendering. The formation of the so-called amyloid by the higher concentrations of parchmentising acid is largely prevented by the presence of formaldehyde.

The addition of formaldehyde to sulphuric acid of crêping strength (108°Tw. or 63·4%) also produces novel results; the fabric shrinks considerably but develops some transparency and a crisp handle.

Some of the most interesting effects are obtained on well-bleached, singed cloth which has been embossed or calendered and then treated with formaldehyde-acid solution; the calendered parts acquire a lustrous appearance and a linen-like feel, which are retained after washing. On previously embossed cloths, the parts which have not been subjected to pressure react more readily and become transparent, producing damask effects.

The action of formaldehyde solution as a diluent for sulphuric acid is rather peculiar; the usual strength of H_2SO_4 for parchmentising is above 110°Tw. (64·26%), and it is possible to dilute solutions of 130°Tw. (72·8%) to 105°Tw. (62·06%) with formaldehyde solution, but yet retain the parchmentising action.

Barrett and Foulds of Tootal Broadhurst Lee Company also found that the stiff results obtained by treating cotton fabrics with H_2SO_4 of 133°Tw. (74%), in presence or absence of 0·5% of 40% formaldehyde solution, could be softened by a second treatment with weaker acid, i.e. less than 110°Tw. (64·26%); partial softening may be obtained with sulphuric acid of 80°Tw. (50%), but this takes longer. A typical example is to treat for 5 seconds in the stronger acid, and then pass the fabric directly into the weaker acid (90°Tw. or 55%), where it is allowed to remain for 1 minute. The cloth is then washed and finished in the usual way.

The action of sulphuric acid and formaldehyde on calendered or embossed cloths formed the basis of the "K-mas" finish, which was very popular for some years.

One slight disadvantage of parchmentising embossed fabrics for pattern effects is that where the pattern is large, the transparent nature of the part which has been more severely affected by the acid is apt to be over-emphasised. This may be obviated by the methods described in B.P. 510,083 by Bancroft, Foulds, and Roscoe. Urea and paraformaldehyde are added to the acid, and after application to the embossed fabric, the washing process produces some methylene urea (see page 315), which gives an opalescent effect instead of the transparent pattern ordinarily formed. The amount of urea and paraformaldehyde may vary from 2 to 6% on the weight of the acid. No precipitation occurs when the molecular proportions of formaldehyde to urea exceed 2 : 1.

The method is illustrated by adding 13 g. of urea to 100 c.c. of 160°Tw. H_2SO_4 (86%) containing 26 g. of paraformaldehyde; the urea should be added slowly and the mixture kept cool. The resulting solution is still equivalent to 130°Tw. H_2SO_4 (72·8%), but the parchmentising action is slower. When cotton fabric is treated with the solution for 30 to 60 seconds and washed in cold water, an opaque but parchmentised effect is obtained, and the opacity is not removed by subsequent mercerisation.

Although considerable attention has been devoted to the treatment of cotton with sulphuric acid of 105° to 108°Tw., it is possible to utilise other dispersing agents for cellulose. The sulphuric acid may be replaced by phosphoric acid (123° to 130°Tw.), hydrochloric acid (40°Tw.), nitric acid (85° to 94°Tw.), or warm solutions of zinc chloride (168°Tw.).

For the treatment of rayon, it is necessary to use less concentrated solutions than those employed with cotton. For example, sulphuric acid of 82° to 106°Tw. covers the range, although 82°Tw. H_2SO_4 is without action on cotton. The maximum concentrations of other acids for the treatment of rayon are phosphoric acid (106°Tw.), hydrochloric acid (32°Tw.), and nitric acid (64°Tw.).

Before leaving the discussion of the treatment of cotton with moderately concentrated sulphuric acid, it may be well to emphasise that these effects are only obtained with fabrics from which the surface hairs have been removed, and, in addition, fabrics in which a uniform and high degree of absorbency has been attained. It is also important that the cloth should not have been degraded during its preparation.

NITRIC ACID

Nitric acid is occasionally used in the finishing of cotton cloths. Its action was investigated by Knecht (J.S.D.C., 1896, *12*, 89), who observed that when cotton was steeped for a few moments in HNO_3 (*d* 1·415) it became gelatinous, and on washing with water, shrinkage occurred with an increase in lustre and strength. About the same time, these effects were patented by Scheulan (D.R.P. 109,607 of 1896), who protected treatment under tension; Thomas and Prevost (D.R.P. 129,883 of 1900) specified the use of 43°Bé HNO_3 (85°Tw. or 70·6%).

From these and other specifications, concentrations of 67·5 to 74·4% appear to afford a suitable range for mercerising. Knecht (ibid., 1904, *20*, 68) found that up to 62°Tw. HNO_3 (48·5%) there was scarcely any action on cotton, but at 82°Tw. (67%) the action of the acid resembles that of sodium hydroxide of mercerising strength; there is a sudden increase in action at 76°Tw. (61%). Budnikoff (Faser. u. Spinn., 1923, *5*, 64) confirmed many of Knecht's observations; when cotton is treated with HNO_3 of 40° to 41°Bé (77° to 80°Tw. or 61·7 to 64·5%) for 30 seconds its strength is increased by 20% for a shrinkage of 13%. If the treatment exceeds this length of time, the strength of the cotton is diminished.

The hardening of paper, particularly filter paper, with nitric acid is commonly carried out in many works, but the chief technical application to cotton cloth was that of Philana A.G. of Basle; the "philanising" process is described in the processes of Schwartz, as outlined in B.P. 136,568, 136,569, 144,204, 144,563, and 150,665. The corresponding American specifications are U.S.P. 1,384,677, 1,398,804; 1,400,380, — 1.

Unbleached and unmercerised cotton cloth is treated at room temperatures with nitric acid of more than 65% strength, and then rapidly washed when shrinkage takes place. The details of time and temperature vary with the type of cloth, and examples range from

65 to 75% of acid for periods of from 1 to 5 minutes. The treatment may be prolonged up to 30 minutes provided the temperature does not exceed 20°C.; with concentrations of HNO_3 above 75% (88°Tw.) the time of treatment must be very short. The finished product has a harsh, warm character resembling wool; the pale yellow colour from the treatment may be removed in the subsequent bleaching process. The process appears at its best on unbleached material; there is always some difficulty with true and apparent strengths of cotton which has been allowed to shrink, but breaking loads of treated cotton fabrics, corrected for shrinkage, show 100% with unbleached material and 52 to 60% for bleached, dyed, or printed cotton, estimated on the original cloth (Textilber., 1925, 6, 662).

Although the main effect is due to the action of nitric acid without tension, other substances such as dissolved cellulose, starch, and proteins may be applied from nitric acid solution, and superior effects are stated to result from passing the acidified cotton into a solution of formaldehyde, dilute acid, alkali, or salt solution before washing with water.

D.R.P. 292,213 by Heberlein describes the use of HNO_3 of 43° to 46°Bé (84·8° to 93·6°Tw. or 70·6 to 83%) on mercerised cotton; this treatment is the basis of the "Hecolan" finish.

SALT SOLUTIONS

Parchmentising agents other than sulphuric acid have found only limited application in textile finishing, but are used on paper to a greater extent (zinc chloride is used for manufacturing vulcanised fibre). The action of reagents such as zinc chloride and calcium thiocyanate on cellulose has been described by Marsh and Wood, Cellulose Chemistry, London, Chapman & Hall, Second Edition, 1941, p. 162).

Figured effects, however, may be obtained by the local application of these salts, which require high concentrations and high temperatures; the difficulty in printing with salt solutions is the production of a satisfactory printing paste, and most ornamentation has relied on the resist method. However, Heberlein, in B.P. 439,749, utilises formaldehyde as an addition to calcium thiocyanate, thickened with starch or cellulose; better penetration is thus obtained and the action increased to a degree. After printing, the cotton fabric is dried and passed through a steam chest or into a bath of calcium chloride solution at 120°C., when the pattern develops through the parchmentising action. B.P. 450,837, also by Heberlein, makes use of cellulose as a thickener for zinc chloride solution when a printing paste is required; an almost saturated solution of zinc chloride may be thickened with cellulose in the form of viscose rayon waste. The addition of formaldehyde reduces the parchmentising effect only, but dilution with water destroys both printing value and parch-mentising action. The printed cloth is dried at 90°C., when parch-mentising takes place and produces the transparent pattern; washing and drying complete the process.

Two typical processes depend on the use of calcium thiocyanate and zinc chloride respectively.

B.P. 196,696 of the Calico Printers' Association and Fourneaux describes a treatment with calcium thiocyanate solution (b.p. 130°C.) followed by hot air or steam for a period of a few seconds to one minute, according to the nature of the material. The harsh effect normally given by hot solutions of calcium thiocyanate may be overcome by mercerising the cotton before or after the thiocyanate treatment; variations of this kind may give either linen-like or wool-like effects, as described in B.P. 228,655.

Zinc chloride solution of 82° to 104°Tw. has been suggested by Cheetham in B.P. 225,680 as a finish for cotton. After impregnation, the goods are dried over hot cylinders, treated in an acid bath, and washed. This process gives an organdie effect, but if the cloth is mercerised before or after the treatment with zinc chloride, then a soft transparent finish is obtained.

MISCELLANEOUS DISPERSING AGENTS

Although the chief dispersing agents for cellulose are moderately concentrated solutions of acid and alkali, there are several other products which have been used, to a minor degree, in textile finishing.

Lustrous and translucent effects may be obtained by the viscose reaction itself being applied to the fabric under restricted conditions of reaction; instead of applying viscose solution to the cloth, the surface of the material is transformed into sodium cellulose xanthate. This method is due to Lilienfeld, and is outlined in B.P. 216,476 and 7; mixtures of carbon disulphide and sodium hydroxide are applied to the cloth in the stretched state. The time of treatment may vary from 15 seconds to a few minutes, according to the required effect which may vary from a lustrous appearance to a stiff finish. One treatment is to apply carbon disulphide in 5 volumes of benzene, squeeze, and then treat with 14 to 20% NaOH solution; alternatively, the fabric may be treated and stretched simultaneously with a mixture of 12 to 18% NaOH and 0·2 to 3% CS_2. Low temperatures are an advantage in this reaction. (See also U.S.P. 1,831,745.)

Cuprammonium hydrate has been utilised in the finishing of cotton goods; its chief application is in the rotproof and waterproof finish by the Willesden process (see page 512), but it has also been used for etching effects by the local removal of the pile on velvets and velveteens of cotton and rayon.

The effect of cuprammonia on cellulose has been studied by Heberlein; according to B.P. 433,751, yarn or fabric may be treated with cuprammonia and then mercerised in the stretched state with sodium hydroxide solution. The mercerisation coagulates the dissolved and swollen cellulose, so that the result of the whole treatment is to produce a smooth film-like layer on the surface of the yarn or fabric. In U.S.P. 1,896,620, attention is drawn to a similar order of treatment; the cuprammonia should contain 20 g. of copper per litre for fabric and 15 g. per litre for the treatment of yarns. In another process, described in U.S.P. 2,002,106, the cotton is swollen by treatment with a solution containing cuprammonium hydrate and sodium hydroxide or other alkali metal hydroxide, in which the free alkali does not exceed 1·5% of the weight of the solution; the swelling action may be interrupted by dilute acid solutions.

B.P. 420,592 by Flight gives an account of a process in which cotton is impregnated with sodium sulphate solution, dried, and passed in open width through a solution of cuprammonia containing dissolved cotton and also sodium hydroxide. The alkaline substances are then neutralised with dilute acid, and the fabric washed, followed by drying on an over-feed stenter or compressive shrinkage machine.

Morton, in B.P. 468,633, has described a linen-like finish produced by impregnating cotton with copper sulphate solution, squeezing, and passing through a solution of ammonia and caustic soda in water. Cuprammonia is formed and the cellulose superficially attacked. After a further squeeze, the fabric is passed through dilute sulphuric acid which precipitates the cellulose and removes copper from the fabric.

Two interesting processes have been protected by Bancroft. U.S.P. 2,111,486 gives an account of the production of stiff crisp effects by impregnating cotton with copper sulphate, ammonia and caustic soda solution; 60 lb. of copper sulphate are dissolved in 116·5 litres of water, to which is added 52·5 litres of ammonia (d 1·2) and the mixture agitated until the precipitate dissolves. The solution is cooled to 15°C. and 95 litres of it are poured into a mixer, together with 66·5 litres of ammonia (d 1·2). A second solution is prepared by dissolving 10·4 lb. of sodium hydroxide in 15 litres of water, cooling, and adding 29 lb. of cracked ice. The two solutions are mixed and contain copper sulphate and caustic soda in the molecular proportions of 1 : 2. Impregnation of cotton with this solution should be short, about 2·5 seconds, to remove the projecting fuzz of surface hairs and partially dissolve the body of the yarns; the fabric is then squeezed and acidified in 7% (by volume) sulphuric acid solution, followed by mercerising under tension. According to a second process, given in U.S.P. 2,157,600, the fabric may be treated with a solution of copper sulphate, ammonia, and caustic soda containing

2 molecular proportions of sodium hydroxide per molecular proportion of copper sulphate; the temperature should be between 5° and 15°C., or even lower. The excess of solution and dissolved cellulose are removed mechanically, the fabric washed, and then mercerised in the wet state with sodium hydroxide solution of concentration greater than 10 N, followed by washing to reduce the concentration to 2 N NaOH, neutralising, washing, and drying.

Arnold Print Works, according to B.P. 489,402, prefer to employ a solution containing a cuprammonium salt dissolved in ammonia, followed by a reagent which activates the previous solution. Suitable cuprammonium salts are the chloride, nitrate, cyanide, bichromate, chlorate, formate, acetate, oxalate, or citrate; a good activating agent is sodium hydroxide solution applied below room temperatures. The cotton fabric may be fed under tension into a bath containing copper sulphate and ammonia, squeezed, and passed into 50°Tw. NaOH solution at 4°C., remaining in each solution for between 3 and 8 seconds; the material is then squeezed, stretched, soured, and washed.

It must be realised that considerable care needs to be exercised when treating vegetable fibrous material with dispersing agents capable of bringing about dissolution of the cellulose; with acids, in particular, it is essential completely to remove them after they have exerted their swelling action, for otherwise if allowed to concentrate on the fabric, considerable damage will be caused.

Treatments with cold caustic soda solutions and also with sulphuric acid are capable of giving valuable finishes, as has been discussed; in many cases, the treated fabric feels rather thin, and the general public has not been educated that this thinness is a sign of the ennoblement of the cotton and not of its impoverishment. In actual fact, many acid-treated products give vastly superior service to the public than the untreated fabrics. It is surprising that these cheap, simple, and convenient processes have not a very wide field of application.

CHAPTER V

FORMALDEHYDE

IN a polymeric form, formaldehyde has been known since 1859, but the simple compound was first prepared by Hoffman in 1867; the method devised was to draw a mixture of the vapours of methyl alcohol and air over a heated spiral of platinum wire. The modern manufacturing process is to pass the methyl alcohol, in vapour form, over copper gauze or through a copper tube packed with copper turnings which are maintained at a temperature of 500°C.

$$CH_3OH + \tfrac{1}{2}O_2 \longrightarrow CH_2O + H_2O$$

The methyl alcohol is generally made by combining carbon monoxide and hydrogen under high pressure and at a high temperature.

Formaldehyde is a gas which liquefies at about —21°C., but, being soluble in water, it is usually sold in a concentrated solution containing 37 to 40% of formaldehyde. It is the most reactive of the aldehydes, probably on account of its low molecular weight. The ordinary solution of 40% formaldehyde generally contains some methyl alcohol (7 to 13%) to hinder polymerisation.

Polymers of formaldehyde are readily formed and exist in two types: (a) hydrated polymers $(CH_2O)_n.H_2O$, and (b) true polymers $(CH_2O)_n$. The most important hydrated polymer is paraform, in which n varies between 6 and 50; it tends to precipitate from aqueous solutions of formaldehyde above 30% concentration. Paraform is slightly soluble in cold water, but dissolves on warming; it contains some 95% of formaldehyde which may be liberated on heating. The α, β, and γ polyoxymethylenes are of less commercial importance, and are made by dehydrating formaldehyde solution with various amounts of sulphuric acid; n is 100 or more, and the γ polyoxymethylene contains some combined CH_3OH, as it is made from formaldehyde which contains methyl alcohol. The polyoxymethylenes are almost insoluble in water, but dissolve in solutions of alkali or of sodium sulphite.

The true polymers, such as α-trioxymethylene, are also insoluble. This compound is made by subliming paraform and sulphuric acid, and may be cyclic in character. Tetraoxymethylene is made by heating polyoxymethylene diacetate *in vacuo*.

A good description of the manufacture, properties, and analysis of formaldehyde has been given by Homer (J.S.C.I., 1941, *60*, 213).

The commercial solutions of formaldehyde usually have an acid reaction; the acidity, due to formic acid, is generally of the order 0·05% equivalent NaOH.

The ubiquitous formaldehyde plays an important part in many finishing operations; indeed, it may be regarded as one of the most essential reagents available to the finisher. Even before the finishing processes are reached, formaldehyde finds a use in the manufacture of regenerated fibres from proteins.

When casein is "spun" into acid and salt solutions, it can be washed in salt and dried; the fibres are apt to be brittle and possess little strength. Formaldehyde-treated fibres may be rendered insoluble in dilute aqueous alkali by heating, when the physical properties of the material are also greatly improved. Now, if the salt-linkages were the only bridges between the molecular chains, treatment with acid or alkali would not merely swell the filaments, but it would dissolve them. Hence, the suggestion that formaldehyde reacts with the amino groups as follows:

$$\begin{array}{c} -NH_2 \\ \\ -NH_2 \end{array} +CH_2O \longrightarrow \begin{array}{c} -NH \\ \diagdown \\ CH_2 \\ \diagup \\ -NH \end{array}$$

is not universally accepted. Unhardened casein dissolves in weak acid and in weak alkali, and it is possible that the course of the reaction is to provide methylol derivatives which later give rise to methylene bridges; the formaldehyde treatment does not destroy the individuality of the filament, but provides another type of bond in addition to the salt-linkages.

$$R-NH_2+CH_2O \longrightarrow R-NH-CH_2OH \longrightarrow R-NH-CH_2-NH-R'$$

The methylene group is somewhat analogous to the cystine bridge in wool; for example, the untreated casein fibre is extremely plastic in water, but the treated fibre exhibits some elastic recovery—if, however, the treated casein fibre is maintained under tension in hot water, it loses its tendency to contract. It is probable that new methylene bridges are formed by hydrolysis of the old bonds under strain. In wool, the cystine bond is permanently broken by hot alkali, but hot acid is required to hydrolyse the methylene bridge in casein-formaldehyde fibres.

Nylon may also be improved by treatment with formaldehyde. B.P. 534,698 relies on the fact that in the "super-polyamide," the molecular chain contains groups capable of reacting with formaldehyde. The chief advantages of the process lie in imparting resistance to degradation by light and increasing the true elasticity of the fibre; a modification of the formaldehyde finish may be employed for water-repellency. The setting action of the simple formaldehyde treatment gives an increased permanence of form which may improve the ability of nylon fibres to recover from deformation, or, alternatively, may be utilised in stabilising the crimp which can be produced by mechanical means. During the treatment with formaldehyde solution, the pH of the bath should not be allowed to fall below 3·0. A suitable bath consists of 10% of aqueous formaldehyde solution and 0·5% of ammonium chloride; the impregnated nylon may be heated for 3 minutes at 150°C. In many treatments, it is preferable to have present a buffer substance, such as potassium hydrogen phthalate.

When nylon is exposed to ultra-violet light for 65 hours it suffers a loss in tenacity and extension of approximately 50%, but the formaldehyde-treated nylon only suffers 8 to 14% decrease. In the finishing treatments, it is not always necessary to use formaldehyde, whose volatile nature and strong odour may be unwelcome; substances liberating formaldehyde may be used as alternatives, and methylol ureas have been employed. The reaction mixture should not be sufficiently acid to hydrolyse the nylon; the pH must not fall below 3.

Special derivatives of formaldehyde, containing long-chain fatty acid residues, may give nylon a water-repellent finish; methylol stearamide has been used for this purpose, and may be applied in 3% solution in alcohol, followed by heating at 150°C.

The reaction between formaldehyde and urea is probably very similar to that between formaldehyde and casein. It is possible first to form a simple condensation product, methylol urea, which in presence of acid and heat may be transformed to the insoluble resinous condensation product where the urea-residues are joined by methylene bridges (see page 392).

The chief textile use of formaldehyde is probably in connection with the formation of urea-formaldehyde resins inside the textile fibre, but there is a limited application of these resins as external coatings. As described on page 316, the urea-formaldehyde reaction may give rise to a white amorphous product which has found application as a delustring medium in textile finishing.

Another indirect application of formaldehyde in textile finishes may be seen in the use of fatty alkyl chlormethyl ethers which react directly with cotton or wool to give softening and waterproofing effects; a fatty alcohol (or amide, or carbamic ester) is treated in benzene with formaldehyde and hydrochloric acid to give the type of product discussed on page 480. The older type of water-resistant finish has, of course, been produced with casein-formaldehyde, and a similar reaction has been suggested for crease-resistant effects, although the conditions of applications are different.

Formaldehyde has also been employed in connection with dyeing.

The after-treatment of many direct dyes with formaldehyde has a pronounced effect on the fastness to washing and to milling, but not to light; a suitable concentration is 1 to 3% of 40% formaldehyde solution. The process is most suited to direct blacks, and the effect is best with those dyestuffs which contain two hydroxyl (or amino) groups, one of which is in the meta position to the other; presumably a methylene bridge is formed between these polar groups and the solubility of the compound is diminished.

Another application of formaldehyde is with the naphthol colours; the "naphthol" is applied to fabric as a sodium salt, which is then treated with a diazotised base, to develop the colour. The sodium naphtholate has a tendency to hydrolise to the free "naphthol" which has little coupling power; the addition of free formaldehyde retards this hydrolysis, and also prevents oxidation when the naphtholated material is not developed immediately in the wet state. Some members of the Naphthol AS series, however, have their dyeing powers destroyed by the addition of formaldehyde.

Reference has been made on page 435 to the production of "animalised" rayon, such as the supplementary fibre "Rayolanda," the production of which is believed to entail the use of a resin from cyanamide and formaldehyde; this is another instance of the use of formaldehyde in dyeing effects.

Phenol-formaldehyde resins have been suggested as mordants, as discussed on page 434, but according to B.P. 511,654, it is possible to combine formaldehyde with a "sulphurised" phenol and a primary or secondary amine to give a product capable of improving the fastness of direct dyeings when applied from 1% solution in acetic acid.

Another interesting use of formaldehyde in dyeing lies in the stripping of colours by compounds such as sodium sulphoxylate formaldehyde.

Reviewing the uses of formaldehyde in textile processes, it is possible to classify these in two ways: (a) where formaldehyde is used with other reagents as an auxiliary or as part of a compound, and (b) where formaldehyde is used as the prime reagent.

(1) Stripping agent in sodium-sulphoxylate-formaldehyde.
(2) Addition to hypochlorite in bleaching (Ristenpart; Textilber., 1923, 4, 373).
(3) Crêping of cellulose derivatives (see page 109).
(4) Stabilising Naphthol AS colours.
(5) Fixing direct dyes.
(6) Mordanting processes, e.g. Rayolanda.
(7) Controlled parchmentising (see page 128).
(8) Starch-formaldehyde adhesives (see page 286).

(9) Delustring by methylene urea (see page 315).
(10) Water-repellents of the Velan type (see page 480).
(11) Resins for coating or for crease-resistance (see page 360).
(12) Antiseptic, in size and starch finishes, and to prevent anthrax from certain raw wools.

As the prime reagent reacting direct with the textile fibre, we have:

(A) Stabilising casein filaments.
(B) Improving nylon.
(C) Rendering wool non-shrink, mothproof, and alkali-stable.
(D) Anti-swelling and stabilising action on rayon, and non-shrink and crease-resisting effects on vegetable fibres generally.
(E) The fixation of sericin on raw silk may also be included here for convenience.

The items listed as (C) and (D) have received sufficient attention to be of some importance.

TREATMENT OF WOOL

The action of formaldehyde on wool has aroused attention at various times, mainly in connection with possible protection from damage by alkali. Kann in D.R.P. 144,485 of 1901, and 146,845 of 1903, stated that about 4% of formaldehyde rendered wool resistant to alkali and also to steam. In these circumstances, however, there is a reduced affinity for dyestuffs, but by the use of weaker solutions, 0·25 to 1·0%, the wool may be protected against alkali without its dyeing properties being affected. The reaction between wool and formaldehyde was stated to take place readily in alkaline liquors, but less readily in acid or neutral solutions (Farber-Zeit., 1914, 25, 73); the formaldehyde was liberated again by treatment with hydrochloric acid, but this probably depends on the conditions under which the combination was effected. Speakman and Peill (J.T.I., 1943, 34, 70) determined that optimum conditions for cross-linking fibres at 50°C. were at pH 6 to 7, in solutions containing 0·732 g. of formaldehyde and 2·31 g. methyl alcohol per litre.

The reaction with formaldehyde had also been investigated by Trotman (J.S.C.I., 1922, 41, 219) with a view to protection of the wool during chlorination, when it was established that the diminution in weight during chlorination with 0·7% chlorine was reduced from 5 to 2·6% if the wool had received a prior treatment with 2% formaldehyde solution; this pre-treatment also brought about a decreased solubility in $N/10$ NaOH of woollen goods damaged during chlorination. Treatment with formaldehyde does not strengthen ordinary wool; indeed, according to Speakman (J.T.I., 1926, *17*, 457; 1943, *34*, 70) there is a slight reduction in extensibility.

The effect of formaldehyde had been examined in some detail by Bell (J.S.D.C., 1927, *43*, 76), who found that the amount of formaldehyde taken up by wool at room temperatures varies with the concentration of the bath and the volume of the solution, but a maximum is reached in concentrations corresponding to 3% on the weight of the wool; about 0·15% of formaldehyde appears to enter into chemical combination. Trotman, Trotman, and Brown (ibid., 1928, *44*, 49) found that the reaction was greater at higher temperatures, and about 0·7% of formaldehyde entered into combination after treatment with 2% formaldehyde solution at 75°C., followed by drying at 100°C.

The wool-formaldehyde compound is not very stable, the combined formaldehyde being reduced from 0·6 to 0·2% after one hour's boil.

Investigations of formaldehyde as a protecting agent against damage by chlorination and by alkali were made later by Trotman (J.S.C.I., 1931, *50*, 463).

The resistance to cold alkali seems good, and even with warm alkali there is considerable resistance after 4 hours at 75°C., as shown by the nitrogen content of the wool.

RESISTANCE TO ALKALI

NaOH%	Nitrogen in CH_2O—wool	Nitrogen in ordinary wool.
0·02	15·76%	14·98%
0·044	15·76%	14·69%
0·068	15·78%	14·92%
0·132	15·75%	14·00%
0·2	15·63%	disintegration
0·4	15·71%	do.

Formaldehyde may therefore be recommended as a protective agent in alkaline wet processes, but large amounts are required to show any effect in scouring. The volatility of formaldehyde necessitates either a pre-treatment or the use of some compound from which it may be liberated; condensation products of formaldehyde and naphthalene sulphonic acids have been employed. Horsfall and Lawrie in B.P. 285,554 suggest 5% of mono- or dimethylol urea on the weight of the wool (or silk) when scouring or when dyeing with vat colours.

The use of formaldehyde in the chlorinating liquor has been patented by von Lumpp (B.P. 13,088 of 1911), but is of little value and merely reduces the amount of available chlorine.

As an agent for imparting non-felting effects, formaldehyde has been found to give temporary results. Treated wool shows less shrinkage when washed than does untreated wool, but is not resistant to milling or felting, owing to gradual hydrolysis of the wool-formaldehyde compound. The initial effect is good; for instance, treatment with 1% formaldehyde at 60°C. for 1 hour gives a product which resists boiling soap for 30 minutes, but there is considerable shrinkage in the next 30 minutes. The treated wool appears to be hydrolysed more or less readily by 0·7 to 0·8% NaOH solutions.

More recently, the condensation of formaldehyde with wool under acid conditions has attracted attention. Finlayson and Perry in B.P. 450,620 have described the treatment of low-grade wool with 20% formaldehyde solution and 3% hydrochloric acid by impregnating, drying at 50°C., and heating at 140°C. for 5 minutes. Lantz and Miller of the Calico Printers' Association, in B.P. 519,343, describe the treatment of wool with an acidified solution of formaldehyde at pH not greater than 2, in order to fix the dimensions of the fabric and prevent shrinkage; in an example, the wool is treated with a solution containing 15% formaldehyde and 3% sulphuric acid, followed by drying and heating at a high temperature.

These processes are similar to those which have been suggested for vegetable fibres, as described later.

It has been shown by Speakman (J.S.C.I., 1930, 49, 209) that the absorption of water by formaldehyde-treated wool shows little difference from that of untreated wool.

Formaldehyde may also be employed for the mothproofing of scoured wool, according to B.P. 549,362 by McLean and Traill of I.C.I. The scoured wool is immersed in dilute formaldehyde solution (0·5 to 10%) at a pH not exceeding 1 when measured at 20°C., but the steeping takes place at 30 to 40°C. for from 2 hours to 2 days, according to the temperature. The treated goods are rinsed and dried in the usual manner.

CELLULOSE-FORMALDEHYDE PROCESSES

The earliest use of formaldehyde appears to have been made by Strehlenert, as described in B.P. 22,540 of 1896. Attention is drawn to the behaviour of artificial silk in the presence of water, when it loses about 90% of its strength. (These remarks, of course, do not refer to modern rayon productions.) This defect is a disadvantage in the wet processing of artificial silk, as, for example, in dyeing. Strehlenert was mainly concerned with cellulose nitrate and suggested the addition of formaldehyde to the solvent for the nitrate, or, alternatively, treating the extruded filaments with formaldehyde. The amount of formaldehyde suggested was 15% of the weight of the cellulose nitrate and the treatment should take place before denitration.

Textile science was not far advanced in 1896 and Strehlenert seems to have been of the opinion that because formaldehyde was capable of rendering gelatin insoluble in water, it would have a similar effect on other substances containing nitrogen, and, in particular, the artificial silk made from cellulose nitrate. Other aldehydes, such as acetaldehyde, paraldehyde, and benzaldehyde are also mentioned in this early patent specification.

Probably the best-known work on the use of formaldehyde with cellulosic fibres is due to Eschalier, and is contained in B.P. 25,647 of 1906; the French documents are B.F. 374,724 and the patents of addition 8,122, 9,904, 9,905, and 10,760. The treatment relates to the strengthening of cellulosic material, particularly the depolymerised cellulose obtained from cellulose in the different solvents, and therefore existing in various stages of dispersion. It is rather interesting that even at this date the idea of regenerated cellulose being depolymerised native cellulose should be expressed, for practically nothing was known of the constitution of cellulose. Albuminoid fibres or materials are also considered to be improved by the treatment with formaldehyde.

The formaldehyde, according to Eschalier, is supposed to polymerise or condense with the cellulosic material and so bring about a strengthening effect which was stated to be quite appreciable in the dry state and especially good in the wet state. The process is obviously directed to the strengthening of regenerated cellulose, the wet strength of which has always been one of its disadvantages, and in 1906 was a very serious defect. There would seem little point in causing the reaction to take place on cotton or linen, because their strength is already high and is peculiar in that it is increased and not decreased on wetting.

The treatment with formaldehyde was suggested in two broad methods. First, in presence of acids or acid salts; and, secondly, in presence of dehydrating agents; in many instances the two ideas are combined, as may be seen from examples. A solution was made of from 1 to 10 parts of 40% formaldehyde in 99–90 parts of acetic acid of 10 to 40% concentration. The artificial silk, as it was then termed, was impregnated in the solution and then placed in a closed vessel in presence of, but not in contact with, calcium chloride, concentrated sulphuric acid, or some other dehydrating agent. The reaction was accelerated by exhausting the closed receiver, which could also be heated for 4 or 5 hours to an internal temperature of some 40° to 50° C. The material was then washed in water and dried.

In other examples, 5 to 25 parts of formaldehyde were mixed with an equal quantity of lactic acid and dissolved in 90–50 parts of water, to make the impregnating bath. In further examples chrome alum, potassium alum, or aluminium alum could replace the lactic acid.

Another variation of this method was to impregnate the artificial silk in 40% acetic acid and then suspend it in a closed receiver above 40% formaldehyde solution for 8 to 10 days at room temperature.

Again, the regenerated cellulose could be strengthened by immersion in a bath composed of 20 to 25 times its weight of glacial acetic acid, to which was added 2/10,000 of 40% formaldehyde solution, and the bath heated for 3 to 4 hours to about 90° to 96°C. and then left to cool.

Instead of water as a medium for dissolving the reagents, it was suggested that other solvents could be used, provided that they had no harmful effect on the cellulosic material, e.g. alcohol, glycerol, acetone, etc.

This process became very well known, particularly in France, where it was referred to as "sthenosage," but never attained commercial success, possibly because the state of textile finishing was not sufficiently far advanced to deal with technical developments so far removed from normal practice, or more probably because the treatment was irregular and unreliable in its effect.

Cross and Bevan (J.S.C.I., 1908, 27, 1187) verified Eschalier's process and found that the amount of formaldehyde fixed varied between 0·35 and 0·8%, the molecular ratio being 1 of formaldehyde: 30 of $C_6H_{10}O_5$, which indicates some structural chemical modification. The strength of the rayon in the dry state was originally 1·25 g./denier, which rose to 1·6 g. after treatment; in the wet state the corresponding figures were 0·37 and 1·1. The extension at break, originally 12·2% in the dry state, fell to 7·8 and the extension of 9% in the wet state fell to 7·6 on treatment.

It was also noted that the dyeing capacity of the material was considerably decreased and irregular. The cost of the process was stated to be $2\frac{1}{2}d.$ per pound.

There was little further work until about 1917, when an American patent, U.S.P. 1,234,720, appeared which was similar in subject-matter to Eschalier's specification.

Bruckhaus (Kunstseide, 1926, 8, 115) also repeated Eschalier's work and found that his products dyed more deeply than the original material in contrast to previous work.

Meunier and Guyot (Compt. rend., 1929, 188, 506) re-examined Eschalier's process and measured the decreased swelling of the viscose material by means of the centrifuge. They put forward the interesting suggestion that the long parallel chains of glucose residues may be joined by each molecule of formaldehyde, thus accounting for the strengthening effect which was produced by very small amounts of formaldehyde. On this scheme two molecules of formaldehyde could join together two chains of 100 $C_6H_{10}O_5$ units.

An examination of Eschalier's process has also been made by Wood (J.S.C.I., 1931, 50, 411), who observed that two distinct stages occur during the reaction. In the first stage the rayon fibres quickly lost their solubility in cuprammonia, but preferentially absorbed a large quantity of copper. In the second and later stage, when the moisture content became small, the fibres were quite inert to cuprammonia and did not swell nor absorb the reagent. Similar phenomena took place with direct dyestuffs, and these points show that the water content and rate of reaction determined the effect produced. This explains the deeper dyeing effects obtained by Bruckhaus, above mentioned, for he evidently did not permit sufficient time to produce a low moisture content.

Formaldehyde was also caused to react with cellulose by means of dichlordimethyl sulphate or chlormethoxysulphonyl chloride and soda cellulose. Continuous degradation of the cellulose took place as the formaldehyde increased towards the maximum value of 17·2%.

RECENT WORK

Technical interest in this type of reaction was revived after the successful development of the crease-resisting process where urea-formaldehyde resins are formed inside the cellulosic material.

Although the publications on the production of crease-resistant cotton and rayon by means of chemical combination between the fibre and formaldehyde are of comparatively recent date, this may be a suitable opportunity of remarking that such crease-resisting effects were first noted by F. L. Barrett, in 1919, in the laboratories of Tootal Broadhurst Lee Co., Ltd.; the defects of the product in respect of brittleness and diminished tensile strength were also noted.

B.P. 452,150 of Bowen, Majerus, and Kellett deals with the production of crease-resisting effects on cellulosic material by treatment with formaldehyde and an acid substance followed by heating at 110°C. or above, preferably between 120° to 160°C. It is stated that in addition to the crease-resisting effect, the new products show considerable resistance to dyeing, and that the shrinkability of the treated material in water, detergents or swelling agents is considerably reduced. A typical example mentions working the viscose material in a 10% solution of formaldehyde containing 0·6% ammonium sulphocyanide for 15 minutes; the goods are then dried and heated at a temperature of 150°C. for 5 minutes. Other times and temperatures are 140°C. for 10 minutes and 120°C. for 15 minutes.

A somewhat similar method was outlined by Heberlein in B.P. 455,472, where acid salts were used in conjunction with a 30 to 40%

formaldehyde solution, followed by heating for 50 minutes at 90°C. or 20 minutes at 120°C. or 4 minutes at 140°C.

B.P. 488,095, also by Heberlein, states that the reaction between cellulose and formaldehyde for producing crease-resisting effects is accompanied by an almost complete freedom from shrinkage, but there is also an undesirable deterioration of the breaking elongation, and in the case of the cotton fibres the tensile strength was considerably reduced. It is therefore suggested that before treatment with the formaldehyde, the cellulosic material should be subjected to the action of a swelling agent and then treated with formaldehyde and a catalyst, whilst in the swollen state. In this manner a 60% improvement in the elongation at break can be made, compared with the straightforward acid formaldehyde treatment. In the case of rayon suitable concentrations of caustic potash may be used for swelling the material and also caustic soda, provided one avoids those concentrations which are known to be detrimental. The rayon is swollen in the unstretched state, washed, and then subjected to the formaldehyde treatment. In the case of the cotton material it is preferable to allow the cotton to shrink to its minimum length in the swelling agent and then stretch it beyond its original length, for the tensile strength of cotton is greater the more tightly the impregnated yarn, for example, is stretched after complete shrinkage. With cotton yarns, it was shown that where the formaldehyde treatment took place on the unmercerised material there was 66% decrease in breaking load, compared with 40% for normal mercerising and 30% for over-stretched mercerising. The acid formaldehyde reaction with the cellulose took place for about 15 minutes at 120° to 125°C. after impregnating in 40% formaldehyde solution containing a small quantity of an acid salt, such as aluminium thiocyanate.

B.P. 445,243 of Böhme Fettchemie discloses the fact that crease-resisting effects may be imparted to artificial silk, cotton, linen, etc., by first impregnating in a solution of a wax-like substance or a natural resin and then passing the impregnated material into a second bath containing about 5% formaldehyde solution, acidified with 5 or 6 c.c. of acetic or formic acid per litre. The impregnated material is then squeezed or centrifuged and dried for 20 minutes in 150°C. A temperature of at least 130°C. is apparently essential; suitable wax-like substances are paraffin wax or beeswax in trichlorethylene, but spermacetti may also be used.

Another process which is based on the reaction of cellulose with formaldehyde in presence of an oil or a fatty acid product has been described by British Celanese, Finlayson, and Perry in B.P. 450,620. This is mainly concerned with cellulosic materials, but also embraces some derivatives and low-grade animal fibres. In an actual example

the cloth is impregnated with a solution containing 20% formaldehyde and 3% hydrochloric acid; the material is dried at 50°C. and
heated for 5 minutes at 140°C., followed by washing and drying.

A limited application of the formaldehyde treatment of cellulose
has been disclosed in B.P. 491,779 of Du Pont, which relates to pile
fabrics with a "non-reactive" back composed of natural silk, cellulose
acetate, or even wool. The object of this particular method is to
render the rayon pile of velvets resistant to crushing. The velvet is
impregnated with a solution of formaldehyde and an acid or an acid
salt catalyst, and then dried at a temperature of 100° to 120°C.;
during the drying and heating process the velvet pile is brushed first
in one direction and then in another, until at the end the pile threads
stand perpendicular to the backing. Various amounts of formaldehyde are given in the examples which range from 8 to 37%; ammonium chloride is a typical catalyst and may be present in 0·25
to 0·5% concentration.

The inventors of this process are apparently well aware of the
disadvantages which normally exist when regenerated cellulose is
combined with formaldehyde, because they refer to the dangers of
weakening the pile to such an extent that it will break off on crushing.
In commercial practice conditions must be chosen which give the
desired degree of resistance to creasing without serious embrittlement, bearing in mind that the products become more resistant to
creasing and more brittle, the higher the concentration of the catalyst
and of the formaldehyde employed, the greater the amount of
solution remaining on the fabric, and the higher the temperature of
final heating. A somewhat significant statement, which may perhaps
be capable of rather wider application, is that a moderate degree of
brittleness in the pile is not particularly objectionable since pile
fabrics are not subjected to much wear. It is stated that there is
no direct relationship between the resistance to creasing and the
increase in weight brought about by the formaldehyde treatment.
The usual products increase the weight of the pile from 1·5 to 18%
and the better products from 4 to 18%. It seems to be of some
importance that the amount of the ammonium chloride catalyst
should be below 0·5%, preferably 0·2 to 0·3% in order to avoid
embrittlement of the pile.

This process of Du Pont, which is also known as the Heckert
process, was intended to produce washable crease-resistant velvets;
the process was operated on a fairly large scale at one time, but
now appears to have been abandoned in favour of that which depends
on urea-formaldehyde for the effect.

B.P. 477,084, by Lantz and Miller of the Calico Printers' Association, again deals with the direct combination of cellulose with
formaldehyde, and three effects are mentioned. First, the improved

resistance to creasing of the cellulosic material; secondly, the anti-shrink property; and, thirdly, the increased fastness to washing of certain dyestuffs, particularly direct and acid dyes. The process is limited to the use of sulphonic acid catalysts, and also avoids the use of temperatures higher than 100° C. by allowing the impregnated and dried material to remain at room temperatures for some 24 hours before washing. The amount of formaldehyde in the impregnation bath varies between 12 and 15%, and the quantity of sulphonic acid from 0·2 to 5%, according to the desired result and the particular acid used. After impregnation the goods are dried by a stenter, or by steam-heated cylinders, at temperatures ranging from 60° to 100° C., and, if necessary, allowed to lie at ordinary temperatures for some hours before washing and drying. It is stated that in these circumstances there is no diminution in the strength of the fibre.

The dialdehyde glyoxal has also been suggested for the production of crease-resisting and stabilising effects by reaction with cellulose; pre-war patents describing the reaction are B.P. 317,085, and 439,294 of the I.G., and B.P. 518,167 by Charbin. More recently, Cluett Peabody have interested themselves in the use of glyoxal as a stabilising agent for rayon as described in B.P. 585,679; the addition of polyvinyl alcohol to glyoxal is covered in B.P. 586,598 and the addition of urea-formaldehyde in B.P. 586,637.

Returning to the treatment of cellulose with formaldehyde, later specifications fall within a somewhat restricted field in which the product is not resistant to creasing, but is nevertheless substantially shrinkproof. These treatments occupy a position intermediate between the sthenosage process and the creaseproofing formaldehyde processes. Typical instances are seen with Heberlein's B.P. 518,872, and also B.P. 526,098 of the Calico Printers' Association, as described on page 257, in the section dealing with the production of shrink-resistant cotton and rayon.

An interesting paper on the action of formaldehyde on viscose rayon has been given by Saegusa (J. Cell. Inst., Tokyo, 1941, *17*, 81), and extensive measurements have been made on dry and wet strength together with resistance to creasing of rayon treated in various ways with formaldehyde in the presence of an acid catalyst. Viscose rayon (2 g.) was soaked for 15 hours in 300 c.c. of formaldehyde solution adjusted to pH 1·7; the sample was then centrifuged until its increase in weight was 70%, and was then heated for 5 hours at 70° C., washed, dried, and maintained in an atmosphere of 65% R.H. Saegusa claims to have prepared monomethylene cellulose in one operation and containing 17% of formaldehyde; when this product was boiled with caustic soda, however, the fixed formaldehyde fell from 17 to 12%, from which it appears that a certain amount of polymerised formaldehyde was contained in the material.

With cotton cellulose Saegusa was only able to combine 5·8% of formaldehyde; in both cases X-ray examination showed the reaction to be uneven. The presence of polymerised formaldehyde is always a difficulty in accurate work on cellulose methylene ether, as some of these products are very hard to remove except by heating *in vacuo* at 170° C.

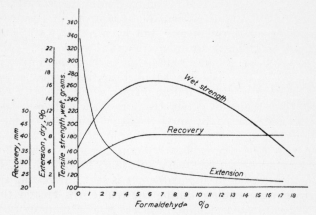

FIG. 108.—Influence of combined formaldehyde on some properties of rayon.

The conclusions reached by Saegusa are:

(*1*) For good resistance to creasing it is essential for the combined formaldehyde to exceed 2%.

(*2*) The extensions of the treated product in both dry and wet state are close together; but extensions of more than 10% can only be obtained when less than 1% of formaldehyde is combined.

(*3*) With quantities of combined formaldehyde between 3 and 9%, the wet strength of the product is 50% in excess of the dry strength (the dry strength itself, however, is adversely affected where more than 3% of formaldehyde is combined).

(*4*) The addition of paraform to the impregnating bath gives increased methylenation.

(*5*) Increased concentration of formaldehyde vapour during heating gives a methylene cellulose (from rayon only) containing 17% of combined formaldehyde.

Gotze and Reiff (Zellwolle, Kunstseide, Seide, 1941, *46*, 331) found that the formaldehyde-cellulose reaction results partly in combination and partly in polymerisation of the aldehyde; the reaction products may be separated by extraction with 10% NaOH for 5 hours. With constant catalyst, increased concentration of formaldehyde favours combination, whereas with constant formaldehyde concentration, an increase in the catalyst also promotes the extent of polymerisation. For practical purposes, it is better to increase the formaldehyde concentration rather than the amount of catalyst. Where formaldehyde is caused to combine with regenerated cellulose, an increase in the combined formaldehyde up to 1% decreases the swelling powers of the filaments, but even 0.2 to 0.5% combined formaldehyde is sufficient for many practical purposes.

Vogel (ibid., 1942, 47, 800) found that by nitration of the methylene cellulose, it was possible to liberate the formaldehyde and obtain an acetone-soluble cellulose nitrate whose viscosity could be measured. The degree of polymerisation of the cellulose was found to have been decreased by methylenation, and the decrease was mainly determined by the nature and amount of the catalyst.

It does not appear possible to obtain crease-resisting effects by methylene cellulose without very substantial degradation; indeed, no commercial fabrics are available. It is very interesting that the damage to native cellulose during the reaction is greater than the damage to regenerated cellulose, which is generally more susceptible. Nevertheless, when regenerated cellulose is combined with small amounts of formaldehyde, some stabilisation is obtained towards the changes in dimensional response to wetting, and the damage is not excessive. The values for water-imbibition may be seen in Fig. 109.

The reaction between cellulose and formaldehyde has been utilised for the production of permanent embossed effects—permanent in the sense of being resistant to washing, laundering, damp-pressing, etc. B.P. 452,149 of Bowen, Majerus, and Kellett gives examples using solutions of formaldehyde between 6 and 10% in conjunction with a catalyst in the proportion of 0.1 to 1% of the impregnating liquid. Suitable catalysts are the non-volatile organic acids, and certain of the mineral acids and their acid salts. The material is impregnated in the liquor at a temperature of 40 to 60° C. and then dried at a temperature of about 60° C. The fabric is then subjected to the mechanical treatment, such as schreinering, glazing, beetling, or embossing, and then heated at a temperature of the order of 130° to 140° C., for about 7 to 10 minutes, according to the temperature. The treated material is subsequently washed with soap or a solution of soap and ammonia in order to remove any traces of formaldehyde.

A somewhat modified method of rendering mechanical effects fast to washing has been described in B.P. 527,888 by Lantz and Miller. The regenerated cellulose material is impregnated with a solution containing formaldehyde and an acid catalyst, but dried below 60° C. to avoid any reaction between the cellulose and the formaldehyde during this operation. The dried material is then subjected to the mechanical treatment without previous conditioning and heated at a temperature not exceeding 105° C. for a sufficient length of time to give the desired result. In general the concentration of formaldehyde in the impregnating solution does not exceed 15%, but may be lower. The acidity of the impregnating bath is adjusted so that it is insufficient to cause reaction between formaldehyde and cellulose

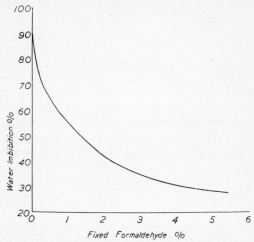

FIG. 109.—Influence of combined formaldehyde on
water imbibition of rayon.

during the impregnation and drying, and with this in view, acids of medium strength, such as aromatic sulphonic acids, or other acids having a dissociation constant between 3×10^{-1} and 1×10^{-4} may be employed. In an example, 0·3% of naphthalene-2-sulphonic acid is given for a solution containing 15% formaldehyde. The impregnated cloth was dried at 55° to 60° C. for 2 minutes, cooled to room temperature, embossed, heated for 1 minute at 90° C., followed by washing and drying.

In B.P. 547,846 of Cilander, attention is drawn to the fact that successful commercial practice of this type of reaction is hindered by the brittleness and weakness of the product. Certain modifications are suggested for the ordinary treatment with formaldehyde and an acid catalyst, but it is still required that sufficient formaldehyde should be used to ensure that the main reaction is that between cellulose and the formaldehyde.

The first suggested addition is an esterifying or etherifying substance, particularly Velan P.F., whose function is to avoid embrittlement of the fibre; a second addition is termed "a means of transmission," and includes small amounts of urea, thio-urea, methylol urea, etc. It is also stated in this specification that various starching, filling, and softening agents may be added to the formaldehyde solution, and also substances such as rubber latex and waterproofing agents may be added to the solution.

For the treatment of cotton, a mixture is suggested of 250 g. of 40% formaldehyde, 100 g. Velan P.F., 30 g. dimethylol urea, 8 g. ammonium sulphate, 28 g. sodium acetate, and water up to 1,000 g. The fabric is impregnated in this solution, dried at 60° C., and heated at 150° C. for 10 minutes, followed by washing and drying.

The brittleness of methylene cellulose has been utilised by Kent (B.P. 524,415) to form powdered cellulose of increased resistance to water, by impregnating the cellulose with formaldehyde in presence of a small amount of acid, freeing from excess liquor, drying and heating until brittle, and then pulverising the product. The temperature and duration of heating should be such as to render it brittle, but should not be so high as to "injure" the material. The product may be used for producing rayon of reduced lustre and substantial freedom from swelling on wetting, according to U.S.P. 2,234,307. Cellulose is treated with 100 parts of 40% formaldehyde solution and 0·5 parts of HNO_3, heated when dry at 100° to 120° C. and ground to 200 mesh. About 2 to 3% by weight of this product is suggested for incorporation in the rayon.

As previously indicated, the reaction between formaldehyde and cellulose is capable of giving two types of result: (a) a non-swelling compound, and (b) a highly swollen product. For non-swelling material the methods of treating with formaldehyde, in presence of an acid catalyst, entail the use of temperatures of the order of 100° C. and above in order to bring about a combination; Eschalier's process results in about 0·3 to 0·8% of formaldehyde being combined with the cellulose to form cellulose methylene ether. Quite recently, however, it has been found possible to form a product containing 3 to 4% of combined formaldehyde, as shown in B.P. 528,740. In carrying out the process the proportion of solution to the cellulose must be such that the latter is always in a fully swollen state; the rate of absorption depends on the concentration of the acid and of the formaldehyde, and these factors are so chosen that the time required for the treatment is less than 2 hours. Where 40% formaldehyde is used in conjunction with sufficient sulphuric acid to give a "normal" solution, the reaction is complete in 10 minutes at 80° C. or in 1 hour at 60° C. Using $N/10$ H_2SO_4 with 40% formaldehyde the same result can be obtained in 1 hour at 80° C. Some details of apparent pH values are as follows: 3·1 at 100° C.; 2·3 at 80° C.; 1·5 at 60° C.; 0·7 at 40° C.; 0·0 at 20° C. When the material has been steeped for the necessary length of time, it is washed and dried. It will be seen, therefore, that this process differs from Eschalier in having no dehydration, and from later processes in the absence of any heating in the dry state.

The properties of the cellulose methylene ether resulting from the above treatment are also different from what has gone before; there is no increase in wet strength and no resistance to creasing. The affinity towards some direct dyestuffs is slightly increased and the product still possesses a high-water imbibition.

These properties or effects are contrary to those possessed by the material treated with formaldehyde and acid, according to the previous methods, but the products also possess the property of combining with nitrogenous materials such as amines, amides, etc., when heated, after which they possess an affinity for those dyestuffs usually employed in dyeing animal fibres. For example, the methylated cellulose may be treated at the boil for a few seconds with a 4% solution of cyanamide at pH 5, followed by drying and heating for 2 to 5 minutes at 135° to 140° C., after which an affinity for wool dyestuffs is exhibited and the dyed material possesses good fastness to washing.

Combination between the high-swelling cellulose methylene ether and nitrogenous compounds is described in B.P. 528,741, also by Boulton and Morton of Courtaulds; it is interesting to note that the high-swelling cellulose methylene ether can be converted into the non-swelling methylene ether by heating in presence of an acid catalyst.

In view of the two types of product, high-swelling and low-swelling, together with the possibility of passing from the former to the latter, it is possible to draw some interesting comparisons between the reaction of formaldehyde and cellulose with that of formaldehyde and urea; the possibility of hydroxymethyl and of methylene derivatives appears a feasible hypothesis. Methylene bridges between the cellulose chains might well have some function similar to that of the cystine link in wool and the general reaction bears some points of similarity to the vulcanisation of rubber. It is also interesting to compare the stabilising action of formaldehyde on cellulose with the production of permanent set of wool on the basis of cross-linkages.

CHAPTER VI
PERMANENT SET

ONE of the most remarkable properties of wool is its elasticity, which increases with the moisture content; when stretched in water to 60 or 70%, wool will return to its original length if placed in cold water again. The extensibility of wool also increases with temperature, the limiting value of 100% being reached in steam.

The changes in the load-extension curves of wool produced by steam or hot water are permanent to cold water; that is, the curve of the normal fibre does not return in cold water. In other words, when wool is stretched in cold water it is highly elastic, but the behaviour of wool which has been stretched for a time in hot water or steam is different; it becomes set and does not recover in cold water, even in absence of tension.

This behaviour has been utilised in textile finishing processes from very early times, and is often described as permanent set. As will appear later, true permanent set requires the prolonged action of steam, and it is now becoming common to refer to the set which is permanent to cold water as temporary set.

The fact that wool stretched in steam or hot water shows a highly diminished tendency to return to its original length, even when immersed in cold water, received little scientific attention until the work of Harrison (Proc. Roy. Soc., 1918, *494*, 460), who attributed the effect to the plasticising action of steam or hot water, whereas Shorter (Trans. Farad. Soc., 1924, *20*, 228) considered that steam had an annealing effect.

The first systematic examination of the setting phenomenon was made by Speakman (ibid., 1929, *25*, 169), when it was established that the recovery of wool in cold water, from strain applied at various temperatures up to 79° C., depended on the degree of strain; the greater the strain, the more slowly does the wool return to its original length. Further, the tendency to return to the original length decreases with increasing time of subjection to strain. Where the rate of recovery in cold water was concerned, the tendency to acquire set increases with rise of temperature during strain up to 80° C. In addition to these three factors, the slow retraction in cold water on release from strain makes it difficult to define the exact temperature at which set is imparted to wool.

This difficulty is increased when recovery from strain is examined at high temperatures, for set which is permanent to cold water is not necessarily permanent at higher temperatures. For example when wool was extended 40% in water at 86°C., it assumed a set of 30% to water at 18°C., but returned to its original length in water at 86°C. This property was found to be typical of temperatures up to 90°C., so that after the crabbing process, for example, the wool is set except when subjected to temperatures above that on the crabbing roller. Above 90°C., however, the strained fibres contracted somewhat, but recovery was incomplete, and some measure of true permanent set was realised. This may be seen from the figures in the table.

CONTRACTION OF FIBRES WHEN STEAMED BEFORE RELEASE

45 minutes steaming		15 minutes steaming		23 minutes steaming	
Time	Extn.	Time	Extn.	Time	Extn.
0·0 mins.	39·6%	0·0 mins.	39·3%	0·0 mins.	7·9%
1·6 mins.	31·8%	0·7 mins.	35·2%	0·6 mins.	6·4%
3·6 mins.	29·4%	1·7 mins.	31·5%	1·6 mins.	5·7%
5·6 mins.	27·9%	2·7 mins.	29·0%	3·6 mins.	5·2%
8·6 mins.	26·2%	3·7 mins.	26·7%	7·6 mins.	4·4%
14·6 mins.	23·7%	4·7 mins.	23·8%	21·6 mins.	3·6%
65·0 mins.	20·5%	7·7 mins.	21·5%	70·6 mins.	3·2%
84·0 mins.	20·0%	10·7 mins.	19·0%	93·6 mins.	3·2%
172·0 mins.	20·0%	13·7 mins.	17·4%	—	—
—	—	20·7 mins.	15·4%	—	—

This aspect of the setting process was also examined by Astbury and Woods (Phil. Trans. Roy. Soc., 1933, *A232*, 333), who found that when stretched wool is set by caustic soda solution or by steam for a few minutes, the effect can be reversed by removing the tension and leaving the fibre in NaOH solution, or in steam, when contraction to less than the original length takes place; this effect was termed *super-contraction*. Super-contracted fibres can be stretched to twice their original length in cold water and show complete elastic recovery in cold water.

If, however, the normal hair is stretched in steam for about 30 minutes, there is no super-contraction; the hair becomes set and the elongation is not removed by steaming the released fibre. This true permanent set is produced by steam, but not by NaOH.

Super-contraction of wool fibres which have been stretched in steam or hot water may be achieved by NaOH or Na_2S solutions, by steam or hot water at a higher temperature, after the stretching force is removed. Super-contraction first increases with time of relaxation and then decreases; in steam the relaxation time for maximum super-contraction of 30% is short, about 2 minutes, but relaxation in water at lower temperatures requires a longer time.

From Fig. 110, it is clear that wool must be held stretched in steam for at least 20 minutes to realise any true permanent set; the set from hot water or short exposures to steam is destroyed by subsequent steaming in absence of tension so that contraction to less than the original length takes place.

It should be emphasised that the process takes place in two stages: first, breakdown of cross-linkages; and, secondly, rebuilding.

When wool is stretched, the long peptide chains uncoil and certain cross-linkages of the grid are put under stress; when steamed in this

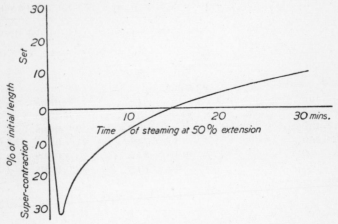

FIG. 110.—Super-contraction and set of wool on steaming.

state, hydrolytic breakdown of the cross-linkages takes place, so that, if the tension is removed, super-contraction occurs. As the steaming is continued with the wool in the stretched state, the broken cross-linkages reform in new and unstressed positions and inhibit, to a considerable extent, the normal contractive force of stretched wool. In X-ray photographs of wool stretched in steam, it was noticed that certain of the spots were drawn out into short streaks, and by consideration of the spots which were so extended and those which were not, it was shown that the disruptive effect of steam, or cold dilute alkali, is confined to one direction, namely, that associated with the cross-linkages. The possibility of super-contraction always precedes that of set, and neither is developed until the phenomenon above described appears in the X-ray photographs.

The chemical mechanism responsible for permanent set has been examined and elucidated by Speakman (J.S.D.C., 1936, 52, 335, 380, 423; 1937, 53, 237). Experiments on setting at various pH values revealed that the maximum setting properties of fibres are developed at pH 9·2; control of pH had not previously been generally exercised in the textile finishing processes of crabbing and blowing, and uneven effects may easily result from various amounts of alkali in the fabric depending on the scouring and rinsing technique. The high degree of the permanence of the set obtained by boiling for 30 minutes in 0·05 M borax solution is seen by the fact that there was little difference between the values of the set persisting after 2 minutes and 60 minutes release in boiling water.

From these results it appears that setting should be carried out at pH 9·2 or the highest figure below this value consistent with the necessary strength of the fabric; borax solutions of 2% concentration afford a simple means of realising this value.

The fact that no set is produced in hydrochloric acid at pH 1, on the other hand, tends to the assumption that as one of the reactions in setting must be hydrolytic in character owing to the necessity for heat and moisture (or alkali), it should affect the cystine linkage which is known to be alkali-sensitive. The breakdown of linkages between the peptide chains, which precedes the rebuilding of linkages necessary for permanent set, is due to hydrolysis of cystine linkages.

Astbury and Woods (loc. cit.) had previously shown that permanent set is the result of two successive reactions, the first of which is characterised by the fact that it leads to super-contraction; Speakman, however, showed that reactions which break the cystine linkage also lead to super-contraction. Sodium sulphide, sodium bisulphite, silver sulphate, and potassium cyanide solutions all gave super-contraction; indeed, the shrinkage produced by sodium bisulphite had been patented by Elsaesser (D.R.P. 233,210). The behaviour of sodium sulphite was anomalous on account of its inability to break salt linkages, but super-contraction was effected on de-aminated fibres, showing that this property is associated with breakdown of both salt and sulphur linkages. Similarly, de-aminated fibres showed rapid contraction in borax solutions at pH 9·2, where the normal fibres do not contract on account of the persistence of salt linkages.

The first reaction in permanent setting, therefore, is hydrolysis of the cystine linkages

$$R-S-S-R + H_2O \longrightarrow R-SH + R-S-OH.$$

Now the rebuilding of new linkages to give permanent set is not merely a reforming of the salt linkages, for the permanent set resists steam; further, the set fibres fail to contract in boiling HCl at pH 1 when salt linkages are broken. Astbury had also shown (see page 153) that although set fibres contract in NaOH solutions, this does not depend on the reversion of β- to α-keratin, so that the linkages responsible for permanent set are not produced by re-formation of cystine linkages. The new linkages are formed by interaction between the salt and sulphur linkages or their hydrolysis products.

$$R-S-OH + R'-NH_2 \longrightarrow R-S-NH-R' + H_2O.$$

The fact that the free amino groups of arginine and lysine side-chains play an important part in the rebuilding process was demonstrated by showing that fibres from which these groups had been removed failed to take a permanent set in steam. Similarly, fibres from which sulphur had been removed also failed to take permanent set, thus showing the important role of the sulphur linkages.

The process of setting fibres in steam or boiling water, therefore, is assisted by alkali, which facilitates hydrolysis of the disulphide bond, and is opposed by reagents which attack or combine with basic side-chains or sulphur linkages to prevent their interaction.

With alkalis, the optimum pH is 9·2, but sodium sulphite and bisulphite may also be used at totally different values, to produce permanent set; sodium bisulphite solution is even more effective than borax at pH 9. The chemical mechanism is as follows:

$$R-S-S-R + NaHSO_3 \longrightarrow R-S-Na + R-S-SO_3H$$
$$R-S-SO_3H + R'-NH_2 \longrightarrow R-S-NH-R' + H_2SO_3.$$

From these reactions it appears that the same linkages are present in the set fibre as when alkali is used, but the intermediate reaction products are different.

In view of the great reactivity of boiling solutions of sodium bisulphite, which is sufficient to destroy the wool, Speakman considered it possible that concentrated solutions might be utilised for permanent set at lower temperatures where destructive attack would be minimised. Both sulphite and bisulphite solutions are capable of imparting permanent set at 50°C.

When wool fibres are stretched in water, the long peptide chains are uncoiled against the resistance of the salt and sulphur linkages; stress is thus thrown on these side-linkages. If the fibre is transferred to acid or alkaline solution, the salt linkages are broken and the stress on the cystine link is diminished; the strain on the cystine linkage will, therefore, be at a maximum between pH 5 and 7, where the salt linkages are most stable. Solutions of sodium sulphite and bisulphite were mixed in varying proportions to give constant reducing power but varying pH, and it was established that the amount of permanent set produced in these media, reached a maximum at pH 5·95.

This work was extended to provide methods of setting animal fibres at low temperatures, as described in B.P. 453,559, 453,700, 453,701, and 456,336. The general method is to break the cystine linkages by acid and alkaline reducing agents at low temperatures (35° to 50°C.) and then reunite the cystine side-chains in the relaxed structure. Fibre relaxation may be effected by sodium sulphite, sodium bisulphite, or alkaline reducing agents at a pH above 10, and the rebuilding may be brought about in three ways: (a) mixtures of sulphite and bisulphite at pH 6 rebuild R—S—NH—R' linkages at 50°C., (b) disulphide linkages may be re-formed with oxidising agents, or (c) treatment of the relaxed fibres with solutions of salts of multivalent metals may produce linkages of the type R—S—M—S—R'.

Returning to the consideration of permanent set, it will be recalled that the set imparted by water below 90°C. is not really permanent, but may be reversed according to the temperature of the water in which the wool is subsequently placed, and the time and temperature conditions of the original set, together with the percentage extension imparted to the wool.

Now the change from α-keratin to β-keratin which is generally produced by stretching may also be produced by any kind of strain, including the type of squeezing resulting from pressure; hence, a permanent set may be produced by steaming wool in the compressed state, and this is often utilised to avoid the appearance of creases and other irregularities which would come from the release of latent strains in the cloth. In view of what has been stated about the elastic properties of wool in water and in steam it may be well to differentiate between certain of these effects. The London Shrinkage process (see page 188) is carried out with cold water and no stress of tension is applied to the wool; strained fibres will therefore contract unless they have been permanently set. The ordinary process of steaming is also effected without tension, and is applied for a short time only; the actual temperature of the wool during this process is relatively low (about 50° to 60°C.), and the object of the process is to release strains in the fibre and permit contraction.

The processes used to impart permanent set are crabbing, blowing, and boiling. The crabbing process involves the use of hot water and tension, and in the full crabbing process the effect is enhanced by wet blowing. The blowing process depends on the effect of steam at 100°C. on wool under tension for a prolonged period; pressure-blowing is a variation of this process. Boiling also involves the treatment of wool under tension with water at 100°C. for a short time or at 75° to 80°C. for a long time.

The ordinary process of steaming does not impart permanent set and must not be confused with blowing or decatising; the usual objects of steaming are to prepare the goods for raising, cutting, or pressing, as well as to remove the thin, papery handle and superficial lustre which result from blowing, and so restore the fullness of the material. On a steaming mill, the cloth is drawn by plush-covered rollers over an open trough with a perforated base connected with a steam supply, from which rises a mist of warm steam through which the cloth is repeatedly passed. The steam-box is closely related to the dewing machine, which owes its name to the old method of moistening wool by exposing in fields overnight; this method was followed by plaiting or cuttling alternate layers of dry and moist wool and allowing the mass to stand. In the dewing process, the moisture is applied by a fine spray; whatever the method adopted, it not only conditions the wool, but also removes the gloss and papery finish which may result from blowing or pressing. Steaming is also combined with brushing when the nap is raised prior to cutting.

SETTING PROCESSES

The chief processes for imparting permanent set to wool are:

(*a*) Crabbing.
(*b*) Blowing or decatising.
(*c*) Potting or roll-boiling.

In the operations of crabbing, blowing, and boiling, the cloth is usually wound on a roller under tension, so that a greater pressure is built up on the inner part of the roll than that which obtains on the outside; it is for this reason that it is generally advisable to give the piece a double treatment during which it is unwound and reversed so that a uniform finish is obtained. The pressure during these processes improves the lustre of the goods, and clarifies the weave when a wrapper is used. Cotton wrappers which have a slightly raised and "structureless" surface may be used in order to avoid any mutual embossing of a pronounced weave which would obscure the desired effect; if the woven design is subdued, then a wrapper is not necessary.

The tension applied in the preliminary winding is important and must be sufficient to pull out the creases and cockles of the fabric before it is set by hot water; the tension is longitudinal, so that a certain weft shrinkage occurs, but some machines are provided with devices for adjusting the width of the cloth as it is wound on to the roller. One type of crabbing and winding machine comprises a pair of endless chains carrying hooks or pins on to which the selvedges are pressed by a circular brush; the stretched cloth then passes over a steam-box and is wound on to a roller or beam, which, if necessary, may be supplied with a heavy jockey roller. The tenter-crab can thus be used as a complete machine for a mild crabbing process, or as an accessory to crabbing, blowing, or potting processes of greater severity.

The crabbing process may also be utilised to develop certain structural features in fabrics of the lining type.

CRABBING

The crabbing process is directed to obviating any distortions of the yarn and cloth which might arise in wet processes due to the release of the latent strains in the wool which, it will be recalled, is highly elastic. In particular, many goods would curl, shrink unevenly and crease were they not given some measure of permanent set. Further, many fabrics are often "cockly" as they come from the loom, and these distortions must be removed.

The actual conditions of crabbing must be determined to some extent by the subsequent processes through which the pieces have to pass; if the wool has to be scoured, milled, and bleached, it will not have to withstand higher temperatures than 40° to 45°C., but if the piece is intended for dyeing, then it might be subjected to a boiling dyebath for some hours. In the second instance, it would be useless to give a short crabbing process before dyeing.

According to one crabbing process, the pieces are passed through boiling water at full width and under tension, and then run on to a beam for some time and allowed to cool. An alternative method is to wind the pieces under tension on a perforated iron cylinder which is immersed in water and the water boiled by passing in steam; the pieces are then allowed to cool and are generally run on to a second cylinder, and the process repeated in order that both ends of the goods should be evenly treated. This second method is sometimes referred to as a full crabbing process.

In the ordinary crabbing machine there are two or three troughs supplied with hot and cold water or steam, and each trough contains a crabbing roller with a weighting roller above; at the end of the machine is situated a perforated cylinder for steaming. The fabric runs over an expanding roller on to the first crabbing roller under suitable tension and pressure, where it revolves in the boiling liquor for the required length of time. It is then wound on to the second crabbing roller, and the process repeated; the goods are allowed to cool slowly on the final roller. Many variations are possible in the crabbing routine. For instance, when the goods have been wound on the first roller and the temperature of the water raised to a point above that which the wool will encounter in any subsequent finishing process, the cloth may be rotated under pressure from a jockey roller running on the crabbing roller. In some crabbing machines, the cloth is wound on perforated rollers through which the hot water is pumped during the rotation of the roller in the trough.

A continuous crabbing process has been devised whereby the cloth is passed at full width over a series of small rollers through a trough of hot water, and then cooled in cold water.

The crabbing liquors may range from water to soap or alkali, but if crabbing takes place on scoured goods, then water alone is generally used; most crabbing takes place with worsteds, however, and these generally contain relatively small amounts of oil, so that it is possible to omit scouring and pass directly from the crabbing process to the dyeing treatment with cheap cloths. When goods have been crabbed in the grease they are more difficult to scour, if scouring is necessary, so it may be advisable to add a little detergent to the crabbing liquor, but this should not exceed 1% Na_2CO_3; the amount of detergent should not be sufficient to produce lathering in the crabbing process itself.

As previously mentioned, 2% borax solutions give crabbing liquors of the correct pH for the best effect; it is not very common to add borax, however, for many fabrics are already slightly alkaline.

The tension and pressure applied to the fabrics during crabbing are very important factors, for if the tension is excessive the handle is adversely affected; a certain amount of watermarking may also be caused, and this may not become apparent until the goods have been dyed. On the other hand, too little tension may bring about a preferential treatment on or near the selvedges, and this again may not be apparent until the goods have been dyed and revealed darker edges and sometimes cockled selvedges.

If the treatment is carried out too quickly or the temperature of the water raised rapidly, then there is a tendency to produce "ended" pieces, although this danger may be obviated to some extent by a larger roller, or by re-winding and double-crabbing.

The crabbing process is not complete until the goods are cool, and in some cases they are put on one side to cool naturally; if the rolls are placed upright, the fabric may slip and unwind, and in the horizontal position care should be taken to avoid drainage producing uneven effects. It is possible to remove excess of water by suction before placing the rolls to cool, and this will obviate drainage difficulties.

BLOWING

Blowing consists in subjecting the cloth to the action of steam, which is forced through the fabric under pressure; this process is also termed decatising—a term which is used somewhat loosely. The process is capable of many variations. Although the blowing process utilises steam, it must not be confused with the simple steaming operation, the object of which is merely to remove excessive lustre, and the thin papery handle from previous processes, as well as to prepare for pressing and cutting. In the blowing or decatising process, the steam is applied to the fabric while it is in a state of strain, so that some permanent set is produced. The purpose of the blowing operation is to set the woven structure in a regular and permanent manner, the lustrous effect is secondary and results from the improved regularity of the structure, together with the slight flattening. The fabric is wound on a perforated roller whose perforations are covered with a cotton or canvas wrapper; the winding takes place under tension, which must not be excessive or "pressure marks" will result. A wide wrapper is then applied and the ends firmly bound with cord. Steam is blown through the roll of fabric for from 8 to 15 minutes; the wool becomes plastic, strains are relieved, and the various tensions relax to give a stable balanced product. This state is fixed by cooling, which is usually carried out by blowing cool air through the roll. It is essential that the cloth should be blown dry before removal. As with most of these treatments, it may be necessary to re-wind the fabric and blow again, so that both ends receive approximately the same treatment. This second treatment is usually of shorter duration since the fabric is generally hot from the first blowing.

The blowing process may also be utilised for the production of embossed effects, by blowing the wool while in contact with a rubberised matrix sheet. It is obvious that the correct tension during winding is of the utmost importance, and the cloth should be wound so that the raised pattern on the matrix sheet is in contact with the surface of the cloth to be embossed without the intervention of a wrapper. The matrix sheet is generally made of rubberised cotton or linen, to which rubber pads are fixed to make the pattern; the thickness of these pads may be 0·25 inches for thick fabrics and 0·125 inches for medium cloths. The matrix sheet is pierced with holes in positions which will not interfere with the impression, and these holes allow the steam to escape.

Blowing in the wet state is broadly equivalent to crabbing for the general fixation of the woven structure, and, indeed, sometimes forms the final stage of a crabbing process; blowing in the grease is often employed as a rapid alternative to crabbing, and one which is less troublesome. Dry blowing forms part of a later sequence of finishing processes and generally follows cutting, perhaps after brushing and steaming; the development of a permanent lustre is one of the prime objects of this type of finish.

The lustre obtained by pressing is not permanent unless set by decatising, and the pressure-apparatus is sometimes used for this purpose. The pressed cloth is tightly wound against a fine cotton wrapper on to a perforated shell and a heavy end-cloth is wound on top of the finished roll to afford protection to the whole, and to apply pressure to the outer layers of the wool. The perforated cylinder is then placed in a jacketed cylinder which is closed and evacuated; steam is admitted through the perforated cylinder on which the cloth is wound, and passed for 2 or 3 minutes after which the direction of the steam is reversed to pass through the roll from the outside by suction. The cylinder is rotated during the whole

11

period of steaming. The process is completed by removing the perforated roller from the pressure cylinder, pumping out the steam from the cloth, and cooling by drawing air through the roll of fabric. In this process, the passage of the steam in both directions through the cloth gives an even result with one winding.

In ordinary dry-blowing or decatising, it is possible to follow one of two courses—self-blowing or wrapper-blowing—but the former is of somewhat limited application and is generally used to impart a little shrinkage. Wrapper-blowing obviates or removes surface distortions, increases the lustre of the cloth, and imparts a type of press-finish from the tension of winding; the amount of shrinkage in width is less with wrapper-blowing than with self-blowing. The winding of the cloth under tension produces an internal pressure between the layers so that the fabric becomes thinner, and may have to receive a further finish, such as ordinary steaming, to restore its fullness.

The general method is to wind the wool fabric, interleaved with a fine cotton apron or wrapper, on to a perforated cylinder which is already protected with a cotton wrapper; the roll of cotton and wool is then covered with the cotton wrapper whose extending sides are bound with cord so that when steam is blown into the cylinder it must pass through the body of the cloth and not escape at the selvedges. The older machines had two cylinders whose diameters were from 6 to 10 inches, but the modern tendency is towards a single large cylinder whose diameter may be 36 to 40 inches; the larger cylinder makes it possible to avoid double-blowing, and also permits greater shrinkage since the internal pressure is less, due to fewer layers on the cylinder.

The time of steaming may be varied according to the result required, but is usually from 1 to 5 minutes. The steam is generally removed by a vacuum pump, but if only partially removed, a duller effect may be obtained.

The lustrous effect is due to the swelling which occurs under the influence of heat and moisture, and this swelling presses the fibres against the smooth constricting wrapper; excessive treatment is apt to produce a thin, smooth, limp, and slippery fabric, and may also impair the strength of the wool itself. The feel and handle of the wool varies to a certain extent with the nature of the cotton wrapper or apron. When raised fabrics are blown or decatised, it is essential that the direction of the nap should not be disturbed during the winding on to the cylinder, as any such disturbances of the nap will be fixed by blowing.

POTTING

Potting, or roll-boiling, is used to produce a soft handle and a smooth glossy surface, as, for instance, on billiard cloth. This finish is generally employed on dress-faced cloths, such as doeskins, beavers, and pilot cloths, and is therefore coupled with milling, raising, and cropping beforehand. As potting imparts a high degree of permanent set, it may be regarded as a process related to crabbing.

The goods are treated on a perforated iron roller, whose perforations are covered with a cotton or canvas wrapper. The fabric is wound on to this roller at full width, and free from creases; a certain amount of tension must be applied during the winding process, and this varies according to the type of cloth. The roll of fabric is then covered with a wrapper of cotton or canvas, and both ends are securely tied with cords. The rolls are placed vertically in a cistern of water which is gradually brought to 60°C., and maintained at that temperature for at least 3 to 5 hours, or possibly 2 or 3 days. The goods are lifted from the cistern when the boiling is complete, and allowed to drain and cool in an upright position, after which the cloth is unwound, and the process repeated with the centre of the roll on the outer layers. When the fabric is allowed to cool slowly on the rolls, a smooth glossy face is produced, but if this is not required, the hot cloth may be unwound through cold water to give the soft handle only.

The full potting treatment is a somewhat drastic process, and may be replaced by forced pumping in crabbing; over-treatment gives a thin papery effect which may be rectified by steaming.

BEAMING

Beaming may be regarded as a mild form of potting, and is generally used to remove crimps or other marks which have arisen during scouring, milling, or dyeing; the defect is preferably removed as soon as it is observed. The goods are run through hot water and stretched in the weft direction by an expander roller or tenter crab before running on to a wooden roller or beam; the woollen fabric is followed by a cotton wrapper of greater width and the ends are bound with cords and the goods allowed to cool over a period of 12 to 48 hours. With lightweight woollens, a steaming treatment may replace the hot water.

CHAPTER VII

MILLING

The ability to felt is probably the most characteristic feature of wool; it is so obvious that it has been known from the earliest times, and forms the basis of probably the first permanent finish. This felting property may be utilised in finishing processes to alter the fabric in respect of body, elasticity, strength, and appearance, and to provide a new texture which may become the foundation for further finishing treatments.

It seems probable that felting originated in the primitive methods of facilitating the washing of fabrics by pounding, when it would be found that effects other than cleansing were realised; the pounding methods appear to have been carried out by trampling the cloth underfoot also, for this technical process featured among the many curious mural decorations of Pompeii. The original term for the process was "fulling," which signifies a treading action and persists in the French *fouler*; the term "walker" was also used, and is still seen in the German *Walken*. The treading action is reproduced in the stocks which are sometimes called fulling stocks, but the introduction of rotary machines brought with it the word "milling," which now applies to all the compressive processes whereby the wool fabric is caused to felt. The term "fulling" still persists in the U.S.A.

It has been suggested that where fabrics are concerned, milling should be regarded as the process, and felting as the resulting phenomenon; however, a lack of precision is typical of many definitions in textile technology. Milling and felting have become practically synonymous, but, strictly speaking, felting is the process of making felts from fibres which are formed into a compact mass by pressure, and thus make a fabric without the processes of spinning and weaving.

Now different types of wool vary in their ability to felt depending on the length, fineness, scaliness, waviness, and other physical properties; it is well known, for instance, that Merino wool is superior to Crossbred in respect of milling properties. Yarn structure also plays an important part, for in general yarns of an open nature facilitate felting. Hence, worsted yarns with parallel fibres felt less readily than wool yarns formed from a cluster of fibres already intertwining with each other; the fibrous density is lower, and fibres from adjacent yarns make contact more easily than in the worsted construction. Obviously the question of twist, too, plays a part, for loosely spun yarns will felt more readily than hard-spun material.

The effect of weave is largely a matter of the frequency of intersections, for the plain weave is more difficult to mill than the twill, and so forth; standard weaves are adopted for certain milling effects.

The extent of felting may be varied to give a variety of effects ranging from a shrinkage treatment to form a more compact and softer cloth to a more severe processing whereby the yarn structure is burst and the fibres are matted together, obscuring the weave completely; the latter effect is more easily realised in the stocks. The milling machine may be utilised to give cover to the fabric without much shrinkage or to obtain shrinkage without imparting much cover.

MILLING THEORY

One of the earliest attempts to collect the various theories of milling was made by Löbner (Studien und Forschungen über die Wolle, 1898), and it appears to have been suggested by Youatt (page 225) that the actual fibre shortens and telescopes itself under the influence of moisture. Ditzel, however (Deutsche Wollengewerbe, 1891, *23*, 1), milled some wool fibres in a bag with a piece of woollen cloth made from the same type of fibre under such conditions that the piece of cloth showed a shrinkage of 16% in length and width; the free fibres showed no diminution in length.

The fundamental cause of felting was discovered by Monge (Ann. de Chimie, 1790, *6*, 300) who found that during the milling process the wool hairs always migrate in the direction of their root ends; he attributed this tendency to their imbricated surface.

Ditzel also noticed that if the wool fibre is rubbed between finger and thumb in the direction of its length, then it travels in the direction of its root; this is because all the scales project towards the tip of the fibre and oppose motion in that direction. It was also established that when locks of wool were arranged (*a*) with root ends facing each other, and (*b*) with tip ends facing each other, and milled in bags, the first arrangement resulted in the root ends milling fast together, but with the second arrangement the tip ends separated and the root ends moved to opposite corners of the bag. Hence, it is clear that the wool hairs travel in the direction of their root ends during milling.

Further work on fibre travel was carried out by Arnold (Leip. Monat. f. Textilind., 1929, *44*, 463, 507, 540), who confirmed and extended the ideas of Ditzel to show that during the felting process the fibres stretch and move in a similar manner to that in which an earthworm crawls; this is known as the *Regenwurmtheorie*.

In addition to the manner whereby the fibres move, there are other factors which are of importance in the consideration of milling. Shorter (J.S.D.C., 1923, *39*, 270) has drawn attention to the fact that the wool fabric is a collection of "self-tightening mechanisms," for each fibre in the cloth will have places of tight and loose entanglement; hence fibre travel will diminish the distance between the entanglements by drawing them together if the scales are properly orientated. If it should happen that the scale structure is not directed so as to draw the entanglements together, then they should

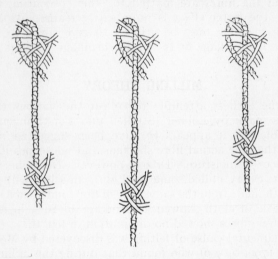

FIG. 111.—Diagram illustrating the felting of wool.

be moved apart and extend the fabric; however, the lack of rigidity prevents this, so the fibre loops and so forms further entanglements with other fibres as milling proceeds.

The theory of Arnold envisages some creeping even against a certain amount of tension, but the views of Shorter are concerned with the travel of the fibre in the slack state only.

Speakman (J.T.I., 1933, *24*, 273) has pointed out that the interpretation of milling shrinkage by consolidation is possible by combining Arnold's views on felting with those of Shorter on milling, so that the actual mechanism is not unlike an elastic sewing thread which draws up the fabric on recovering from extension.

It appears, therefore, that the two main features in wool which account for milling shrinkage are the scale structure which produces unidirectional travel, and the property of wool of being stretched but recovering from extension.

It has also been suggested by Martin (Proc. Phys. Soc., 1941, *53*,

186) that the orientated frictional effect arises from the particular arrangement of the atoms forming the surfaces of the scales.

The pressure of the milling rollers, or of the stocks, forces the fibres into close contact whereby the scales of the adjacent fibres find the necessary mutual friction. The movement during milling is due to the intermittent nature of the pressure which causes the hair to stretch, moving in the direction of its root end, but the elasticity of the moist hair is such that the fibre contracts when the pressure is released. This contraction takes place in the direction of the root end, so that a steady movement of the fibre results, drawing other fibres together to form a close and compact mass.

As the only fibres which can be successfully milled are those with a surface scale structure, it must be assumed that the scales are largely responsible for the felting and shrinkage of fabrics in the milling machine.

It has also been suggested by Youatt that, under the influence of heat, pressure, and moisture, the fibres were forced into such intimate contact that the scales actually interlocked at the serrations and were held in position by the "saw-edge" effect; this view has persisted to a most alarming extent, and is often illustrated by diagrams in technical publications. In actual fact, there is no evidence whatsoever for this type of contact, which is never seen under the microscope.

As considerable power is required to produce felting in the milling machine, the importance of mechanical compression should not be overlooked; there is a forcible displacement of the fibres. Further, although the milling shrinkage depends primarily on the scale structure of wool, the ease of extension and the power of recovery are important factors in fabrics of similar composition and construction.

In view of the importance attached to scale structure and its influence on milling, it might be expected that the rate of shrinkage in the milling machine would be largely determined by the difference in frictional resistance to movement in the direction of root and tip. It is well known, for instance, that merino wool, with well-defined and projecting scales, felts much more rapidly than mohair, with its less distinct scales which adhere more closely to the fibre.

A useful term "The Directional Frictional Effect" or the "D.F.E." has recently been adopted by many investigators; it is a quantitative measure of the difference between the maximum and minimum coefficient of friction of wool hairs, i.e. rubbing from tip to root, and rubbing from root to tip respectively.

Speakman and Stott (J.T.I., 1931, 22, 339) devised an apparatus for measuring the "scaliness" of fibres, by mounting them on a small wooden bridge with the scales all pointing in the same direction; the fibres were then raised with small pieces of wood so that the structure resembled the bow of a violin. The scaliness was estimated as the percentage difference in friction in the two directions. No strict relationship was found between scaliness and milling properties, except with extreme types, such as merino and mohair; with closely related wools, such as Wensleydale, Oxford Down, and Southdown, the order of scaliness was the reverse of the order of milling properties.

The experiments were repeated under water (ibid., 1933, *24*, 273), with the fibres mounted on a glass bridge with the following results: in all cases, the scaliness under water was found to be greater than in the air, and this may be due to the increased flexibility of the wet fibres. However, it was found that the order of scaliness of the different wools is not the same in water and air, and this may be due to increased scale projection brought about by swelling. Even these results showed imperfect correlation between scaliness and milling properties, and the same inverse relation with Wensleydale, Oxford Down, and Southdown wools.

Now for the same degree of scaliness, the milling properties of wool should increase with their fineness, but this does not account for superiority of Wensleydale in milling, for it is coarser and less scaly than Oxford Down or Southdown. The shrinkage of cloths from these three wools on milling had been determined by Speakman and Goodings (ibid., 1926, *17*, 607):

Milling Shrinkage

Wensleydale	33·7%
Oxford Down	28·0%
Southdown	16·3%

On the basis of fibre travel being closely associated with milling shrinkage, then the length of the fibre must play a part in the process; Wensleydale wool is longer than Oxford Down or Southdown. Speakman (ibid., 1933, *24*, 273) determined the effect of fibre length by cutting a Wensleydale top into shorter lengths (5·5 cm. as against the original 13 cm.) from which yarns and fabric were made; when milled under identical conditions the shrinkage was greater with the longer wool (13·4% compared with 6·6%).

Hence the length of the wool hair is of great importance in considering its milling properties, and has been investigated further by Speakman and Sun (J.T.I., 1936, *27*, 171). Although the freedom of the fibres and their tendency to migrate must decrease with increasing fibre length, the shrinkage caused by contraction of stretched fibres will increase with increase in fibre length. With

Australian merino wool of different lengths, but in yarns of the same count and twist, the rate of milling shrinkage decreases with increase in fibre length. This is contrary to the results from Wensleydale wool, but may be attributed to the greater scaliness and crimpiness of merino fibres; there seems to be no simple relation between fibre length and milling properties.

In addition to scaliness, fineness, and length, the amount of crimp or curliness and spirality will play a secondary part in milling shrinkage; the longer fibres produced by extension in spinning will tend to recover their crimp on wetting and, moreover, there is a greater possibility of mutual entanglement with highly crimped fibres.

As the order of scaliness of the wools differed in the two media, air and water, it later occurred to Bohm (J.S.D.C., 1945, *61*, 278) that it might be different again in the conventional milling media. Accordingly six types of wool were selected to give a gradation of known felting power, and the D.F.E. measured in 5% sodium carbonate solution. The results are seen in the following table where the wools are arranged in order of decreasing milling efficiency.

FELTABILITY AND D.F.E.

	Maximum Coefficient of Friction	Minimum Coefficient of Friction	D.F.E.
70s Cape Merino . . .	0·276	0·206	0·070
70s Australian Merino Skin . .	0·267	0·203	0·064
50s New Zealand Pieces .	0·384	0·328	0·056
50s New Zealand Matchings .	0·317	0·269	0·048
48s Lustre Weather Skirts . .	0·328	0·292	0·036
48s Shropshire Matchings . .	0·278	0·262	0·016

It is clear therefore that there is a complete correspondence between milling efficiency and the D.F.E. in 5% soda ash solution.

There are, of course, other factors which determine the shrinkage of wool in milling. It is well known that the rate of shrinkage is at a minimum in water around the isoelectric region and increases with increase in acidity or alkalinity of the solution. It would appear that fibre swelling is associated with this behaviour, which has been investigated by Speakman, Stott, and Chang (J.T.I., 1933, *24*, 273). It was established that milling is most rapid at about pH 10 on the alkaline side of neutrality and that the maximum rate of milling is given by soap, which may not act in virtue of alkalinity alone; milling experiments with sodium carbonate and hydroxide solutions, however, demonstrated that milling is most rapid at pH 10, but the data for soap indicate a specific action in promoting milling shrinkage, apart from the pH of the solution. Hence, it is not possible successfully to replace soap with soda or caustic soda where milling shrinkage is required, except for milling in the grease, which is fundamentally a variation of soap milling. On the acid side of neutrality, the rate of shrinkage on milling starts to increase at pH 4, and continues to increase with decreasing pH, whereas on the alkaline side of neutrality milling reaches a maximum rate around pH 10.

Although there is a fairly close parallel between swelling and milling properties in solutions of varying pH, there is also the question of temperature to consider, for Harrison had shown that the rate of milling with soap or acid is most rapid at 46° to 49°C. (W.I.R.A. Publication No. 9, 1921, p. 15), increasing with rise of temperature and then falling. Speakman, however, found that the swelling of wool fibres in water first decreases with rise in temperature, reaching a minimum at 37°C. and then increases. Hence, swelling does not determine the milling properties.

This was confirmed by experiments on milling shrinkage in solutions of acid and salt; although salt has the property of depressing swelling, its presence increases the rate of milling shrinkage.

Now Speakman had previously shown (Trans. Farad. Soc., 1933, *29*, 148) that the effect of acid or alkaline solutions was to facilitate the extension of wool to a very high degree, and a remarkable similarity was shown between this ease of extension and milling shrinkage. Fibres are most difficult to deform in solutions between pH 4 and 8, and show minimum rate of milling shrinkage in the same region; for example, Igepon A which gives a pH of 6·5 in aqueous solution is not advised as a milling agent. The parallel between ease of extension and milling properties also persists when some of the temperature effects are considered; for instance, the ease of extension and rate of milling both increase with rising temperature up to 45°C.

The ease of extension in water continues to increase up to 100°C., whereas the rate of shrinkage decreases above 45°C.; further, beyond pH 10, milling shrinkage decreases with increasing alkalinity of the solution, but the ease of extension continues to increase. The temperature effect is no doubt due to difficulty in recovery from extension at temperatures above 45°C., and this critical milling temperature may be attributed to the increasing ease of extension being overwhelmed by decreased power of recovery, as shown by Speakman's hysteresis data for various temperatures.

Similar measurements of recovery from extension at various pH values revealed that with increasing alkalinity above pH 8, milling is first facilitated by increased ease of extension, but at higher pH values the decreased rate of recovery operates against milling efficiency and the rate of milling finally falls with increase of pH.

Measurements of recovery from extension also show why acid milling is more rapid than alkali milling, for the former not only facilitates fibre extension, but does not diminish the power of contraction.

According to Speakman, therefore, extensibility and recovery afford an explanation for the existence of a critical temperature and pH for milling; the fact that soap is a more efficient milling agent than alkali at the same pH is associated with the primary requirement for milling shrinkage—a surface scale structure. As fibre travel, with stretching and contraction, must be opposed by some frictional resistance from adjoining fibres, shrinkage will be assisted by a lubricant such as soap; oils are of no value because they do not assist fibre extension.

More recent work by Mercer (Aust. J. Council Sci. Ind. Res., 1942, *15*, 285) and by Carter and Grieve (W.I.R.A. Publication No. 6, 1944, p. 17) has indicated that there is no maximum temperature up to 60° and 70°C. respectively, for the alkali felting of yarn and knitted hosiery; this rendered it difficult to apply the whole of Speakman's theory as outlined above.

However, Bohm (J.S.D.C., 1945, *61*, 278) clarified the situation by measurements of the D.F.E. of New Zealand Merino wool over the range pH 1 to 11, and obtained a very close relationship between the effect of pH on the milling efficiency and on the D.F.E. This was confirmed by comparing curves showing the changes in D.F.E. over the pH range, with curves representing the effect of pH on the milling of yarn and the felting of cloth. It appears, therefore, that the felting power of wool depends mainly on the magnitude of the D.F.E. in the milling medium, and that the effect of pH on the felting power of the milling liquor is due to the influence of the pH on the magnitude of the D.F.E.

Speakman, Chamberlain, and Menkart (J.T.I., 1945, *36*, 91) have also shown that the scaliness of wool fibres increases with decrease of pH below 4, while above pH 9 it first increases and then, above pH 11, decreases. The measurements were made on the lepidometer, an instrument for measuring the creeping power of individual fibres under a rubbing action similar to that exerted by finger and thumb.

Schofield (J.S.D.C., 1930, *46*, 368) has pointed out that the course of the milling operation is usually followed by measuring the shrinkage in either or both warp and weft directions, and however important these shrinkages may be, one of the chief objects of milling is to increase the cover of the cloth by bursting the yarn structure and liberating fibres which may become entangled and felted.

The increase in thickness of the material and the diminution in porosity are factors which need consideration. Schofield's method of determining porosity is to measure length, width, and thickness of standard portions of the fabric and hence the volume; the mass may be found by weighing. The volume of actual wool is obtained by dividing the mass by the density of wool (1·31), and this volume subtracted from the volume of the standard portion gives the volume of the interspaces or voids in the structure; this volume is termed the porosity.

Now time-shrinkage curves of milling have been determined by Schofield (Scouring and Milling, 1920, p. 171) and by Barker and Barker (J. Text. Science, Leeds, 1926, *1*, 79), but no laws of shrinkage were deduced. As a result of further work, however, Schofield suggested that change in porosity is the primary factor in cloth felting, and that time-porosity data show an exponential relation which is the fundamental law of felting.

This matter has been criticised by Chamberlain and Woods (J.S.D.C., 1931, *47*, 289). Johnson (J.T.I., 1938, *29*, 7) examined the rate of milling of cloths of various weaves, and found that the results could be represented by an equation, due to Schofield, of the type

$$da/dt = k(x - a)$$

where t is the time in minutes, x is the limiting percentage shrinkage, a is the percentage area shrinkage at time t, and k is a constant characteristic of the rate of shrinkage of the cloth.

Not all investigators agree on the fundamental reasons for the felting of wool; indeed, Justin Mueller, in a series of papers (Bull. Soc. Ind., Mulhouse, 1906, *76*, 72, to Rev. Gén. Mat. Col., 1938, *42*, 378), considers that the epithelial scales play no part in felting, nor does the crimp of the wool. He assumes that each fibre is covered by a layer of protein substance which he terms protogel, and that this substance becomes gelatinous during the felting process, causing the fibres to adhere together and so become matted. It cannot be said that these views have found many supporters.

No discussion on felting theory would be complete without some reference to the carrotting of rabbit and hare fibres to induce felting; the process of imparting feltability is brought about by treatment with mercuric nitrate in nitric acid, hydrogen peroxide, per-acids, and per-salts.

Berg (Textilber., 1937, *18*, 438) examined fur fibres, with and without carrotting, sealed them in tubes in water where they were boiled for a few minutes. Heating caused the carrotted fibres to curl and intertwine.

There is an obvious anomaly in the fact that carrotting agents bring about breakdown of the disulphide bond facilitating extension and assisting felting, whereas similar breakdown prevents the felting of wool fibres. Speakman, however (J.T.I., 1941, *32*, 83), has explained this in the light of the peculiar contour of the fur fibres which have a pronounced bulge near the tip; this bulbous region will prevent migration of fibres in the direction of their roots. Carrotting is actually restricted to the tips or upper half of the fibre, and assists felting by softening or plasticising the bulbous region which normally restricts fibre travel.

THE MILLING PROCESS

There are two main types of machine for bringing about the felting of wool: (*a*) stocks and (*b*) the rotary milling or fulling machine.

In the STOCKS, the piece of cloth is entered in bulk and the stocks or hammers pound the cloth; under the influence of heat, moisture, and pressure, the threads and fibres are moved about intermittently and felting is induced. The shrinkage is determined broadly by the time of treatment, and occurs in length and width at the same time, but there is no means of separate control of the dimensions of the cloth. An account of these machines is given on page 31; they are made in various sizes to accommodate from one to four pieces of fabric, depending on the weight of the material.

In the ROTARY machine, the fabric is entered and treated in rope form; two rollers draw the cloth through the machine and considerable pressure may be exerted on the top roller. The material then passes into a trough or spout with a loosely fitting lid which is weighted so that compression is exerted on the warp of the folded fabric, causing a decrease in length. When the material emerges from the spout, it slides down an incline to the bottom of the trough, from which it is lifted to pass through the draftboard usually fitted with an automatic stop-motion which separates the pieces, and would stop the machine in case of entanglement. The ropes of fabric then pass over guide rollers into a throat, which may consist of adjustable flanged rollers or adjustable diamond-shaped guides; in both cases, however, pressure may be exerted in the weft direction and so influence the weft shrinkage. The fabric is drawn through the rollers or guides to the main rollers above-mentioned, and the cycle of operations continued.

It will be seen, therefore, that, excepting temperature, much more control may be exercised over the material in the rotary milling machine than in the stocks. The latter give a softening effect to the material which is quite characteristic, but the former gives more cover in the same time, or, alternatively, the same amount of cover in a much shorter period.

Although the extent of milling in the rotary machine may be controlled in respect of length and width by adjustments to the spout and throat, it must be remembered that there are other factors to consider, such as the type of soap used, and the amount of moisture present; an insufficiency or excess of water interferes with the normal milling operations, which depends to a large extent on friction. Again the history of the fabric may influence the milling process, particularly if the goods have been subjected to a setting process beforehand, for a high degree of permanent set imparted by crabbing may seriously retard the felting effect; if setting is inadequate, however, its effects may be completely destroyed by the milling process.

Rotary milling machines, in general, give a much higher output than the stocks.

In both machines, the shrinkage and milling is controlled by stopping the machine at intervals to measure length and width and examine the pieces. Milling is not a standardised process and considerable care and skill are required for good work.

As previously indicated, in the milling machine the fabrics are treated in rope form, being sewn to form loops or endless chains; these are known as drafts. In the single draft system the piece of cloth runs through the machine as a single strand, whereas in the double draft system the piece is made into two loops to form a double strand. This drafting may be utilised to influence the course of milling, for in the single strand system the shrinkage in width is reduced on account of less resistance in the throats or eyes, whereas in the double draft system width shrinkage is hastened by the friction of twice the amount of cloth in the throats.

The two-draft system is generally followed, but with certain cloths it is possible to exceed this with advantage. For example, a piece of cloth may take 4 hours to mill when run in two drafts, but this may be reduced to 2 hours by running in three drafts on account of the better pressure. Similarly, two pieces running in four drafts on a two-piece machine give better production than one piece running in two drafts; the two pieces may also be milled in six drafts with further saving in time. For four- or six-draft running, it is preferable to treat the two pieces separately in the same machine and run them as two separate pieces of two or three drafts and not as one piece of four or six drafts; better balance and more accurate drafting is thus obtained.

During the milling of the piece goods in rope-form, rigs, creases, and crimps are apt to appear; these consist of permanent marks running in the warp direction. Often they are seen as shallow depressions with less fibrous covering than the rest of the fabric.

The cause of these defects is a lack of uniform treatment during processing, and once these crease-marks are formed it is almost impossible to eliminate them. A common precaution during milling is to stop the machine periodically, open the pieces, and stretch the creased regions so that the fabric does not always run in the same folds. It must not be forgotten that the actual structure of the woven fabric sometimes forms the deciding factor in rigging.

With some goods, it is essential to straighten the pieces by shaking out from time to time, and also to reverse the direction of passage through the machine. If the pieces are allowed to run too long without changing, local felting may start on a fold and ruin the appearance of the goods; it will be seen, therefore, that with some cloths a considerable amount of actual handling is necessary during the milling process. Contributory factors in the formation of mill-rigs are excessive pressure on the rollers, or allowing the pieces to run dry, which produces too much friction. Curling selvedges may also result in streaks along the edges of the goods; this may be due to faulty cloth construction, but may be obviated by sewing the selvedges together to make a bag. Bagging the material may also be necessary to preserve the face of some cloths from chafing, in which case the face side should be inside. Rotary draftboards are also available.

Mill-rigs may also be produced by contraction in the width without simultaneous warp shrinkage.

From these observations, it will be seen that there should be less rigging or creasing in the stocks, and this is certainly the case; many worsteds are fulled in the stocks on this account. On the other hand, it is difficult to full to specified length and width in the stocks; if the pieces are piled lengthwise, there is greater shrinkage in the warp, and if piled weft way, then shrinkage in width occurs.

MILLING

Milling processes may be divided into two chief classes:

    (*a*) Acid milling.
    (*b*) Alkaline milling (including soap milling).

Both of these methods may be carried out in stocks or in rotary milling machines.

The three essential requirements for felting to occur are moisture, heat, and pressure; moisture appears to act in virtue of its ability to facilitate extension and recovery; that is, to improve the elastic properties of wool. Up to a point, this behaviour is improved with increase in temperature, but the effect of heat also produces plasticity and flexibility, which assists felting. The effect of pressure causes the wool fibre to travel; pressure is always intermittent in milling, and produces contraction with subsequent extension on account of the elasticity of wool, so that the fibre travels in the direction of its root end, becomes entangled with other fibres, and causes felting.

Heat is produced by friction from the pressure devices in the machine, and care must be taken to ensure that the goods do not overheat.

The moisture is provided in the form of alkaline or acid solution, and, in the former case, soap is commonly used. The concentration of soap usually depends on the required shrinkage and the felting capabilities of the wool, but as a guide, 5% soap solution may be required for slight felting and 10% soap for the heavier effects for uniform cloths; these figures refer to 70% soap and not 100% soap, and are calculated on the liquor used for treatment. The soap may vary in alkalinity according to the nature of the goods; if scoured wool is under consideration then a neutral soap may be used for milling, but otherwise an alkaline solution may be employed containing 0·5 to 1% of sodium carbonate.

As one function of the soap is to reduce the friction, care must be taken to avoid excess or the goods will slip and fibre movement, and hence felting, will be reduced.

ALKALI

ALKALINE MILLING may be carried out either with soap or with alkali alone; the latter is used when milling in the grease, and is actually a form of soap milling, in that the soap is formed by interaction between the alkali and the grease and oils, instead of being applied as such.

When milled in the grease, the fabric is first wetted with sodium carbonate solution of 6° to 7° Tw. by passing through the lecker; this comprises a box or trough for the liquor and a pair of rollers to ensure even distribution and remove any excess. This machine may also be used for impregnating with hot soap solution as a preliminary to soap milling. Milling in the grease takes place in the ordinary milling machine, but as it may be a somewhat dirty operation, it is usual to reserve certain machines for this purpose.

Milling in the grease generally takes place with lightweight goods and with uniform fabrics; there is a 30% saving in cost over soap milling and also an increased output, largely on account of the fact that there is no previous scouring process. The handle of the milled goods is rather firmer than from soap milling.

It is important to realise that in all forms of milling the woven fabric only runs in about its own weight of liquor, and any excess must be avoided; if too wet, the milling process is retarded, and if the fabric is too dry, then there is a loss in weight on account of flocking. Similarly, a low temperature retards milling, but a high temperature produces mill-rigs and uneven rolling.

Sometimes it is possible to run the pieces dry in the machine and then add lukewarm soda-ash solution to ensure thorough wetting before milling starts.

Soap

SOAP MILLING is the method most widely adopted; the cost is higher than for greasy or acid milling, but softer cloths are obtained with much less risk of damage. There is minimum wear and tear on both fabric and machines.

A full scouring treatment is not necessary beforehand, and, indeed, residual soap is an asset to milling, but it is better to start with clean cloth, for dirty fabrics mean more soap for milling. Where the pieces come from the scouring machines, a thorough hydroextraction is essential, for an excess of water reduces the concentration of the soap which is applied, and with weak solutions it is necessary to make frequent additions of soap during milling and the cloth becomes too wet to mill properly.

Oleine types of soap are generally preferred for maximum softness and handle, but if firmness is required, then the stearine soaps are used. In general, solutions of 10% concentration are employed, and 2·5 gallons of solution are adequate to start a piece of 100 lb. in weight. The temperature generally takes some time to rise, so that it is customary to close the doors of the milling machine after the first soaping. If the fabric becomes dry or there are signs of excessive flocking, then further small additions of soap solution may be made during milling. The temperature of the soap solution should never be more than lukewarm with coloured goods, or bleeding is apt to occur.

It may be necessary occasionally to add some loose fibres to the back of the fabric during treatment to compensate in some measure for those removed by friction and so preserve the weight of the goods.

Where the finishing of heavy overcoating material is concerned, it must be remembered that surface effects are not required, but rather a thorough treatment to "blind" the weave to a large extent and impart protection to inclement weather.

The cloths are first scoured with soap and alkali; olive-oil soap and sufficient sodium carbonate solution of about 4°Tw. to provide a good scouring liquor are commonly used. Where four pieces are run together in the dolly, the goods should be run in straight drafts and not crossed in pairs; after wetting in warm water for 10 minutes or thereabouts, the machine is drained, both drain and dolly valves being opened. The valves are then closed, the soap and alkali added, and the scouring process allowed to proceed for 30 to 45 minutes, after which the goods are washed in warm water for a further 30 minutes.

Where lecking machines are available, the goods are squeezed in the soap solution ready for milling, but if such machines are not available, the fabric should be hydroextracted before being placed in the milling machine. Indeed, it is often customary to hydroextract in any case.

Where the soap has not been applied in the lecking machine, it may be poured on to the cloth in the milling machine from a can as slowly and evenly as possible, as correct soaping is an important requirement for good milling.

In the single type milling machine, the pieces should be run in two drafts, and care should be taken to ensure that the drafting is accurate. With machines large enough for two pieces it is possible to sew them together and run them as four drafts, but better balance results from running the goods separately as two separate pieces centred in the machine. The ends of the two pieces are threaded through the centre holes of the four-hole draftboard, through the machine and through the remaining two holes, when the ends are stitched. Where the goods are run as two separate pieces, the shortening of certain drafts is less serious than if the goods are milled as a two-piece length. Many of the overcoating fabrics have to be milled so that there is a reduction in length of 10 yards and a reduction in width of 6 inches or more; heavy weighting is therefore necessary on the lid of the machine.

About 2 hours' running is generally required for these cloths, but they should be measured constantly after the first hour; if advisable, they may be shaken out or even reversed should evidence of mill-rigging or uneven felting appear.

When milling is complete, the goods should be cuttled or plaited by hand and then transferred to the scouring machine for the final scour in straight drafts, as before, to prevent extension in length. Warm sodium carbonate solution is used to remove the soap from the milled cloth, and a little fresh soap solution is added later to assist in the cleansing of the cloth. After scouring for about 30 minutes, a little ammonia solution may be used to assist efficient washing for a further 10 or 15 minutes, after which the pieces are washed with warm water for about 2 hours in order to remove all soap and alkali. The temperature of the wash-water is gradually reduced during the rinsing period, but sudden cooling is apt to produce undesirable surface effects and should be avoided.

Striped flannels may only require a slight amount of milling, but they are sometimes not responsive to this process, and difficulty may be encountered in obtaining the required width. A good scour is necessary before milling, and it is usual to carry out this process in two periods of about 30 minutes each; at the end of the first period the liquor will require changing, since it is apt to be discoloured with dyestuff from the yarn-dyed material.

After the scour, the goods may be taken directly to the milling machine and soaped as they start running, or they may be soaped separately in the lecking machine. In any case, the pieces should lather quickly and milling may be continued for 30 to 60 minutes; these goods generally lose about 3 or 4 yards in length, and may be brought to the required width since there are no further wet processes, such as dyeing, to be carried out. It is considered advisable to run this class of material in three drafts on the machine and avoid a small mouthpiece, since it is easy to form bad creases in medium-weight cloths. The amount of moisture in the cloth needs very careful control; the fabric should be moist, but not wet, and care should be taken to avoid dryness, on the other hand, owing to the heat developed by friction. Fluffing on the draftboard is a useful guide to the state of the material. The Williams-Peace combined scouring and milling machine is very suitable for this class of work.

After milling, the goods should be scoured again, adopting the double-cross method, first with warm sodium carbonate of 3°Tw. to remove the soap, and then with warm water for about 2 hours.

In the treatment of fancy goods, it is preferred to put them directly into the scouring machine rather than impregnate in the lecking machine first, and so avoid bleeding of dyes as the cloth lies in an alkaline state; once impregnated they should be kept in motion. It is difficult to give definite concentrations for the alkaline scouring liquor, but 6°Tw. sodium carbonate solution may be taken as a general guide; the liquor is run on to the goods in the proportion of about 20 gallons per 100 lb. of cloth. The amount of liquor should be sufficient to give a ring of suds when the cloth is pressed between the thumb and forefinger. Scouring may take from 20 to 30 minutes, according to the weight of the material.

It is important that the suds should be washed away slowly at first, and the volume of water only increased towards the end of the washing process. Fresh soap solution is then added in the proportion of about 8 oz. of soap per gallon of water for each 100 lb. of cloth; after a further 30 minutes' scour, the cloth should be washed again as before. The material is then ready for the application of soap for milling; about half a gallon of soap solution per 100 lb. of wool is adequate, and the cloth may be allowed to lather in the scouring machine before removal and hydroextraction. The fabric is then milled in the rotary milling machine with the tops and doors open to keep the temperature low and avoid bleeding of the colours. After milling, the goods are transferred to the scouring machine, again washed with water to remove the soap, and again scoured with fresh soap for about 15 minutes, and then well washed. It is false economy to attempt the final scour with the residual soap from the milling operation, if a bright and clean effect is required.

ACID

ACID MILLING is very suitable for uniform fabrics and heavy cloths such as felts for printing and paper-making machines. Not only is it possible to mill these heavy fabrics more rapidly and efficiently with acid than soap, but the felting is more uniform throughout the mass; this is due to the difficulty of replenishing the soap in the heavy fabrics when they have started to felt, as thorough penetration by fresh soap is hindered by the matted surface. It is not necessary to add fresh acid to the pieces as milling proceeds, but only water to replace that lost by evaporation.

In addition to the advantages of acid milling for heavy fabrics, the method is also useful with cross-bred wool, which is difficult to mill in any case; these goods are generally softer after acid milling than after soap or alkali milling.

Some general advantages are that there is a saving in chemicals since it is not necessary to wash as thoroughly after milling as with alkali or soap, which are very difficult to remove from wool; a residue of acid, within certain limits, is not harmful to wool.

For most yarn-dyed and coloured-woven goods, and particularly for white goods with coloured effects, such as blankets with coloured borders, the acid milling method is preferable as there is less possibility of bleeding in presence of acid before, during, or after the milling operation, than with soap or alkali milling. In all cases, the loss in weight is less when the acid process is used as compared with soap milling and the strength of the fabric is greater.

The chief disadvantage appears to be that the goods must be thoroughly scoured beforehand and rinsed free from soap or alkali.

Where a four-piece dolly is used, the pieces should be entered in the machine and crossed in pairs, as this ensures a frequent change of the folds in the goods. The fabrics in rope form are generally rinsed in lukewarm water for about 15 minutes and the dirty liquor drained away; soap and sodium carbonate solution may then be added and the goods scoured for 30 to 45 minutes, followed by washing in warm water for a further 15 minutes with the drain of the machine open to ensure thorough rinsing. After this rinsing process, the drain should be closed again and fresh soap added, together with ammonia, when the goods should lather up again immediately and scouring be continued for a further 30 minutes. A very complete washing process then follows, using warm water, for a period of about 2 to 3 hours, after which the alkalinity of the cloth should be tested. If neutral, all water should be drained away and fresh water added to reach the level of the bottom scouring roller; the machine may then be set in motion and the necessary amount of acid added, say, 2 lb. of D.O.V. per 100 lb. of wool.

Mixing of acid and water may take 10 minutes, after which the drain-box may be opened so that the dilute acid trickles through to the cloth in the bottom of the dolly, when the goods are allowed to run for 15 to 20 minutes. The acidified water is then drained away and the cloth rinsed to help distribute the absorbed acid more evenly during a period of 15 minutes or thereabouts. The fabric is then taken from the machine and squeezed or hydroextracted ready for the acid milling process.

At the start of the milling process it is not necessary to add any further liquid, but when heavy milling is carried out it may be necessary to add water to replace that lost by evaporation; this is generally left to the experience of the operative.

For every 100 lb. of cloth, about 3 lb. of B.O.V. or 2 lb. of D.O.V. will be required, suitably diluted to about 0·2 to 0·5% sulphuric acid. It is important that the milling machine should contain sufficient cloth to set up the necessary friction and produce a rise in temperature, otherwise milling will be very slow. The temperature of the acid milling process is generally much higher than that employed when milling in the grease or with soap. Once the temperature has risen, it must be maintained, and a careful watch must be kept on the length of the goods, which is apt to diminish rather suddenly towards the end of the process, and may result in excessive shrinkage if the weights on the spout lid are not adjusted.

After milling, the pieces are rinsed for 15 minutes or so in a scouring machine, using warm water. It is essential that cloths containing wool and cellulose fibres should be neutralised after acid milling as subsequent drying of cellulose fibres containing acid is liable to cause degradation; where sodium carbonate has been used to neutralise the acid, any excess of this compound should be removed from the wool by rinsing with an adequate supply of warm water.

THE MILLED FABRIC

Begg (J.S.D.C., 1920, *36*, 38) has given the following data on the tensile strength of goods milled in various ways:

STRENGTH OF MILLED GOODS

Treatment	Tensile strength	Extension
Acid milled	290 lb.	2·50 in.
Soap milled	242 lb.	2·37 in.
Grease milled	242 lb.	2·31 in.

Acid-milled material is considerably stronger than goods milled with soap or in the grease; this fact is utilised in the production of cloths for uniforms.

Yewdall (J.T.I., 1933, *24*, 173P) has given some interesting data on this point, which may be illustrated by weft strengths.

COMPARISON OF MILLING METHODS

Material				Grease	Soap	Acid
Greasy cloth	.	.	.	73·4 lb.	73·4 lb.	73·4 lb.
Scoured cloth	.	.	.	—	58·6 lb.	58·6 lb.
Milled 30 mins.		.	.	56·0 lb.	61·3 lb.	68·5 lb.
60 mins.		.	.	58·5 lb.	66·7 lb.	76·0 lb.
90 mins.		.	.	64·2 lb.	70·3 lb.	83·1 lb.
120 mins.		.	.	68·9 lb.	75·8 lb.	92·5 lb.
150 mins.		.	.	75·0 lb.	82·4 lb.	99·5 lb.
180 mins.		.	.	84·2 lb.	87·9 lb.	105·7 lb.
210 mins.		.	.	84·3 lb.	87·9 lb.	109·5 lb.

It will be noted that the fabric milled in the grease is weakest; on further milling, when the cloth ceased to contract, it lost strength.

In most cloths, the warp is stronger than the weft, both before and after milling, but the effect of sulphuric acid seems to produce a greater increase in weft strength than warp strength, so that acid milling may be used to bring about a more even balance between the tensile strengths in the two components of the fabric.

Another advantage arising from the use of acid-milling methods is the increased extensibility at break given to the fabric; this extension is greater in the weft direction, and this may be due to the lower tensions on the weft in weaving, and also to the fact that cloths are generally milled to a greater extent in the width than in the length.

COMPARISON OF EXTENSION AT BREAK AFTER MILLING

Material				Grease .	Soap	Acid
Greasy cloth	.	.	.	1·64 in.	1·64 in.	1·64 in.
Scoured cloth	.	.	.	—	1·70 in.	1·70 in.
Milled 30 mins.		.	.	1·99 in.	2·26 in.	2·33 in.
60 mins.		.	.	2·34 in.	2·37 in.	2·45 in.
90 mins.		.	.	2·42 in.	2·48 in.	2·56 in.
120 mins.		.	.	2·58 in.	2·62 in.	2·74 in.
150 mins.		.	.	2·65 in.	2·72 in.	2·87 in.
180 mins.		.	.	2·73 in.	2·82 in.	3·09 in.
210 mins.		.	.	2·76 in.	2·98 in.	3·26 in.

A further important advantage in acid milling is the saving in time to reach the required dimensions; the increased rate of milling shrinkage enables a greater output to be obtained from the plant. Yewdall (loc. cit.) has compared grease and acid milling on a woollen cloth as used for uniforms from yarns of medium Saxony quality.

Comparison of Grease and Acid-Milling

	Grease-milled	Acid-milled
Grey, length	65·5 yd.	65·5 yd.
width	75·0 in.	75·0 in.
weight	140·0 lb.	140·0 lb.
Scoured, length	—	67·5 yd.
width	—	70·0 in.
weight	—	91·0 lb.
Milled, length	61·5 yd.	56·5 yd.
width	54·0 in.	55·0 in.
weight	87·0 lb.	89·0 lb.
Time of milling	10·0 hours	3·25 hours

The cloth milled in the grease took three times as long to reach the required dimensions as that subjected to acid milling; the acid-milled fabric contracted in length 5 yards more than that milled in the grease. With acid milling, of course, the cloth must first be scoured, and this time must be included for an accurate comparison.

Milling times for a cloth of Cheviot quality gave a further interesting comparison, the weft data being given in the following table:

Comparison of Milling Methods

Stages	Grease	Soap	Acid
Greasy cloth . . .	70 in.	70 in.	70 in.
Scoured cloth . . .	—	67 in.	67 in.
Milled 30 mins. .	67 in.	64 in.	62 in.
60 mins. .	64 in.	61 in.	58 in.
90 mins. .	62 in.	59 in.	56 in.
120 mins. .	60 in.	57 in.	54 in.
150 mins. .	58 in.	56 in.	53 in.
180 mins. .	57 in.	54 in.	52 in.
210 mins. .	56 in.	53 in.	51 in.

It will be noticed that the cloth milled with acid reached the required width in 90 minutes, that milled in soap took 150 minutes to reach the same width, but the fabric milled in the grease needed 210 minutes. Length shrinkages on the same material showed that the acid- and soap-milled material contracted to 22 and 23 inches respectively from 36 inches in 210 minutes, whereas the grease-milled fabric contracted to only 26 inches in 180 minutes, after which there was no further contraction in length.

It is possible to use acetic or hydrochloric acids in place of sulphuric, but with equal weights (4·5%) of acid on the dry scoured wool, sulphuric acid gave the best results both in respect of strength and rapidity of milling shrinkage. In a series of tests on worsted material with sulphuric, acetic, and formic acids, the last-mentioned gave least contraction and the weakest cloth; sulphuric acid again produced the best results.

Variations in the strength of acid used naturally affect the physical properties of the milled material, namely, the amount of contraction, the extension at break, and the tensile strength. Some interesting results have been obtained from the treatment of a cloth made from Saxony noils:

COMPARISON OF VARIOUS METHODS OF MILLING

		Soap	1·5%	Sulphuric Acid 3%	4·5%
Width					
Scoured cloth		68 in.	68 in.	68 in.	68 in.
Milled 20 mins.		64 in.	63 in.	61 in.	60 in.
40 mins.	Width	61 in.	60 in.	58 in.	57 in.
60 mins.		59 in.	58 in.	56 in.	54 in.
Extension					
Scoured cloth		2·12 in.	2·12 in.	2·12 in.	2·12 in.
Milled 20 mins.		2·15 in.	2·21 in.	2·38 in.	2·53 in.
40 mins.	Extension	2·46 in.	2·48 in.	2·58 in.	2·64 in.
60 mins.		2·69 in.	2·62 in.	2·71 in.	2·79 in.
Strength					
Scoured cloth		52·2 lb.	52·2 lb.	52·2 lb.	52·2 lb.
Milled 20 mins.		55·7 lb.	58·0 lb.	63·7 lb.	63·9 lb.
40 mins.	Strength	58·3 lb.	60·3 lb.	65·4 lb.	64·8 lb.
60 mins.		61·4 lb.	62·6 lb.	66·8 lb.	68·4 lb.

The amounts of acid are estimated on the weight of the dry cloth.

From these data it appears that the soap-milled cloth contracts least during the milling process, and that the amount of contraction increases with the amount of acid; the lowest amount of acid gives results comparable with those from soap milling. As would be expected, the extension at break of the samples varies with the amount of shrinkage they underwent during milling. The results of measurements of tensile strength show that the weakest acid solution has given a stronger fabric than that obtained from soap milling; the tensile strength of the acid-milled fabrics increases as the concentration of acid increases.

Harrison (Wool Industries Research Association Report No. 4, 1919, p. 7) has shown that when milling with sulphuric acid, the milling increases with concentration of H_2SO_4 up to 4·9%, but diminishes after 19·6%.

Yewdall (loc. cit.) has found that when woollen material is milled with sulphuric acid of increasing strength, there is an increase in contraction with solutions up to 6%, above which there is no further contraction. The tensile strength, however, continues to increase with solutions up to 8%, but drops sharply with stronger solutions.

The increase in tensile strength of milled fabrics is apparent rather than real, on account of the great amount of shrinkage; the preceding data do not refer to the same number of threads, but to strips of the same width, and this width will contain various numbers of threads depending on the amount of shrinkage. This question has been examined by Wilkinson and Law (Journal Leeds University Textile Association, 1915, p. 77), when it was established that the strength of a milled cloth is less than would be expected from calculations based on the number of ends and picks after milling. Starting with 100% as representing the strength of warp and weft in the greasy state, a scoured cloth was found to show 83% in the warp and 67% in the weft; this may be due to more severe action on the weft by the rollers. The fully milled material showed 56% in the warp and 33% in the weft. This loss in strength is not revealed in the fabric on account of the shrinkage, but it must not be assumed that milling produces a real increase in strength.

Part of this real loss in strength may be due to loss of material and also to the bursting of the yarn structure which displaces the fibres from the thread. Midgley (Journal Dept. Text. Inst. Bradford, 1918, p. 21) maintains that the loss in strength only takes place in woollen cloths; a woollen yarn of initial breaking load of 63 lb. fell to 51 lb. after milling, whereas a worsted yarn increased from 143 lb. to 154 lb. on milling. The structure of the material is of fundamental importance.

CHAPTER VIII
THE UNSHRINKABLE FINISH
FOR WOOL

WHEN wool goods are washed, there is a very considerable reduction in area, which is commonly termed shrinkage—indeed, it may be stated that the great defect of wool in popular opinion is associated with this shrinkage.

The diminution in area on laundering is primarily due to two causes: (*a*) the relaxation of extension brought about during the manufacturing processes, and (*b*) the felting of the wool fibres. It is important to distinguish between these two phenomena and in order to avoid confusion over the use of a single term, "shrinkage," it is becoming common to refer to relaxation shrinkage and milling shrinkage.

RELAXATION

The RELAXATION SHRINKAGE is due to stretching of yarns and fibres during spinning, knitting, or weaving, after which the material is maintained in the stretched state; even in the normal processes of scouring and bleaching the goods may still be maintained under tension or possibly stretched further as in the "boarding-out" process with hosiery garments. Ultimately, however, the finished garment is washed without mechanical restraint and contracts in dimensions as the strains are released under the lubricating action of the soap solution. Naturally this relaxation shrinkage will vary with the structure of both yarn and fabric, but it may even reach 20% in loosely constructed material. It is important to realise that non-felting processes do not affect this relaxation shrinkage; indeed, in certain circumstances the wet fabric may be caused to extend by severe mechanical handling during the ordinary chlorination process, and show a high relaxation shrinkage although substantially non-felting. Excessive stretching in finishing chlorinated woollen material will produce great relaxation shrinkage on washing.

MILLING

MILLING SHRINKAGE is due to the felting of the wool hairs, as discussed on page 165. Although the terms "milling" and "felting" are well understood, they are not defined precisely. It seems generally accepted that felting as a process applies to the production of a fabric by entangling the mass of fibres without spinning or weaving, and so forming a felt fabric. Milling, on the other hand, refers to the treatment of fabrics to give extra cover and body associated with the milled finish where the weave may be completely obscured; in this connection, milling may be regarded as the process and felting as the effect. Where laundry shrinkage is concerned, however, the felting phenomenon is a disadvantage of wool, and there has arisen an almost subconscious definition of milling as a desired effect positively reached, as opposed to felting as an unrequired result of washing wool garments.

The FELTING of wool on laundering is fundamentally due to fibre entanglement and therefore depends to a large extent on the arrangement of the fibres; a free fibrous mass felts more easily than a fabric, and a loose knitted structure tends to felt more easily than a woven cloth. Hence the problem of non-felting wool is more acute, in general, with knitted fabric than woven cloth. This is complicated by two further factors, for fine wools are more generally used in knitted fabrics and felt more easily than coarser wools, but also it is customary to utilise lightly twisted yarns in knitted fabric as compared with woven structures. A loosely twisted yarn contains more projecting hairs than a hard-spun yarn, so that it is easier for these hairs to become entangled on washing, and so draw the structure together by the well-known property of elastic movement and fibre travel possessed by wool.

Prolonged and severe washing, however, gradually disrupts the yarn so that the fibre travel causes wool hairs to project even from hard-spun yarns, and these projecting hairs become entangled and so draw the structure together, causing contraction in area, and felting. The variety of the wool and the type of yarn and fabric account for differences in felting on laundering.

As previously explained (see page 166), the felting of wool is associated with its scale structure and elastic nature; the latter permits extension and contraction during laundering, whereas the former causes travel in the direction of the root end, as the tips of the scales point towards the tip of the wool, and these projections present frictional resistance to fibre travel in the direction of the tip.

Fundamentally, therefore, it is possible to prevent felting by destroying the elasticity of the fibre or affecting the scales so that they no longer influence the direction of travel or assist entanglement. It is now generally accepted that fibre elasticity is due to the coiled nature of the polypeptide chains which uncoil on stretching but return again by reason of the strains on the cross-linkages between the main chains; any chemical attack on the molecular structure which prevented uncoiling would affect the elasticity of the wool and interfere with one of its most valuable properties. Hence, most processes have been directed to altering the surface properties of the wool and preventing unidirectional travel and entanglement; most often the edges and surfaces of the scales are affected and possibly the wool substance immediately under the scales.

As will appear later, many chemical treatments have been devised for producing non-felting wool, but in general a completely non-felting wool is only realised at the expense of wool quality, as shown by loss in weight, decreased durability, yellowness, harsh handle, increased lustre, increased affinity for water and dyes, and susceptibility to alkali. Hence, most processes tend towards minimum treatment consistent with resistance to a test equivalent to some twenty or thirty launderings. Even under these conditions there is often a loss in weight of 1 to 5% which may occur during the process or in the subsequent launderings.

Substantially, but not completely, non-felting wool has the advantage of retaining a great deal of the elasticity of the wool and also providing some compensation for wear, in that as abrasion takes place, a slight felting or shrinkage on washing imparts longer life than would result from completely non-felting material.

Without some non-felting treatment, the wool material after repeated launderings becomes so dense and compact that the reduction in area causes it to be unwearable; further, the compact nature of felted material is such that there is a loss of elasticity in the fabric and the matted material is very difficult to wash clean.

RELAXATION SHRINKAGE

The essential feature of relaxation processes is to permit well-moistened wool to dry slowly and without restraint; the two principal methods of imparting shrinkage initially are by cold water or with steam.

LONDON SHRINKAGE

The LONDON SHRINKAGE process is probably the best-known treatment involving the use of cold water and, as originally carried out, consisted in folding the cloth in layers between dampened wrappings and allowing it to stand for a certain number of days according to the amount of potential relaxation present in the material. The modern method, however, accelerates the process by impregnating the wrapper with water on a damping machine in the usual manner by rubber bowls, and then winding the wrapper, together with the wool cloth to be damped, on to a roller; the machine is then reversed and the damped cloth is cuttled or plaited and allowed to stand for some time before passing on to the hanging drier. An alternative method is to plait or cuttle alternate layers of woollen cloth and damp wrapper on to a wooden platform and then compress the pile to ensure thorough moistening, after which the pile of cloth is allowed to stand for 12 hours before drying.

The drying operation after the London shrinkage is carried out on a hanging frame from which the cloth is suspended in loops or folds by laths or poles. In the old-fashioned method, the cloth was allowed to dry in the open air of the room in which the drier was situated, but air-circulators were later installed. The use of hot-air drying in festoon machines is a recent development, but the finish of the cloth is less mellow.

When completely dried, the cloth is pressed, book-fold fashion, for 10 to 12 hours under a pressure of about 3,000 lb.

STEAMING

STEAMING methods have been devised to expedite the relaxation shrinkage, and one of the simplest of these is to blow hot steam into the fabric until it is thoroughly wet, after which it is plaited down and allowed to cool. Wool fabrics may also be steamed on cylinders, plaited down, and allowed to cool before drying on a festoon drier. The open steaming method is preferable for heavy cloths, napped goods, and pile fabrics, but the cylinder method is better for suitings, tweeds, and similar cloths. The relaxation shrinkage of lightweight goods may be reduced by decatising, when they are wound, with a cotton wrapper, round a perforated cylinder and steam blown through the material. This is suited to goods with a "face" finish, for it is possible to set the cloths with a minimum shrinkage and retain the original appearance.

Some of the problems of relaxation shrinkage have been discussed by Cryer (J.T.I., 1935, 26, 331P). If relaxation shrinkage has not been adequate, and the cloth is tailored and pressed, there will be a reduction in the size of the garment, and if this amounts to more than 2% in length or width, it is a serious matter. Relaxation shrinkage may often reach 8%.

Experiments with a Hoffman press showed that 50 to 75% of the residual shrinkage was obtained on one pressing, and the remainder on the second or third pressing where well-shrunk cloths were tested, but with improperly shrunk cloth five to seven pressings may be necessary to reach finality. The humidity of the atmosphere in which the cloth is hung after pressing is important, as is the amount of moisture in the cloth when received; material with 20% moisture content may contract 1% on drying to 14% moisture content.

Cryer's experiments tend to show that the most efficient method of shrinking cloth is by wetting in hot water, cold water comes next, and placing between damp wrappers (London shrinkage) third; the least efficient is simple pressing on the Hoffman press. With immersion treatments, greater shrinkage is obtained by higher temperatures, longer immersions, and numerous treatments; the intermittent nature of shrinkage is apt to be surprising, for even after a relaxation treatment of 14 hours in hot water, followed by drying, a repetition caused further contraction. Hence, the occasional necessity for double shrinkage. With most cloths London shrinkage seems best, for although water gives a greater shrinkage it disturbs the face of the fabric, whereas London shrinkage does not roughen the cloth or alter its level nature. The hot pressing which follows London shrinkage may extend the cloth 1% and so impart a potential shrinkage which may be obviated by moderate pressure.

COMPRESSIVE SHRINKAGE

COMPRESSIVE SHRINKAGE methods have also been applied to wool; for instance, Wrigley, Melville, and Kellett, in B.P. 529,579, have described a mechanical treatment whereby the woollen or worsted material is nipped twice while travelling at different speeds, the area between the two nips being confined in a closed space so that buckling cannot occur. When the compressed fabric emerges from the apparatus, the natural resilience of the wool causes it to lengthen directly the compressive force is removed, although it remains much shorter than it was originally. This lengthening may be controlled to a certain extent by steaming the cloth in the contracted state immediately it emerges from the machine; steaming at 5 lb. pressure for 1 hour, followed by cooling in water, is sufficient to impart the necessary set. The process is described in B.P. 542,446.

As a result of this treatment, the fabric becomes heavier and denser, with a substantial increase in elasticity. Purely as a new finish, the effect is interesting and valuable.

On account of the compressive shrinkage in the direction of the length of the fabric, the tendency to shrink in length by felting during washing is eliminated or very substantially reduced; the process does not prevent felting and shrinkage in the weft direction. The following results indicate the effect of the process on grey serge material:

COMPRESSIVE SHRINKAGE AND STEAMING

Shrinkage on leaving machine	Shrinkage after steaming	Shrinkage after milling for		
		2·5 hours	3·5 hours	4·5 hours
0%	0%	18%	18%	23%
21%	19%	21%	21%	22%
24%	22%	21%	22%	23%
27%	24%	21%	21%	22%
29%	28%	22%	22%	23%
31%	31%	22%	22%	23%

In this example, which illustrates the invention, it will be seen that the untreated material decreases 23% in length on milling, but if that amount of shrinkage is mechanically induced into the material and set before milling, then the fabric is stable.

Controlled compressive shrinkage, of course, has been applied to cotton goods, as described on page 248.

NON-FELTING WOOL

Numerous processes have been devised for the production of non-felting wool, and some of these are so recent that it is not possible to decide which is the best. Indeed, it may well be that no one process is equally suited for all goods. Non-felting treatments are mainly applied to knitting wools and hosiery—a term which includes all knitted fabrics and not only socks and stockings. The treatment of woven piece goods is comparatively small in quantity.

Hosiery may be divided into two broad classes: (*a*) for men's underwear, and (*b*) for women and children, corresponding to the coarse and fine trades respectively. The coarser goods are easier to treat, and not only are the finer goods more difficult to process, but the demands in the way of finish and handle are much more stringent. Hence, it may be that the more expensive non-aqueous processes will be more suited to the finer goods on account of the mild nature of the treatment and reduced possibility of interference with the quality of the wool, whereas the cheaper chlorination processes are more satisfactory for the coarser trade.

There can be no doubt, however, that the chlorination process is exceedingly cheap compared with its competitors and the greater part of non-felting wool still appears to be treated by the wet chlorination process.

CHLORINATION

The chlorination of wool originated with John Mercer in connection with the printing of delaines. The unequal absorbency of cotton and wool for certain colours, such as Prussian blue, was a serious hindrance to further developments; but in 1839 Mercer discovered that by passing the cloth through a weak solution of free chlorine (made from bleaching powder and hydrochloric acid) the wool acquired a great affinity for the colours required. A mixture of sulphuric acid and potassium bichromate produced the same effect, but left a slight stain, so that chlorine was adopted as the oxidising agent for general use.

Messrs. Fort were able to produce many new styles in which they had a monopoly for some time, but Mercer communicated the process to friends in the trade and it became standard practice in

England, Scotland, and France. In 1848, it was described as the most important discovery hitherto made in dyeing and printing woollen goods. This invention was not patented, but given to the industry without any reservation whatsoever.

There is no record, however, that the woollen goods treated in this manner had lost their ability to felt or mill; indeed, it has not been possible to find when and where the process of wet chlorination for the unshrinkable finish was discovered. It seems reasonable to assume, however, that the non-felting property followed automatically on the chlorination of wool for printing, and therefore ranks as a discovery or observation and not as an invention; it is extraordinary that it should not have been mentioned until sixty years after Mercer's work. The non-felting property was not mentioned by Knecht (J.S.D.C., 1902, *18*, 41) in his work on the treatment of wool with chlorine gas, but Vignon and Mollard (Compt. rend., 1906, *142*, 1343) were certainly aware of this effect which could be produced by gaseous chlorine, chlorine water, or acidified solutions of bleaching powder. Prolonged action was stated to dissolve the wool, but a limited action caused a 10% loss in weight, with a greater affinity for dyes and reduced felting properties assumed to be caused by destruction of the projecting points of the scales.

Stansfield (J.S.D.C., Jubilee No., 1934, p. 166) states that arrangements were made for the production of non-felting wool by wet chlorination about 1899 in the case of a firm of finishers in the West Riding of Yorkshire, and also another in Scotland. Edwards and Hardcastle (ibid., 174) consider that the slump in trade after the Boer War caused a demand for cheap hosiery, and it was about this time that wet chlorination was introduced. The process consisted in treating the wool with a solution of a hypochlorite and hydrochloric acid, followed by an anti-chlor.

The non-felting process does not appear to form the basis of a patent specification; this may be due to the fact that it was a discovery arising from the use of Mercer's process without any inventive step, or, alternatively, that the period of its origin was one of secret processes when information and recipes changed hands for a cash payment. Some non-felting woollen goods were sold under registered trade names about 1908.

Briefly, when wool is steeped for about 30 minutes in an acidified solution of hypochlorite it loses its power of felting or milling. Chlorination takes place so quickly that it is difficult to obtain a uniform effect; two alternative methods have been devised to obviate this defect. In the first, the fabric is run on the winch machine and the chlorine liquor is added at intervals; in the second method, a large volume of liquor is prepared and the fabric is immersed in this and agitated rapidly. It is usual to employ 2 to 5% of active chlorine calculated on the weight of wool; at the end of the process, the goods are washed with water and then treated with a dilute solution of sodium bisulphite to destroy any residual chlorine, followed by a final rinsing process.

The anti-chloring treatment with sodium sulphite or bisulphite solution can improve the non-felting effect beyond that produced by the chlorination; this should be considered in conjunction with the recognised fact that a peroxide bleaching treatment applied to chlorinated wool can also improve the non-felting property (Can. Text. J., 1937, 54, 37).

Chlorination is accompanied by some damage to the wool, so that in commercial practice it is customary to carry the action only to the stage where the wool has lost most of its tendency to felt without being unduly impoverished. Generally, if the treatment is taken to that point where zero shrinkage is attained, then the wool is definitely damaged in subsequent washing treatments; the colour becomes yellow and the wool acquires a slimy handle when placed in aqueous solutions of weak alkali such as soap or ammonia. The material possesses a harsh feel in the dry state and does not wear well; over-chlorination appears to loosen the epithelial scales and these are removed in subsequent wear and washing. A further possible defect is the loss of elasticity so that treated garments tend to lose their shape.

If the chlorination treatment is carried too far, not only does the material suffer a loss in weight and become thinner in handle, but it is possible to exceed the limit of zero shrinkage and produce an over-chlorinated wool which does not shrink, but actually extends in area on washing. The expansion of such fabrics on washing is probably due to the lack of scales on the overtreated fibres which permits some slippage and extension of the yarn on wetting.

Absorption of Chlorine

Wool is capable of absorbing very large amounts of chlorine either in the gaseous state or from solutions. In experiments carried out by the W.I.R.A. in 1925, it was found that wool was able to absorb almost 30% of its weight of chlorine either from bleaching powder solution or from chlorine water; in these circumstances, however, there was a loss in weight of the wool amounting to 13%.

Courtot and Baron (Compt. rend., 1935, 200, 675) have shown that long exposure to an excess of chlorine or bromine in water causes 60% of the wool to dissolve; iodine is practically inactive although absorption occurs.

The action of chlorine seems to proceed progressively inwards, as shown by Herzog (Textilber., 1928, 9, 33), and varying degrees of chlorination are revealed by varying depths of penetration rather than by a partial action on the whole fibre. The thickness of the chlorinated layer can be seen in cross-sections which have been stained; the epidermal scales, which are 0·8μ thick, are scarcely affected.

Attempts have been made to control the rapid absorption, even in the earlier days of chlorination, by adding the chlorine at intervals. For instance, Pearson (J.S.D.C., 1909, *25*, 81) dissolved sodium hypochlorite in water so as to have a 4 to 5% solution of available chlorine, and 0·1 to 1 lb. of this solution when acidified was used for every pound of wool. The hypochlorite liquor was added in two or three portions instead of all at once, and the exhausted liquor was run off after 5 or 6 minutes. The hydrochloric acid was added gradually in the proportion of two-thirds of the volume of hypo-chlorite for the first addition and one-half for the second and third additions.

(Pearson also found that when chlorinated wool was rubbed against untreated wool it produced a charge sufficient to disturb the gold leaves of an electroscope whereas ordinary wool did not; he suggested "electric" belts with wool warp and chlorinated wool weft.)

Another process was that devised by Schofield in 1914 in which an aqueous solution of chlorine was applied to flannel piece goods in the ordinary rope scouring machine; chlorine gas was dissolved in water and the solution titrated. The solution was slowly fed into the water of the scouring machine, the pieces running in the ordinary way for 30 minutes, and this had the advantage of giving about thirty squeezings and re-saturations with a very level treatment. Schofield has given details of this process in his book, *The Finishing of Wool Goods* (1934).

Damage in Chlorination

For many years the wet chlorination of wool was carried out as a purely empirical process. The first attempt to place the treatment on a scientific basis was made by Trotman (J.S.C.I., 1922, *41*, 219).

The general complaints about chlorinated wool were that it was not completely unshrinkable, it lost weight during the process, and was unsatisfactory in wear. Examination of various wool fibres showed that there was modification of the scale structure due to chlorination, the scales fitting more closely to the cortex; with over-chlorinated wool, damage to the scales may be seen, which in some cases may be so severe as to remove the scales. Trotman suggested that damage could be estimated quantitatively by a scale count, and found that commercial unshrinkable fabrics contained from 5 to 50% of damaged fibres. The tensile strength and extension at break of the treated wool do not appear to be affected until over 50% of the fibres are badly damaged.

Chlorinated wool has an increased affinity for dyestuffs, but this is extremely slight if the process is carried out carefully, and a strong affinity for dyes indicates extensive damage. Another defect of chlorinated wool is its bad wearing properties, which are due to attack on the scale structure. It was also recorded that when chlorinated wool is placed in water it wets, swells, and assumes a soft and almost slimy handle; there is also an increase in moisture content due to chlorination. The wetting power, the slimy handle, and the increased regain vary with the percentage of damaged fibres.

The solubility in alkali was found by Trotman to be a useful test of damage due to chlorination; the solubility was estimated by immersion for 3 hours at room temperature in $N/10$ NaOH solution. Wool showing 5% damage lost 3·5% in weight in these circumstances and wool showing 50% damage lost 14·5% in weight. Strong swelling in $N/10$ alkali, with a soft slimy feel, was found to be characteristic of damaged wool.

There are two main methods employed for assessing the damage in wool, and both of them depend on microscopic examination and a scale count. In the first method an undamaged fibre is returned as zero and a damaged fibre as one unit; by examining 100 fibres and taking the total the percentage damage is obtained and the maximum figure permitted is from 5 to 10%, according to the class of wool. The second method of counting is to divide the fibres into various groups; undamaged fibres are counted as zero, partly damaged fibres as half a unit, and badly damaged fibres as one unit. The maximum figure allowable on this system is 35 to 40%.

This method has recently been extended and made easier by staining with Kiton Red G. The dyed sample of yarn is wound spirally around a wooden pencil and a longitudinal cut made by means of a cutter consisting of two safety-razor blades 0·3 mm. apart. The fibre sections are then examined under the microscope and graded into one of five classes, according to whether they are white, light pink, pink, pink-red, or deep red; these classes are graded 0, 0·25, 0·5, 0·75, and 1.

The estimation of damage on chlorinated hosiery has been discussed by Edwards (J.T.I., 1933, *24*, 1), and an attempt made to correlate these physical methods of assessing damage with chemical methods.

One of the best-known chemical methods is the Pauly test, a quantitative application of which has been described by Rimington (J.T.I., 1930, *21*, 237); the reagent is an alkaline solution of diazotised sulphanilic acid.

Edwards found that the number of damaged fibres determined by physical means was almost proportionate to the degree of chlorination of the fibre, and although the Pauly test is quite workable over the desired range (0 to 4% chlorine) it is less sensitive for high degrees of damage. It does not appear that the chemical method will replace the scale count for commercial testing.

Hirst and King (J.T.I., 1933, 24, 174) made use of cloth-strength measurements to estimate damage; these are difficult to relate to wearing properties because chlorination and drying increase the surface friction of the material and may show improved strength even when the wearing properties are impaired.

Chemical analysis showed that during the chlorination process, protein nitrogen is gradually dissolved; sulphur is also dissolved and the proportions of sulphur and nitrogen in the wool changed.

SOURCE OF DAMAGE

Trotman drew attention to the fact that the damage to chlorinated wool may be produced both during the chlorination process and in later processes, such as washing, which were capable of removing the damaged scales.

Many of the so-called standard processes were found to be exceedingly vague; the three general methods appear to depend on treatment with hypochlorite followed by acid, treatment with acid followed by hypochlorite, or treatment with hypochlorite and acid together.

The neutralisation of bleaching powder produces hypochlorous acid which is decomposed by further mineral acid giving rise to chlorine; with limited amounts of acid, a mixture of hypochlorous acid and chlorine is produced. With many of the old commercial processes, the production of hypochlorous acid or chlorine was entirely a matter of chance, and depended upon the quantity of acid carried into the solution of bleaching powder by the wool itself.

Methods of Control

Trotman established that different grades of wool require different treatments, so that the maximum amount of chlorine (estimated on the wool) must be found by actual experiment; on the other hand, owing to the destructive action of chlorine, the solution employed for the chlorination of wool should not contain more than 0·6 g. of available chlorine per litre.

In many commercial processes, quantities greatly in excess of this were used and brought about damage to the wool; excess of either hypochlorous acid or chlorine causes destruction of the scales, loss in weight during the process, poor resistance to wear, and a high solubility in alkali. There appears to be no direct relation between shrinkage and destruction of scales, but the felting power decreases as the scale damage increases.

ACIDITY

Where no CONTROL OF ACID is exercised, the solution may contain either hypochlorous acid or free chlorine, according to the pH of the solution; Trotman and Trotman (J.S.C.I., 1926, *45*, 111) showed that when wool was treated with solutions containing available chlorine, there was a rapid absorption followed by a more gradual absorption. When free chlorine is present, this initial absorption is so rapid that the process tends to be uncontrollable, and damage is produced very quickly, even by the absorption of as little as 1% of chlorine. Hence, solutions of bleaching powder or sodium hypochlorite, when used with hydrochloric acid, are apt to cause damage. The rate of absorption of chlorine by wool is affected by the presence of mineral acid, and depends on the pH value of the solution.

If, however, hypochlorous acid free from chlorine is used, the initial rate of absorption is slow, so that the process is capable of control, as described in B.P. 239,360, for example. A convenient method of making hypochlorous acid solution is to treat bleaching powder solutions with excess of boric acid; exact neutralisation was difficult because most indicators are decolorised by chlorine and the glass electrode was not available at the time of these experiments. Trotman used rosolic acid as an indicator, but it may be stated that the addition of boric acid to bleaching powder solution gives pH values of 7 to 8.

With hypochlorous acid, there was little loss in weight, until over 4% of chlorine on the weight of the wool, had been absorbed. This makes it possible to produce reasonable unshrinkability to ordinary washing, utilising a comparatively small percentage of available chlorine as hypochlorous acid; the process appears safe with quantities of chlorine which, if produced from hypochlorite and acid, would cause extensive damage.

It appears from this work that the action of hypochlorous acid is quite different from that of free chlorine; when the latter is used, the number of damaged fibres increases with increasing concentration, but with hypochlorous acid solution, there is little difference produced by varying the volume of liquor.

The difference between chlorine and hypochlorous acid may also be realised from the experiments of Meunier (Chim. et Ind., 1924, *40*, 266), who showed that wool will absorb chlorine from solution in carbon tetrachloride; Trotman and Trotman, however, demonstrated that hypochlorous acid was not absorbed from carbon tetrachloride solution unless a little water or a little hydrochloric acid was added. A further difference between the action of free chlorine and hypochlorous acid (J.S.C.I., 1928, *47*, 4) is that wool treated with the latter does not condense with semicarbazide, whereas wool treated with chlorine in presence of HCl or H_2SO_4, still contains carbonyl groups which condense with semicarbazide.

As discussed later (see page 211), there is a further difference between the action of hypochlorous acid and of free chlorine on wool, as shown by the Allwörden effect.

Summarising the previous work, it appears that the chief problems connected with the unshrinkable finish are:

(a) Control.
(b) Damage.
(c) Lack of unshrinkability.
(d) Wearability.

Trotman (J.S.C.I., 1931, 50, 463) considers that in a well-treated fabric the area shrinkage should not exceed 10%, and the material should not felt; the damaged fibres should not exceed 20%, the strength, elasticity, colour, and handle should be unimpaired, and the wearing power should be at least 75% of that of the original material. Apparently considerable damage is due to the presence of absorbed chlorine which depends on the concentration of the solution. When the chlorine is gradually liberated, the damage is slightly reduced. For instance, the gradual addition of hypochlorite to hydrochloric acid gives less damage than when the two reagents are present from the beginning. When the quantity of acid required is reduced to the minimum, better results are obtained, but the damage is still in the neighbourhood of 25 to 30%. Experiments on the slow liberation of chlorine from persulphates and chlorides, or by trade products such as Aktivin and Peraktivin, led to the conclusion that it was impossible to chlorinate wool to give a high degree of unshrinkability without producing 20 to 30% of damaged fibres.

The use of hypochlorous acid free from chlorine has been shown to give unshrinkability without excessive damage; in order to obtain a high degree of unshrinkability it is sometimes necessary to use 5% of available chlorine estimated on the weight of the goods.

The early methods of commercial treatment necessitated the use of a small volume of liquor of high concentration, and whereas dilute solutions of hypochlorous acid containing 5 g. available chlorine per litre may be used with safety, the damage produced increases with concentration due to the gradual liberation of free chlorine. Experiments to keep the pH of the liquor between 6 and 7 showed that it was not possible to keep the percentage of damaged fibres below 24, but this is much less than in presence of acid. Fairly good results were obtained when the sodium hypochlorite was made faintly acid with sodium dihydrogen pyrophosphate. Fatty acids when added to a solution containing 3% of available chlorine (estimated on the goods) gave shrinkage of the order of 10% with 15 to 20% of damaged fibres. Similar results were obtained in presence of salts which are hydrolysed by water.

When on the alkaline side of neutrality there was considerable damage, but milling shrinkage was removed; the use of alkaline solutions of hypochlorites is revealed in U.S.P. 1,781,415. In general, the action of the alkaline solution is much slower than that of acid solutions, but the wool is apt to be discoloured.

The use of protective agents, such as protective colloids, tannic acid, formaldehyde, and quinone, did not give satisfactory results, but some interesting effects were obtained by the addition of phenol to the hypochlorous acid, for in many cases the damage did not exceed 15%; the hypochlorous acid was made by adding boric acid to a solution of bleaching powder.

In most wet chlorination processes, it is customary to use acidified hypochlorite solutions, but it is generally undesirable to use such an excess of acid that the pH falls below 3 where evolution of chlorine gas readily occurs and contaminates the atmosphere. Where solutions of pH 5 to 4 are utilised, only hypochlorous acid is formed, and it is common practice to obtain a pH in this region. Indicators are unreliable for this purpose, and many works have no glass electrodes available.

Ridge and Little (J.T.I., 1942, *33*, 59) have tabulated the proportions of acid necessary to reduce the pH to 5:

SODIUM HYPOCHLORITE SOLUTION AT pH 5

Acid	For 1 lb. available Cl	For 1 lb. NaOCl (15%)	For 1 gallon NaOCl (15%)
HCl (100%) . . .	0·53 lb.	0·08 lb.	1·00 lb.
(36°Tw. or 36%) .	1·47 lb.	0·221 lb.	2·8 lb.
(28°Tw. or 28%) .	1·89 lb.	0·284 lb.	3·6 lb.
H_2SO_4 (100%) . .	0·715 lb.	0·107 lb.	1·35 lb.
(96–97%) . .	0·735 lb.	0·110 lb.	1·40 lb.
(94–96%) . .	0·75 lb.	0·112 lb.	1·42 lb.
(77–78%) . .	0·92 lb.	0·138 lb.	1·74 lb.
Acetic (glacial). . .	1·2 lb.	0·18 lb.	2·27 lb.
(80%) . . .	1·5 lb.	0·225 lb.	2·85 lb.

BLEACHING POWDER SOLUTION AT pH 5
(free from suspended lime)

Acid	For 1 lb. of available chlorine
HCl (100%) . . .	0·53 lb.
(36%)	1·47 lb.
(28%)	1·89 lb.
Acetic (glacial) . . .	1·2 lb.
(80%)	1·5 lb.

In actual fact, the quantities in these tables depend to some extent on the alkalinity of the hypochlorite, the precise concentration of acid, and the accuracy of measurement; hence, there may be some deviation with products of different origin and composition.

It must also be realised that the mineral acids do not give stability of pH, as the solutions are unbuffered in this slightly acid region, but with acetic acid, the system is well buffered near to pH 5 and does not change to any appreciable extent during processing. Aluminium sulphate is useful for buffering at pH 4.

It is not possible to give a general recipe which can be applied to all types of wool, nor to all textile structures; for instance, a particular wool in the form of yarn may require 2% of chlorine, but may require more when the yarn is treated in the form of hosiery.

In commercial processes, it is customary to use sodium hypochlorite and hydrochloric acid solutions, so that the bath will consist of a mixture of chlorine, sodium chloride, and hydrochloric acid.

The effect of acid and salt on the chlorination process has been examined by Trotman (J.S.C.I., 1933, 52, 159). For example, neutral chlorine water, containing 3% of chlorine on the weight of the goods, gave an unshrinkable finish in 20 minutes with negligible damage, but when the concentration of acid was gradually increased, the damage increased up to a certain concentration, after which further acid produced no greater damage; the maximum concentration of acid was approximately 0·6 g. per litre, and above this figure the quantity of chlorine absorbed by the wool was still the same.

From these experiments, it appears that chlorine water, which is free from mineral·acid, produces no damage, and that the addition of small quantities causes damage, but the addition of more acid has no further detrimental action. The presence of hydrochloric acid increases the initial rate of chlorine absorption.

Addition of sodium chloride tends to diminish the damage, especially when a high (e.g. 5%) percentage of chlorine is present in order to produce the necessary reduction of shrinkage. When hydrochloric acid and sodium chloride are increased simultaneously, each exercises its separate effect.

Chlorine water generally contains about 0·1 to 0·16% of hydrochloric acid, and when this is replaced by acetic acid, by the addition of sodium acetate, the mixture produces commercial unshrinkability without more than 10% of damaged fibres. If chlorination is carried out at 37°C. only half as much chlorine is required as at atmospheric temperatures, and the damage is small.

The observations regarding the effect of acid have been confirmed by Edwards (J.S.C.I., 1932, 51, 234), who found that large amounts of acid caused no increased absorption of chlorine. It is not necessary to use more acid than that required to liberate all the chlorine from the hypochlorite, making allowance for the presence of NaOH and Na$_2$CO$_3$; nevertheless, a small excess of acid seems to preserve the whiteness of the wool.

DILUTION

The EFFECT OF DILUTION was also examined, using 5 g. of wool in various volumes of the hypochlorite bath, each bath containing 4·25 c.c. of N NaOCl and 5·4 c.c. of HCl. The following results were obtained, as shown in the table:

EFFECT OF DILUTION

Vol. in c.c.	Chlorine absorbed (g.)	Total chlorine absorbed %
100	2·80	93
200	2·27	75
300	2·01	66
400	1·66	55
500	1·33	44
600	1·19	39
800	1·03	34
1,000	0·89	29

The results show that the volume of liquor affords a control of the chlorine absorbed. At the greater dilutions, the absorption of chlorine was slower, and this indicates that better control may be obtained by treatment in a dilute bath for a long time. Experimental results of 5 g. wool in 500 c.c. of water were chosen as a compromise between control and practical working; with these values about 50% of the total chlorine is absorbed by the wool in 45 minutes. Edwards suggests that for coarse goods in 5 lb. lots, it is possible to treat 100 lb. of coarse wool in 1,000 gallons of water containing 12 gallons 7 pints of N sodium hypochlorite and 15 gallons 4 pints of N hydrochloric acid. The goods should be treated for 45 minutes, washed, and dechlorinated in a mixture of sodium sulphite and sodium bicarbonate. After the goods are removed from the bath, the volume may be restored to its original value by water, and the necessary amount of sodium hypochlorite and acid in the same ratio as before should be added to bring the bath to its original strength.

Commercial hypochlorite usually sets free about 150 g. chlorine per litre, so that it is 4·23 N while commercial hydrochloric acid is 9 N.

In more convenient quantities, 5 lb. of coarse wool was immersed in 50 gallons of water containing 697 c.c. of commercial hypochlorite and 393 c.c. of commercial acid. The wool was treated for 45 minutes and then dechlorinated. Titration with thiosulphate showed that there was 2·5% of available chlorine left, and the bath was restored to 4·6% by adding 316 c.c. of hypochlorite and 178 c.c. of acid. The fabric absorbed 2·90% of available chlorine and showed 28% damage. A shrinkage test gave a reduction in area of 7·4%. A sample treated in the next bath absorbed 2·18% of chlorine and showed 26% damage with 7·7% area shrinkage.

The employment of slightly alkaline solutions of hypochlorite has been mentioned on page 199, and seems to be moderately popular in the U.S.A. For example, socks are treated in rotary drums of stainless steel; a preliminary wetting in 1% borax solution is followed by the gradual addition of hypochlorite over a period of 10 to 15 minutes so as to give a concentration of 4·5%. The pH of the liquor lies between 9 and 7·5. After working the socks in the liquor for about 20 minutes, sodium bisulphite is added as an antichlor and the socks worked for a further 5 to 10 minutes. Two rinses in water for about 5 minutes on each occasion complete the process.

Variety of Wool

It has long been known that different qualities of wool require different treatments in the chlorination process. This point was investigated by Edwards, using fourteen different wools, and it was determined that fine goods require 1·85% of chlorine, medium goods need 2%, and coarse goods need 2·3%. The amount of damage increases both with the chlorine and the finer quality of wool, and from the examination of commercial samples Edwards concluded that 30 to 35% damage was the maximum which could be allowed if the fabric was to retain good wearing properties.

The chlorination of wool has also been examined by Speakman and Goodings (J.T.I., 1926, *17*, 607) with a view to ascertaining the amounts of chlorine required to produce unshrinkability on wools of widely differing milling properties. Chlorination was not carried beyond 4% chlorine on the weight of the wool, for even with 3% there was definite over-chlorination with the unpleasant slimy feel in water. The following results were obtained:

EFFECT ON DIFFERENT WOOLS

Wensleydale		*Oxford Down*		*Southdown*	
% chlorine used	% shrinkage	% chlorine used	% shrinkage	% chlorine used	% shrinkage
Untreated	33·7	Untreated	28·0	Untreated	16·3
0·39	33·9	0·44	26·8	0·38	15·6
0·91	29·5	0·84	22·6	0·72	12·5
1·50	22·5	1·02	18·8	1·07	9·8
1·73	21·3	1·53	12·8	1·37	7·1
2·13	17·8	1·78	10·5	1·90	5·2
2·24	18·4	2·30	7·1	1·95	4·4
2·58	12·9	2·42	6·3	2·39	2·9
3·07	12·0	2·80	4·9	2·73	4·5
3·62	10·5	3·40	1·2	3·40	1·3
—	—	3·44	−2·5 (increase)	3·44	3·1

It will be seen that small quantities of chlorine, about 0·3% on the weight of the wool, produce little or no effect on the felting properties; the initial action, therefore, is a period of inhibition, but this is soon followed by a period of rapid reduction of shrinkage, followed by a period of slow reduction of shrinkage. This final stage is probably due to the slow diffusion of the hypochlorite solution into the inner fibres of the yarn as compared with the preferential absorption of chlorine by the exposed fibres on the outside of the yarn. This diffusion factor seems to be largely responsible for the difficulty of obtaining absolute unshrinkability, without some damage.

The Negafel Process

The difficulties of the ordinary methods of wet chlorination are the lack of uniform treatment and the damage to the wool which varies according to the type of goods, the temperature, the initial concentration, and the pH of the liquor.

Clayton and Edwards (B.P. 537,671) have found that formic acid is a valuable agent for liberating the active chlorine from the hypochlorite solutions, and liquors of this type behave differently from the ordinary acid chlorinating bath containing mineral acids or even acetic, boric, or other weak acids. In many respects, of course, the lowest member of a homologous series behaves differently. When hypochlorite/formic acid liquors are allowed to act on wool under controlled conditions they give excellent anti-felting properties and do not degrade or discolour the wool as when mineral acids are used. On the other hand, chlorinating liquors containing acids of low ionisation constants are either too slow for commercial use or do not give satisfactory non-felting.

It is believed that the formic acid method is the basis of the "Negafel" process.

Clayton and Edwards suggest that if part of the damage to wool is produced by oxidation, then the greatest damage will be produced from liquors of the highest oxidation potential. Comparative tests of hypochlorite/hydrochloric acid liquor and hypochlorite/formic acid liquor show that the oxidation potential of the former is twice that of the latter. The role of the formic acid is not easy to determine; it may serve as a potential anti-oxidant apart from its effect on the pH of the solution, but it may be that the formic acid has considerable influence in freeing the long-chain protein molecules from their normal mutual attraction, thus creating new surfaces for absorption as originally suggested by Speakman and Hirst (Nature, 1931, *127*, 665).

In the Negafel process it is also advisable to make use of a buffering agent consisting of the sodium or other soluble metallic salt of the acid possessing reducing properties, such as formic or lactic acid, and also, if desired, urea, thiourea, or thiodiglycol, which are capable of preventing oxidation of the fibre.

Wetting agents may also be employed to reduce the interfacial tension between the scales and the chlorinating liquor. In actual working it has been found preferable to treat the wool while it still contains its grease, oil used in the manufacturing operations, and any precipitated fatty acids derived from soap or soap residues, as such substances exert a protective action on the cortical cells of the fibres, but do not prevent absorption of the active halogen.

Whereas in many wet chlorination processes it is customary to treat the scoured wool in the wet state, Clayton and Edwards prefer to treat the material direct from the knitting machines or looms; alternatively, if it is essential to scour the material before chlorinating, then such scouring should be effected with reagents which do not swell the wool fibres.

The process is generally carried out between 5° and 10° C. and the total amount of available halogen varies according to the type of wool. The absorption of chlorine takes place steadily around pH 4, and for this reason the initial pH of the liquor is adjusted to about 4, using sodium formate as the main buffer; with certain types of wool, after 6 to 10 minutes' treatment, it is necessary to add an acid of fairly low ionisation constant in order to keep the pH of the whole system constant, and so reduce to a minimum the tendency of the fibre to swell without interfering with the exhaustion of the remainder of the chlorine in the bath. The action is allowed to continue until the liquor only gives a slight reaction when tested with starch potassium iodide paper.

The recipe for treating 100 lb. of tubular knitted wool fabric is as follows:

300 gallons of water are placed in a suitable machine and cooled with ice to 5° to 10° C. Sufficient sodium or calcium hypochlorite solution is then added to give a concentration of approximately 2% available chlorine calculated on the weight of the material to be treated. Formic acid is next added to give a pH of about 3 to 4, together with 0.5% of a sulphonated higher fatty acid wetting agent, and the dry fabric containing manufacturing oils, etc., entered directly into the liquor as quickly as possible. After the fabric has been worked in the liquor for 6 to 10 minutes, a further addition of formic acid or an addition of orthophosphoric acid is made so as to keep the pH of the liquor about 4, at which point the last traces of chlorine in the liquor are absorbed by the fabric during working for a further short period. Finally, the fabric is cleared by adding sodium bisulphite or sulphite solution to the exhausted chlorinating liquor or to a fresh liquor, rinsed, and scoured, bleached, etc., as required.

Raw merino wool, before scouring, may be treated in a somewhat similar manner for 5 to 10 minutes at 5° to 10°C., or with a chlorine-water liquor containing approximately 2% available chlorine, 0·1 to 0·2% of sodium formate, and 3% formic acid calculated on the weight of the wool, for 5 to 10 minutes at 5° to 10°C. A circulating liquor system may be used, if desired, but in such a case the wool-liquor ratio should be about 1 : 20, and the chlorinating liquor should be added at a medium rate to the circulating liquor. Finally, the wool is cleared with sodium sulphite solution, rinsed, and passed directly to a scouring plant in which it may be scoured at twice the normal speed used when scouring non-chlorinated merino wool.

This process is stated to have definite advantages compared with the usual hypochlorite/mineral acid processes. The treated wool maintains its weight and has good wearing properties, being practically free from chemical damage and possessing good colour. The treatment is uniform and easily controlled with less effect on the colour of both dyed and undyed wools than the older processes.

It is also stated that goods containing wool in admixture with other natural fibres, artificial fibres, synthetic fibres, or rubber can be treated satisfactorily.

The Negafel process seems to be based on four main factors: a reducing acid, such as formic acid or lactic acid, which lowers the oxidising power of the hypochlorite or chlorine, protective agents such as urea, natural or artificial protective colloids such as the wool fat, and control of pH at 4 or the isoelectric region of wool.

A previous specification by von Lumpp, B.P. 13,088, in 1911, made use of hypochlorite neutralised with acetic acid, formic acid, lactic or oxalic acid, together with 2 to 2·5 parts of formaldehyde per part of active chlorine; the chlorine is completely exhausted from solution and the formaldehyde partly exhausted according to this invention.

Protective agents such as Perminal NF or Lanasan FB in wet chlorination processes have been mentioned by Heywood in Australian Patent 111,599. Wool is treated for 10 minutes at 60°C. in 0·1% solution of the Perminal or Lanasan, and then immersed, without rinsing, in a cold solution of 2 pints of sodium or calcium hypochlorite solution (36°Tw.), and 0·5 pints of hydrochloric acid (32°Tw.) in 300 gallons of water.

The use of gelatin as a protective agent has been described by Trotman (J.S.C.I., 1931, 50, 463; 1932, 51, 66), who states that the structural damage caused by chlorination may be obviated by the addition of a neutralised solution of gelatin to the chlorinating bath; he supposes that some chloramines are formed by interaction of gelatin with chlorine. Chloramine formation with the wool substance had previously been suggested, but shown to be a wrong idea from the work of Trotman and Wyche (J.S.C.I., 1914, *43*, 293), who found de-aminated wool was neither more nor less sensitive to chlorination than normal wool.

A later process (B.P. 557,600) by Clayton and Edwards is another modification of the wet chlorination treatment; wool is treated in a solution of calcium or sodium hypochlorite at less than pH 10·5, and gradually acidified by the addition of carbon dioxide.

Slow Chlorination

Reference has already been made to control of the rapid absorption of chlorine by wool through the simple means of adding the chlorine slowly at intervals instead of at one time. Trotman (J.S.C.I., 1931, *50*, 463) has investigated the possibility of the slow liberation of chlorine from persulphates and chlorides as a means of reducing damage (see page 198), but without any great advantage; trade products such as Aktivin or Peraktivin were also examined.

Organic *N*-chloramides have been investigated by Feibelmann and the results protected in a series of patents, namely, D.R.P. 563,387, 647,566, and 656,112. U.S.P. 1,892,548 describes the chlorination of wool with *p*-toluenesulphodichloramide, which is insoluble in water, but may be applied from alkaline solution or suspension. Apparently 0·5 to 3 parts of *p*-toluenesulphodichloramide in 1,000 parts of water is sufficient for all requirements; the solution is first prepared by dissolving in alkali and then 15 parts of concentrated hydrochloric acid are added to precipitate the dichloramide yielding a milky liquid in which the wool is soaked until the active chlorine is consumed. (Peraktivin or Dichloramine T is *p*-toluenesulphodichloramide.) In another example 1 lb. of Peraktivin was taken for 25 lb. of wool; 1 gallon of cold 10% Na_2CO_3 solution was used to dissolve the Peraktivin and the solution was then diluted to 35 to 40 gallons of cold water, after which 1 gallon of HCl (34°Tw.) was slowly added. A milky solution was produced in which the wool was circulated until the liquor became clear. The process is completed by washing. The Hypol method probably depends on either the foregoing treatment or the following process.

Aktivin has also been suggested for this purpose, but its aqueous solution becomes turbid at first when acidified with HCl, owing to the formation of the sparingly soluble dichloride; this gradually decomposes with liberation of chlorine. In an actual example, a wool fabric was treated with sufficient Aktivin or Chloramine T, to yield 3% of chlorine; the colour of the wool was good, but the damage amounted to 45 to 50%.

An important list of compounds containing active chlorine has been given by Chenicek (Interchemical Review, 1945, *4*, 13).

An interesting variation of the wet chlorination process has been described by Speakman and Whewell (B.P. 551,310), in which conditions are so arranged that during a multiplicity of treatments there is substantial exhaustion of the chlorine before it penetrates the wool. The solution should contain from 0·5 to 1·5% of available chlorine arranged in four baths through which the wool is drawn; the passage through one bath occupies about 10 seconds, and the amount of liquor is both limited and evenly distributed by squeezing. Reaction is confined to the surface of the wool under these conditions.

HYPAK PROCESS

The Hypak process, according to Rordorf (Spinn. u. Weber, 1937, 55, 20), is based on the addition of certain organic compounds to the hypochlorite liquors; these organic compounds are intended to absorb the chlorine which is liberated on acidification and then slowly deliver it to the wool so that the aggressive action of the chlorine is decreased. For 10 Kg. of wool it is necessary to employ 300 l. of water containing 1·5 Kg. of concentrated H_2SO_4; the Hypak bath is made by dissolving 200 g. of Hypak in 10 l. of water. The cleaned wool is immersed in the acid bath for 10 minutes and then removed, when 4 l. of the Hypak solution is added to the acid bath, and the wool immersed again for 15 minutes with constant agitation. After the removal of the wool, 3 l. of Hypak solution are added and the wool again immersed for 15 minutes. The wool is removed for a third time, the residue of the Hypak solution is added, and the wool immersed for a final period of 15 minutes. After removing the excess of liquor, the wool is given the usual anti-chlor and washing treatments. It is stated that the Hypak method causes less damage than the usual chlorination processes.

A process which is similar to, if not identical with, the Hypak treatment has been described in B.P. 482,656 of Landshoff and Meyer. Additions to the chlorinating bath include ammonia or compounds which include one or more amino or imino groups, as, for instance, primary or secondary amines, amino or imino carboxylic acids, carboxylic amides, urea or substitution products of these compounds. Amino or imino compounds which have fibre-protective or protective colloid properties are particularly advantageous. Other suitable additions include compounds in which the hydrogen atoms of the amino or imino groups have been replaced by radicles which promote surface-active effects, as, for example, fatty acid or alcohol radicles containing more than eight carbon atoms.

If comparative tests are made with a series of solutions containing the same amount of active chlorine, but increasing amounts of the added compounds, it is found that the time to consume the chlorine increases throughout the series, but the felting capacity of the treated wool is not reduced to the same extent; there appears to be an optimum concentration of the nitrogeneous compound, the correct concentration of which may be found by a few preliminary trials.

An example of the method describes treatment of 25 g. of wool in 750 c.c. of water containing 4 c.c. of NaOCl (13·5% active chlorine), 0·25 g. of amino-acetic acid, and 4 g. of H_2SO_4. A period of 90 minutes was required to consume the chlorine, which in absence of amino-acetic acid, was absorbed in 10 minutes. In another example, wool was treated with a similar solution, but in which the amino-acetic acid was replaced by the same quantity of acetamide. Commercial lysalbinic acid may be used, and also protein degradation products obtained from the degradation waste of leather which has been tanned by inorganic tanning agents.

Batches of wool were also treated in forty times their weight of a liquor containing 8% of H_2SO_4 and 4% of active chlorine in the form of NaOCl; amino-acetic acid was added in quantities of from 0·1 to 0·6 g. per litre in steps of 0·1 g., and it was established that minimum felting was obtained from a concentration of 0·8 g. per litre of amino-acetic acid. Similar experiments with urea showed that a concentration of 0·8 g. per litre gave minimum felting. Stronger felting occurs with wool treated in the presence of both higher and lower concentrations of these additions to the usual chlorinating baths.

PROTON PROCESS

Another interesting process depending on the slow liberation of chlorine makes use of a substance Alrochlor BH paste and also a small amount of formaldehyde. Assuming that Alrochlor paste is sodium sulphamate, this would react with hypochlorous acid at room temperatures to give a comparatively stable compound, $NHClSO_3Na$, which decomposes on warming to give a chloramine, NH_2Cl. The chloramine will decompose in water to give ammonia and hypochlorous acid; the use of formaldehyde may prevent an undue rise in acidity as well as combining with the ammonia to bring about more complete hydrolysis.

Depressed Swelling

The very great affinity of wool for chlorine is probably associated with the swelling of wool in water and in aqueous solutions of hypochlorites. A few methods have been devised to depress the swelling of wool and so promote uniformity of treatment.

Hirst and King (J.T.I., 1933, *24*, 174) found that when salts were added to the chlorinating bath, the rate of absorption of chlorine was reduced and a more uniform treatment was obtained. Trotman (J.S.C.I., 1933, *52*, 159) has stated that additions of common salt had no effect on the rate of absorption of chlorine (see also page 200), but this difference of opinion may be due to the possible use of neutral solutions by Trotman. Hirst and King established that the rate of absorption of chlorine in presence of acid was more rapid and more uniform than in its absence, which agrees with Trotman's statement that even 0·1% of HCl in chlorine water causes considerable fibre damage. From this standpoint, Trotman prefers chlorine water buffered with sodium acetate, but Hirst and King seem to prefer chlorine alone as the strength of the treated wool is good and the non-felting effect is equal to that from equivalent amounts of bleaching powder and hydrochloric acid.

In the experiments of Hirst and King, the ratio of liquor to wool was 40 : 1, for in commercial practice the ratio usually lies between 30 : 1 and 100 : 1. Some interesting data were recorded, but they are difficult to classify on a systematic basis. Where no additions of salt were made, however, the use of boric acid gave poor colour and low unshrinkability; acetic acid gave good unshrinkability which was nevertheless inferior to that produced in presence of hydrochloric acid, where bleaching powder was used. Hypochlorous acid seems to give less unshrinkability than that resulting from equivalent amounts of bleaching powder; the colour is inferior to that from bleaching powder and hydrochloric acid.

The depressing action of salt enables higher concentrations of chlorine to be used without undue loss in strength, although saturated solutions of $CaCl_2$ are not so satisfactory as NaCl or Na_2SO_4; with lower concentrations the results from solutions containing $CaCl_2$ give the impression of greater strength for a given degree of unshrinkability. Where solutions of chlorine gas were used in place of bleaching powder, saturated Na_2SO_4 solutions seem to give the best result, and $CaCl_2$ showed the least effect.

With the depression of swelling in presence of salt solutions, the rate of chlorine absorption is considerably reduced, so there should be a much smoother action on the fibre. However, undue repression of swelling may reduce the degree of unshrinkability obtained from a given percentage of chlorine.

Restricted swelling also plays a part in the process outlined in B.P. 550,541, by Marsh, Wood, and Cowley of the Tootal Broadhurst Lee Company. Briefly, a preliminary treatment of the wool with a synthetic resin enables it to withstand the action of hypochlorite liquors to a much greater extent than untreated wool; there is also improved resistance to degradation by alkali.

The preferred form of the invention is to apply the resinous condensation product as a water-soluble condensate of low molecular weight which will penetrate the fibre, where it is condensed by a heat treatment to form an insoluble resist which protects the interior of the fibre, probably by preventing swelling in water, so as to impede or prevent diffusion of reagents into the wool substance.

Solutions of urea-formaldehyde condensation products have been found very suitable for this purpose, and after they have been resinified, the fabric may be treated with any reagent which is known to impart non-felting properties to wool.

In an example, 100 g. of urea was dissolved in 200 c.c. of 40% formaldehyde solution (previously neutralised), 9 parts of concentrated ammonia solution added, and the mixture refluxed for 3 minutes, followed by rapid cooling. This mixture was diluted by adding 40 parts of water to 60 parts of the soluble condensate, and 2 to 3% of ammonium hydrogen phosphate added (calculated on the undiluted solution). A woollen fabric was impregnated with this solution and, after removal of excess liquor, it was dried and heated for 3 minutes at 130°C. The increase in weight amounted to 12%. The resin-treated wool was immersed in acidified hypochlorite solution at pH 4·5, and of such concentration that the available chlorine was 5%, calculated on the weight of the wool. The ratio of liquor to cloth was 50 : 1, and the duration of the treatment was 20 to 30 minutes. After processing, the cloth was washed and given an anti-chlor treatment with sodium bisulphite solution. The cloth exhibited considerable resistance to felting when washed, and it was noteworthy that there was an absence of the slimy handle usually associated with chlorinated wool; the colour of the treated wool was good.

If necessary, the resin may be removed by treatment with deci-normal hydrochloric acid at 60°C., followed by washing and drying.

It will be noted that the amount of chlorine employed is somewhat greater than that generally utilised for the chlorination of wool.

The resin technique may also be employed with other non-felting agents, such as gaseous chlorine or bromine, solutions of alkalis, oxidising agents, reducing agents, or enzyme preparations; where non-felting agents are applied from non-aqueous solvents, as described on page 224, there is afforded a double protection to the wool, and it may be found necessary to increase the time of reaction to produce the desired effect.

In most cases, it is better to remove the resin preparation which might otherwise interfere with the dyeing operations subsequent to the anti-felting treatment; on the other hand, in certain circumstances, the resin may afford a valuable improvement to the physical properties of the material.

Some of the samples treated according to this process (resin, followed by chlorine) were tested after removal of the resin, and showed a milling shrinkage of 0% compared with 28% for the untreated material: the resistance to abrasion was unimpaired.

The Allwörden Effect

An interesting observation first made by Allwörden (Z. Angew. Chem., 1916, *29*, 77) was that when undamaged wool was treated with chlorine water a series of small bubbles or blisters was observed protruding through the scales when the fibre was examined under the microscope. Allwörden assumed that these blisters were caused by a carbohydrate constituent of the wool, situated between the cortex and the scales, and this substance was termed "elasticum." This hypothetical substance was assumed to affect the behaviour of the wool in milling and other finishing processes and was considered to be readily removed by alkali.

Allwörden suggested that the behaviour of the wool in chlorine water could be used as an indication of the extent of damage by alkali.

This effect may be taken to indicate that the wool has not been damaged by alkali, but, on the other hand, undamaged wool does not always give these blisters; the work of Speakman (J.T.I., 1926, *17*, 607) indicates that the product is some protein substance formed by the action of chlorine on the wool, and as the action of chlorine on different wools varies considerably it is only to be expected that there will be some variations with Allwörden's test.

According to the hypothesis of Allwörden, the removal of the "elasticum" is accompanied by a loss of the felting properties of wool; the unshrinkable finish produced by chlorination was assumed to be due to the destruction of the "elasticum" by chlorine.

The modern view of the Allwörden effect, as discussed on page 217, is that acid is formed which gives rise to swelling and produces blisters in accordance with the Donnan theory of membrane equilibrium.

GELATINISATION

One of the common suggestions as to the cause of the non-felting property of chlorinated wool is that the outer scales of the fibre have been eaten away to a greater or less degree by the action of chlorine, and the projecting tips of the scales have been eroded. Examination of commercial chlorinated wool, however, lends little support to this theory unless excess of chlorine has been used.

Speakman and Goodings (J.T.I., 1926, *17*, 607) have examined the action of chlorine and hypochlorous acid on wool, as Trotman (see page 197) has shown that the action of these two substances differs in many respects although both reagents produce non-felting wool.

When wool is treated with chlorine water the blisters of the Allwörden effect are obtained, and they begin at the free edges of the scales and continue above the surface of the scales next along the fibre. The membrane surrounding each blister is not a distended scale, as Allwörden supposed, but a protein decomposition product. In the early stages of the reaction the number of blisters is equal to the number of scales, but later coalescence takes place.

Hypochlorous acid does not give this effect.

The chlorination of wool does not finish with the treatment with chlorine or hypochlorous acid, as the goods are dechlorinated and washed in soap or sodium carbonate solution or both. From the moment of contact with the alkaline solution the outer layers of the fibre swell with great rapidity until the whole fibre is surrounded by a sheath of jelly; in this way it is possible to determine the degree of penetration of the chlorinating agent into the wool. Examination of the swollen fibres shows that the scales lie on the outside of this jelly layer in a more or less undamaged condition, depending on the conditions of chlorination, but when the swollen fibres are washed free from alkali, and dried, they return to their normal size.

These experiments indicate that the scales are more resistant than the cortex to the attack of chlorine, and that the layer of cortical cells within the cuticle is attacked by chlorine and swollen by the subsequent action of soap or soda. The intervention of a layer of jelly between the scales and the cortex is considered to be the cause of non-felting, as when subjected to mechanical treatment the scales cannot cause the necessary fibre travel because of their weak attachment to the fibre.

The formation of a layer of jelly by the consecutive action of chlorine and soap is responsible for the bad wearing properties of some chlorinated wools; such jelly layer and the surrounding scales are easily worn away by the chemical action. The slimy feel of over-chlorinated wool is also due to the formation of a layer of jelly surrounding the fibres.

Speakman and Goodings considered that some of the difficulties of non-felting wool could be eliminated by a process capable of causing the jelly layer to shrink and harden on to the core of the fibre, if sufficient chlorine had been used to cause gelatinisation of both the scales and the outer cortex. It was found that chlorinated wool could not be improved by treatment with condensing agents such as formaldehyde and quinone, but that certain mordanting agents applied after the soap or soda treatment produced improvements. The best results were obtained with chrome mordants which indicates that the bad wearing properties of chlorinated wool may be remedied in so far as dyed goods are concerned by the use of chrome mordant dyes.

Gaseous Chlorination

The main difficulty of treating wool with chlorinating solutions is that the chlorine attacks the wool rapidly and vigorously, but the rate of penetration of the solution into the fibrous mass is relatively slow; the result of this is that the outside fibres of the woollen material are apt to be over-treated whilst the inside fibres are often untreated. The difficulties with regard to the use of aqueous solutions have caused attention to be devoted to the possibility of using gas.

Dry wool reacts only slowly with chlorine gas, which nevertheless can penetrate into wool or into woollen yarns quite readily. In 1897,

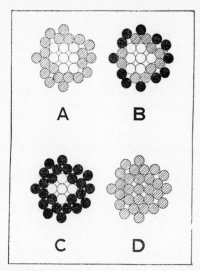

Fig. 112.—Diagrams representing cross-sections of chlorinated yarns; A to C indicate increasing degrees of wet chlorination without treating all fibres, and D indicates the ideal light treatment of the fibres throughout the yarn.

Meister, Lucius, and Brüning (B.P. 11,917) found that a silky gloss could be obtained by allowing damp wool to react with a definite amount of chlorine. Knecht and Milnes (J.S.D.C., 1902, *18*, 41) found that dry chlorine had little action on dry wool, but reaction occurred as the moisture content of the wool increased and hydrochloric acid was formed. Meunier and Latreille (Chim. et Ind., 1923, *10*, 636) also studied this reaction and found that there was little effect by chlorine unless the wool was moist, in which case its elasticity and tensile strength were impaired and the ability to fix acid and basic dyes was increased; the felting properties were also affected according to these investigations. For commercial treatment wool was dried in air at 85°C. for 20 minutes, and while warm exposed for 12 hours to 5% of its weight of chlorine gas; it was then washed with water, 1% sodium bisulphite solution, and finally with water.

About 1933, the dry chlorination process was investigated by the

Wool Industries Research Association and a modified method protected in B.P. 417,719, 475,742, and 495,098. Considerable quantities of wool have been treated, according to this method. The
uniform treatment of the wool is brought about because the rate
of reaction between the dry wool and chlorine is slow, and the
penetration is helped by conducting the reaction in a partial
vacuum. Provided the moisture regain of the wool is below 10%,
the process works satisfactorily. The dry wool is placed in an autoclave, the door closed, and the greater part of the air removed by
pumping; the required amount of chlorine gas is then passed into
the evacuated vessel, and measured by a meter on the way. The
gaseous contents of the autoclave are circulated by a pump. When
the treatment is finished the excess chlorine is blown away through
an absorbing tower, the door is opened, and the wool removed. The
complete treatment takes about 90 minutes.

When the wool is removed from the autoclave the non-felting
process is complete, but as the material contains a small amount of
hydrochloric acid, this is generally neutralised or removed before
the next stage in the ordinary manufacturing process. The actual
working conditions will vary somewhat according to the capacity
of the autoclave, but with small apparatus of 10 cubic feet capacity,
and taking a charge of 35 to 40 lb. of wool, the vessel was evacuated
so that the pressure within the apparatus was approximately 6 inches
of mercury. One lb. weight of chlorine was admitted over a period of
45 minutes to 1 hour, when the pressure reached a figure of approximately 12 inches of mercury. The apparatus was then allowed to
stand for half an hour, during which time the pressure fell to about
9 inches of mercury; at the end of this time air was admitted to
atmospheric pressure, and a stream of air pumped through to remove
any free chlorine or hydrochloric acid in the autoclave.

With wet chlorination, the reaction takes place so rapidly that
the outside fibres are fully treated before the liquor has reached the
inside fibres (see Fig. 112). The core of untreated fibres means that
the wool will felt ultimately. The treatment with chlorine gas aims at
treating all the fibres lightly and avoiding the complete treatment of
any of them (see Fig. 112 D).

The wearing properties of the fibres of dry chlorinated wool, when
made into fabrics, compare very favourably with those of the same
fabrics in the untreated state, and when treated tops have been spun
into yarn they appear to be about 10% stronger than similar yarns
made from the same wool before chlorination. Dry chlorinated wool
dyes more rapidly than untreated wool and the handle is slightly
harsher, but this can be remedied by treatment with a surface-active
softening material.

According to B.P. 559,263 of Brandwood, initial drying of the wool is not necessary and the material may contain 40% of moisture. The wool is wound into packages and subjected to the action of chlorine gas (1 to 3% on the weight of the wool); the gas is mixed with a large volume of air at 5 lb. pressure and the chamber is finally cleared of residual chlorine by compressed air. The process is completed by washing.

BROMINATION

The substitution of bromine for chlorine in the treatment of wool was demonstrated by Trotman (J.S.C.I., 1933, *52*, 159), and it was shown that the product exhibited little structural damage although the degree of unshrinkability was satisfactory. Callan (ibid., 544) had obtained similar results.

The advantages claimed for bromination as opposed to chlorination are as follows:

(1) Bromine is absorbed very readily by wool from aqueous solutions.
(2) The structural damage produced is less than that caused by an equivalent quantity of chlorine.
(3) The unshrinkability is satisfactory.
(4) The handle of the treated material is good and it responds readily to bleaching.
(5) Aqueous solutions of bromine are less irritating than solutions of chlorine or of sodium hypochlorite and hydrochloric acid.

Trotman and Bell (J.S.C.I., 1935, *54*, 30) continued these investigations on bromination and their results indicated that in all respects bromination is superior to chlorination. The following table shows the percentage of damage and absorption given by increasing concentrations of bromine and chlorine:

COMPARISON OF CHLORINE AND BROMINE

% Cl. or Br.	% absorbed	% damage
3 Br.	100	2·6
3 Br.	100	2·9
5 Br.	100	5·0
5 Br. and NaOAc	—	2·2
7 Br. and NaOAc	97	6·0
10 Br. and NaOAc	82	7·0
20 Br. and NaOAc	89	20·0
25 Br. and NaOAc	87	22·0
1 Cl(NaOCl and HCl)	—	30·0
2·5 Cl(NaOCl and HCl)	—	42·0

2·5% of chlorine seems to be equivalent to 5·75% of bromine, and any percentage produces less damage than the chemical equivalent of chlorine; where small percentages of bromine are used there is no need to add sodium acetate, but with 5% or more the damage is reduced.

Bromination of woollen yarn with 2% of bromine showed that there was no loss in tensile strength nor diminution of extensibility. The amount of water absorbed by brominated yarn was less than that absorbed by chlorinated yarn, and, generally speaking, the affinity for dyestuffs of brominated wool was found to lie between that of untreated wool and chlorinated wool.

It appears that treatment with bromine can reduce the shrinkage of a Botany fabric sufficiently for trade purposes without producing more than 5% of damage. The following results afford a comparison of treatments with 2% of bromine and 2% of chlorine:

COMPARISON OF CHLORINATION AND BROMINATION

	Brominated	Chlorinated	Untreated
% damage	9·0	45·0	—
% shrinkage	11·6	7·1	29·0

Although Callan (loc. cit.) has recorded that bromination of wool on a commercial scale was carried out industrially as long ago as 1914, it does not appear to be the general practice. It is interesting to note, therefore, that this method has again received attention more recently, as described by Ericksson (Am. Dyes. Rep., 1940, 29, 641), U.S.P. 2,326,021. The advantages of bromination are that there is less structural damage than with equivalent amounts of chlorine and that bromine does not affect tensile strength, elongation, nor absorption of water.

Preliminary experiments on hose made from 40s worsted yarn gave very interesting results when treated with 9·6% of bromine estimated on the weight of the wool, the bromine being applied in aqueous solution which amounted to 25 times the weight of the wool; the time of treatment was 5 minutes at 21°C. No shrinkage was noticed when the treated socks were washed by hand for 10 minutes in alkaline soap solution at 55°C., and even after 40 minutes of machine milling at 60°C. there was no shrinkage, but only a slight change in "loftiness." None of the brominated hose shrank in dyeing, but the untreated material lost 7% in dyeing and 15% in milling.

The amount of unshrinkability produced with various percentages of bromine is shown in the following table:

EFFECT OF BROMINE ON SHRINKAGE

% Br.	% shrinkage Dyeing	Fulling
0·0	6·8	15·5
2·5	5·1	10·2
5·6	2·2	5·5
9·8	1·9	2·0

As for most purposes with knit goods, a total shrinkage of 5% is adequate, it appears that a satisfactory product may be obtained by treatment with 5 to 6% of bromine.

Ericksson has devised a brominator to produce bromine water from liquid bromine as required; the brominator is filled with the necessary amount of bromine for treatment of the wool and pumped into the water reservoir of the machine as required. The absorption of bromine by wool is a very rapid process, and may be reduced by lowering the temperature or lowering the pH. Tests with various acids showed that it is advisable to maintain the pH below 2. Experiments with 5% of sulphuric acid, and 7% of bromine at 10°C. give satisfactory results; there was no change in tensile strength and only a slight reduction in extension at break of yarn treated by this method.

IODINE

Iodine appears to react much more slowly with wool than is the case with either chlorine or bromine. vom Hove (Angew. Chem., 1934, *47*, 756) made an examination of the effect of dry chlorine, bromine, and iodine in the vapour state or in inert solvents. He concluded that the active halogen penetrates to the interior of the fibre where it forms halogen-hydrogen acid with water and oxydises the fibre. With iodine the oxidation is considerably slower than with the other halogens so that iodine penetrates almost exclusively by adsorption.

Haller and Holl (Textilber., 1936, *17*, 493) concluded, contrary to vom Hove, that iodine does not attack the tyrosine nucleus of wool. They also showed that wool is less reactive to iodine than to chlorine or bromine, and distinguished between adsorbed and combined iodine by removing the former by boiling the wool in water. The absorption of iodine from non-aqueous solutions was also investigated.

vom Hove (*supra*) also examined the Allwörden reaction and found that the blisters can be enlarged by the addition of hydro-chloric acid, reduced by washing in water, but cannot be produced in the absence of water; the blisters are also reduced by salt solutions. It appears that the blisters are produced by halogen-hydrogen acids giving rise to swelling of the type visualised by the Donnan theory of membrane equilibrium and the Proctor-Wilson theory of swelling.

It seems that iodine is of no value in the production of non-felting wool.

OXIDISING AND REDUCING AGENTS

Under strongly alkaline conditions, hypochlorite functions as an oxidising agent (pH 9); under acid conditions (pH 5) the effect is essentially chlorination. Where the solution is neutral, the hypo-chlorite functions both as an oxidising and a chlorinating agent.

The prime reaction in wet chlorination is probably as follows:

$$R-S-S-R+Cl_2 \longrightarrow 2R.SCl$$

The suggestion of Speakman (page 211) that the non-felting finish depends on the formation of a gelatinous degradation product of keratin, on or under the scale structure of the fibre, was extended (Nature, 1938, *142*, 1035) to show that this may be accomplished by any oxidising agent which is capable of breaking down the disulphide bond and a number of instances were cited. Trotman and Trotman (J.S.C.I., 1926, *45*, 111) considered that the characteristic action of hypochlorous acid was due to the liberation of nascent oxygen. Now, although hydrogen peroxide is a strong oxidising agent, it does not seem capable of producing substantially non-felting wool. However, this oxidising agent is able to make a contribution to the non-felting finish, for goods bleached with peroxide are more easily treated than unbleached wool. Ozonised air produces little non-felting action until 20% of the scales have been destroyed, but complete unshrinkability was not obtained in spite of great discoloration; persulphates also produce some effect when used in concentrations exceeding 1 g. per litre, but again with structural damage and discoloration. In the *Manual of Dyeing*, Knecht, Rawson, and Lowenthal state that permanganate is capable of producing non-felting wool, but here again there is discoloration and some tendering of the wool.

Sodium chlorite has been used for reducing the milling shrinkage of wool, according to Mason and Thompson of the I.C.I. (B.P. 561,475); the wool is first treated in an aqueous solution of sodium chlorite and then with HCl at 90° to 95°C. The goods are finally bleached with a sulphite compound.

Speakman's views with regard to the breakdown of the disulphide bond with various agents were taken a stage further on the occasion of the Mather lecture (J.T.I., 1941, *32*, 83) and the possibility of all chemical treatments which produce non-felting wool doing so in virtue of disulphide bond breakdown was outlined. These theories have received strong confirmation by the recent work on alkali treatments, discussed on page 231, but the evidence from reducing agents, alone or in conjunction with enzyme preparations, is also interesting.

REDUCING AGENTS

REDUCING AGENTS are capable of producing non-felting wool in certain circumstances, but, in general, it is more difficult to obtain good results than with oxidising agents.

Jones, in B.P. 501,292, has described the treatment of wool with hot aqueous solutions of alkaline sulphites to which ammonia or ammonium carbonate may be added; sodium chloride may also be added to increase the effect.

The wool may be treated with normal sulphites of sodium or potassium, but at the higher temperatures of 90° to 100°C. they produce greater discoloration than ammonium sulphite; in some cases, particularly where dyes have to be considered, it may be desirable to work at 70° to 90°C. The concentration of the solution may vary according to requirements, but in general, it ranges between 0·05 and 2% ammonium sulphite.

One advantage of this treatment is that it may be effected at the same time as the dyeing process.

The general method may be seen from actual examples; for the treatment of 100 lb. of wool, a bath of 300 gallons of boiling water should be prepared containing 3 lb. of sodium sulphite and 19 oz. of ammonium chloride. Another example replaces the ammonium chloride with 24 oz. of ammonium sulphate, whilst a third bath contains 2 lb. 1·25 oz. of a mixture of 104 parts of sodium hydrogen sulphite, 17 parts of ammonia, and 53 parts of ammonium chloride. In all cases the bath should be adjusted to pH 8 by the addition of ammonia or ammonium carbonate; the time of treatment should be 30 minutes.

The use of stronger reducing agents has been suggested in B.P. 541,965 by Crowder and Marsh of the Tootal Broadhurst Lee Co., and care must be taken to avoid over-treatment with fibre damage. Substances such as sodium hydrosulphite, stannous chloride, and titanous chloride are mentioned.

The use of stannous chloride in 10% aqueous solution, acidified with hydrochloric acid, gives non-felting results when the wool is treated in 15 times its weight of the solution, either for 3 hours at 70°C. or for 16 hours at 18°C.; the wool is well washed after treatment. Stannous chloride may also be used in non-aqueous media; for example, wool was treated for 30 minutes in a boiling solution of 10% stannous chloride in butyl alcohol, the excess liquor was removed and the goods washed. In another example, wool was treated with a solution of 10 g. of stannous chloride in 40 c.c. of butyl alcohol and 60 c.c. of white spirit, after which it was removed and washed after removing excess of the reagent.

In general, where these strong reducing agents are used it is preferred to employ acid conditions for the most pronounced effect, whether the aqueous or non-aqueous method is utilised; bleached woollen goods are more susceptible to treatment than the unbleached material, and this applies, of course, to most non-felting treatments.

It is possible to activate the wool by reducing agents, or by oxidising agents, before the chlorination process. In B.P. 570,582 by Raynes and Stevenson it is stated that the wool may be treated with an aqueous solution of a stannous compound followed by chlorination in a solution of an alkaline earth hypochlorite. B.P. 569,730 refers to a preliminary treatment with permanganate, before the chlorination. The modern method appears to be that described in U.S.P. 2,429,082, where wool is treated with potassium permanganate and sodium hypochlorite together in alkaline solutions; the simultaneous use of these compounds gives a uniform effect with less yellowing than is obtained by the conventional methods.

Although FORMALDEHYDE is a strong reducing agent, this ubiquitous compound does not exert its reducing properties on wool, but combines with the amino-groups present to impart some resistance to alkali. Trotman (J.S.C.I., 1922, *41*, 219; 1931, *50*, 463) and Trotman and Brown (J.S.D.C., 1928, *44*, 49) have examined the behaviour of formaldehyde-treated wool which may contain up to 0·6% of combined formaldehyde, and exhibits some resistance to shrinkage and felting; the effect is not permanent. The initial effect is pronounced for wool stockings soaked in 1% formaldehyde solution for 1 hour at 60°C. showed no shrinkage on boiling in soap and water for 30 minutes, but in the next 30 minutes there was a diminution of 1·5 inches in length. The formaldehyde treatment may be valuable in obviating the shrinkage which occurs in ordinary scouring or dyeing.

It is possible that shrinkage on further washing is due to hydrolysis of the condensation product of formaldehyde and wool, for although the formaldehyde-treated wool resists cold alkali, it is hydrolysed by solutions containing more than 0·7 to 0·8% NaOH.

The addition of formaldehyde to the chlorination bath has been patented (see page 205), but it seems to exert no protective action, and only reduces the amount of active chlorine present. Previous treatment with formaldehyde, however, has a slight advantage over the ordinary chlorination process, for although the number of damaged fibres is not diminished, the alkali-solubility of the product is improved; further, during the chlorination process, the loss in weight in solutions containing 0·7 g. of chlorine per litre was 5·4% with ordinary wool, but only 2·6% with formaldehyde-treated wool.

ENZYMES

BIOCHEMICAL METHODS are capable of producing non-felting wool by utilising proteolytic enzymes; indeed, it has been known for some time among felt hat manufacturers that noils from sweated wools have poor felting properties. This sweating process loosens the root ends of the wool by the action of proteolytic enzymes on the epidermis; these enzymes also attack the surfaces of the wool fibres. Proteolytic enzymes have also been used to disintegrate wool into its component cells, in a manner analogous to the retting of flax.

Trotman (Bleaching, Dyeing and Chemical Technology of Textile Fibres, Griffin, London, 1925, p. 196) has stated that the effect on the surface of wool produced by proteolytic enzymes is similar to that of hypochlorous acid and chlorine in that there is visible degradation of the edges of the scales. Craven, in B.P. 290,805 (see also page 236), suggested that wool should be bated with pancreatic enzymes before treatment with basic aluminium or chromium salts for non-felting results.

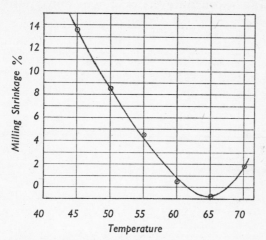

FIG. 113.—Influence of temperature on destruction of felting powers of wool when treated with papain at pH 7·4 (30 minutes).

In general, wool is fairly resistant to the action of enzymes, and this may be due to the bridging of the polypeptide chains by disulphide bonds, for it has been shown by Michaelis and Goddard (J. Biol. Chem., 1934, *106*, 605) that when the disulphide bonds were broken by reducing agents, then the polypeptides were rapidly hydrolysed by trypsin into their constituent amino-acids. The problem of producing non-felting wool by enzymes is therefore a double problem; first, the effect of reducing agents to open the wool structure, and, secondly, the proteolytic action of the various enzymes.

Middlebrook and Phillips (J.S.D.C., 1941, *57*, 137) have given an interesting account of their work which led to a detailed examination of the effect of papain and sodium bisulphite. Papain is the dried juice of the papaya-tree, which is grown in Ceylon, British East Africa, and the British West Indies; it was found to have an intense action on wool in presence of sodium bisulphite. The reduced form of papain was found to attack wool more rapidly than the oxidised form, and it has been suggested that the action of reduced papain on reduced wool is specific. Other reducing agents, such as hydrogen cyanide, sodium hydrosulphite, sodium thiosulphite, and hydrogen sulphide, have also been used to activate papain, but none of these was found to equal sodium bisulphite as an accelerator of the reaction between papain and wool.

Now the rate of reaction increases with the concentration of sodium bisulphite, but 1% of bisulphite permits of a convenient speed.

Papain does not penetrate the wool fibre, but is adsorbed on the

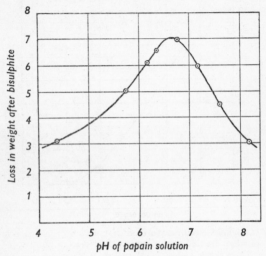

Fig. 114.—Effect of pH on absorption of papain by wool.

surface from colloidal solution; the maximum adsorption was found to occur at pH 6 to 7. With bisulphite-enzyme solutions the rate of attack diminishes on either side of the range pH 6 to 7, but within the range of pH 6 to 8, the unbuffered solutions do not alter appreciably within a period of 30 minutes, possibly on account of the inhibiting action of the degradation products of wool on the atmospheric oxidation of the bisulphite. Both carbonised and bleached wools are more readily attacked by papain than is the case with untreated wool.

Experiments on the extent of non-felting produced showed that when knitted wool was placed in solutions of 1% sodium bisulphite containing various amounts of papain for 30 minutes at 65°C., concentrations of 0·01% papain brought about a considerable reduction in felting, but the full effect was not realised until the concentration of papain reached 0·02%. It will be noted that papain is rather exceptional among enzymes in that the temperature for its action is high, the optimum being reached at 65° to 75°C., according to Willstater (Zeit. f. Physiol. Chem., 1924, *138*, 184). Investigation of the action of a solution of 1% bisulphite and 0·05% papain on the weight of the liquor showed the highest activity at 65°C.

Treatment with 1% bisulphite and 0·025% papain for 30 minutes at 55°C. brought about a loss in tensile strength amounting to about 7%, whereas a treatment at 50°C. for 60 minutes caused 11% reduction in strength; sodium bisulphite alone, however, causes a similar decrease in strength.

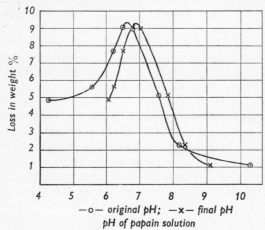

—o— original pH; —x— final pH
pH of papain solution

FIG. 115.—Effect of pH on loss of weight of wool when treated with papain at 65°C.

An interesting additional effect of the treatment is the bleaching produced at the same time as the non-felting result. Whereas sodium bisulphite solution of pH 4 to 7 is capable of bleaching wool, the effect is not permanent and may be reversed by washing in soap, but when papain is added to the bisulphite solution, not only is there a better bleaching action, but the effect shows a very high degree of permanence to washing and resembles hydrogen peroxide in this respect.

The activity of the solution may be further increased by the addition of urea or cysteine, either added as such, or in the form of cystine.

The enzyme process under consideration has been protected in B.P. 513,919 by Phillips and Middlebrook of the Wool Industries Research Association.

The working details of the invention may be seen by an examination of the examples. One hundred parts of loose wool may be treated for 10 minutes at 65°C. in a solution of pH 6·7, obtained by dissolving

1·25 parts of papain in 5,000 parts of water with the addition of 50 parts of sodium bisulphite and 30 parts of anhydrous sodium carbonate. After removal from the solution, the wool is rinsed in running water, hydroextracted, and dried. Wool fabric may be treated by immersing 100 parts of the scoured material in a solution of 0·325 parts of papain in 1,250 parts of water with the addition of 12·5 parts of sodium bisulphite and 2·1 parts of sodium hydroxide; the pH of the solution is 6·7 and the wool is treated for 45 minutes at 65°C., followed by washing and drying.

Although the use of papain is generally preferred, it is also possible to use trypsin in presence of sodium sulphide for a long time relative to that necessary for papain. Thus, 100 parts of wool may be treated for 3 hours at 37°C. in a solution of 2·5 parts of trypsin in 250 parts of water, with the addition of 0·4 parts of sodium sulphide and 0·12 parts of ammonium chloride, followed by washing and drying.

It is generally found that unless the wool loses about 1 to 3% of its weight during the treatment, its felting properties are not entirely destroyed, so that conditions must be chosen in which 1 to 3% of the wool passes into solution. (This is the Perzyme process.)

It is well known that fine wools felt much more readily than the coarse wools, but at the same time they are much more readily damaged by papain; it appears, therefore, that the papain treatment is more suited to the coarser varieties. On the other hand, the process appears to offer considerable scope in the treatment of mixed goods, for papain is without action on the fibres of native or regenerated cellulose which are very susceptible to damage by chlorine. A further interesting point is that fabrics composed of wool and silk in the gum may be degummed and rendered non-felting in one operation, for although bisulphite-papain solutions attack silk gum, they do not affect the silk fibre itself.

An interesting effect may be obtained when wool which has been chlorinated is subsequently treated with papain; a silk-like material is produced which has an attractive handle. This method is stated "to take the tickle out of wool." (This is the Chlorzyme process.)

TREATMENT IN NON-AQUEOUS LIQUIDS

It is well known that water exerts a considerable swelling action on wool, and in this manner substances of small molecular weight may be carried to the inside of the fibre. It has been realised that one of the difficulties of treating wool with aqueous solutions of hypochlorites is to limit the reaction to the surface, for the interior of the wool hair is more susceptible to chemical attack than the scales. Further, as the scale structure plays a large part in the felting phenomenon, it would also appear reasonable to limit the reaction to that structure, if possible without damage. One method of avoiding a highly swollen structure with its attendant liability to chemical attack is to treat the wool with gaseous reagents, as described on page 212.

More recently, however, considerable attention has been devoted to the use of non-aqueous (and non-swelling) liquors which do not necessitate the somewhat complicated methods associated with the use of gases. Some interesting work by Speakman (Proc. Roy. Soc., 1931, *132*, 167) in connection with the swelling of wool in various alcohols as revealed by the work necessary to extend the fibre, showed that above propyl alcohol, in the series of alcohols, there was no swelling, and hence no penetration into the wool substance. It is interesting to see that certain non-penetrating liquids have been used as solvents for reagents which would otherwise damage the wool severely; not only have hypochlorites been utilised, but also substances such as sulphuryl chloride and even caustic alkali, whose action on wool is generally regarded as very harmful and drastic.

The use of chlorine (or bromine) in an inert solvent has been suggested in B.P. 556,872 by E. R. Trotman of Wolsey Ltd. The wool is conditioned to contain 13% of moisture, and then immersed in a solution of chlorine in an organic liquid with which the chlorine does not react. For example, chlorine may be passed into 1,000 c.c. of carbon tetrachloride until 0·125 lb. of the gas has been absorbed; this solution is added to 5 gallons of white spirit to make a liquor in which 5 lb. of wool may be immersed for 1 hour. The solution generally contains from 1 to 3% of chlorine estimated on the weight of the wool. After the requisite length of time, the wool is withdrawn and drained or centrifuged, and washed in a solution of a sulphated fatty alcohol and sodium carbonate. (See also page 197.)

ORGANIC HYPOCHLORITES

Two of the earliest methods of treating wool with non-felting reagents in inert solvents have been described in U.S.P. 2,132,342 and 2,132,345. The first of these documents was filed in November 1929 and the other in March 1930, but neither of them was published until October 1938.

U.S.P. 2,132,345 describes the treatment of wool with organic hypochlorites of which tertiary butyl hypochlorite and tertiary amyl hypochlorite are preferred. The speed of the chlorination may be controlled by adjusting the moisture in the wool before treatment, and, if necessary, the material may be first impregnated with an acid buffer as, for example, sodium acetate.

In the examples, it is suggested that the material may be immersed in butyl hypochlorite or amyl hypochlorite for about 2 hours. Such processes, of course, are very expensive and attempts have been made to economise by using a mixture of 50% butyl hypochlorite and 50% carbon tetrachloride at 40°C. for 30 minutes, or a solution of 6% of butyl hypochlorite in carbon tetrachloride at 46°C. for 90 minutes.

U.S.P. 2,132,342 points out that the tertiary butyl hypochlorite treatment is not easily controlled, the reaction requires a long time and excessive quantities of reagent; a better method is to treat wool with a mixture of organic hypochlorite and certain alcohols. Tertiary butyl hypochlorite and methyl alcohol are stated to be satisfactory, but in order to obtain a better control it is preferable to incorporate this mixture in an inert solvent such as carbon tetrachloride. The chlorinating agent in the reaction of butyl hypochlorite and methyl alcohol with wool is of a different character from that which operates with butyl hypochlorite alone; when tertiary butyl hypochlorite is mixed with methyl alcohol a violent reaction takes place after a short time and the rate of the chlorination reaction with butyl hypochlorite and methyl alcohol is much more rapid than with butyl hypochlorite alone. It is very probable that the actual chlorinating agent is methyl hypochlorite.

The process may be illustrated by an example in which 15 g. of wool of normal moisture content are immersed in a solution of 10 c.c. of tertiary butyl hypochlorite and 8 c.c. of methyl alcohol in 300 c.c. of carbon tetrachloride; the wool should be placed in the bath within a few minutes of its being prepared. The time of reaction may be varied to regulate the amount of chlorine which it is desired to use; at 23° to 26°C. wool will absorb from the above solution 0·5% of chlorine in 11 minutes or 2% in 35 minutes. The amount of chlorine absorbed by the wool may also be controlled by varying the amounts of butyl hypochlorite, methyl alcohol, and carbon tetrachloride. It appears that the reaction must be controlled within certain limits, for when wool with the normal moisture content is chlorinated to fixed percentages of chlorine on the wool in excess of 4%, the wool is damaged.

According to this process, where the reaction is partly controlled by the use of an inert diluent, the absorption of 0·5% of chlorine by the wool is sufficient to render the material unshrinkable under ordinary washing conditions.

In view of other processes which will be described later, it is interesting to note that the use of other alcohols, such as ethyl alcohol, is less satisfactory.

One of the interesting features of this specification is that the presence of a small amount of water is not detrimental; but any substantial quantity of water will cause damage, so that it is preferred to employ anhydrous reagents and condition the wool.

SULPHURYL CHLORIDE

One of the most important advances in the production of non-felting wool has been outlined in B.P. 464,503, 474,846, 480,775, and 483,707. This series of patents protects the Dri-Sol process, which has been described in detail by Hall (J.S.D.C., 1939, 55, 389).

Briefly, the process consists in treating wool with a solution of sulphuryl chloride (SO_2Cl_2) in white spirit, as a result of which the wool loses its felting properties without suffering appreciable damage. The change in properties occurs during the immersion in the sulphuryl chloride solution and not during the subsequent washing with water; this is demonstrated by washing out the sulphuryl chloride with an excess of the organic solvent instead of water. Further, if the change took place in presence of water during washing, then sulphuric and hydrochloric acids would be formed, but numerous experiments have shown that it is not possible to reduce the felting properties of wool by treatment with an aqueous solution of the hydrolysis products of sulphuryl chloride.

In addition to the important point of a non-felting wool substantially free from damage, the results of the process were shown to be much more even than in the case of wet chlorination. With the latter process, the rapid action of chlorine on the wool makes it almost impossible to ensure that the innermost fibres of a yarn, particularly a tightly twisted yarn, receive the same treatment as the outside fibres; the sulphuryl chloride solution in white spirit wets the wool immediately so that the fibrous mass is evenly affected and all the fibres receive the same treatment even when the wool is greasy.

Another disadvantage of wet chlorination is that the water penetrates the individual fibres with which it comes into contact and swells them, thus carrying the chlorine into the cortex which is very susceptible to chemical attack. The molecule of white spirit, however, is believed to be too large to penetrate into the inside of the wool fibre, so that the action of the sulphuryl chloride will be almost entirely limited to the surface and the cortex will escape attack. Speakman (J.T.I., 1933, 24, 167P) has shown that molecules larger than those of n-propyl alcohol cannot penetrate into the dry wool substance.

Although sulphuryl chloride dissolves without reaction in carbon tetrachloride, trichlorethylene and tetrachlorethane, the choice of solvent is largely decided by economic considerations, and two brands of white spirit or petroleum distillates were found very satisfactory; one product distilled at 200° to 252°C. and had a density of 0·778, whereas the second boiled at 160° to 265°C. and had a density of 0·817. The low degree of inflammability enables white spirit to be used with little risk of fire.

There are several factors which influence the degree of non-felting which may be produced by treatment with SO_2Cl_2 in white spirit, the most important being the concentration of SO_2Cl_2, the liquor to cloth ratio, the time and temperature of treatment, and the original moisture content of the wool. The usual method of procedure is to steep air-dry wool in a 2 to 2·25% solution by volume of sulphuryl chloride in white spirit, initially at 15°C., for an hour; the liquor to wool ratio may vary from 7 : 1 for knitted fabric to 16 : 1 for loose wool. The temperature may rise to 26°C. or thereabouts, but the rise in temperature will be less as the ratio of liquor to wool is increased.

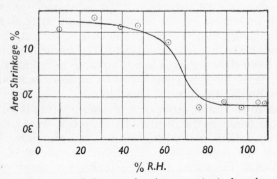

FIG. 116.—Influence of moisture content of wool on treatment with sulphuryl chloride.

At the end of the steeping period, the liquor is run off, and the wool centrifuged until it contains not more than 1·5 to 2 gallons of residual liquor per 100 lb. of air-dry wool. The wool is then thoroughly washed with warm water which may, with advantage, contain a little of a modern detergent, such as Lissapol, Igepon, or Gardinol; if the wool is to be bleached with hydrogen peroxide subsequently, it must be neutralised with ammonia or dilute sodium carbonate solution. The spent liquors may be collected, cooled to 15°C., and brought up to strength again by the addition of the necessary amount of SO_2Cl_2; generally, the initial concentration of SO_2Cl_2 is reduced about 50% during the treatment. The chemical losses for 100 lb. of air-dry wool are about 8 lb. of SO_2Cl_2 and 2 gallons of white spirit. The liquor may be used almost indefinitely, and any moisture which accumulates in the spent liquor may be allowed to settle and can be withdrawn periodically.

The sulphuryl chloride solution in white spirit has a corrosive action on all metals, and therefore it is necessary that the plant should be constructed of resistant material, such as ebonite, vulcanite covered material, hard rubber, stoneware, or synthetic resins.

For full control of the process it is advisable to condition the wool beforehand, and this may be accomplished by exposure to an atmosphere of 24°C. and 65% R.H. for 24 hours. It is interesting to note that below about 50% R.H., the up-take of moisture is such that the sulphuryl chloride has practically no action in reducing the felting properties of wool.

As a result of the sulphuryl chloride treatment, there is an improvement in the breaking load of the wool hair, and also an increased extension at break; the softness and colour are only very slightly affected and the former may be corrected by treatment with a suitable agent, such as Soromine O, Sapamine KW, or soluble oils. In this connection, the I.C.I. in B.P. 540,613, suggest the addition of suitable softeners such as octadecyl isocyanate, to the sulphuryl chloride liquor.

The sulphuryl chloride treatment may be followed by bleaching with sulphur dioxide or hydrogen peroxide in the usual manner.

Comparisons of the sulphuryl chloride and wet chlorination treatments by Hall (J.S.D.C., 1939, 55, 389) have given some very interesting data. With wet chlorination, the exhaustion of the bath is greater as the initial concentration of the chlorine is less, but the reverse holds with sulphuryl chloride. Wet-chlorinated wool suffers a decrease in sulphur content and is partially soluble in $0 \cdot 1$ N.NaOH solution, but the product of the sulphuryl chloride treatment loses no sulphur and is much less soluble in alkali. Chlorinated wool is apt to lose its epithelial scales, particularly in subsequent washing, but wool treated with sulphuryl chloride retains its scales intact although some may be slightly damaged. Hence the latter product is much more durable than chlorinated wool.

Generally, wool which has been made non-felting has an increased affinity for acid dyes, but the sulphuryl chloride treatment gives an even-dyeing product compared with chlorinated wool; in cold dyeing, chlorinated wool dyes more deeply than untreated wool or the product from the SO_2Cl_2 treatment, but the distinction is less obvious with hot dyeing.

Hall has tried a variety of substances in organic solvents, but none was so effective as sulphuryl chloride. Chromyl chloride CrO_2Cl_2, for instance, may be used in carbon tetrachloride. As an alternative to the use of white spirit, it is possible to use sulphuryl chloride vapour or a mixture of sulphur dioxide and chlorine.

From the practical standpoint, the older wet chlorination processes were forced to strike a compromise between non-felting and impoverishment of the wool, and so were limited to a product of reduced tendency to felt; the sulphuryl chloride process, on the other hand, gives a non-felting wool without sacrifice of quality.

Another non-aqueous process which may be mentioned has been described in U.S.P. 2,213,399, where NITROSYL CHLORIDE, NOCl, is utilised, either as a gas or dissolved in a solvent. Conditioned wool is immersed for an hour in 2% solution of nitrosyl chloride in a suitable solvent, washed with the solvent, dried, and then washed with water, neutralised, rinsed, and finally dried. Nitrosyl chloride is an obnoxious substance, and it may be difficult to avoid coloration of the wool.

Returning to the consideration of sulphuryl chloride, this substance has been utilised by Speakman, Nilssen, and Elliott (Nature, 1938, *142*, 1035) to explore the actual chemical mechanism by which wool is made non-felting. It will be remembered that the modern view of the structure of wool includes long polypeptide chains bound together by side-chains which form cross-linkages; in addition to the salt linkages, the cystine link, $R\text{---}CH_2\text{---}S\text{---}S\text{---}CH_2\text{---}R$, plays a most important role in the behaviour of wool. A somewhat analogous substance, dibenzyl disulphide, was treated with sulphuryl chloride in white spirit at 37°C. to form dibenzyl disulphoxide and finally benzyl chloride and benzyl sulphonyl chloride.

$$C_6H_5.CH_2.S.S.CH_2.C_6H_5 \longrightarrow C_6H_5.CH_2.S.SO_2.CH_2.C_6H_5$$
$$\longrightarrow C_6H_5.CH_2.Cl + C_6H_5.CH_2.SO_2.Cl.$$

These compounds were isolated and identified as the main reaction products, so it is evident that the disulphide linkage is permanently broken. Speakman and his co-workers suggest that very similar changes occur in wool, and that the property of non-felting is due to this cleavage of the disulphide bond. If this theory is correct, then non-felting wool may be produced by permanent breakdown of the disulphide bond, but the most satisfactory method will be to limit the reaction to the outer layers of the fibres by using the reagent in organic solution, as shown by Hall.

In support of this theory, Speakman has shown that non-felting wool may be produced by treating wool with various substances which are known to bring about permanent breakdown of the disulphide bond, and so form a gelatinous degradation product of keratin, on or under the scale structure of the fibres; chlorine peroxide, potassium permanganate, manganese heptoxide, and Caro's acid under correct conditions are capable of rendering wool unshrinkable. The permanganate was applied from acetone solution; an old specification, namely, B.P. 5612 of 1907 by Kammerer, utilised 10% aqueous permanganate acidified with sulphuric acid. Returning to Speakman's work with sulphuryl chloride and dibenzyl disulphide (J.C.S., 1940, p. 641), it is interesting to note that thionyl chloride, which is not suitable for making wool unshrinkable, has no significant action on dibenzyl disulphide.

PLATE **XVII**

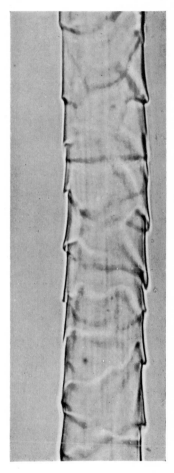

FIG. 117.

FIG. 118.

Scoured Wool.

Courtesy of Mr. J. Manby, F.R.P.S.

PLATE XVIII

FIG. 119.   FIG. 120.

Chlorinated Wool.

Courtesy of Mr. J. Manby, F.R.P.S.

PLATE XIX

 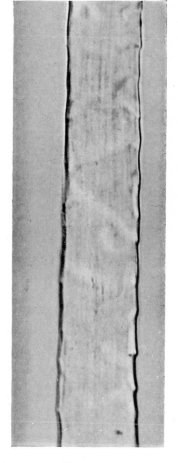

FIG. 121.   FIG. 122.

Over-chlorinated Wool.

Courtesy of Mr. J. Manby, F.R.P.S.

PLATE XX

 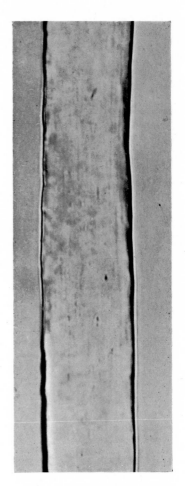

FIG. 123.   FIG. 124.

Heavily Over-chlorinated Wool.

Courtesy of Mr. J. Manby, F.R.P.S.

ALKALI

The action of alkali on wool has long been known to be deleterious; ammonia, borax, sodium carbonate, and sodium hydroxide in dilute solutions need extreme care if their harmful action is to be avoided in the ordinary treatment of wool. Whereas dilute sodium hydroxide rapidly destroys wool, more concentrated solutions do not have this effect; NaOH solutions of 34 to 46·5% (75° to 100°Tw.) have been shown by Kertesz (Farber Zeit., 1896, 9, 35) and also by Buntrock (ibid., 1898, 11, 69) actually to strengthen the wool instead of destroying it. Naturally it is necessary to wash the wool quickly with dilute acid and water to pass through the dangerous concentrations as rapidly as possible. During the treatment with alkali, the temperature must not exceed 20°C. or great loss of strength occurs.

Schneider, in B.P. 6152 of 1907, suggests the use of sodium hydroxide solutions of 1° to 32°Tw. at 5° to 10°C. for an hour to increase the affinity of wool for dyestuffs, but it is in this region of concentrations that other investigators have found the most severe effects.

Schneider also noted in B.P. 11,834 of 1908, that as the affinity for dyes increased, the resistance to felting in subsequent washing was also increased, and he stated that wool treated in this manner compared favourably with wool treated with gaseous chlorine; Schneider did not use solutions of greater concentration than 64°Tw. (38%).

The action of strong alkali on wool has been investigated more recently by Freney and Lipson (Council for Scientific and Industrial Research, Australia, Pamphlet 94, 1940), who established that wool does not disintegrate when immersed for 30 minutes in solutions of 52 g. of NaOH per 100 c.c., but in 40 g. of NaOH per 100 c.c., the wool is attacked in 10 minutes. The chief difficulty is to remove the alkali from the wool without damage; the best method seems to be to squeeze out the excess of alkali and then plunge the wool into a large excess of aqueous dilute sulphuric acid solution.

In the experiments of Freney and Lipson, wool was treated with concentrated alkali by immersing small hanks of yarn in 10 parts of the alkaline solution for the specified time, followed by washing with running water, acidifying and rinsing. The yarn was then knitted and the fabrics washed to estimate the shrinkage.

TREATMENT IN AQUEOUS NaOH FOR 10 MINUTES

Concentration	Temperature	Milling shrinkage
52%	Room	Slight
40%	—	Moderate
58%	—	Marked
58%	45°C.	None

A high temperature or moderate concentration of alkali tend to produce non-felting wools, but these conditions also cause damage, for the yarn treated at 45°C. with 58% NaOH was unattractive in appearance and inferior in handle. Similar non-felting results were obtained with solutions of potassium hydroxide, but not ammonia.

According to Matthews (Textile Fibers, Wiley, New York, 1924, p. 157) lime-water is capable of producing non-felting wool, but the quality of the material is adversely affected and there is a loss of sulphur; baryta gives similar results.

Alkali and alcohol

Freney and Lipson (loc. cit.) examined the effect of ALKALI IN ALCOHOL and found that wool was not damaged by treatment with 0·05% NaOH or KOH in alcohol for 24 hours or with 5% NaOH or 7% KOH for 5 minutes; nitrogen and sulphur contents were unchanged, and no sign of damage could be detected under the microscope. Little shrinkage was found with wool treated in 1 or 2% NaOH in ethyl alcohol.

With more concentrated solutions of alkali, such as 5% NaOH or 7% KOH, in methylated spirits, better results were obtained; for example, with a caustic potash treatment for 1 to 2 minutes, followed by neutralisation in alcoholic sulphuric acid (5% by volume), as immersion in aqueous acid was not reliable. Air-dry wool containing 12% moisture was found to be a satisfactory starting product in respect of moisture content, but Freney and Lipson considered that moisture-free alcoholic liquors were unsatisfactory for non-felting effects.

For semi-industrial trials, 14 lb. of commercial KOH were dissolved in 1 gallon of water and diluted with 19 gallons of methylated spirits containing 2 lb. of glycerin, the object of which was to avoid the dark reddish-brown coloration which appears in its absence. Through this solution, 8 lb. of dry wool tops (14·5% regain) were run and the time of treatment arranged to give 75 seconds immersion, after which the wool was squeezed and passed into a second bath containing 1 gallon of commercial sulphuric acid (18 lb.) diluted with 19 gallons (133 lb.) of methylated spirits. A third bath consisted of continuously flowing fresh water. The consumption of reagents for 24 lb. of wool was 3·2 gallons of alkali solution, or 1·6 lb. of KOH, 3 gallons of methylated spirits, 0·3 lb. glycerin, and 1·25 lb. of H_2SO_4.

In a continuous treatment the temperature should be controlled to 25°C. ±2°C.; the strength of KOH should be 4 to 6%, and the time of treatment 1·5 to 2·5 minutes. The water content of the reagent may be 2 to 6%.

If a steeping technique is adopted, however, the tolerances for a period of 3 minutes immersion are 0·5 to 1·25% for the concentration of KOH, and 0 to 7% for the water in the reagent.

B.P. 538,428 of Hall and Wood of the Tootal Broadhurst Lee Co. describes a process for treating wool with an alkaline substance in an organic liquid containing little or no water. In an example, NaOH is dissolved in butyl alcohol to give 0·6 g. per 100 c.c.; wool previously conditioned over saturated brine was immersed for 60 minutes in this alkaline solution at 20°C., centrifuged and plunged into acidulated water, followed by rinsing and drying. Untreated knitted wool, when washed in soap and water, showed a shrinkage of 34% in area, but the treated material only diminished 7% in area.

Various organic media are suggested in the specification, but particular attention is drawn to the aliphatic alcohols which contain 3 to 8 carbon atoms; all kinds of alkali substances appear to be mentioned: metallic lithium, ethylene diamine, benzyl trimethyl ammonium hydroxide, and diphenyl iodonium hydroxide.

It is believed that the alkaline treatment produces a temporary swelling or partial gelatinisation of the surface of the wool fibres so that they acquire reduced tendency to felt; any such swelling or gelatinisation of the interior of the fibres would adversely affect the wool quality, so the reaction is limited to the surface by the use of suitable solvents which do not penetrate wool.

Solutions of SULPHIDES of alkali metals in organic solvents have been suggested in B.P. 539,057 by Parker, Farrington, and Stubbs of the Bleachers' Association, and Speakman. A suitable non-felting treatment is to immerse air-dry wool in 0·5 parts of potassium sulphide dissolved in 100 parts of isopropyl alcohol at 22°C. for 1 hour.

Alkali-alcohol-paraffin

A most interesting process has been described by Hall and Wood in B.P. 538,396, the basic idea of which seems to be the use of alkali dissolved in a mixture of organic liquids, one of which is a solvent for the alkali, the other being a poor solvent or non-solvent. A typical mixture is SODIUM HYDROXIDE, BUTYL ALCOHOL, WHITE SPIRIT.

The advantages of this ternary mixture may be seen from the examples. For instance, wool treated with 0·64% NaOH in butyl alcohol gave an area shrinkage of 7% when milled, but the parallel case of treatment with 0·64% NaOH in 1 volume of butyl alcohol and 9 volumes of white spirit showed an area shrinkage of only 0·8%; untreated wool showed 34% shrinkage in area when milled under the same conditions. It is believed that the presence of the diluent or non-solvent is beneficial because it tends to force the alkali on to the wool.

Corresponding results for alkali in glycol monoethyl ether with and without white spirit, show 25% area shrinkage from the binary mixture and 1·6% from the ternary mixture. The differences between ethyl alcohol and ethyl alcohol with white spirit are not so great. From the standpoint of penetration into the wool substance and possible damage, it would appear that the butyl alcohol and white spirit mixture is to be preferred.

An important practical feature of this process is that the diluent or non-solvent forms the major part of the liquor with which the wool is treated.

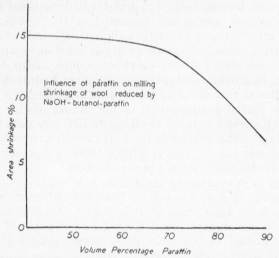

FIG. 129.—Influence of paraffin on the action of NaOH and butanol in their effect on the milling shrinkage of wool.

Now adequate control of the results is possible because the conditions of treatment may be varied quite widely. This control may be exercised through (a) the composition of the reagent in respect of alkali content and the amount of solvent and non-solvent, (b) duration of treatment, (c) temperature, (d) alkali concentration, (e) ratio of liquor to cloth, (f) moisture content of the reagent, and (g) moisture content of the wool.

It is preferred to use reagents which contain little or no water as its effect is generally harmful to the wool, but this may be corrected to a certain extent by decreasing the time and temperature of treatment. With regard to the moisture content of the wool, the best conditions for treatment are when the wool contains 12 to 18% of water.

The action of the alkali treatment increases with rising temperature and with increasing time of treatment. Below 10°C. the action is slow, but above 60°C. the rapid action is harmful to the wool; a suitable temperature range for ordinary treatment is 15° to 20°C. A convenient time of treatment is 1 hour.

A good method for treating the conditioned wool is to prepare a solution containing 6 g. of NaOH in 100 c.c. of butyl alcohol and dilute this with 9 volumes of white spirit. After treatment of the wool in 8 parts of this liquor for 1 hour at 18°C., the excess liquor is removed and the alkali in the wool is washed out with water (or acidulated water), followed by acidification, washing, and drying.

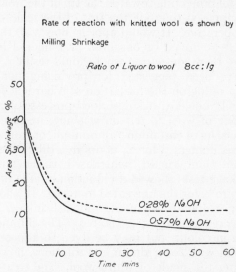

FIG. 130.—Effect of time of treatment in NaOH, butanol and paraffin on milling shrinkage of wool.

The effect of some variations of this treatment may be seen in the table.

EFFECT OF TIME AND TEMPERATURE

Time of treatment	Shrinkage on drastic washing after treatment at various temperatures					
	10°C.	15°C.	20°C.	25°C.	30°C.	35°C.
0 . . .	35%	35%	35%	35%	35%	35%
1 min . .	21	15·6	12·0	10·6	6·0	6·0
5 ,, . .	15	11·8	10·5	10·2	5·0	5·5
10 ,, . .	14	11·0	10·0	8·0	3·0	4·0
20 ,, . .	11	10·5	9·0	4·0	2·0	0·5
30 ,, . .	10	8·8	8·0	3·5	0·0	—
40 ,, . .	10	8·8	7·5	3·0	—	—
50 ,, . .	9	8·0	7·0	2·5	—	—
60 ,, . .	9	4·0	3·5	0·0	—	—

The ratio of liquor to wool was 15 : 1.

The product of this type of treatment differs from the non-felting wool produced by chlorination, in that the latter acquires a wet slimy handle when wetted in slightly alkaline aqueous liquor; on the other hand, the former becomes slightly stiffer and fuller, but this effect disappears again on drying when the original handle is restored.

SCALE COATINGS

It has already been stated that an important factor in the felting of wool is the fibre travel, which is unidirectional on account of the scales of the wool projecting towards the tip of the wool; chlorination is commonly supposed to erode the tips of the scales and so render fibre travel inoperative. It would appear, however, that if the scale projections were removed or obscured or rendered inoperative by physical causes, then non-felting wool should result.

Methods have been suggested for producing non-felting wool, apparently depending on the formation of a hardened surface.

Craven, in B.P. 290,805, has described processes for reducing the natural tendency of wool to felt on washing; in general, he makes use of the basic salts of chromium, aluminium, or iron. For example, wool flannel was immersed for 24 hours in a dilute basic solution of iron ammonium alum, rinsed, neutralised, rinsed and dried; comparative shrinkage tests showed a reduction in area of less than 2% compared with 10% for the untreated material. In another example, basic chromium sulphate was used, and a shrinkage figure of 12% (untreated) was reduced to 2·5% (treated). The chrome-treated wool is greyish-blue in colour, but may be dyed to almost any required shade; treatment with basic aluminium solutions, however, does not appreciably alter the shade of white wool. The treated material is less hygroscopic than the original wool and has a fuller handle and character.

Another process for inhibiting the tendency to shrink or felt, and again depending on the formation or deposition in the wool of a solid which impedes the necessary fibre movement, may be seen from B.P. 475,422 of Brown. The scoured or cleansed wool is treated with a solution containing boric acid, urea, formaldehyde, glycerol, and water; the wool is worked in the solution for 8 to 15 minutes at 12° to 20°C., dried in an oven to complete the condensation, and then lightly scoured, rinsed, and dried. The condensation product formed is probably methylene urea.

Markert, in D.R.P. 676,276, has suggested several applications of 1% cellulose acetate in acetone solution for producing non-felting effects on wool.

RESINS

The production of non-felting wool by the internal polymerisation of certain resins of the thermoplastic type has been described by

Speakman and Barr in B.P. 559,787. The fabric is wetted in water and suspended above a mixture of monomeric methyl methacrylate and water; this mixture is warmed so that the monomer is deposited on and within the wool fibres where it polymerises. A more rapid action may be brought about if the wool is previously impregnated with ammonium persulphate. The time of treatment varies with the effect desired; for example, for good non-felting with methyl methacrylate an increase in weight of about 40% is required, but with styrene 13% is adequate.

The fabric also exhibits a decreased affinity for water vapour when treated in this way, but B.P. 418,449 of British Celanese also discloses the treatment of foils, films, and other articles of organic materials with monomeric compounds which are caused to polymerise in and on the articles rendering them impervious to moisture.

Solutions of anhydrocarboxyglycine in an organic solvent at room temperatures have been employed by Baldwin, Barr, and Speakman, as outlined in B.P. 567,501 (J.S.D.C., 1946, 62, 4). The solvent is removed by drying, and the impregnated fibre is baked at 90° to 140°C. to complete the condensation.

Another interesting process for producing non-felting wool is due to Johnstone and van Loo of American Cyanamid, as outlined in B.P. 562,977 (U.S.P. 2,329,622) and described by Johnstone (Am. Dyes. Rep., 1944, 33, 301). It depends on the treatment of wool with an aqueous dispersion (5 to 15% on the weight of the wool) of an alkylated methylol melamine. This product is made by condensing melamine with formaldehyde and then alkylating with, say, methyl alcohol. After impregnation and drying, the wool is heated for a few minutes at 100° to 150°C. to condense the resin.

It is important to appreciate that urea-formaldehyde resins only give a partial reduction in shrinkage, and also that the methyl ether of dimethylol urea behaves in a similar manner. The water-soluble methylated methylol melamines, however, give good results which will withstand repeated laundering; the resin appears to be distributed through the fibre.

THE "D.F.E."

As previously stated, wool hair shows a difference in the coefficient of friction when the direction of rubbing is reversed. Monge (Ann. de Chimie, 1790, 6, 300) seems to have been the first to record this observation, and attributed it to the scale structure of the hair, where the tips of the scales all point to the tip of the hair, the scales overlapping like tiles on a roof.

This fact has been used to explain the felting powers of wool which depend on unidirectional travel, and has dominated the picture from 1790 onwards. The term Directional Frictional Effect (the D.F.E.)

was suggested by Martin (J.S.D.C., 1944, *60*, 325) who considers that the D.F.E. may be due to the surface chemical composition of the scales and not only to their structure. Various methods of measuring the scaliness of the fibres and their D.F.E. have been mentioned on page 168.

With regard to non-felting wool, the inclined-plane method has been used by Whewell, Rigelhaupt, and Selim (Nature, 1944, *154*, 772) to demonstrate that the result of certain commercial non-felting processes was to bring about a reduction in the D.F.E.

A method devised by Mercer (ibid., 1945, *155*, 573) may be used with single hairs; a single fibre, mounted on a bow, was carried forward at a definite speed while pressed against a cylindrical piece of ram's horn with the required load, the horn being mounted on a clock spring, whose deflection measures the frictional force. Non-felting processes all reduce the D.F.E. in alkaline solutions, but they do not all act in the same way. For example, wet chlorination and bromination reduced the D.F.E. to approximately zero by decreasing the anti-scale coefficient more than the with-scale coefficient, but both are reduced. The sulphuryl chloride treatment causes the anti-scale coefficient to approach the with-scale coefficient without greatly affecting the average value. Alcoholic potash behaves in a different manner by bringing about an increase in both coefficients, and the with-scale coefficient becomes almost the same as the anti-scale coefficient.

Bohm (J.S.D.C., 1945, *61*, 278) determined the D.F.E. for a uniform sheet of several hundred fibres, whose scales all point in the same direction, against a glass surface immersed in various aqueous media. Sulphuryl chloride caused a marked diminution in the D.F.E.

Lipson and Howard (J.S.D.C., 1946, *62*, 29) took the method of Mercer a stage further, measuring the D.F.E. in soap and sodium carbonate solution, but the ram's horn was also treated with the particular reagents for producing non-felting wool. With the treated horn and the untreated fibre, the anti-scale friction was reduced to 25% of the original value by sulphuryl chloride, bromine and chlorine; with alcoholic alkali, the anti-scale friction was reduced to 50% of the original value. Hence it is not necessary to treat the hairs themselves to reduce the D.F.E., and this observation supports Martin's hypothesis.

With treated hairs and untreated horn, sulphuryl chloride raised the with-scale coefficient but gave very low figures for the D.F.E. Alcoholic alkali raised the anti-scale coefficient and doubled the with-scale coefficient, but the D.F.E. was still substantial. The D.F.E. approaches zero with chlorination, the with-scale coefficients having risen.

The most important results, however, are those where both horn and fibre have been treated. All the halogen processes and sulphuryl chloride give very low D.F.E. values, and reduce with-scale and anti-scale friction to similar values. Alcoholic alkali behaves differently, for it raises the anti-scale friction by 50% and doubles the with-scale friction.

Lipson also found that when the horn was treated with sulphuryl chloride it becomes gelatinous; a similar effect appears after chlorination when the horn is treated with sodium bicarbonate solution. No such effect was observed with alcoholic alkali, whose mode of reaction seems to differ from that of the other reagents.

CHAPTER IX
ANTI-SHRINK COTTON

THE shrinkage of cotton goods on laundering has long been one of the major problems requiring attention by textile technologists. All of us, at one time or another, have been subjected to annoyance by the shrinkage of our personal clothing during laundering, collars and shirts in the case of men, undergarments and frocks with women.

Part of this shrinkage was undoubtedly due to the severe stretching of cotton goods during their manufacture, stretching which was deliberately undertaken in many cases to produce the maximum possible length and width. Even without any purposeful and drastic stretching for the profit motive, a certain amount of tension must inevitably be exerted on the cloth during the finishing operations as it passes through the various processes.

It was customary at one time to follow two main expedients for obviating the shrinkage of cotton goods: (a) to wet the goods and dry them without tension on some form of slack dryer—usually a loop drier, (b) to wash the material before making into garments. The first expedient was at the expense of the "finish" or pristine beauty of the original fabric, which was apt to be covered with little creases or "crows' feet," and appear unfinished and unmerchantable; further, only part of the potential shrinkage was removed in this way, and further shrinkage took place on washing. The second expedient also destroyed the finish and only removed part of the potential shrinkage.

In some cases it was usual to make garments on the large size, and so allow for subsequent shrinkage. The difficulty here was that the garments were first of all too large; the method was unreliable, as all cloths do not shrink evenly, so that the final fit was a matter of chance.

The shrinkage of cotton and rayon materials is essentially different from that of the animal fibres; in wool, for instance, large shrinkages are possible because the actual molecular architecture permits of considerable distortion on account of the folding and unfolding of the chain-molecules which comprise the keratin. Again, the presence of scales and crimps is responsible for a considerable diminution in area on account of fibre contraction and travel producing the phenomenon of felting.

It is often assumed that the shrinkage of cotton goods is merely a relaxation of the tension and extension inherent in the manufacture of cloth; in other words, the water acts as a molecular lubricant causing the micelles, fibres, and yarns to contract to the position of minimum strain from which they were originally stretched during spinning and weaving.

Some of the fundamentals governing the shrinkage of cotton goods have been explained by Collins (J.T.I., 1939, *30*, 46P) on the basis that shrinkage is not only due to the release of strains imposed during manufacturing processes, but to the swelling produced on wetting which brings about an internal rearrangement of the material resulting in external shortening. For example, when cotton hairs absorb water they show an extension of 1% and an increase in diameter of some 20%; the swelling is reversible. Examination of the shrinkage of stretched fibres showed that the true contraction only amounted to 2% or so, and this does not account for cloth shrinkages of the order of 10%. Further, when the stretching of cloth is considered, the fabric stretches first, then the yarn, and, finally, the fibre as the breaking-point is reached.

Now in cotton yarns the hair passes around and along the yarn, so that when the yarn diameter is increased by the swelling action of water, the fibre must either pass around or along the yarn to a less degree. If the first condition was realised, the yarn would untwist, but it is not free to do so in most cases, hence the fibre, in order to pass around the yarn as before, must shorten its path along the yarn, i.e. the yarn must shrink. With twistless yarn, there is no tendency to stretch the fibres as the yarn swells, and hence little shrinkage is encountered; but even with yarns of normal twist (not exceeding a twist-factor of 5) yarn shrinkage on wetting rarely exceeds 2%. This again does not account for the high shrinkage of fabrics.

The above remarks apply to cotton materials only, but with rayon there is the possibility of greater swelling and shrinkage effects; it is well known that many rayon fabrics exhibit considerable extension on wetting, and contraction on drying. Indeed, casement curtains with rayon warps vary in length according to the humidity of the atmosphere. With rayons, there is a corresponding behaviour in the fibres themselves, and relatively large shrinkages occur on wetting material which has been stretched in a damp condition before drying. Rayon from regenerated cellulose is much more extensible than cotton; it is composed of dispersed cellulose and absorbs more moisture; further, the chain-molecules are short and arranged more or less at random. With cotton, however, the long chain-molecules approach helical arrangement. In many instances, the shrinkage of rayon goods may be accounted for by fibre and yarn shrinkage, particularly where stretching has taken place during manufacture. Unlike cotton, rayon may exhibit up to 9 or 10% yarn shrinkage.

Apart from the question of regenerated cellulose, however, it is

16

not possible to account for the relatively large shrinkage of fabrics by the small shrinkage of the constituent fibres and yarns; the explanation of cloth shrinkage lies in the fabric structure. In this connection, an account of the geometry of cloth structure by Peirce (J.T.I., 1937, *28*, 45) is of interest.

Woven fabrics are characterised by the fact that the yarns of warp and weft bend round one another and, in general, the warp yarns bend round the weft yarns to a greater extent; the difference between the cloth length and the yarn length is accounted for by the crimp of the yarn. When the cloth is wetted, the yarns increase in diameter, and if the crossing weft threads were to remain the same distance apart, as in the dry state, then the warp would have to extend. Such extension would require force for its accomplishment, just as with the fibres in a swollen yarn, but as there is no such force, and the cloth is under no constraint, the weft threads move closer together in order that the warp yarn can remain the same length. The cloth, therefore, shrinks in the warp direction.

Alternatively, where the warp threads are straight, then the weft threads are crimped and the fabric shrinks weft-way. With one set of straight threads and one set of crimped threads, a cloth must contract one way or another on wetting.

In most fabrics the warp yarns are finer than the weft, and therefore bend more easily; secondly, they are closer together for good cover, and are less able to bend the weft threads. Hence, the stable structure is that in which the warp crimp is high and weft crimp is low. The considerable tension on the warp during the wet processing of piece goods, particularly in drawing the cloth through the various machines and about the works generally, extends the cloth lengthwise. It is well known that this stretching takes place; indeed, it is common practice for manufacturers to expect an increased yardage from the finisher and to debit him with the "missing" length if only the original yardage is delivered. The stretched structure has a low warp crimp and is therefore unstable; when washed, the cloth takes up a more stable position, being free from restraint, and so shrinks. Relatively large shrinkages of 10% may occur in cotton cloths.

(It is customary to express shrinkage of this type as *linear* shrinkage; the felting of wool, on the other hand, is often expressed as *area* shrinkage.)

As previously mentioned, some cases of shrinkage occur merely on exposure to a humid atmosphere, but greater and more rapid shrinkage takes place on wetting with water. Simple immersion in water, however, depends for its efficiency on the period of immersion and the wettability of the material, and may not be satisfactory either as a test of potential shrinkage or as a means of producing unshrinkable cloth. Hot soapy liquors are more reliable, particularly if the fabric is subjected to fairly vigorous handling during the treatment. The effect of mechanical agitation may produce an additional 2% of shrinkage over that obtained by thorough wetting alone.

Sometimes it has been found that cotton materials are not completely shrunk on the first wash, but continue to shrink in further washes. This seems to depend to some extent on the intensity of

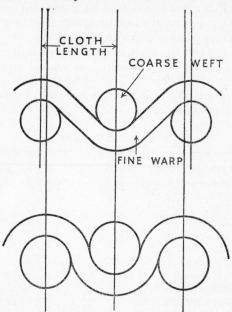

FIG. 131.—Diagram illustrating the shrinkage of woven fabric.

the washing treatment, but it may be that there are local strains due to yarn adhesion which are not capable of easy removal until the more general strains have disappeared. In general, the shrinkage attained after the first two or three washes is the maximum that is likely to occur in actual practice. A fully-shrunken cloth is in a loose state, and may easily be extended about 1% during the handling in the wet state and the subsequent ironing process. Even when dry, a fully-shrunk material is not difficult to extend; this is due to the collapse of the swollen material on drying to leave some free space in the structure. For these reasons, zero shrinkage is not generally desirable.

The major cause of fabric shrinkage, as previously stated, is due to the swelling of the threads on wetting; the thickened warp yarns require more space to enable them to pass over and under the swollen weft yarns, hence they must adopt an undulating path—the cloth shortens or shrinks.

It would appear, then, that this shortening may be produced by *mechanical* means as a final finishing operation, or, alternatively, the cotton may be given some *chemical* or *physico-chemical* treatment which will prevent either or both the swelling or contraction.

Modern anti-shrink treatments are based on these two methods, the first of which, it must be understood, is in reality a pre-shrinkage treatment—that is to say, the manufacturer has the goods mechanically shrunk before passing them on to the consumer.

It may be of interest to note the approximate amount of potential shrinkage which has to be considered in dealing with the problem of cotton goods. The following examples are taken from data supplied in a trade pamphlet issued by the Bradford Dyers' Association, and may be regarded as typical:

LAUNDRY SHRINKAGE

Cloth	Potential shrinkage
Dress Materials	4 to 7%
Nurses' uniforms . . .	6 to 8%
Overalls ⎫	
White coats ⎪	
Khaki coats ⎬	6 to 12%
Bib overalls ⎪	
Boiler suits ⎭	
White semi-stiff collars . .	6 to 8%
Poplin shirts	3 to 7%
Cellular shirts	4 to 8%
Casements (various) . . .	4 to 12%
Furnishings (various) . . .	6 to 16%

Methods of determining laundry shrinkage and some tentative textile standards have been described (J.T.I., 1941, *32*, S13). It should be noted that in the laundering of many fabrics made from cotton and rayon the full shrinkage is not always realised in the first wash; frequently, the fabric will shrink in the first three launderings, but the shrinkage becomes progressively less, and reaches stability with a ratio of final shrinkage to initial shrinkage of 1·4. This value, of course, depends on the intensity of the laundering treatment, but means that if a cloth shrinks 5% in the first wash, then it is likely to shrink 7% before reaching dimensional stability.

ADAPTED STENTERS

Early suggestions for the production of anti-shrink cotton materials during the stentering operation depend upon some form of endless chain which runs in a vertical plane; at the entering end of the stenter, the lower run of the chain describes a curved path as it moves round to the upper line of running, i.e. the top of the stenter. In the case of a chain which is fitted with pins or small spikes, these pins will be close together whilst following their horizontal course, but in moving round the curve they will separate to a greater or less extent according to the arc of curvature. The principle is simple, and may be compared for illustration with the fingers of the hand in the fully extended position compared with the fingers of the hand

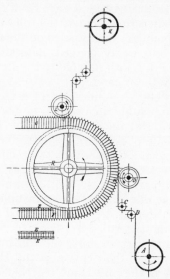

FIG. 132.—Diagram of the Payet stenter.

close together. If cloth is impaled on the fingers or pins in the extended position, and afterwards the pins or fingers come close together carrying the cloth on them, then obviously there must be a contraction of the cloth.

This idea was first put into practice by Payet, B.P. 333,182. An endless chain of pins formed each side of a stenter and moved in a vertical plane. At the entering end of the stenter, these chains moved round a circular wheel, so that any motion from the upper to lower position was described by a semicircular vertical path, during which the intervals between the pins were greater than on the horizontal course. For the maximum contractive effect, the previously moistened cloth was fed tangentially at the mid-point of the semicircle, and as the chain moved round, the pins came closer together, contracting the cloth in the warp direction. A series of ripples or small loops was thus created as the cloth proceeded up the stenter, where it was dried in the normal manner, but during the passage of the cloth the chain-rails were caused to diverge, as is usual at stenters, and the slight extension of the weft removed the ripples in the warp direction, and this produced a stable cloth which had been contracted warpway.

This stenter could be used in the ordinary way; that is, without warp contraction, by feeding the cloth on to the highest point of the stenter rail. The general principle is seen from the illustration, the pins being farthest apart at H and coming together at the point I and remaining together during the passage from I to G and onwards. For operation as a contracting stenter, the roll of wet cloth A is fed to the stenter at the point H, and impaled on the pins by the roller D (covered with some soft, easily pierced material); for operation as a normal stenter, then the cloth K is fed to the stenter at the point I, and again impaled by the roller L.

B.P. 335,861 describes a modification of a stenter which nevertheless operates fundamentally in a similar manner. The chains pass over curved guide plates at the entering end of the stenter, and the curvature of these guide plates varies progressively from maximum to zero, so that by varying the position at which the cloth is fed on to the pins as they pass over these curved plates, any predetermined contraction can be imparted to the cloth. Immediately above the curved plates, two metallic supports were installed containing holes or notches into which the brushes which pressed the cloth on to the pins could be fitted, and according to the contraction required, these brushes were fitted into various slots, and this impaled the cloth on the pins at various parts of their curved path. Here, again, the wet cloth was contracted as the pins came together on their horizontal course, and drying in this state produced a cloth which would not shrink further on subsequent laundering.

A further development may be seen in B.P. 346,782, the fabric being extended in width and permitted to recede or shrink in length during drying. Individual pins were mounted so that each was capable of angular displacement relative to its neighbour, and the pins were carried on chains or bands which were guided round a curved surface adjacent to the feed-on position of the fabric. The pins engaged the fabric at certain spaced distances, and as the chains moved from the vertical to the horizontal path, this spacing decreases in a definite ratio. The curvature was controlled in this apparatus by means of a cam rail. The pins are carried on bands which may be gripped by the clip chains of the ordinary clip stenter after the fabric has been impaled on the pins; the clip chain drives the bands and is used to produce the desired width between the selvedges of the fabric.

These modified stenters cause a positive shortening of the cloth in the direction of its length, due to the increase of crinkle in the warp threads consequent upon a partial reduction of crinkle of the weft threads; the positive contraction of the warp which is given by the feeding device is absorbed by the slight extension of the weft during the drying process, so that the cloth is delivered in a flat condition when dry.

Over-feed

The OVER-FEED system of producing unshrinkable cloth on a stenter is due to Krantz, and was described in D.R.P. 458,322 and B.P. 305,616. This is a simple modification of the pin stenter, and is still in use.

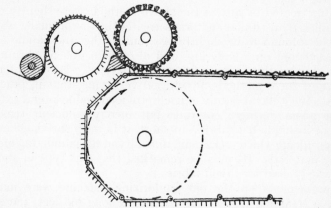

FIG. 133.—Diagram of the over-feed principle.

The wet cloth is fed on to the machine at a higher rate of speed than that of the stenter itself, so that no longitudinal tension is applied when the fabric is gripped by the machine, nor during the drying process. At the intake of the stenter the fabric is fed into the machine in the usual manner near a guide roller, but is then gripped near the edges by two feed rollers, which are driven by a train of pinions in such a way that the surface speed of these rollers exceeds that of the pin chains by a definite amount which can be varied by altering the gearing. A pressure brush forces the fabric on to the pins of the slower moving pin chain, after which the cloth passes into the drying chamber proper, and as drying proceeds and the cloth shrinks, the distance between the selvedges is diminished. It will be noted that tension is released in both directions.

The original Sanforizing process also depended on the over-feed system, and was described in the various U.S. patents, 1,734,896, 1,734,897, 1,837,408, 1,800,604, 1,950,398.

The wet fabric was fed on to the stenter slightly faster than the speed of the machine, and this produced sufficient "slack" to accommodate the shrinkage produced by the subsequent stretching of the weft. The amount of shrinkage could therefore be controlled. The relative rate of feeding and running, however, was not the only point to be considered, for it was necessary that the amount of slack between the pins should correspond to the amount of shrinkage required; this was effected by a brush roller made in two parts, one of which floated on the slack fabric and impaled it on the pins, after which the heavier brush wheel forced the fabric into full engagement with the pins. During stentering, the cloth was extended weft way as usual, and there being no warp tension, the crinkles were taken from the warp.

Cloths treated by any of the above methods were slightly thicker and fuller than similar materials treated in the ordinary way; the lustre was found to be slightly less, but neither the handle nor the lustre suffered on laundering, and also there was no shrinkage of the material within a limit of approximately 1%. It is an interesting feature of these methods of contractive drying, that in practically all cases the weft takes care of itself provided undue lateral extension is not given during stentering, but merely sufficient tension to produce a simple flat fabric—in short, it is warp shrinkage and not weft shrinkage which is the main difficulty in the laundering of woven textile materials. (It may be remarked that this type of stenter is now widely used for rayon fabrics.)

Improvements on the old Sanforizing machine were made by fitting a steaming unit at the end of the long (90 feet) pin stenter where the goods were again moistened in order that shrinkage in width could take place before passing to the Palmer machine, which dried the fabric, gave it the final shrinkage, and also imparted a lustrous effect.

COMPRESSIVE SHRINKAGE

The modern method of controlled compressive shrinkage seems to have occurred more or less simultaneously to Sanford Cluett of Cluett, Peabody and Co., and to Messrs. Wrigley and Melville of the Bradford Dyers' Association. The basic patent seems to be U.S.P. 1,861,422 of Cluett, and this possesses a very broad claim; other Sanforizing patents are U.S.P. 1,861,423, 1,861,424, 1,971,211, 1,944,001. On the other hand, the methods of Wrigley and Melville which led to the Rigmel process were protected in B.P. 371,146, 371,976, 372,803, 400,950, 402,087, 420,030. The processes are based on the same principle, but the methods of operation are different; the patent disputes which took place in certain countries ended in an agreement between the two parties, who now work harmoniously together in pursuing the modern policy of controlled compressive shrinkage.

Sanforizing

The fundamental departure from modifications or adaptations of stenters relies on the new idea of making use of a wave formation; consideration of any wave-form of an elastic material which describes a sinuous path shows that the convex surface is extended and the concave surface is contracted. If, however, cotton material is placed on the extended crest of the wave formed by the elastic material and moves with it into the contracted trough, being held in contact with the elastic material during that movement, then the cotton

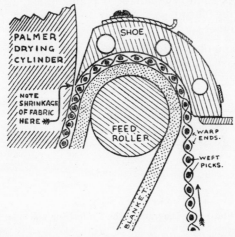

Fig. 134.—Simplified diagram of the Sanforizing method of producing shrinkage.

material will be contracted by compression. In the Sanforizing process, shrinkage is achieved by passing the cotton fabric on to a movable elastic felt blanket which is in a state of tension; when the tension on the blanket is released, it assumes a shortened condition, and the cotton fabric is forced to conform to this compression as it is held firmly in contact with the blanket by the drum of a modified Palmer machine.

When a thick blanket is curved tightly around a 2-inch shaft, the blanket expands on its outer surface. If a piece of cloth is placed on this outer surface at two points about 3 inches apart, and then the blanket and cloth removed together and stretched, it will be found that the cloth is longer than the blanket between those two points. Similarly, on the Sanforizing machine, with the exception that the cloth is confined by the surface of the Palmer machine, and as a result, instead of there being an excess of cloth when the blanket reverses its curvature, the fabric contracts in order to conform to the contracted surface of the blanket by rearrangement of the yarns due to the compressive action to which they have been subjected.

The thickness of the blanket determines the longitudinal contraction of the cloth. Generally, blankets of three thicknesses are available:

(a) 0·275 inch, which is mainly used for bleached shirting, and having a shrinkage range up to 3·5 inches per yard.
(b) A heavier blanket 0·4 inch thick, used on materials having shrinkages of 3·5 to 5·0 inches per yard.
(c) An extra heavy blanket, 0·45 inch thick, used on materials having shrinkages of 3·9 to 5·6 inches per yard, e.g. denims.

The main drum of the machine can be either 60 inches or 84 inches in diameter, according to the material for which it is intended.

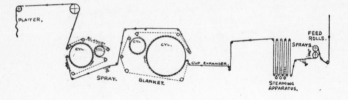

DOUBLE PALMER SHRINKING RANGE.

FIG. 135.—Diagram of the Sanforizing machine.

Before passing the cloth through the Sanforizing range, it must be tested in a standardised manner in order to determine the warp and weft shrinkage it will undergo on washing, for which the Sanforizing range is adjusted to cope with the potential shrinkage of the material.

The cloth is fed into the Sanforizing range through the feed rollers of a mangle, whose function it is to hold back the material and only allow the blanket to contract it the required amount, as otherwise the blanket contracts the cloth to the maximum capacity of the blanket, i.e. it is possible to over-shrink the material. From the feed rollers the cloth passes between sprays which moisten it, thereby rendering the yarns soft and plastic and more easily compressed by the felt blanket; this moistening is assisted by a steaming apparatus called a skyer. The cloth then passes through a short clip expander or stenterette about 3 feet 6 inches in length which controls the width of the goods as they are fed on to the blanket of the modified Palmer. This small stenter runs on a track so that it may be pushed back in order to adjust the shoes, etc., on the Palmer machine. The delivery end of this expander is adjusted laterally in order to obtain the desired width as determined by the standard wash test.

The cloth then passes to the felt blanket over the feed roller, and is placed in firm contact with the stretched surface of the blanket by electrically heated shoes; if cold shoes were used, the friction of the steel would overcome the friction of the blanket and less shrinkage would result.

The cloth, in contact with the stretched surface of the blanket, passes to the main steam-heated cylinder of the Palmer machine, so that when the stretched surface of the blanket is contracted by reversal of curvature, the fabric is contracted also. Feed rollers of different diameters are available for various thicknesses of cloths under treatment.

Having passed round the drum of the Palmer machine, the finished material may be passed on to an auxiliary finisher which is an additional Palmer unit for use when both sides of the material are to be finished alike or when additional shrinkage is required. It is not necessary always to use this auxiliary finisher; hence, the existence of two models of the range—Simplex and Duplex.

There is a device for keeping the blanket running in a straight path on the cylinder, and also an indicator giving the tension on the blanket. The electrically heated shoes are lifted from the blanket automatically when the machine is stopped, thus eliminating scorching.

It is essential that the fabric is thoroughly dried before leaving the Sanforizer, otherwise it will elongate. It is claimed that the proper use of the Sanforizing range enables shrinkage on laundering to be reduced to 0.75% or less.

Rigmel

The RIGMEL machine appears to be the first to rely solely on the principle of compressive shrinkage. It gives more lustre than the ordinary Sanforizing machine, because the cloth is held against a thick rubber sheet during the compressive shrinkage; there is no danger of blanket-marks on very fine cloths.

On account of the thickness of the rubber and its great elasticity, it is comparatively easy to pass from the extended to the non-extended state as the endless rubber sheet moves round a pair of rotary drums. The outer surface of the rubber apron will be extended as it passes over the peripheral surface of half the circumference of the drums until it reaches its straight path on leaving the surface of the drums.

Hence, if the damp cloth is held in contact with the rubber apron compressive shrinkage will take place. A pressure plate is mounted above the drum to which the fabric is first fed, forcing it into contact with the surface of the rubber apron; this plate is made with its leading edge reaching over a portion of the curved periphery of the rubber apron on one side and a similar portion of the straight path of the apron on the other side, thus conforming to the path in which the apron travels. The pressure plate is heated.

The cloth which is to receive the shrinkage treatment is fed into the machine so that it enters between the pressure plate and the rubber apron in the position corresponding to 9.50 on the clock-basis of estimating positions on the circumference of a circle. The gripping surface of the contracting rubber engages the fabric as it passes

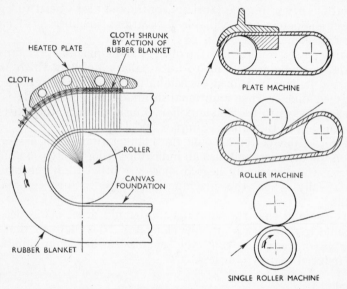

PRINCIPLE OF RIGMEL MACHINE　　　TYPES OF RIGMEL MACHINE

FIG. 136.—Diagrams of the Rigmel method of compressive shrinkage.

under the heated pressure plate and carries it forward. The contraction of the rubber forces the weft threads into closer proximity to each other, and therefore causes the warp threads to follow a more sinuous path, so shortening the length of the fabric.

Shrinkage is thus produced by forcing the cloth to partake of the contractile motion which is given to the surface of the rubber apron by a change of curvature.

Rigmel machines were shown at the British Industries Fair in 1937, and present a compact appearance. The drums appeared to be 18 to 24 inches in diameter, and thus much smaller than the Palmer drum of the Sanforizing machine. The shoes of the latter are small compared with the large pressure plate of the Rigmel machine; the rubber apron was approximately 2 to 3 inches thick.

The chief difference between the two machines lies in the use of

PLATE XXIII

FIG. 137. Guiding head of stenter showing over-feed arrangements.

Courtesy of Mather & Platt.

FIG. 138. Rigmel machines.

Courtesy of the Bradford Dyers' Association.

To face page 252.

PLATE XXIV

FIG. 159. The Sanforizing Plant.

the wool blanket as compared with the rubber apron, but the Sanforizing machine in its ordinary form depends on the reversal of sharp curvature from the small roller on which the shoes fit to the very gradual reverse curvature of the large drum of the Palmer machine, whereas the Rigmel machine produces the same result in passing through a relatively small quadrant. Actually, there is a small Palmer machine in conjunction with the Rigmel machine, but it plays no part in the shrinkage, being only employed to dry the fabric completely and set the cloth in a stable state.

The most effective form of pre-shrinkage, therefore, owes much of its success to the combination of British and American ideas. It may be remarked that rubber, as the medium of control, is confined in England to the Rigmel plant.

Although the term "Sanforizing" has been used for purposes of convenience, it should be stated that "Sanforized" is actually a cloth of measured shrinkage relating to specific wash-testing procedure allied to specific tolerances in the sample under test; both Sanforized and Rigmel are Trade Names.

PHYSICO-CHEMICAL METHODS

The crease-resisting process of Foulds, Marsh, and Wood of the Tootal Broadhurst Lee Co., Ltd., depends for its success on the production of synthetic resins inside the textile material to which they are applied. Although the novelty of the effect is striking on account of resistance to creasing having hitherto been confined to animal fibres, yet there are other valuable properties associated with the product, some of which have been described elsewhere. Crease-resisting cotton or rayon goods also possess a high degree of resistance to shrinkage, and this is an inevitable result of the standard crease-resisting process. This fact was announced in 1932.

It is noteworthy that the mechanical processes, such as contractive drying and compressive shrinkage, which are successful with cotton goods are not successful in the case of rayons, particularly spun rayons. The crease-resisting process, however, gives a substantial degree of resistance to shrinkage with spun rayons, and in many cases the potential shrinkage is reduced from 12 to 2% or less.

The formation of synthetic resins in close association with the cellulose itself has been studied by later workers and definite claims for unshrinkability have been made. For instance, Raduner and Co., in B.P. 445,891, utilise a partial condensate of urea and formaldehyde to impregnate the textile fabric, which is stretched on a stenter and heated in order to harden the resin and fix the dimensions of the material. In one example, bleached, mercerised cotton cloth in the wet state was passed several times through a 20% solution of a urea-thiourea-formaldehyde condensation product containing a catalyst and squeezed after each impregnation until 200% of the dry weight of the fabric was obtained. The cloth was then dried on a stenter and caused to assume a merchantable length and width, after which it was heated to between 120 and 140°C.; this heat treatment fixed the dimensions of the cloth, which was then washed, rinsed, and dried in the ordinary manner. Whereas an untreated cotton voile had a potential shrinkage of 7 to 9%, a similar material according to the above method only had a potential shrinkage of 0·09 to 1·8%.

Other patent specifications appear to utilise the same idea; for instance, B.P. 480,171 by Lantz and Morrison of the C.P.A. use a urea-formaldehyde resin under such circumstances that no more than 8% of resin is formed, calculated on the weight of the fabric. Lightly condensed reaction mixtures are used.

For example, 250 parts of urea were mixed with 625 parts of formaldehyde and 500 parts of water. The mixture was made slightly alkaline and allowed to condense for 15 minutes at 40° to 65°C., cooled and neutralised. 125 parts of formalin were added to this condensate, which was made up to 2,500 parts with water. The impregnating bath consisted of 40 parts of the above solution, 3 parts of glacial acetic acid, and 57 parts of water. Impregnation is carried out so that the fabric retains 110% of the liquor, after which it is dried under warp and weft tension and then heated for 50 seconds at 200°C., followed by washing and drying.

Examples illustrating the effects on various cloths show that in the case of staple fibre the potential shrinkage was reduced from 13·2 to 2·7% for a resin content of 5·5%; a viscose crêpe fabric with a potential shrinkage of 9% showed only 3·8% after treatment with 6% synthetic resin. A cotton voile had its potential shrinkage reduced from 6 to 3% as a result of treatment with 3% synthetic resin, whilst a poplin had its shrinkage reduced from 7 to 2% by incorporating 2% of resin.

B.P. 456,307 of Farberei Sitterthal also utilises synthetic resins for the production of textiles which resist shrinkage on laundering.

B.F. 790,614 of the I.G. discloses that fabrics of vegetable material may be rendered unshrinkable by impregnation with a mixture of 1·6 Kg. of starch in 18 litres of cold water to which has been added a solution of 150 g. of dimethylol urea and 15 g. of ammonium oxalate. The fabric is dried at 120°C. and then washed in the usual manner. Far-condensed resins have also been suggested for rendering crêpe fabrics unshrinkable; the resins were prepared by boiling mixtures of urea and formaldehyde for between 4 and 5 hours, according to Japanese patent 100,072. After drying and heating, the impregnated fabric should be passed through weak mineral acid to complete the condensation. This type of treatment is apt to produce a stiff handle which is not very attractive. Another suggestion for the employment of highly condensed resins for the prevention of shrinkage of textile material has been made by Borgetty in U.S.P. 2,050,156. The water-soluble condensation product of urea-formaldehyde is so applied that the interwoven threads are bonded together solely at their contacting surfaces by a transparent covering of synthetic resin.

As mentioned elsewhere, it is possible to produce dispersions or emulsions of far-condensed urea-formaldehyde resins, which, when applied to cloth, do not stiffen the material; resin emulsions, of the urea-formaldehyde type described in B.P. 512,187, are capable of producing resistance to shrinkage in the textile materials to which they are applied.

Acetone-formaldehyde resins may also be utilised to produce unshrinkable cellulosic materials, as described in U.S.P. 2,159,875.

It is important to realise that the mechanical methods of producing unshrinkable cellulosic textile materials are inoperative in the case of regenerated cellulose whether in the form of continuous filament or spun rayon. There are certain essential differences between cotton and rayon; the latter absorbs more moisture and swells to a greater extent in water; it consists of a dispersed form of cellulose made up of shorter chain-molecules than in the case of cotton, and therefore is less stable in the mechanical sense. Not only shrinkage difficulties have to be considered, but also the question of *extension* on hot pressing. The physical form of rayon, with the smooth surface and lack of convolutions, prevents the effects of mechanical pre-shrinkage being permanent; indeed, fabrics of rayon which have been subjected to the compressive shrinkage methods are apt to extend visibly as they come off the machine.

In general the resin treatments are capable of reducing the potential shrinkage of rayon fabrics to the order of 2%, which is often sufficient for most practical purposes. If a higher degree of unshrinkability is required, then it is possible to combine mechanical shrinkage with resin treatments. For instance, during the normal processing of the resin-treated goods they may be dried on a stenter fitted with an over-feed device or some contractive method of imparting shrinkage during the stentering. Again, it is possible to combine the resin treatment with controlled compressive shrinkage, as in the Sanforizing or Rigmel processes.

This enables the residual shrinkage to be removed in the only satisfactory manner for rayon and at the same time has certain advantages in that the combined process does not lose the same yardage as with the mechanical process alone. Controlled compressive shrinkage actually contracts the cloth in the direction of its warp; that is to say, that a cloth with a potential shrinkage of

7% is reduced 7% in length during the processing. On the other hand, a combination of resin treatment and compressive shrinkage would allow of the same unshrinkability without such a high loss in length during the process. This point is of importance for cotton goods as well as for the spun-rayon materials, which, as previously stated, cannot be treated by mechanical means alone to render them unshrinkable.

Combinations of compressive shrinkage and resin treatment are capable of giving very good results; a final operation of compressive shrinkage (Sanforizing) on goods which have already received the resin treatment is quite common practice.

B.P. 538,665, however, makes use of the heating sections of the Sanforizing process to complete the resinification of the resin treatment; the shoes before the Palmer machine may be heated up to 200°C., whilst the drum itself may operate at a temperature of 130° to 150°C. The combined process is stated to give unshrinkability for a 2·5% reduction in length during processing, compared with 7% reduction in length by mechanical shrinkage alone in the case of cotton goods. For spun rayon (which cannot be treated by mechanical means) the combined process only reduces the length of the goods by 7·5% during processing, whereas the potential shrinkage of the untreated material was 16%.

Before leaving the question of physico-chemical treatments which impart resistance to creasing, it may be mentioned that cellulose ethers have also been applied to textile materials in order to reduce the laundry shrinkage.

CHEMICAL METHODS

Consideration of the fundamental principles of the shrinkage of textile materials has shown that the most important single factor is the swelling which takes place when the goods are immersed in water. Obviously, therefore, goods which do not swell, or only swell to a small extent, are not likely to create difficulties in laundering. This is the case with cellulose acetate rayon, whose absorption of moisture and swelling in water is much lower than that of cellulose itself. Goods made from acetate rayon rarely give rise to complaints of shrinkage when laundered.

This resistance to swelling is mainly due to the blocking of the hydroxyl groups of cellulose by the acetyl groups of the acetate, and it is only to be expected, therefore, that other methods of blocking hydroxyl groups should have been investigated with a view to preventing swelling, and therefore shrinkage.

Methylene cellulose formation is one of the simplest and easiest methods of reducing the swelling of cellulose itself, and depends on the treatment of cellulose with formaldehyde in presence of an acid catalyst. The original reaction was first outlined by Eschalier in 1903, and is well known, having been described on many occasions. Both cotton and viscose rayon fabrics when treated with formaldehyde do not shrink so much in ordinary washing as do the untreated materials; unfortunately, however, the goods are apt to be damaged by acid attack during the treatment.

B.P. 455,472 of Heberlein states that viscose and cotton materials may be rendered proof against laundry shrinkage by treatment in a bath containing 30 to 40% formaldehyde solution catalysed with about 1% of aluminium sulphate or aluminium thiocyanate; the goods are dried and then heated for, say, 50 minutes at 90°C. or 20 minutes at 120°C. or 4 minutes at 140°C.

B.P. 488,095 refers to the considerable deterioration of breaking elongation which always occurs with these formaldehyde processes, and discloses that this may be avoided by subjecting the textile material to the action of a swelling agent before the formaldehyde treatment. Over-stretching is advised and figures are given to show the effect of these swelling treatments on the cotton yarn. Formaldehyde treatment on unmercerised cotton gave a percentage loss of 66%, on mercerised cotton of 40%, and on over-stretched mercerised cotton of 30%.

A further specification of Heberlein, B.P. 518,872, refers more particularly to the treatment of rayon to render it shrinkproof by treatment with formaldehyde solutions of concentration equivalent to 50 to 200 g. of 40% formaldehyde per litre, i.e. a lower concentration of formaldehyde than that generally employed previously. Condensation of the cellulose takes place in the presence of an acid or acid-producing catalyst, and the heating may fall within the range of 90° to 160°C.

The Calico Printers' Association have also produced anti-shrink materials containing methylene cellulose. B.P. 460,201 specifies oxidising agents such as nitric or perchloric acids or their ammonium salts. In one example of the method a viscose taffeta is prepared with aluminium acetate and then steamed for 1 hour, after which it is impregnated with 16% formaldehyde solution containing 2% nitric acid, dried and heated for 50 seconds at 200°C. The goods are then washed and are stated to exhibit resistance to creasing and to shrinkage. The aluminium oxide formed in the fabric is supposed to be a protective agent. In B.P. 477,084 the catalyst is an aromatic sulphonic acid; impregnation with 15% formaldehyde solution and 3% of orthoaminophenolparasulphonic acid, followed by heating for 40 minutes at 80°C., gives a high degree of resistance to shrinkage.

B.P. 526,098 of the Calico Printers' Association, Lantz and Miller, states that it is desirable to limit the amount of formaldehyde which combines with the cellulose where resistance to shrinkage is required without any resistance to creasing; it is considered that not more than 0·1 to 1·75% of formaldehyde should be fixed in rayon and not more than 0·1 to 0·4% in native cellulose, such as cotton or linen. The formaldehyde concentration in the solution need not exceed 15%, but may be even lower. The catalyst may be any kind of free acid and the formaldehyde solution is preferably rendered acid to pH 2 at ordinary temperatures, but in order to avoid acid attack on the cellulose, it is wise to use acids of medium strength, such as the aromatic sulphonic acids and various organic acids whose dissociation constant lies between 3×10^{-1} and 3×10^{-4}. The temperature of drying depends on the acid catalyst selected, but should not exceed 130° in general. When the reaction has been completed, the fabric should be washed in a weakly alkaline solution in order to remove any uncombined formaldehyde and the acid catalyst.

Two examples illustrate the process, which it is believed forms the basis of the Grafton crêpe finish. Viscose rayon crêpe was impregnated with 15% formaldehyde solution containing 2·5% tartaric acid. The pH was 1·83. The impregnated material was then dried at 110°C. for 12·5 minutes while stretched to its final dimensions. The cloth was then washed in weak sodium carbonate solution, soaped, and dried. The amount of combined formaldehyde was 1·5%, and laundry tests showed zero shrinkage in the weft compared with 12% shrinkage in the case of similar but untreated material.

Cotton furnishing material was impregnated with a solution containing 3% of formaldehyde and 0·13% of sulphonic acid, squeezed until 70% of the solution remained in the cloth, and then dried for 6 minutes at 105°C. The cloth was then washed, rinsed, and dried as above. The formaldehyde content of the fabric was 0·1% and its warp shrinkage was 2%, compared with 11·4% for the untreated material.

According to B.P. 518,872 of Heberlein, the concentration of the formaldehyde solution for shrinkproofing should be 50 to 200 g. per litre of 40% formaldehyde solution; the Calico Printers' Association prefer to use 15% formaldehyde solution at a pH below 2. For rayon, the combined formaldehyde should lie between 0·5 and 1·5%, and for cotton between 0·1 and 0·4%, not exceeding the latter.

Although material made from cellulose acetate does not give rise to shrinkage difficulties, as stated above, yet it must be remembered that some partially saponified cellulose acetate rayons are more susceptible. These, too, may be treated according to the methylene cellulose reaction as outlined in B.P. 450,620.

The Sanforset process which arose in the U.S.A. during 1939 and 1940 is very probably a combination of controlled compressive shrinkage with cellulose methylene ether formation, specially developed for the treatment of rayon.

CHAPTER X

SOFTENING

ALL native fibres are associated with some oily, fatty, or waxy substance in the raw state, and its function appears to be mainly protective; the fibres are lubricated by the fatty product which is usually water-repellent also. With the exception of silk, the fibres become harsher when the fatty matter is removed, and, indeed, it is very difficult to spin either cotton or wool from which the wax or grease is absent. On the other hand, most of the grease must be removed from wool before spinning.

Softness is very frequently required in textile materials, particularly in fabrics used for clothing, so that it is not surprising that attempts have been made to "soften" cloths which have been deprived of their natural fat or wax during the processes of bleaching, dyeing, or printing. Further, certain colouring matters are apt to impart a dryness and an unpleasant handle to the textile material which must be corrected before the goods can be regarded as satisfactory.

During many finishing processes, substances are added to the textile fabric for purposes of weighting, filling, binding, and stiffening; most of these additions require the presence of some softener for the best effect. Another use of softeners is in connection with mechanical finishes, such as calendering, where smoothness and brightness are required.

Some chemical finishing processes, in particular, the chlorination of wool, are apt to give a harsh handle to the material, and here again a softening treatment is most desirable.

Softeners, therefore, may be applied as a finish in themselves, to impart softness, smoothness, fullness, suppleness, and flexibility, all of which affect draping properties, or, alternatively, as a method of modifying other finishing materials.

Although many hundreds of preparations are available for softening textile materials, it is noteworthy that they are all based on long-chain fatty compounds in one guise or another. The earliest application of the fatty products was as a soap or, alternatively, as an emulsion; Marseilles soap and olive-oil emulsions being typical examples. Similar fatty substances were then produced in the form of the sulphonated oils ranging from the old Turkey red oil to the modern Calsolene Oil HS; the sulphonated oils were stable to hard water, which obviated some of the difficulties encountered with soaps and emulsions of fats.

The sulphonated oils merely deposited themselves on the surface of the fibres for which they had no real affinity, but later work has resulted in the manufacture of fatty compounds which have substantive properties and can be applied from dilute solutions which are capable of exhaustion. Still more recently, compounds with a fatty basis have been prepared in such a form that they will combine with the fibre to which they are applied and provide a permanent softening effect.

Fundamentally, the softening of textiles depends on the surface application of oils, fats, or waxes in one form or another. It is not always easy to express in words the exact differences between various softeners, but an excess of almost any softener gives a greasy effect, sometimes termed "slazy"—textile English is not noted for its elegance, as may be seen from many peculiar terms in common use. Words such as bulky, full, mellow, soft, thin, reedy, papery, harsh, hard, and boardy are actually less confusing in practice than might be expected, provided local or even personal interpretations are understood.

Softening agents may be divided into the following classes:

(a) Emulsions of oils, fats, and waxes (in many cases the emulsifying agent itself possesses softening powers).
(b) Soaps (these too can be used as emulsifying agents).
(c) Sulphonated oils.
(d) Sulphated alcohols.
(e) Fatty acid condensation products.
(f) Quaternary ammonium compounds (some of these have substantive properties and others are capable of actual chemical combination with the fibre).

Another class of softening material relies on increased moisture in the fabric for its effect; the material becomes less rigid and more plastic. Compounds such as glycerol and certain hygroscopic inorganic salts are sometimes used for this purpose.

OILS, FATS, AND WAXES

Oils, fats, and waxes used for softening, whether directly as emulsions or indirectly in the form of various compounds, have a common characteristic in their fatty component; waxes are the esters of fatty acids and fatty alcohols, whereas many fats are the glycerides of fatty acids. Hence, from spermaceti and carnauba wax it is possible to obtain cetyl or ceryl alcohol and palmitic or myristic acid; oils and fats, such as olive oil, tallow, cotton-seed oil, etc., provide glycerin and fatty acids, as, for example, palmitic, oleic, or stearic acid.

The fatty acids are of two main types, $C_nH_{2n+1}COOH$ or $C_nH_{2n-1}COOH$, according to whether they are saturated or unsaturated, and usually the number of carbon atoms in the chain is high and varies from 10 to 18. The fatty alcohols, on the other hand, are generally saturated and have the general formula $C_nH_{2n+1}OH$. Alkali transforms the fatty acids into soaps, which, in addition to their detergent action, have great value as softeners; the saturated series is preferred, for rancidity is apt to occur with the unsaturated soaps when they are applied to fabrics and allowed to oxidise by "ageing."

Special methods of hydrogenation are capable of transforming fatty acids to fatty alcohols which can be sulphated to give soluble products of high detergent action and softening ability—the so-called synthetic soaps. Hence fatty alcohols can be obtained from waxes, or from the fatty acids derived from oils, fats, and waxes.

Many of the natural fatty substances give mixtures of more than two fatty acids or alcohols when hydrolysed or saponified; for use as softeners, it is not necessary to isolate the pure compounds, and the resulting softening preparation is often all the better for being a mixture.

Some of the following formulae are of interest in connection with the fatty compounds used in textile finishing:

FATTY COMPOUNDS

Hydrocarbon	Fatty acid		Fatty alcohol	
Octane	Caprylic	$(C_7H_{15}COOH)$	Octyl	$(C_8H_{17}OH)$
Decane	Capric	$(C_9H_{19}COOH)$	Decyl	$(C_{10}H_{21}OH)$
Dodecane	Lauric	$(C_{11}H_{23}COOH)$	Lauryl	$(C_{12}H_{25}OH)$
Tetradecane	Myristic	$(C_{13}H_{27}COOH)$	Myristyl	$(C_{14}H_{29}OH)$
Hexadecane	Palmitic	$(C_{15}H_{31}COOH)$	Cetyl	$(C_{16}H_{33}OH)$
Octadecane	Stearic	$(C_{17}H_{35}COOH)$	Stearyl	$(C_{18}H_{37}OH)$
Eicosane	Arachidic	$(C_{19}H_{39}COOH)$	Eicosyl	$(C_{20}H_{41}OH)$

The saturated normal fatty acids are typified by palmitic, but myristic and stearic acids are also fairly common. Ceryl alcohol $C_{26}H_{53}OH$ is obtained from beeswax, and cetyl alcohol from spermacetti.

Oleic acid is the most widespread of the fatty acids, and it is unsaturated $C_{17}H_{33}COOH$ or $CH_3(CH_2)_7CH : CH(CH_2)_7COOH$; the corresponding oleyl alcohol is $C_{18}H_{35}OH$ or $CH_3(CH_2)_7CH : CH(CH_2)_7 CH_2OH$, and is obtained from sperm oil.

Ricinoleic acid is an unsaturated hydroxy acid whose formula is $CH_3(CH_2)_5CH(OH)CH_2CH : CH(CH_2)_7COOH$. Other common unsaturated fatty acids are linoleic acid $CH_3(CH_2)_4CH:CHCH_2CH : CH(CH_2)_7COOH$ and linolenic acid $CH_3CH_2CH : CHCH_2CH : CHCH_2CH : CH(CH_2)_7COOH$.

In the commercial preparation of fatty acids, the crude products are separated into two classes, the oleines and the stearines; the oleine is the liquid portion and the stearine the solid portion at room temperatures. As might be expected from these names, the oleine, or red oil, is mainly oleic acid, whereas the stearine contains a large proportion of stearic acid. Some confusion is apt to exist between the oleine which denotes oleic acid, and olein oil, which is a Turkey red oil formed by the sulphonation of castor oil, as discussed on page 266.

Tallow has found extensive application as a finishing agent, as it is able to counteract the stiffness and harshness which would be imparted to fabrics by many filling and weighting preparations; its chief use is with cotton goods. Tallow is both cheap and abundant, and capable of giving excellent softening under certain conditions, particularly when suitably emulsified. If coarse and uneven emulsions are employed, the results are disappointing, and the preparation of a suitable emulsion is not easy. A somewhat specialised technique, however, enabled the I.C.I. to market a thick paste known as Waxol T, which consists of a concentrated stabilised neutral emulsion of tallow; its stability to hard and soft water is good, and it only needs dilution with warm water (45° to 50°C.) before use. The concentrated product should be stirred with 3 to 4 times its weight of soft water to form a thin, uniform cream, which may then be diluted to any required concentration even with water of 14° of hardness. From 1 to 4 lb. of Waxol T per 100 gallons of finishing liquor is usually sufficient, but the quantities may be varied to suit the requirements of the finisher. In conjunction with other finishing agents, it has been found that these preparations may be applied to a greater extent without dusting or loss of suppleness if Waxol T is present in the "mixing"; as a straightforward softener, however, a smooth soft handle is given to all types of cotton, rayon, and linen. Many tallow preparations become yellow and develop unpleasant odours when stored, but these drawbacks are almost absent with Waxol T, whose storage properties are excellent.

Waxes, such as beeswax, paraffin wax, or carnauba wax, have a widespread use for imparting softness and suppleness to textile materials. The best results are generally obtained when the wax is applied from a stable and finely emulsified form, conditions which are fulfilled in Waxol P of the I.C.I. This product is available as a smooth white paste, which on dilution with warm water gives emulsions of excellent stability, even to alkali and to electrolytic salts; the addition of starch, dextrin, gelatin, or gum has no deleterious effect on the stability of the emulsion.

For a stock emulsion, the Waxol P may be stirred with 3 to 4 times its weight of soft water at 40° to 50°C. until a smooth thin cream is obtained, which is then diluted to the required amount with water; for most purposes, 1 to 2 lb. of Waxol P per 100 gallons of water should be adequate, but in presence of other finishing materials it may be necessary to increase the amount to 2·5 to 5 lb.

There can be little doubt that such emulsified fats and waxes fulfil a useful purpose in providing the means for a uniformity of finish in virtue of the even distribution of the wax or tallow throughout the finishing preparation, and thus on the goods when finished.

Cirrasol SA and LC of the I.C.I. are believed to be neutral fatty compounds emulsified with some of the new emulsifiers; the SA variety is primarily of value for rayon, and the effect is midway between that of a soluble oil and a wax. Cirrasol LC is of value for wool and linen, but both of these preparations may be used with any of the textile fibres. As a straightforward softening about 1 to 4 lb. of Cirrasol per 100 gallons of liquor is adequate, but this should be increased to 5 to 15 lb. per 100 lb. of solid when the Cirrasols are used with starch, dextrin, gelatin, or the newer ether finishes. The Cirrasols are stable to hard water, but should not be used with Epsom-salt finishes.

The Amoa product "Tallowmulse," as its name implies, is a tallow emulsion with good softening and penetrating powers. Other Amoa products for use in softening preparations are Castor ABW, Moawax, and Moapol, which are softening emulsions capable of utilisation with various waxes.

SOAPS

Soaps have been in use for about 2,000 years, and there is reason to believe that they were first used as pomades; modern soap manufacture dates from about 1790.

The term "soap" may be applied in general to the metallic salts of the higher fatty acids, but in particular it is confined to sodium and potassium salts.

Fats are the glycerides of fatty acids, and when saponified with alkali may give rise to three different products in addition to the glycerol.

$$\begin{array}{l} CH_2O.CO.R^1 \\ | \\ CH.O.CO.R^2 + 3NaOH \longrightarrow CHOH + R^1COONa + R^2COONa + R^3COONa \\ | \\ CH_2O.CO.R^3 \end{array} \quad \begin{array}{l} CH_2OH \\ | \\ \\ | \\ CH_2OH \end{array}$$

Within recent years fatty acids have been produced by treating fats with various agents, such as acids, steam, lime, or enzymes; these fatty acids are readily transformed into soaps as required in the textile finishing works.

The common hard soaps are sodium salts of fatty acids, the potassium salts forming soft soaps; the term "soft" does not necessarily imply the potassium salt, for a hard soap may come from the saponification of a hard fat like tallow, but with the same fatty acid, the sodium salt is harder than the corresponding potassium salt.

The sodium salts of the fatty acids exhibit soapy properties when the molecular chain is sufficiently long, but as the number of carbon atoms in the chain increases there is a diminution in solubility. The lathering powers are also connected with the number of carbon atoms, lauric acid (C_{12}) being outstanding.

Soaps form the basis of many softening preparations which may be made from olive oil, tallow, palm oil, coco-nut oil, etc., and naturally these differ considerably in their properties. At one time, many softenings were made from coco-nut oil and from tallow, but latterly the use of stearine has been popular.

Soaps are slightly soluble in cold water, but dissolve readily on warming; cooling the solution forms a gel which liquefies again on warming. The appearance of turbidity is associated with the melting-point of the fatty acid from which the soap is made.

SOAP SOLUTIONS

Fatty acid		Titer of soap				Turbidity in soap solution
Lauric	$C_{11}H_{23}COOH$	44°C.	.	.	.	40 to 45°C.
Myristic	$C_{13}H_{27}COOH$	54°C.	.	.	.	50 to 55°C.
Palmitic	$C_{15}H_{31}COOH$	62°C.	.	.	.	60 to 65°C.
Stearic	$C_{17}H_{35}COOH$	71°C.	.	.	.	65 to 70°C.
Arachidic	$C_{19}H_{39}COOH$	77°C.	.	.	.	75 to 80°C.
Oleic	$C_{17}H_{33}COOH$	14°C.	.	.	.	20 to 30°C.

The titer of a soap is the temperature at which its molten fatty acid solidifies on cooling.

It will be noted that with oleates, the presence of the unsaturated radicals produces a more liquid soap, but it is preferable to avoid the use of highly unsaturated compounds as softeners, for they tend to oxidise and give rancid and sticky products. In the saturated series, the hardness is related to the aliphatic residue, so that it is possible to vary the softening effect by a choice of soap or a blend of soaps.

As the sodium and potassium soaps are salts of weak acids and strong bases, they hydrolyse in aqueous solution, and in dilute solutions they are distinctly alkaline; the degree of hydrolysis increases in passing up the series from laurate to stearate. Further, the action of soap is determined to some extent by the fibre to which it is applied; with wool, the fibre absorbs more alkali than acid, and so becomes alkaline even from a neutral soap. The soap bath thus becomes charged with acid soap.

The alkalinity of soap solutions is not their chief defect, for they are decomposed by mineral acid or any acid which is stronger than the fatty acid of the soap. Again, the action of many soluble metallic salts on soap solutions is to give an insoluble metallic soap, as with the calcium and magnesium salts in hard water, forming sticky products which adversely affect the handle of the goods and bring about discoloration on ageing.

These disadvantages are mainly associated with the presence of the carboxyl group, and some very interesting methods have been suggested for overcoming these defects.

Many of the soap softeners use the soap itself as the emulsifying agent for the fat or fatty acid which they contain; hence, the production of a soap by heating coco-nut oil with alkali, will enable further quantities of coco-nut oil to be emulsified by that soap.

One of the best-known softeners is that from borax and stearine which does not possess great alkalinity. It may be prepared by dissolving 2 lb. of borax in 100 gallons of water and adding 10 lb. of stearine (commercial stearic acid; m.p. 53° to 54°C.). The mixture may be boiled until homogeneous, and then diluted to 150 gallons for use at 60° to 90°C.

Another simple softener may be made by emulsifying stearic acid with potassium stearate. A suitable stock solution may be prepared, whose solid content contains 75% of potassium stearate and 25% stearic acid, and diluted to 0·5 to 1% concentration before use. Products of this type have certain points in common with the so-called super-fatted soaps which are manufactured for their emollient properties.

The production of triethanolamine soaps has made it possible to use their great powers of emulsification for the preparation of many soap-emulsion softeners. There are literally hundreds of preparations available.

Triethanolamine soaps are prepared very simply by mixing molecular proportions of triethanolamine with the fatty acid, such as oleic, palmitic, or stearic acid. With stearic acid, a solid product is obtained, but for many purposes the semi-liquid triethanolamine oleate is preferred on account of its high powers of emulsifying fats and oils. If emulsions are required for softening purposes in textile finishing, it is often more efficient to mix the oleic acid with the oil or wax and then add the triethanolamine with the necessary amount of water.

For calender finishes with ordinary soaps in conjunction with starch the high temperatures often used cause a yellow discoloration, but this may be avoided by the use of triethanolamine soaps. A typical recipe from B.P. 431,275 is to mix 2 parts of triethanolamine stearate (or palmitate), 0·5 parts of ethylene glycol, 1 part of cetyl alcohol, 1 part of Turkey red oil, and 96 parts of water-soluble starch.

Triethanolamine soaps are also useful for application to acetate rayon when it is desired to avoid the development of static electricity.

SOLUBLE OILS

The so-called sulphonated oils were the first step towards over-coming the weakness of soaps towards hard water; Turkey red oil was the forerunner of these compounds and owes its origin to the work of Mercer in 1846, when "sulphated oils" were made from olive oil and sulphuric acid.

Modern Turkey red oil is made by treating castor oil with sulphuric acid, and neutralising the product with sodium, potassium, or ammonium hydroxide. The reaction is rather complicated, but is essentially the formation of a sulphuric acid ester

$$C_6H_{13}CH(OH)CH_2.CH:CH.C_7H_{14}.COOH \longrightarrow C_6H_{13}CH(O.SO_3H)CH_2.CH: CH.C_7H_{14}COOH$$

With olive oil, which is the triglyceride of oleic acid, the sulphuric acid reacts at the double bond

$$C_8H_{17}.CH:CH.C_7H_{14}.COOH \longrightarrow C_8H_{17}.CH(O.SO_3H)CH_2.C_7H_{14}.COOH.$$

The introduction of the sulphuric acid residue renders the fatty acid soluble in water, and imparts a certain amount of resistance to acid compared with soap; the SO_3H group is also capable of forming soluble calcium and magnesium salts. Hence, in circumstances where a soap softening would be precipitated, the sulphated oils are stable; they are therefore useful softeners with finishing prepara-tions containing Epsom-salt. The original oils contained 3 to 7% combined sulphuric acid, and this has been increased in the Monopol soaps, and also Prestabit V oils, but at the expense of the fatty character; the wetting powers are greater, however, and also the resistance to lime and acid.

Allied products may be made by amidation or esterification of the carboxyl groups in ricinoleic acid, followed by treatment with sulphuric acid. Avirol AH extra is the sulphuric ester of butyl ricinoleate, and Humectol C, the sulphuric ester of the amide of ricinoleic acid.

As previously mentioned, the soluble fatty softeners on a soap basis comprise a polar head and a long fatty hydrophobic tail; the polar head penetrates the fibre, leaving the fatty tail to lubricate and soften the surface. In soaps, the polar group is at the end of the molecule, but with the sulphated oils of the type under discussion, the polar group is in the centre of the molecule; hence, other things being equal, there will be a greater accumulation of fatty or hydrophobic chains on the surface.

Calsolene Oil HS of I.C.I. utilises this principle, as shown by its formula

$$CH_3.(CH_2)_3.CH(C_2H_5).CH_2\diagdown$$
$$CH.O.SO_3Na.$$
$$CH_3.(CH_2)_3.CH(C_2H_5).CH_2\diagup$$

A similar compound on the same molecular architecture is

$$CH_3.(CH_2)_7.O.CO.CH_2$$
$$|$$
$$CH_3.(CH_2)_7.CH.SO_3Na$$

Aerosol OT, which is popular in the U.S.A., is the dioctyl ester of sodium sulphosuccinate

$$C_8H_{17}.OOC.CH_2$$
$$\phantom{C_8H_{17}.OOC.}|$$
$$C_8H_{17}.OOC.CH.SO_3Na.$$

SULPHATED ALCOHOLS

The fatty acids, with their terminal COOH groups, are weak in respect of ability to disperse lime soaps, but the corresponding alcohols contain terminal OH groups which may be modified by the introduction of a solubilising SO_3H group to form a sulphuric ester, which in its turn can form a sodium salt. The sulphated fatty alcohols thus combine detergent properties with resistance to lime; they are also good softeners.

For example, cetyl alcohol can be converted to the acid sulphuric ester and neutralised to form sodium cetyl sulphate $C_{16}H_{33}.O.SO_3Na$. It is unfortunate that the term "sulphonated" is often applied to these products, giving rise to some confusion; the sulphate is $R.CH_2.O.SO_3Na$, whereas the sulphonate is $R.CH_2.SO_3Na$. Further, the sulphuric esters are formed by treatment with chlorsulphonic acid at 30°C., whereas the sulphonate is formed by reaction with strong sulphuric acid at 150°C.

The range of suitable alcohols, obtained by hydrogenation of the fatty acid, comprises those containing from 10 to 30 carbon atoms in the chain, the commonest being lauryl alcohol $C_{12}H_{25}OH$, myristyl alcohol $C_{14}H_{29}OH$, and cetyl alcohol $C_{16}H_{33}OH$. The maximum detergent action is seen in the products from the C_{18} alcohols. Although the sulphated alcohols are relatively insensitive to acid and to lime, this only applies to warm solutions, but although the lime salts of the sulphated fatty alcohols are deposited on cooling, they do not possess the objectionable sticky characteristics of the ordinary lime soaps.

Some well-known preparations are the Lissapols, Gardinols, the sulphated Lorols and Ocenols; Gardinol LS is sodium oleyl sulphate and Gardinol WA is sodium lauryl sulphate.

Many of these preparations are referred to as textile assistants or auxiliaries; they have penetrating, wetting, dispersing, emulsifying, and softening properties, and their functions are not always sharply differentiated.

Lissapol C, for example, is a long-chain compound with a polar SO_3Na group, and thus possesses great interfacial activity; the length of the chain has been chosen for highest detergent efficiency. The product is sold in the form of a thick paste which is readily soluble in hot or warm water to give a neutral solution, stable to acid and alkaline solutions, and to hard water. Lissapol C has a marked softening action on materials which have been heavily weighted with Epsom-salt, a typical recipe being 0·5 to 1% of Lissapol C paste in 30 to 50% Epsom-salt solution.

For general finishing and softening purposes about 0·5 to 1 lb. of Lissapol C paste is sufficient for 100 gallons of liquor; in many cases the Lissapol will have been utilised as an assistant in previous process of scouring, milling, dyeing, etc., and may be allowed to remain or, alternatively, it may be added with the final rinsing water.

Amco is also believed to be a sulphated fatty alcohol.

CONDENSATION PRODUCTS

Fatty acid condensation products have also been used for the formation of compounds which have good wetting and softening ability; they also possess detergent powers. The best-known examples are the Igepons.·

Igepon A is prepared by esterification of oleic acid with an aliphatic oxy-sulphonic acid, and its probable formula is $C_{17}H_{33}COOCH_2CH_2$-SO_3Na, whereas Igepon T is a condensation product of oleic acid with an amino-sulphonic acid, and is stated to be $C_{17}H_{33}CONHCH_2$ CH_2SO_3Na, or $C_{17}H_{33}CON(CH_3)CH_2CH_2SO_3Na$.

Another condensation product from a fatty acid is Lamepon, which is derived from oleic acid and protein hydrolysates; its formula is $C_{17}H_{33}CONHR_1(CONHR_2)_nCOONa$.

The Soromin products of the I.G. are mainly condensation products of fatty acids and ethylene oxide; Soromin FL, however, is obtained from stearic acid and a mixture of polyamines.

The Meliorans are mainly compounds of fatty aromatic ketones, of probable formula $C_{15}H_{31}.CO.C_6H_4.SO_3Na$; the Ultravons are derived from o-phenylenediamine and are considered to have the following type of formulae:

$$C_{17}H_{35} \overset{NH}{\underset{N}{\diagdown}} C_6H_4SO_3Na \qquad\qquad C_{17}H_{35} \overset{NH}{\underset{N}{\diagdown}} C_6H_3(SO_3Na)_2$$

Ultravon K.   Ultravon W.

Another interesting compound is Medialan A, an oleyl sarcosine, of probable formula $C_{17}H_{33}.CO.N(CH_3).CH_2.COONa$; this is used as a milling agent.

Lissapol LS of the I.C.I. is believed to be the sulphonated compound of a fatty acid condensation product; though primarily a detergent, it has very good softening properties.

Another interesting type of softener has been described in B.P. 511,441 of the I.G., and depends on the formation of fatty diguanides. The starting-point is dicyandiamide, which may be regarded as a polymerisation product of cyanamide

$$NH_2.C : N \longrightarrow NH_2.C.NH.C : N$$
$$\overset{\parallel}{NH}$$

Condensation with octadecylamine gives the octadecyldiguanide

$$C_{18}H_{37}.NH.C.NH.C.NH_2$$
$$\overset{\parallel}{NH} \quad \overset{\parallel}{NH}$$

Although this may be applied to textiles as a softener, it is better to improve its solubility in water by treatment with ethylene oxide to give a product which may be used as the salt of organic carboxylic acids.

$$C_{18}H_{37}.NH.C.NH.C.NH.CH_2.CH_2.OH$$
$$\overset{\parallel}{NH} \quad \overset{\parallel}{NH}$$

In hard water, a dispersing agent free from acid groups should be present to prevent precipitation of the softener.

A special type of condensation product has been suggested for use in the crease-resisting process, according to U.S.P. 2,284,609 of American Cyanamid. The products are N-alkylol amides of the higher fatty acids; for example, 1% solutions of N-ethanol stearamide are recommended. These compounds may be made by the methods outlined in B.P. 306,116, 337,737, and 337,774 of the I.G. A typical example is to mix one molecular ratio of monoethanolamine with one molecular ratio of NaOH in 20% solution, and then treat the product with one molecular ratio of stearyl chloride, with stirring, when $C_{17}H_{35}CO.NH.C_2H_4OH$ slowly forms.

CATION-ACTIVE SOFTENERS

Softening agents rely for their efficiency on surface active properties, and in the case of the compounds modelled on soap, the fatty chain is in the anion; such compounds are anion-active.

Some cation-active softening compounds have been prepared by the Society of Chemical Industry in Basle, and termed Sapamines. A buttery compound, $NH_2.CH_2.CH_2.NH.CO.C_{17}H_{33}$, mono-oleyl ethylene diamine, was prepared by condensing oleic acid with ethylene diamine, but the Sapamines are based on the reaction between asymmetric diethyl-ethylene diamine and an acid chloride, such as stearyl chloride.

Sapamine CH is $C_{17}H_{33}.CO.NH.C_2H_4.N(C_2H_5)_2.HCl$, Sapamine L is the corresponding lactate, and Sapamine A the acetate. Sapamine BCH and Sapamine MS correspond to

$$R\diagdown\begin{matrix}CH_2.C_6H_5\\ \\Cl\end{matrix} \quad \text{and} \quad R\diagdown\begin{matrix}CH_3\\ \\SO_4.CH_3\end{matrix}$$

respectively, where R denotes the base

$$C_{17}H_{33}.CO.NH.C_2H_4.N(C_2H_5)_2.$$

An advantage in the use of the asymmetric diethyl derivative of ethylene diamine instead of ethylene diamine lies in the possibility of a further treatment of the condensation product with benzyl chloride or dimethyl sulphate to make a quaternary ammonium compound which is cation-active. For example, with dimethyl sulphate and the Sapamine base, it is possible to have

$$C_{17}H_{33}.OC.NH.CH_2.CH_2.N\diagdown\begin{matrix}CH_3\\(C_2H_5)_2\\SO_4.CH_3\end{matrix}$$

which probably represents Sapamine MS, which has excellent substantivity. It will be noted that the nitrogen atom is pentavalent.

It is not possible to use these cation-active softeners in conjunction with soap as precipitation occurs; however, all the Sapamines are not cation-active. For example, Sapamine FL is the sodium phthalate of diethylaminoethyloleylamide and anion-active.

Sapamine KW is probably the trimethylammonium-methylsulphate of monostearylmetaphenylenediamine, obtained by heating stearic acid and meta-aminodimethylaniline, followed by the addition of dimethyl sulphate to the product.

The Sapamines are exceedingly good softening agents.

Other bases have been employed for the manufacture of softeners; for example, o-phenylenediamine (see page 269).

Anion-cation active softeners have also been prepared for use in softening, and two typical examples are lauryl pyridinium lauryl sulphate $C_{12}H_{25}N(C_5H_5)SO_3OC_{12}H_{25}$, and lauryl pyridinium laurate $C_{12}H_{25}N(C_5H_5)OOC.C_{11}H_{23}$.

Yet again some non-ionised surface-active compounds have been made and have valuable softening properties; these are completely synthetic and do not originate from natural fats or waxes. The Igepals are the best-known examples, the general formula being $R.O.(C_2H_4O)_{5-10}.CH_2OH$, where R is a hydrophobic aliphatic hydrocarbon chain of 12 to 16 carbon atoms. A somewhat similar type of chemical compound is the well-known dyeing assistant Peregal O, $C_{18}H_{37}.(C_2H_4)_n.OC_2H_4.OH$, prepared by condensing ethylene oxide with octadecyl alcohol.

QUATERNARY AMMONIUM COMPOUNDS

Work on the quaternary ammonium compounds has led to a special type of softening agent, the forerunner of which is the well-known I.C.I. product "Fixanol." This is cetyl pyridinium bromide, which was put forward as an agent for improving the fastness to water of direct dyeings on cotton material. Such a compound, however, is also of value as a softener on account of the fatty chain which is incorporated in the molecule, and, moreover, it possesses a pronounced affinity for textile fibres.

Fixanol is readily soluble in hot or boiling water, but it should be used in cold or lukewarm (40°C.) solution; 0·5 to 1% solutions, calculated on the weight of the goods, are adequate.

Whereas all the foregoing materials suffer from the defect of impermanence, more recent developments have produced reagents which are capable of chemical combination with the textile fibres, and so give a permanent softening action. Many of these are associated with water-repellent finishes (see page 480), for the fatty chain when combined with the textile fibre may confer hydrophobic effects as well as softening. The key substances to most of these reactions are the α-halogen methyl compounds.

For instance, halogen ethers of the type R—O—CHX—R¹ may be treated with tertiary bases to give quaternary ammonium salts which are soluble in water; R may be an alkyl radical, and R^1 a hydrogen atom or hydrocarbon radical, but X is a halogen atom. Either R or R^1 must contain at least 8 carbon atoms. A simple example is seen in the treatment of octadecyl alcohol and formaldehyde with dry hydrogen chloride in benzene; the resulting stearyl chlormethyl ether reacts with pyridine to give a water-soluble quaternary ammonium salt. When this is applied to textile material and heated, pyridine is liberated and the chlormethyl alkyl ether reacts with the fibre to form a derivative which is fast to alkali. A compound which has attracted considerable attention in this connection is octadecyl-oxymethyl-pyridinium chloride; this has frequently been stated to form the basis of Velan PF (Zelan in the U.S.A.). However, the long-chain fatty alcohols are not the only starting-points, for carboxylic acid amides or carbamic esters of general formula $R.CO.NH.R^1$ or $RO.CO.NH.R^1$ may also be treated with formaldehyde and dry hydrogen chloride to give products which form quaternary ammonium salts such as stearamido-methyl pyridinium chloride

$$C_{17}H_{35}CO.NH.CH_2.\underset{\underset{Cl}{|}}{N}.C_5H_5$$

which is equally likely to form the basis of Velan PF. There are numerous variations on this theme.

Velan can be applied to almost every kind of fibre to give a permanent soft water-repellent finish, or an attractive softness, according to the method of application. The general method is to apply the solution or dispersion of Velan together with sodium acetate; the material is then squeezed, dried, baked, and washed. The softening effect alone may be obtained by impregnating and drying at low temperatures, but such a finish is not fast to washing or dry-cleaning. A permanent soft effect without water-repellency requires the full process, but with lower concentrations of Velan.

For rayon, acetate rayon, and silk, a solution of 0·25 to 1 lb. of Velan PF in 100 gallons of water is adequate; sodium acetate should be added in the proportion of 5 oz. of the crystalline acetate (or 3 oz. of the anhydrous product) per pound of Velan PF. The goods may be dried in any convenient manner, and then baked at 120° to 150°C. For cotton and linen, about 0·5 to 2 lb. of Velan should be used per 100 gallons of water, and similar amounts are suitable for wool and worsted.

Uniform heating is essential, and the duration of heating varies inversely with the temperature; at 120°C. a period of 5 to 10 minutes is sufficient, but this may be reduced to 1·5 to 3 minutes at 150°C. Naturally, thicker fabrics require a longer time than thin materials. A final wash may be necessary to remove any unchanged Velan or the by-products of the reaction; a warm dilute alkaline soap solution may be used, followed by a thorough rinsing.

Although Velan PF powder may be pasted with water alone, it is better to use a mixture containing 1 volume of methylated spirit and 4 volumes of water at 40°C.; 1 to 2 gallons of this mixture will be required for every 10 lb. of Velan.

It may be remarked that for the softening of chlorinated wool, which is generally rather harsh, the cation-active quaternary ammonium salt softeners, such as Sapamine KW, Fixanol, and

Velan PF, are very effective. A soft pleasing finish may also be given to goods weighted with urea, or finished with dextrin or gum, if 0·25 to 1 lb. of Velan is incorporated in every 100 gallons of the finishing solution.

In spite of the great advances in the understanding of the function of softeners, and the numerous commercial preparations of improved properties which have been made available, there can be little doubt that softeners from tallow, oils, and the various soaps are still the most numerous in common use.

Sulphonated oils give the best penetration with a fine soft type of handle; tallow penetrates less and gives a mellow feel, but the softest results are obtained from the stearine softeners which penetrate least.

HYGROSCOPIC COMPOUNDS

Softening preparations previously discussed all depend on the presence of a compound containing a fatty radical in some form or other. A different method of softening textiles depends on the use of hygroscopic substances, and is based on the fact that the physical properties of textile fibres are strongly influenced by their moisture content; hence, a less rigid and therefore softer product may be obtained, assisted by the swelling of the fibre with increase in moisture content.

The chlorides of zinc, calcium, and magnesium were commonly used at one time, particularly zinc chloride, which also possessed antiseptic properties. To a limited extent, they are still employed as softeners, but their disadvantages are now well known. Being inorganic chlorides, they are apt to decompose at high temperatures, as in hot calendering, and liberate hydrochloric acid, which will damage vegetable fibrous materials. Further, the deliquescent nature of these salts is liable to result in the attraction of too much moisture and produce conditions which favour the formation of mildew, particularly in presence of starch; zinc chloride is an exception on account of its antiseptic nature.

Glycerin is frequently used as a softener, but if employed in excess, a somewhat sticky effect is produced; allied compounds, such as the various glycols, are occasionally employed for softening purposes. Glycerol is capable of absorbing 30% of moisture from the air, and therefore increases the softness and flexibility of the material in which it is incorporated. About 1% is adequate in most cases, but 2% is often used with stiff fabrics or cloths which have been heavily back-filled.

Another organic compound which was frequently used at one time on account of the full and mellow handle it produced was glucose;

18

presumably the effect here, too, was due to the attraction of water. The use of glucose needs care, on account of its reducing action at high temperatures, and is therefore rarely used with coloured goods. It is cheaper than glycerol, however, and often replaces it.

In general, and subject to the above comments, the deliquescent materials are chiefly employed with flannelettes and with coloured-woven goods; they are rarely used with white, dyed and printed cloths. Glucose, for example, is sometimes employed in the finishing of flannelettes, to which it imparts a thick and mellow effect; it is also used in presence of weighting materials such as magnesium sulphate and sodium sulphate. Obviously, calcium chloride cannot be used with these compounds on account of the double decomposition which would occur with precipitation of calcium sulphate.

CHAPTER XI
STARCH AND STARCHING

THERE are numerous types of starch which may be obtained from the seeds of wheat, rice, and maize, from the pith of plants (sago), or from roots and tubers (tapioca and farina); the term "starch," without qualification, refers to wheat starch.

In France, the term *amidon* refers to starches from cereals, and *feculose* to starches from roots, tubers, and stems. (Feculose is also a trade name for the lowest members of the acetates of starch which resemble gelatin in physical properties.)

Potato starch or farina is extensively manufactured in Europe in a large number of small factories near the potato fields; the potatoes are thoroughly washed to remove all dirt, and are then vigorously mashed or rasped so as to rupture the largest possible number of cells which contain the starch. The watery pulp is washed free from loose starch and again mashed and washed, this time on sieves which separate the raw milk-starch from the fibre. The starch may be separated from the wash-water by a centrifugal method or by sedimentation on long inclined tables. Further refining by washing and sedimentation takes place after which the starch is dried.

Wheat starch is not easy to separate from the associated gluten which swells in water to form a sticky mass which is apt to retain the starch also. The gluten may be destroyed by fermentation, but in the more modern methods, the mass is kneaded under water, when the starch is liberated and carried away. The starch is purified by washing, sieving, and sedimentation; in some cases acidified water may be used, as this has a dispersing effect on the gluten.

Maize starch, known as corn starch in the U.S.A., cannot be made in a similar manner to wheat starch, for whereas the gluten of the latter can be kneaded into a tough coherent mass, that of the former remains in a finely dispersed state requiring special treatment for its removal. The usual modern method is to soak the grains for 30 to 40 hours to soften them, but in water containing 0·3% of sulphur dioxide at 40° to 60°C. The grains are then crushed and washed in a V-shaped tank with a screw conveyor. The coarse solid matter is ground with water in a mill and sieved, the starch being concentrated from the milky liquid by sedimentation on inclined tables.

Rice starch offers further difficulties in its preparation, as its granules are very small and take a long time to settle, so that the centrifugal method is generally preferred to sedimentation. The grain is steeped in dilute ammonia or sodium hydroxide solution until sufficiently soft for disintegration, and is then ground and passed to settling tanks or centrifuges. Where tanks are utilised, it may be necessary to add a little formaldehyde to inhibit fermentation during the time necessary for sedimentation. After removal of the gluten layer, which surrounds the starch, the washing and separation processes are repeated.

Each variety of starch may be recognised by the characteristic shape and size of its granules, together with the stratification, when examined under the microscope; numerous photomicrographs have been published, and attention may be drawn to those by Radley (Starch and its Derivatives, Chapman and Hall, London, 1940). The size of the granules varies from 2μ to 100μ.

Maquenne and Roux (Ann. Chim. Phys., 1906, 9, 179) succeeded in decomposing starch into two distinct substances which they termed amylose and amylopectin; the former showed the characteristic blue coloration with iodine, and was soluble in boiling water, but amylopectin had to be boiled for dispersion, and made a viscous liquid. These two substances recall the work of Nageli, who postulated two compounds in the starch granule, an interior granulose and an exterior starch-cellulose (Die Starkekorner, Zurich, 1858). Later, Meyer (Botan. Zeit., 1881, 39, 841) termed these two substances α-amylose and β-amylose respectively.

Starch is insoluble in cold water and only swells, but the action of heat on the suspension brings about gelatinisation; the granules swell very considerably, and with some starches, such as potato starch, the granules burst and release starchy material from the interior of the granule, and this passes into solution. The ordinary starch paste, therefore, is not homogeneous, as it consists of granules in various stages of swelling and disintegration; the paste-forming properties were assumed to be due to the amylopectin, which is suspended in the solution in a swollen state. In the thin pastes, which may be prepared by a short period of boiling, the amylopectin may settle, but with longer periods of preparation, below 100°C. the amylopectin swells and remains suspended, and thus increases the viscosity of the product. As will appear later, further heating brings about a diminution in viscosity which may be accelerated by acid conditions and retarded by weak alkali.

The breakdown of granule structure may also be accomplished by stirring, as shown by variation in viscosity which falls as the granules diminish in size. Granules of wheat starch, however, do not burst, and the paste remains full of large gelatinous vesicles; this explains some of the properties of wheat starch when applied to textiles.

Different investigators have given different temperatures for the temperature of gelatinisation of various starches; this may be due to different experimental conditions, but also because large granules tend to swell before small granules, possibly on account of the different ratio of amylose to amylopectin. Gelatinisation point is that at which anisotropy disappears.

GELATINISATION OF STARCH

Starch	Temperature
Potato	65–68°C.
Tapioca	70–74°C.
Sago	72–74°C.
Maize or corn	75–77°C.
Rice	80–83°C.
Wheat	80–82°C.

Some interesting data on the strength and physical properties of starch films have been provided by Neale (J.T.I., 1924, *15*, 443).

MECHANICAL PROPERTIES OF STARCH FILMS

	Strength (Kg/cm.^{2})	Extension %	Young's Modulus (dynes/cm.$^2 \times 10^{-10}$)
Farina (potato starch) . .	414	4·2	3·25
Maize starch	468	4·0	3·8
Sago starch . . .	400	2·6	3·12
Farina and castor oil (4%)	365	3·4	2·5
Farina and glycerin (3%)	381	4·3	2·65
Farina and tallow (2%) .	380	2·2	3·8
Farina and Japan wax (4·6%)	320	1·8	3·2

The general elastic behaviour of starch films seems similar to that of ductile metals; maize, farina, and sago show almost identical elastic properties. Glycerol, castor oil, and tallow soften the starch films, but there is a loss in strength if more than 5% of these softeners is incorporated in the starch film; the presence of Japan wax tends to make the starch film weak and brittle.

Some of the fundamental work in connection with starch originates from two main sources: (*a*) the conversion of starch to sugar by Kirchoff in 1812, and (*b*) the isolation of diastase (malt amylase) in 1833. Most of the subsequent work has been an investigation of the intermediate decomposition products of starch.

. As previously stated, the paste-forming properties of starch have been attributed to the amylopectin, and when the paste is treated with amylase there is a great drop in viscosity and a loss of opalescence. Other methods of bringing about a fall in viscosity are to boil the paste for prolonged periods or to grind the material.

When starch pastes are allowed to stand, they deposit solid matter which is not coloured by iodine or readily attacked by malt extract;

the deposit is not soluble in water at ordinary temperatures, but requires heating under pressure. The deposition is known as the retrogradation of starch, and may be increased by certain enzymes. The retrograded starch is assumed to result from the aggregation of the colloidal particles of amylose. It has been suggested that the retrogradation of amylose is due to the precipitation of the longer and less soluble chain-molecules when the solution is cooled, but this simple explanation is not sufficient to account for the whole effect. This effect may be retarded by treatment with formaldehyde, but it is also possible to oxidise starch so that it will dissolve in cold or warm water and give clear permanent solutions.

The chemical heterogeneity of starch was shown by extraction with hot water, without forming a paste. The water-soluble portion precipitates spontaneously or retrogrades, and thus exhibits colloidal instability by passing to a water-insoluble form. In the soluble form, the amylose is rapidly hydrolysed to maltose by enzymes such as malt diastase, but the insoluble form is unattacked. On the other hand, the original starch is hydrolysed by malt diastase into two products, sugars like maltose, and also dextrins which resist further degradation.

It appears to have been assumed for many years that all the maltose was derived from the amylose component and that the other constituent, amylopectin, which is only converted to a soluble dextrin, is responsible for the paste and gel-forming properties of starch.

There is a great deal of confused and conflicting evidence regarding the properties of the various fractions of starch which purport to be either amylose or amylopectin; these two substances can only be separated by great ingenuity and skilful manipulation. Indeed, it is only within the past few years that they have been isolated in a degree of purity which is acceptable to organic chemists. Hence, a clear picture of the constitution and structure is only now starting to emerge.

Structure

Like cellulose, starch has the empirical formula $(C_6H_{10}O_5)_n$, but it contains small amounts of phosphoric and silicic acids in addition. It has been suggested that the phosphoric acid is connected to the hydroxyl groups of the starch by an ester combination; it has also been shown that amylose generally contains little or no combined phosphoric acid. Silicic acid is probably combined in a similar manner.

Starch is composed of chains of α-glucose residues and therefore differs from cellulose, which consists of β-glucose residues, although in both cases the residues are united at the $1 : 4$ positions. With starch, the repeating unit in the molecular chain is maltose, whereas in cellulose it is cellobiose.

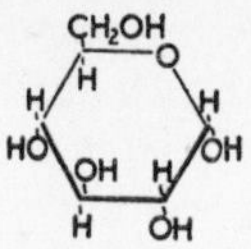

d-glucose 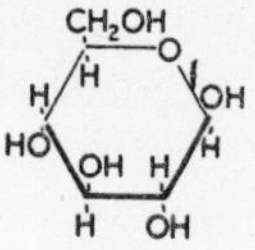 β-glucose

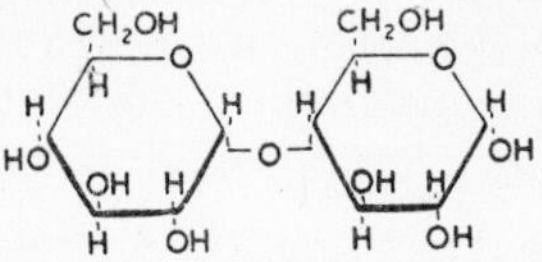

Maltose

Although the chemical nature of starch is not very greatly different from that of cellulose, its behaviour is by no means the same. Starch swells in water when the temperature is raised and becomes a gel with a very high water-content; at the same time, some part of the starch with a lower degree of polymerisation partly dissolves to the sol state. The viscosity of starch is much lower than that of cellulose in equivalent concentrations, and this may be accounted for by a branched or coiled chain structure.

Starch in solution does not exist in the form of micelles or aggregates of chain-molecules, but more as separate and dispersed chains; amylopectin, with its higher degree of polymerisation, is dispersed in the amylose which has passed into the sol state.

The constitution of starch has been established by Haworth and Hirst, together with their co-workers; some important contributions to the problem have been given by Haworth, Hirst, and Webb (J.C.S., 1928, 2681), Hirst, Plant, and Wilkinson (J.C.S., 1932, 2375), Haworth, Hirst, and Oliver (J.C.S., 1934, 1917), Haworth, Hirst, and Isherwood (J.C.S., 1937, 577) and Hirst and Young (J.C.S., 1939, 1471). On this basis of chain-molecules, starch should possess reducing powers which would be less the greater the length of the molecular chain; many workers failed to find evidence of reducing properties in starch, but Richardson, Higginbotham, and Farrow (J.T.I., 1936, 27, 131), however, showed that unmodified starch does possess reducing properties. It is well known, of course, that modified starch possesses reducing properties.

Although sago starch has higher reducing powers than maize or farina starch, it is not possible to distinguish between the different varieties by reducing powers alone. In general, the viscosities of unmodified starch pastes do not bear any simple relation to the reducing power, but among the sago pastes, whose viscosities are lower than those of maize or farina, the lower the viscosity the higher is the reducing power. With acid-modified farina, there seems to be a simple relation between viscosity and reducing power. In the early stages of hydrolysis a small increase in reducing power corresponds to a large decrease in chain length, and although the rapid diminution in viscosity of starch pastes has long been known, it was attributed to the formation of a soluble starch by disaggregation or liquefaction which preceded and differed from hydrolysis. Richardson, Higginbotham, and Farrow, however, have shown that soluble starch must be regarded as a degradation product of starch and only differing from unmodified starch and other degradation products in the average length, and distribution, of the chain-molecules.

According to the views of Haworth, based on end-group determinations, the simple chains of starch should be made up of 25 glucose units, but the work of Richardson, Higginbotham, and Farrow pointed to the necessity of about 1,000 glucose units to the chain-molecule. Staudinger (Naturwissenschaften, 1937, *25*, 673) came to the conclusion, from viscosity and osmotic pressure data, that the higher value was more nearly correct, and suggested that the structure was not that of straight chains but of branched chains. The chemical evidence for this hypothesis was supplied by Freudenberg (Ber., 1938, *71*, 2505; 1940, *73*, 609), from which it now appears that starch contains branched configurations, but with branching through the carbon atom in the 6 position of the various glucopyranose units.

Meyer (Helv. Chim. Acta, 1940, *23*, 845) returned to the examination of the amylose-amylopectin hypothesis which had been somewhat disregarded for many years and, by an elegant system of hot water extraction and retrogradation or spontaneous precipitation, was able to isolate a fraction which could be completely converted to maltose and therefore consists of straight chains. The branched structure does not apply to amylose, but to the residual starch which is not extracted by hot water. It was later found by Schoch (Cereal

Chem., 1941, *18*, 121) that the amyloses could be selectively precipitated by the addition of butyl alcohol to dilute starch pastes. In this manner it was found that maize, potato, and tapioca starches consist of 21 to 23% of straight chains and 77 to 79% of branched chain-molecules. The amylopectin fractions are branched to such an extent that only about 52% of maltose is produced from the purest fractions by treatment with β-amylase.

The isolation of the amyloses in crystalline form has been described by Kerr and Severson (see Paper Trade Journal, 1942, *115*, *TAPPI*, 292); there are also other important contributions (J.A.C.S., 1943, *65*, 142, 193). Some of the chief characteristics of the two types of structure have been tabulated by Kerr, as shown in the following table:

COMPARISON OF AMYLOSE AND AMYLOPECTIN

	Straight-chain Amylose	Branched-chain Amylopectin
Solubility in water	Soluble as isolated	Soluble after separation from amylose
Colloidal stability	Spontaneous pptn. above 0·5% concn.	Stable in 5% solution
Gel properties	5% solution sets to tough irreversible gel	Forms soft gels which re-dissolve
Viscosity of dilute solution	Low, but increases enormously with concentration	High, but a simple function of concn.
Protective colloid effect	Low	High
Iodine colour	Intense blue	Reddish purple
Estimated Mol. Wt.	35,000 or 200 units.	350,000 or 2,000 units
Effect of enzymes		
(a) Liquefying α-amylase	Attacked slowly; retrogrades and becomes resistant	Readily changed to dextrins
(b) Saccharifying β-amylase	95 to 100% conversion to maltose at low concn., but retrogradation at high concentrations to resistant form	Conversion to 52% maltose and 48% soluble dextrins

The enzymes which are used for the treatment of starch, as referred to in the table, may be divided into two main classes— liquefying and saccharifying. The liquefying enzymes have a great capacity for liquefying raw starch, but have poor sugar-forming properties; on the other hand, the saccharifying amylases convert solubilised starch and dextrin to sugars, but have relatively less liquefying action on raw starch.

The present view of starch, therefore, is that it consists of two components, one being highly branched and forming the major part of most starches; the other part is unbranched and amounts to about 25% of the whole. These two constituents differ in physical, chemical, and enzymatic properties. The variation in ability to form a starch-iodine complex has provided a means for the analysis of the two components, and has also demonstrated that they differ widely from one another, with no region of mixed properties; hence there is no product with an intermediate degree of branching.

Amylopectin exists as a branched chain of 24 to 30 glucose residues; the branching occurs about two-thirds of the distance along the short chain, and it seems as if there are 40 repeats of the chain in the branched structure as shown in the diagram.

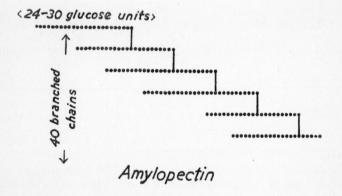

With modified or degraded starch, the number of branches in the branching system is less than with amylopectin, but the length of the short chains (i.e. the branch) is probably the same. In dextrin, on the other hand, the number of branches is still large, but the length of the short chain has been reduced to about one-third of the original value.

Amylose probably consists of longer unbranched chains containing more than 100 glucose residues. Amylose gives films and fibres, and its acetate also provides films and fibres; these are important in structural studies but have no commercial significance. Amylose has been crystallised from aqueous solutions at room temperatures, in a form similar to that of the natural tuber starches. The unit cell is orthorhombic (a) 6·0 Å, (b) 10·6 Å, and (c) 9·1 Å; there are eight glucose units per unit cell in four chains, with alternate chains running in opposite directions and the —CH_2OH groups *trans* to each other. When precipitated by alcohol, the unbranched chains form complexes, the chains form helices with the complexing agent inside the helix; the —CH_2OH groups are *cis* to each other.

Viscosity

An interesting study of the viscosity of starch pastes has been made by Richardson and Waite (J.T.I., 1933, *42*, 383). Whereas the viscosity of ordinary liquids may be determined by measuring the time occupied in driving a known volume of liquid through a narrow tube relative to the time required for a liquid of known viscosity, this simple treatment is inapplicable to starch pastes; the fall-ball method is preferred, but with standard conditions of flow it is possible to assign an apparent viscosity.

With unboiled pastes, the viscosity depends on the rate of stirring and the age of the paste; the viscosity falls as the age increases. There are, therefore, three types of change of starch: (*a*) a rise in viscosity by swelling and disruption of the granules; (*b*) a fall of viscosity with agitation; and (*c*) a fall of viscosity on storage of the paste, due to hydrolysis.

Farina pastes have high initial viscosities which fall rapidly with stirring, but sago pastes have a low initial viscosity and a less rapid rate of fall; maize gelatinises less rapidly than sago or farina, and the viscosity also falls less rapidly. Its initial viscosity is intermediate between farina and sago, but the rate of fall is the least rapid. In all cases, an increased rate of stirring leads to lower viscosities, and the mechanical agitation apparently hastens the disintegration of the granules.

The rate of change of viscosity during storage was shown to depend on the pH of the paste. With sago, the stable region is from pH 7 to 8, farina is more stable at pH 5, and maize or corn starch pastes at pH 4·5 to 6·5; pastes of higher acidity are subject to a rapid fall in viscosity. More alkaline pastes too, suffer a decrease in viscosity, except where soap is the alkaline medium. Most pastes are used at their natural pH, which seems satisfactory except in the case of sago, where the pH is 4·8. In certain circumstances, soaps have a stabilising effect; in low concentrations they behave as mild alkalis, but as the concentration of soap in the paste increases the viscosity reaches a minimum and then rises rapidly. Soap also delays the gelatinisation of the raw starch, as well as increasing the stability of the paste; it may react in such a manner as to prevent the access of water to those points which are active when swelling or are susceptible to acid hydrolysis.

The effect of neutral salts is also interesting, farina pastes being very sensitive; the effect is slight on sago pastes. Although pastes of farina are more viscous than those of sago, for the same concentration, the viscosity is lowered by the addition of salt; at the same time, the stability is increased so that farina pastes with salt are as stable as sago pastes. A similar reduction in viscosity on the addition of soluble salts has been noted for sols of gum arabic, soluble starch, and agar; the fall in viscosity may be due to a diminution of hydration of the colloid. A curious anomaly has been observed, however, for whereas the viscosity of sago paste changes more rapidly with time when salt is added, the reverse is true for farina. Now, as farina is valued on account of its high viscosity in spite of its low stability, where high viscosity is required the paste should be made with pure water, but if stability is wanted, a small quantity of a salt such as sodium sulphate may be added to the mixture, lowering the viscosity, and making a stable paste.

SOLUBLE STARCH

The chemical modification of starch has not been examined to the same extent as cellulose, but it is well known that the action of acid causes an increase in reducing power and a fall in viscosity; these are accompanied by an increase in solubility, and it seems that the so-called SOLUBLE STARCH differs from the natural starch in possessing a lower average chain-length.

One of the earliest chemical modifications of starch on a commercial scale was made in 1896 by Siemens, when various oxidising agents were employed. It was suggested that the modified starch be called "thin-boiling starch." This development was followed by others involving the use of enzymes and the use of dilute acids. The modified starches produced by oxidation are superior in colour to those made by acid hydrolysis; it is not yet clear if the two types of modified starch have the same chemical composition although the mechanical properties seem very similar. From consideration of the modified celluloses, the products of acid treatment should differ chemically from the oxidised starches.

The usual viscous solution of natural starch is not produced by dissolving soluble starch, which not only gives a limpid solution, but one which does not tend to be very viscous as the concentration is increased.

The modified starches have been discussed recently by Jambuser-wala (J.T.I., 1938, *29*, 149; 1939, *30*, 85; 1940, *31*, 1).

Attempts have been made to modify starch by physical means, such as grinding or heating, to give products which swell and form pastes with cold water; the net result, however, is not particularly different from the paste made by heating the natural starch with water. Treatment with oxidising agents, however, gives products which are soluble in hot water, but have less adhesive power than the solutions from the untreated starches; some of these "soluble" or "thin-boiling" starches require the addition of small quantities of alkali for complete solubility. Aktivin (the sodium derivative of p-toluene sulphochloramide) is believed to find wide commercial application in the preparation of soluble starch, as there is no substantial formation of dextrin or sugars.

Among the many commercial forms of "soluble" starch, some Dutch preparations have been described in detail by Dalendoord (J.S.D.C., 1932, *48*, 275).

DEXTRIN

DEXTRIN, or British gum, may be prepared from starch in two main ways: (*a*) the dry method, sometimes termed torrification; and (*b*) the wet method.

According to the first method, the starch may be heated alone or in presence of a small amount of inorganic acid; temperatures of 180°C. or above are employed, the starch giving up its moisture, turning a yellow-brown colour and becoming soluble in water. The addition of a little inorganic acid before heating, however, allows the reaction to take place at a lower temperature, and gives an improved product in respect of odour and colour. The first product is soluble starch, which then passes through various stages which merge into one another, but may be broadly distinguished by the colour reaction with iodine solution, which is graded from blue with soluble starch, through violet to a reddish-brown colour for dextrin.

Maize, potato, and tapioca starches are mainly used for the manufacture of dextrin, full details of which have been given by Radley (Starch and its Derivatives, Chapman and Hall, London, 1940).

When the temperature in the roasting apparatus has reached about 120°C., a small amount of moisture appears as steam, followed by a sudden evolution of a cloud of steam which is accompanied by a rise in temperature of 5° to 10°C., after which dextrinisation proceeds very rapidly. To avoid the process proceeding too far, the dextrin is discharged from the roasting apparatus and cooled rapidly.

The wet process for preparing dextrin depends on the treatment of starch suspensions with acids or other hydrolytic agents, such as enzymes; the sugar formed by enzymes is maltose, but acids give a certain amount of dextrose which is more hygroscopic than maltose and liable to cause cracking in the adhesive film. Where the acid process is used, the aqueous starch suspension is simply heated with hydrochloric or sulphuric acid until the hydrolysis has reached the required stage, as shown by viscosity tests and the iodine reaction; the mass is then cooled and the acid is neutralised. Where enzymes are used in place of acid, the starch paste is treated with the necessary preparation; malt diastase is used at pH 4·6, and pancreatic diastase at pH 6·9. The temperature of the conversion is usually 65° to 70°C., and the hydrolysis is stopped by heating to a higher temperature for a short time to destroy the activity of the enzyme.

The properties of the dextrin vary according to the method of treatment and there is no definite method of characterisation. Some dextrins give stable solutions, but with others the solutions increase in viscosity on standing; again some dextrin solutions give more viscous aqueous solutions than others, and some solutions dry more quickly than others. Commercial dextrin generally contains some unchanged starch, and the chief difficulty in its manufacture is to obtain a stable product without the formation of substantial amounts of dextrose. As shown above, some dextrins approximate to soluble starch and others to glucose.

WATER-RESISTANT STARCH

If formaldehyde is added to a hot starch paste, it does not set on cooling, and the viscosity of the liquid stirred at room temperatures changes more slowly.

The action of formaldehyde has received some attention, as shown by patent specifications.

B.P. 414,576, of the I.G., relates to the treatment of textiles with starch paste and formaldehyde in presence of an acid-reacting substance; alternatively, the fabric may be treated with a reaction product of starch and formaldehyde still capable of giving a paste. In both cases, the treated material is dried at an elevated temperature. As an example of the one-stage process, the fabric may be treated with 100 parts of starch paste to which has been added 15 parts of 30% formaldehyde and 0·5 part of oxalic acid, and then dried at 100°C.

The preparation of starch-formaldehyde pastes may be effected by treating 125 parts of potato starch for 24 hours with 75 parts of 30% formaldehyde solution, followed by drying at 50°C. under reduced pressure; a paste is then made with 8 parts of this product 42 parts of potato starch, and 1 part of ammonium thiocyanate in 1,000 parts of water at 60°C. The treated fabric should be dried at 100°C.

Starch-formaldehyde compounds were examined by Classen in 1897; the action of 40% formaldehyde solution was to give a colloidal solution which was not water-resistant, but the heating of starch (100 parts) with formaldehyde (1·8 parts) at 76°C. for 60 minutes in a closed vessel gave a water-resistant product which was, however decomposed by dilute acid.

Water-resistant starch products have also been prepared by the action of formaldehyde on starch which has been subjected to extreme dehydration, according to B.P. 522,672 and 523,566 of the

Corn Products Refining Company. The preliminary dehydration may be effected by long contact with dry air at an elevated temperature, after which the starch is mixed with formalin containing not more than 60% water; the solution should be at pH 2 or less. For example, starch may be dehydrated at 130°C. for 20 hours, and then mixed with its own weight of 40% formaldehyde and sufficient hydrochloric acid to give a pH of 1·8; the product may be applied to textile material and then heated for 10 minutes at 120°C. Cotton and starch treated in this manner may be steeped in water for some weeks without loss of adhesion.

The product of reaction between starch and formaldehyde is a methylene ether of starch; attempts have been made to make many other ethers of starch, but none appears to have reached extensive commercial application.

It is also possible to make many esters of starch, and in particular various acetates have been made in the hope that they will replace the more expensive derivatives of cellulose as coatings and lacquers, but their commercial application is very limited at the moment.

B.P. 466,287 of Schultz describes starch adhesives which are soluble in hot water but insoluble in cold water; they are prepared by spraying raw starch with chloral hydrate (2% of a 30% solution) containing 3% of HCl, followed by heating. The properties of the product depend on the duration of heating, 60°C. for 3 hours giving a syrupy solution which sets at 75°C. from hot water, whereas heating at 90°C. gives a more soluble product, a 10% solution of which solidifies at 35°C.

Attempts have been made to produce a permanent starching of fabrics by incorporating synthetic resins in the starch paste. B.P. 258,357 of British Cyanides suggested the use of urea-formaldehyde products in colloidal solution, and B.P. 385,378 makes use of acetone-formaldehyde condensation products; these methods do not appear to have been practised on a large scale. Fixapret of the I.G., which appeared about 1932, consisted mainly of dimethylol urea and a catalyst, for addition to starch pastes in order to give a permanent starched effect to textiles.

The methylol ureas have been used by Rohm and Haas (B.P. 543,432 and 3) to stabilise modified starch pastes; the starch is partly hydrolysed, mixed with dimethylol urea at pH 7 to 10, and heated at a temperature above 80°C.

TEXTILE APPLICATIONS

The use of starch as a stiffener and adhesive has been known from time immemorial, and according to Depierre (Traité des Apprêts, Paris, 1887, p. 14) it was even used as a textile finish in

800 B.C., but appears to have been forgotten later except as a filling material.

About 1560, the use of starch became popular in France and Holland as a means of stiffening the ruffles of the nobility; the fashion spread to England in Elizabethan days.

The use of starch became so popular for textile dressings and also as a powder for the hair that it had to be forbidden in 1600 and again in 1800.

The early use of starch in the textile industry was as a size in weaving, and this practice was firmly established about 1750; the next development, which followed quickly, was as a thickener in hand block printing.

The crude wheat starch was followed by potato starch when the textile trade started to use it as a finish for cloth.

The shortage of sugar after the Napoleonic Wars led to investigations of starch as a source of glucose, during the course of which the "thinning" of starch by enzymes was studied, leading to products which were more suitable for textile purposes. Renewed interest brought about further developments, and maize starch was produced, becoming the chief textile starch about 1880.

Although a comparison of "roasted starch" with natural gums had been made in 1804, according to Morgan (Am. Dyes. Rep., 1940, 29, 494), it was a fire in a textile mill in Dublin which led to the discovery of dextrin or British gum in 1821; some starch was roasted in this fire, and it was observed that the roasted starch was more soluble and gave interesting results on cloth. Increasing demand and the shortage of natural gums led to its manufacture on a large scale.

In spite of recent developments in numerous synthetic finishing agents, starch still remains the commonest and most important finishing agent; its use has been roundly condemned on the grounds that it is not fast to washing, a defect that has been over-emphasised, for washable goods are only a portion of textile production. Nevertheless, there is no justification for selling starch and China clay instead of cotton.

Probably the most outstanding property of solutions of raw starch is their high viscosity, but this may be modified by suitable treatments, as discussed previously. The viscosity, however, must be such that the textile material to which the solution is applied will take up different amounts by varying the degree of penetration into the yarns and fabric. This is more easily done with the thin-boiling starches whose viscosity does not increase unduly with concentration; further advantages are the shorter time of boiling and the lower rate of congealing so that they are more firmly fixed to the fibres.

Each type of starch possesses characteristic properties which are utilised in obtaining different effects in finishing; starch is still the most widely used finishing agent for cotton fabric, particularly white goods, and may be utilised as a filling or stiffening agent, as well as a binding agent for various inorganic compounds such as the well-known China clay. Wheat flour is stated to provide a dressing which is unsurpassed in its ability to retain weighting material, and is capable of holding twice its weight of China clay or barium sulphate without "dusting-off"; the best potato starch will only hold 1·5 times its weight of fillers. This power of holding weighting material has been attributed to the presence of gluten in the flour; wheat flour, however, is rarely used for the finishing of white goods, as it affects the colour of the material and also is susceptible to mildew formation, but it finds an outlet in the sizing of yarns and the finishing of grey goods.

Although wheat starch gives a smooth thick feel to the cloth, imparting firmness and some solidity, it is apt to crack on the surface; the starched goods take a high gloss on beetling or calendering.

Farina or potato starch gives a soft and flexible finish, and in conjunction with a glazing agent, such as borax or wax, is capable of producing a high gloss without appreciable increase in weight. The viscous nature of the farina paste tends to prevent much penetration into the yarns of the fabric, so that the starch is more on the surface, imparting a thick and crisp effect, which "mellows" on ageing and conditioning.

Rice starch, on the other hand, penetrates better and gives a harder finish, with a fullness and firmness which is apt to be regarded as "boardy"; it is of great interest in the laundering industry as a stiffener, for it is less affected by humidity than other starches.

Maize or corn starch, on account of the viscosity of its solution, gives a crisp effect which is slightly harsher than that from farina; although potato starch gives pastes of slightly higher viscosity than maize starch, they must be used the same day on account of instability, but maize starch pastes are relatively stable in viscosity. Maize or corn starch is often employed in conjunction with potato starch or farina. The feel imparted by maize starch is characteristic, even with well-boiled starch pastes, but the soluble starch from maize gives a finish somewhat similar to that from wheat starch.

Tapioca starch gives a thin and soft effect from the typical transparent gel of the paste; the finish is tough and flexible as compared with maize or corn starch, but it is rarely used alone.

Sago starch finds application mainly in sizing, for although it gives a thin firm feel to the cloth, unfortunately it tends to crack, particularly on folding.

The soluble starches are chiefly prepared from maize starch or potato starch and provide valuable finishing agents, giving a great

19

variety of effects. Their solutions are less viscous than the pastes from untreated starch, and so penetrate the material to a greater extent, giving a firm and somewhat leathery handle. On account of their lower viscosity, they may be employed in higher concentrations than ordinary starch without reaching a stage where they are unworkable. Soluble starch, however, cannot be used instead of ordinary starch for filling with China clay and similar material as the binding power is much less, and the mineral filling material will "dust off"; nevertheless, it may be used with ordinary starch and China clay to give a less viscous mixture which flows more readily and is easier to apply.

Dextrin is chiefly used alone for the finishing of dyed goods; it imparts weight and firmness without giving a "starchy" feel to the cloth, but in large amounts it produces the unwelcome "tacky" effect. Starch, on the other hand, is apt to obscure and dull the colours of dyed goods.

Many finishing preparations contain more than one type of starch, and although these are sometimes gelatinised together, it may be preferable to make the pastes separately and then boil the mixed pastes to form a homogeneous mass and so avoid the danger of some of the starch, which swells at the lower temperature, coating the granules which should burst at a higher temperature, and thus preventing true gelatinisation; in such a paste there would always be a danger of subsequent "flaking off." There are commercial preparations of mixed starches, together with about 10% sodium hydroxide, which need very thorough stirring and agitation in water to give a mobile paste, the initial action of alkali being to produce a rubbery mass which later gives place to a fluid paste.

An evaluation of starch preparations for various textile purposes has been made by Schreiber and Stafford (Ind. Eng. Chem., Anal. Ed., 1942, *14*, 227), and methods are suggested for estimating (*a*) the "stickiness" during drying and ironing, (*b*) ease of penetration into the fabric, (*c*) transparency of the starch film, (*d*) effect of crushing the starched fabric, (*e*) the stiffness of the starched fabric, and (*f*) the smoothness of the starched fabric.

In general, preparations of starch are applied for one of two purposes:

(*a*) Stiffening.
(*b*) Binding.

For stiffening, the starch should not lie on the surface, but penetrate into the cloth, so that a viscous solution is not required; in these circumstances, the ordinary starch paste, even at 1 lb. per gallon, is apt to give a surface film with a thin, hard and papery effect, so that thin-boiling starches are to be preferred.

Fillers

Filling materials are often used in conjunction with starch, for if utilised alone they are apt to dust off; in these circumstances, the starch acts as a binding agent.

China clay is probably the commonest of these finishing agents. It is a naturally occurring form of aluminium silicate, of which there are large deposits in Cornwall; kaolin is another name for this product. The pure material is quite white, and when finely ground, is very smooth and free from grittiness. Its density is about 2·2, so that it possesses good covering power; it forms a smooth opaque mass with starch and water, and gives a better and fuller appearance to the fabric than does starch alone.

French chalk, or talc, is a naturally occurring magnesium silicate which can be supplied in the form of a very smooth white powder; its density is 2·5, but it seems more difficult to incorporate in starch mixings than China clay and requires more binding material. It is not so widely used in textile finishing as it tends to float in the mixing, and give finishes which tend to dust off; its covering power is less than that of China clay.

Barium sulphate has a harsher feel than either China clay or French chalk, and is therefore used more as a weighting agent than a filling material; its density is 4·5, so that it does not possess the same covering power. The naturally occurring product is termed barytes in the older publications, and must not be confused with baryta, which is barium oxide. An alternative form of barium sulphate, made from soluble barium salts by precipitation with sulphuric acid or sodium sulphate, is termed "blanc fixe." The harsh feel imparted by these two substances is determined to some extent by the fineness to which they have been ground, but in general the natural product always has a gritty feel.

Calcium sulphate is sometimes used in place of China clay as it is cheaper; nevertheless it has a harsher feel but gives similar cover, its density being 2·3. It is softer than the barium sulphates and is more easily bound to the fabric. The naturally occurring form is sometimes termed "mineral," and the manufactured product is referred to as "satin white"; both forms are represented by the hydrate $CaSO_4.2H_2O$ and must not be confused with plaster of Paris, which is $(CaSO_4)_2.H_2O$.

Although the above insoluble weighting agents may be added in the dry state to the starch solution, it is more general to mix them into a paste with water first; some of the compounds are rather difficult to wet with water when they have once been dried. The usual procedure is to mix the water with the China clay, for example, and stir for some time before allowing the mixture to settle. The supernatant water is then removed and the wet and viscous paste may be added to the starch as required. It is on this account that many recipes refer to a number of "pails" of China clay; in these circumstances, it may be assumed that the proportion of actual China clay is about 4 lb. to the gallon.

Antiseptics

Fabrics finished with flour and starch preparations are readily mildewed if kept in a damp place; deliquescent substances often form part of finishing preparations containing starch and their presence accentuates the tendency towards mildew.

It is often desirable, therefore, to include an antiseptic or disinfectant product in the starch preparation in order to inhibit mildew formation. Generally, it has been found that starches are slightly more resistant to mildew than flours; the work of Morris (J.T.I., 1926, *17*, 1 and 23) is of interest in this connection. The common agents used in the textile industry are magnesium chloride, zinc chloride, zinc sulphate, barium chloride, phenol, cresylic acid, salicylic acid, formaldehyde, and Shirlan (salicylanilide).

The phenolic products suffer from the disadvantage of their characteristic odour, whilst salicylic acid is costly and not particularly efficient. The inorganic chlorides above-mentioned possess certain anti-mildew properties, but their use is attended with some danger if the goods are heated, as in schreinering, when some tendering or damage to the cellulose may occur. Formaldehyde is useful, as it forms an unstable compound with starch under both acid and alkaline conditions. For most purposes, however, the use of Shirlan, or salicylanilide, is to be recommended.

Some of the quantities of various antiseptics which have been suggested from time to time are zinc chloride (6%), boric acid (2%), sodium fluorsilicate (2%), cresol or phenol (0·5%), copper sulphate (0·3%), and salicylic acid (0·3%).

Softeners

With regard to the use of softeners, the reader is referred to an account of these substances on page 259. Attention may be drawn, however, to a particular use of the non-drying alkyd resins in conjunction with starches and gums, by Rohm and Haas, as outlined in U.S.P. 2,203,773. The resin may be formed from glycerol, phthalic acid, sebacic acid, and castor oil, and applied in aqueous dispersion. About 5 parts of 25% dispersion may be applied in 100 parts of water. This addition does not "thin" the starch solution, but tends to thicken it; in addition to softening properties, the resin stops the starch from "dusting" and also reduces the solubility of the finish in water.

APPLICATION

The usual method of preparing the starch mixings is to weigh out the materials, and then stir the starch with a small amount of water, grinding it into a cream which is then passed through a sieve. More water is added and heat applied until gelatinisation takes place; the other ingredients are then added, first the fillers and then the softeners, the former having previously been ground to a fine state of subdivision. Lastly, the final amount of water is added to bring the mixture to the required concentration, when it is boiled and stirred until the required consistency is reached; the time of boiling usually does not exceed 10 minutes, but must be definite in order to avoid inconsistencies. The boiling may be effected by either open or closed steam coils; the former are apt to give the impression of ebullition before the required temperature has been reached, but the latter, on the other hand, tend to give local overheating.

The mixing is then run into the trough or box of the mangle from which it is to be applied. These mangles or machines may be considered in four classes:

(1) Simple stiffening mangles.
(2) Friction mangles.
(3) Back-filling machines.
(4) Back-skimming or back-starching machines.

It is, of course, impossible to dogmatise on the treatment of cotton piece goods with starch preparations, for they cover an enormously wide field, but in general it seems that most thin fabrics are passed directly into the nip of the mangle bowls—the so-called "direct nip" method. In these circumstances, the bottom bowl picks up sufficient of the mixing for application to the cloth. Heavier fabrics are led into the trough and through the mixing, where they are enabled to take up more of the paste than would be possible with the "direct nip."

In both methods, however, the speed of the mangle plays an important part in the amount taken up, as also does the "set" or expression of the mangle; to a minor degree, the type of bowl too, plays a part, for wooden bowls apply less of the mixing to the cloth than do rubber or cotton bowls. Where very heavy mixings are applied to light cloths it is sometimes found that the top bowl is apt to slip and distort the weft threads; this is sometimes accompanied by a very definite "chatter." The so-called Scotch or friction mangle obviates this defect by a geared drive for both top and bottom bowls; the friction effect rubs the finishing preparation into the fabric and gives a heavier effect than is possible from the ordinary mangle without resorting to expensive double and treble passages with intermediate dryings.

It is important that where brass bowls are utilised, they should be kept scrupulously clean, for if verdigris forms on the ends it may become detached and form green spots on the cloth.

With back-filling, as the name implies, the starch mixing is applied to the back of the cloth, filling the interstices to give a compact and improved appearance, but maintaining the "face" of the fabric. This is done by passing the cloth round a large wooden or brass bowl which is partially immersed in the box containing the mixing; the filling preparation is pressed into the back of the fabric by a doctor blade which also removes the surplus. At the back of the machine, a second doctor keeps the bowl clean and free from starch so that the face of the cloth is not affected; in the trough itself, an agitator rotates in the mixing and keeps it in a homogeneous state so that the heavier ingredients of the filling do not separate. It is essential that the doctor blades should be examined frequently, as lint and other small particles of solid material are apt to accumulate and cause streaky effects on account of the local absence of the starch preparation. With the back-filling method of applying finishing preparations, these should be definitely viscous, for a "thin mixing" is apt to penetrate the cloth and give an unwelcome chalky appearance to the face.

The type of back-filling mangle described above is often popularly known as the "Tommy Dodd"; it is illustrated in Fig. 24 (page 36).

When starch preparations are applied by the back-skimming method, the usual machine is the "Betty Dodd" mangle; the fabric does not pass into the trough or mangle box, but is drawn horizontally over a bowl which rotates in the starch mixing. The excess of starch is scraped away by doctor knives. It may be remarked that whilst much depends on the correct operation of the mangle during the back-filling process, the secret of success is really determined by the presence of a smooth homogeneous paste.

Universal mangles are also available and can be utilised for the application of starch and starch preparations in a variety of different ways.

It is customary to arrange the starch mangles in a range with a set of drying cylinders or cans which partially dry the fabric before passing on to a stenter where the cloth is completely dried and stretched to the required width. In ordinary use, the first of these cans might become partly "starched" by picking up the preparation from the wet cloth, particularly where there is an excess of water or insufficient softener; the dried starch would flake off the cans and give an uneven effect to the oncoming cloth. This may be obviated by passing the cloth over water-cooled rollers before meeting the heated cans or by wrapping the first few cylinders with thin cloth to give a more gradual drying action.

Drying and setting to width are accomplished on the stenter frame, which may be fitted with a jig or swing motion in which the chain-rails move backwards and forwards relative to one another and so break the temporary adhesion of the yarns at their points of intersection. This destroys the binding effect of the starch film, and again permits warp and weft to be independent, and gives full play to the elastic nature of woven structures.

Most starched fabrics require a final treatment, such as calendering, to give the best appearance, but the calender may also be utilised to remove any variations in starched cloths, by intelligent use of the amount of water sprayed on the cloth before calendering—if the cloth is too stiff, less water should be applied before calendering than with a softer cloth. Many glazed chintz fabrics rely on a calendered starch finish for their effect, sometimes in conjunction with synthetic resins.

Recipes

The various, and exceedingly numerous, recipes for starch preparations are determined to a very large extent by the type of finish required and the fabric to which they are applied, but range upwards to about 1 lb. of starch to the gallon of the final preparation.

A light mixing suitable for nainsook may be made from 5 lb. of maize starch, 5 lb. of tapioca starch, 20 lb. of stearate softener, and water to 50 gallons.

A heavier mixing for medium-weight cloths is made from 50 lb. dextrin, 30 lb. maize starch, 30 lb. tapioca starch, 50 lb. tallow softener, and water to 140 gallons.

A muslin finish may be prepared from 40 lb. of farina, and 0·5 gallons of Turkey red oil, made up to 100 gallons with water; a cambric finishing preparation, on the other hand, might utilise 50 lb. of maize starch with 0·5 gallons of Turkey red oil, again in 100 gallons of water.

A suggested mixing for Bedford cord fabrics is 80 lb. of maize starch and 1 gallon of Turkey red oil in 100 gallons of water.

Silesias, or cotton twills, have been finished with a mixture of 160 lb. of dextrin, 60 lb. of maize starch, and 2 gallons of Turkey red oil in 100 gallons of water.

Dextrin instead of starch has been used in about 4% solution for voiles, where a crisp effect is required; a softer effect, as for zephyrs, may be obtained from a mixture of 75 lb. of dextrin and 0·5 gallons of Turkey red oil in 100 gallons of water.

It appears to be common English practice to boil these compositions for about 10 minutes, but in the U.S.A. a longer period of about 45 minutes is more usual.

In all the above prescriptions, additions should be made of a small amount of an antiseptic to prevent mildew; at one time phenol was commonly employed to the extent of 0·25 pints per 100 gallons of "mixing." A second subsidiary addition to the main mixture is usually Ultramarine, about 1 pint of 10% paste, per 100 gallons, in order to give a good "white" to the finished product; other tinting materials are Prussian Blue, Indanthrene Blue, and Indigo—acid, direct and basic colours are only used for special purposes, such as tinting to definite shades.

The same great variation in "mixes" may be seen when the starch is used to bind filling materials, and the following recipes are merely illustrative of the general type. This aspect of finishing has been dealt with at some length by Bean in *The Chemistry and Practice of Finishing* (Manchester, 1912), where 48 different cotton samples are exhibited.

A back-filling mix for a cambric may be made from 18 lb. of dextrin, 25 lb. of wheat starch, 25 lb. of farina, 90 lb. of China clay, 50 lb. of calcium sulphate, and 2 gallons of Turkey red oil in 100 gallons of water, together with antiseptic and "blue."

A recipe for a shirting finish includes 60 lb. of farina, 90 lb. of dextrin, 70 lb. of China clay, 4 lb. of coco-nut oil, 70 lb. of calcium sulphate, and 4 gallons of Turkey red oil in 100 gallons of water.

A recipe which may be used for the preparation of book cloth by the back-filling method is as follows: 18 lb. of potato starch, 80 lb. maize starch, 32 lb. of dextrin, 43 lb. of sulphonated tallow softener, 12 gallons of China clay (4 lb. per gallon), 4 oz. of Ultramarine, and water to 100 gallons.

The following mixture has been suggested for cotton twills: 22 lb. of farina, 22 lb. of wheat starch, 90 lb. of China clay, and 2 gallons of Turkey red oil in 100 gallons of water.

Although starch preparations are mainly applied to white material, the following recipe is suitable for black linings: 90 lb. of dextrin, 4 oz. of soda ash, and 4 oz. of Direct Black B in 60 gallons of water.

One of the simplest mixings for back-skimming is 15 lb. of farina, and 30 lb. of China clay in 25 gallons of water.

Buckrams and other really boardy finishes are often the result of farina; a preliminary application of 1 lb. per gallon on a two-bowl geared mangle is followed by drying. Three treatments are often necessary to enable the cloth to stand on end, and care must be taken to keep the cloth free from creases, but nevertheless under relaxed tension to obviate breakages.

The production of a crisp finish on spun-rayon fabrics may be accomplished by using a mixture of 5 lb. of potato starch in 45 gallons of water to which has been added 2 quarts of 40% formaldehyde solution and 2 quarts of sulphonated oil in 5 gallons of water.

ALTERNATIVES TO STARCH

Although the use of starch is still pre-eminent for stiffening and binding finishes for cotton goods, there are certain fabrics, such as nets, laces, and veilings, whose woven construction requires some support without substantial filling. The object is slightly to stiffen the fabric and preserve the woven pattern. For this purpose, glues and gums were often used, but even though considerable amounts of glue are still employed for the finishing of lace curtains and nets, the general tendency is for these products to be replaced by starch and dextrin. A recent exception is in the preparation of adhesive nets to cover windows in war-time and prevent the broken glass scattering; this aspect of finishing has been discussed by Butterworth (Chem. and Ind., 1942, 61, 339, 350).

Both gelatin and glue are prepared from horn, bones, and skins of animals, and the principal difference between these two products depends on the state of the raw material and the care in manufacture; the better products are derived from skins.

In addition to the simple application of these products as stiffening agents, it is possible to utilise their reaction with tannic acid or with formaldehyde to produce a water-resisting finish. Casein may also be used, as it, too, can react with tannic acid or formaldehyde to give an insoluble product; the use of casein and similar products for waterproofing is discussed on page 471.

The use of gums in finishing occupies a minor position; their chief textile application is in printing pastes, but they are occasionally used in conjunction with starch. The chief products are Gum Arabic, Tragacanth, and Tragasol.

Gum arabic is the dried exudation from the acacia tree; it is the only natural gum which is soluble in water. It requires 1·5 times its weight of water to give a viscous solution from which it may be precipitated by alcohol. A limited use of gum arabic solutions is seen in the finishing of real silk fabrics and of some rayons, particularly in giving "body" to the fabric without interfering with the transparency; the cost is generally too high for use with cotton goods.

Gum tragacanth is also a dried exudation which may be obtained in flake form by slicing the bark of the tree or in vermicelli form by puncturing the bark. It swells in cold water to give a thick gel which forms a colloidal solution, but this sets again on cooling; solubility may be achieved by the use of alkali. The viscosity of tragacanth is higher than that of gum arabic, but the adhesive power is less. There is a limited use of this product for the finishing of mercerised shirtings.

Gum tragasol is obtained from the seed of a variety of bean, and its properties are similar to those of gum tragacanth. Again, the chief application is in printing, but there is a small outlet in finishing on account of the transparency, flexibility, and binding power.

Certain extracts from seaweeds have been employed in finishing textiles. Irish moss, in the form of a stiff jelly, is used to give a soft bulky feel to fabrics, and there is an absence of any paperiness; both Irish moss and Iceland moss are compatible with many other finishing agents.

Alginates have also been suggested for various finishes, particularly in view of their reaction with salts of polyvalent metals.

There has been a tendency within recent years to investigate the properties of the cellulose ethers as alternatives to starch, and this aspect of finishing is discussed on page 346. Again, the growing use of synthetic resins has enabled them to be used as stiffening and binding agents, as described on page 363.

Before concluding the discussion of starch and allied substances as stiffening and binding agents, it may be well to repeat that the use of starch as a binder or stiffener is almost confined to the white goods, as it is apt to "cloud" colours; gums, dextrins, and other transparent products are capable of satisfactory application to coloured material.

CHAPTER XII

WEIGHTING

THE weighting of textile fabrics falls into two classes:

(a) Cotton (and occasionally wool).
(b) Silk.

In the first class, the finishing agents for effecting an increase in weight are mainly the sulphates of magnesium and sodium, but with some woollen and worsted fabrics it is customary to employ deliquescent salts, such as zinc and magnesium chlorides. Calcium chloride has also been suggested.

In the second class, advantage is taken of the peculiar affinity for tin salts possessed by silk, and it is possible to bring about a great increase in weight by this means.

WOOL

Treatment of woollen and worsted material to increase their weight is not commonly practised in England, but is frequently carried out in continental Europe. It is important that the handle of the fabric should not be adversely affected, nor should it feel damp after treatment. The usual method of finishing with solutions of the necessary inorganic salts is merely to pad the fabric in an aqueous solution, followed by mangling and drying; the drying process is often carried out on cylinders, whereby a little lustre and stiffness are imparted to the material.

COTTON

The weighting of cotton goods is quite common practice, and its object is to increase the weight of the fabric without bringing about a stiffening effect. The commonest weighting agents are soluble salts, such as Epsom-salt ($MgSO_4$) and Glauber salts (Na_2SO_4). Their weighting properties depend on their great solubility in water enabling highly concentrated solutions to be applied.

Whereas the insoluble inorganic compounds are unable to penetrate the cellulose itself, this is not so with the simple solutions of magnesium and sodium sulphates; the cotton or linen material becomes swollen with the aqueous solution, from which the salts crystallise inside the fibres on drying and so impart a full handle to the goods.

The Epsom-salt finish is commonly practised on coloured-woven goods, such as ginghams, and also with flannelettes. The process is simple, and merely consists in impregnation followed by drying, usually on steam-heated cylinders. On account of the solubility of the magnesium sulphate it is possible greatly to increase the weight of the goods to which it is applied. The highest concentration of $MgSO_4.7H_2O$ for convenience is a solution of 60° to 70°Tw., above which there is a tendency for the salt to crystallise on the bowls of the mangle and on the drying cylinders. Solutions of 20° to 40°Tw. are used for a lighter finish, which may result in an increase in weight of 10 to 15%, and a firm handle, without the stiffness which accompanies starch or dextrin.

The Epsom-salt finish occasionally gives rise to tendering of the cloth to which it is applied, and various theories have been put forward to account for this phenomenon. There is no conclusive evidence to support the idea that weakening is due to crystallisation damaging the individual fibres, but in some cases the crystals may cut the fibres during subsequent calendering.

It has also been suggested that the tendering of cotton containing Epsom-salt when heated, either by hot calenders, hot presses, or the household iron, is due to small amounts of $MgCl_2$ often present as an impurity; undoubtedly this is a contributory factor, but, nevertheless, tendering has been recorded when no magnesium chloride was present. It appears, therefore, that some decomposition takes place at high temperatures with the liberation of sufficient acidity to tender the cotton cloth; there is no risk of damage during storage. It is generally unwise to finish Epsom-salt fillings with a hot calendering, but it is sometimes essential to hot-press garments during manufacture. The risk of damage may be reduced considerably by adding about 3 to 5 lb. of borax to every 100 lb. of the magnesium sulphate used in the original weighting process; sodium carbonate causes partial precipitation of the magnesium as the carbonate.

Sodium sulphate or Glauber salt, $Na_2SO_4.10H_2O$, has also been used as a weighting material in the same way as magnesium sulphate; the tendency to efflorescence is a defect of this salt.

Turkey red oil or, better still, Calsolene Oil HS, is a very satisfactory softener for use in conjunction with Epsom-salt.

As the above compounds are soluble in water, the weighting effect is usually removed in the first laundering treatment.

A typical recipe for an Epsom-salt finish is Epsom-salt 200 lb., glucose (60°Tw.) 1 gallon, zinc chloride (102°Tw.) 1 gallon, with the addition of water to make 100 gallons.

The salt finishes do not impart any particular lustre to the material to which they are applied, and at one time it was customary to give a second treatment with wax emulsions, followed by hot calendering. Emulsions of paraffin, wax, or stearic acid can be made sufficiently resistant to salt solutions to enable them to be incorporated in the finishing solutions; B.P. 293,746, of H. T. Bohme, made use of naphthalene sulphonic acids as dispersing agents which are stable to salt solutions, but most chemical manufacturers have since made use of the more recent dispersing agents to form emulsions which are stable to salt solutions. This new technique enables the material to be treated with a wax-like compound and a soluble salt in one operation and to take a high degree of lustre on subsequent calendering.

More recently, urea has been employed as a weighting agent, particularly for rayon; it is capable of increasing the weight of the goods by 10% or so, and provides a full mellow handle without a feeling of stiffness or powderiness. Velan PF (0·1%) is a good softener for use with urea as a weighting material.

A characteristic feature of finishes which rely on substances of the above type is the change in handle and feel with changes in atmospheric humidity.

SILK

During the degumming of silk, there is a loss in weight amounting to about 25%, but the use of certain natural colouring matters, like logwood or cutch, or of iron compounds such as Prussian Blue, gave an increase in weight which was incidental to the actual dyeing. Owing to the expensive nature of silk, it is only reasonable to suppose that a demand was made for all dyed materials to show a similar increase in weight and so replace some of the scouring losses. In the last century the chief application of weighting was seen in the dyeing of blacks, by the combination of the absorbed tannin with iron salts; the use of colourless tannin extracts enabled a certain amount of weight to be added with other shades.

The introduction of the coal-tar colours marked a departure from weighting as incidental to dyeing and led to the investigation of methods for weighting silk as a finishing process. The use of tin salts is now so well established that even the older method for blacks, with iron salts, tannin, and logwood, is often replaced by treatment with a tin salt in conjunction with cutch as a mordant for logwood.

The early treatments with tin salts were almost entirely confined to the processing of yarn; the chemistry of the process was not fully understood, and the amount of weighting was often so excessive that the goods had deteriorated before they left the shelves of the merchants.

The tendency to harshness of the tin-weighted silks is well known, but there are no complaints regarding the softness of the black silk dyed by the iron-tannin-logwood method.

The actual origin of tin weighting appears to be wrapped in mystery, probably on account of its discovery during the days of secret processes; many patents for improvements of one sort or another were easily upset by establishing "prior user."

The first methods of weighting tin with inorganic salts appear to have followed the course of soaking the raw silk in stannic chloride solution and then giving a fixation treatment with sodium carbonate, after which the raw silk was boiled in soap solution to remove the gum. The increase in weight was only small, and the strength of the silk was often adversely affected. Fixation of the tin with sodium phosphate was introduced later, and in the final treatment a little sulphuric acid was added to the bath, liberating phosphoric acid and increasing the weight of the silk. The treatment with sodium silicate, which was introduced at a later date, brought about a considerable increase in weighting. It was also found that a soaking in aluminium sulphate solution between the last phosphate bath and the final treatment with silicate brought about a further increase in weight.

The method generally practised nowadays is to soak the silk in a solution of stannic chloride (pinking) and sodium phosphate (phosphating) alternately, washing the silk after each treatment with stannic chloride and washing and acidifying after each treatment with phosphate; when sufficient loading has been obtained in this manner, the silk is finally treated with sodium silicate solution.

The chemistry of the process is somewhat complex, and the ultimate product is largely determined by the particular conditions obtaining during the process. Most of the evidence points to the view that the fibroin absorbs the $SnCl_4$, but some writers consider that an additive compound is formed; it seems to be established, however, that the tin chloride is taken up as a whole by the silk, and changes to the hydroxide on washing, when the hydrochloric acid passes into the wash-waters.

There is no such unanimity of opinion about the phosphating stage; Heermann (Farb. Zeit., 1903 to 1909) considers that the sodium phosphate is taken up as a whole with the formation of a tin-sodium phosphate such as $Sn(ONa)_2HPO_4$ which, on washing, breaks down into $Sn(OH)_2HPO_4$. The increased acidity of the phosphate in industrial practice is attributed to the introduction of hydrochloric acid by the silk. Fichter and Heusler (Helv. Chim. Acta, 1924, 7, 587) showed that the amount of sodium ion fixed by a stannic acid gel (in absence of silk) from a phosphate solution bears no relation to the amount of phosphate ion fixed; for a phosphate solution of the usual concentration in practice, the ratio is about $PO_4 : 4 Na$, so that the phosphate bath becomes more acid. The adsorption compound loses relatively more sodium hydroxide than phosphoric acid when washed, so that the wash-water becomes more alkaline.

It is often stated that the function of the phosphate process is to "fix" the stannic acid, and this assumes that the precipitate is rendered insoluble by the phosphate. In actual fact, the phosphated stannic acid gel is dissolved by water, whereas the unphosphated stannic acid does not dissolve; the phosphating process, however, renders the stannic acid gel insoluble in concentrations of hydrochloric acid likely to be found in the pinking bath and in which the unphosphated gel readily dissolves.

Considerable data on the composition of stannic chloride and sodium phosphate baths have been published by Ley (Chem. Zeit., 1915, *39*, 973, 986; 1921, *45*, 645, 676), together with the results of examination of the excess liquors removed by the centrifuge, and also of the wash-waters.

During the weighting processes, the following reactions are considered to occur; first the tin chloride is hydrolysed

$$SnCl_4 \longrightarrow Sn(OH)_4 + HCl$$

Some of the stannic chloride is only decomposed during the subsequent washing.

Treatment with the sodium phosphate forms a basic tin phosphate in the following manner:

$$Sn(OH)_4 + Na_2HPO_4 \longrightarrow Sn(OH)_2.HPO_4 + NaOH$$

The sodium hydroxide liberated reacts with the disodium phosphate to form the trisodium phosphate.

The treatment with sodium silicate converts the basic tin phosphate into a trisilicate of tin.

$$Sn(OH)_2.HPO_4 + Na_2SiO_2O. \longrightarrow (SiO_2)_3SnO_2 + Na_2HPO_4 + NaOH$$

One of the principle reasons for the weakening of silk after the weighting process is the tendency of the tin silicate to pass from the colloidal form to the crystalline state, bringing about some disruption of the fibre.

The general process is first to soak the silk in stannic chloride solution at room temperatures, centrifuge, and wash in hard water; the silk is then treated in dibasic sodium phosphate solution and washed. This process may be repeated two or three times, and it is generally found that each course of treatments brings about an increase in weight of about 20%; after, say, three treatments, the goods are soaked in a solution of sodium silicate, usually containing soap, and this adds a further 30 to 50% to the weight of the silk.

The stannic chloride is generally merchanted in solution form, either of 106°Tw. containing 22% of tin, or of 140°Tw. containing 27% of tin. The so-called pink salt is actually a double chloride of tin and ammonium $SnCl_4.2NH_4Cl$.

It is important to keep the acidity of the stannic chloride solution as low as possible, and it may be necessary frequently to neutralise the solution with ammonia. The usual concentration is about 52°Tw. and it must be remembered that concentrations of 100°Tw. are sufficient to dissolve silk. The temperature, too, must not be allowed to rise, and in some works it is maintained at 12°C. for 52°Tw. stannic chloride solution. A high standard of purity should be demanded in the stannic chloride, as many sulphates, chlorides, nitrates, and nitrites are apt to discolour or to damage the silk. Attention has been drawn by Jones (Dyer, 1933, *69*, 44) to the advisability of washing with hard water after the treatment with stannic chloride solution, followed by centrifuging; he suggests water of 19° of hardness as an aid to the transformation of the stannic chloride into the hydroxide, but it must be remarked that water which is too hard would precipitate some of the tin not fixed by the fibre before it had been removed by washing and so give uneven effects.

The sodium phosphate solution is made by dissolving Na_2HPO_4 in soft water, and is maintained at the necessary concentration by replenishment and also by the addition of sulphuric acid. The usual concentration of sodium phosphate is 12°Tw., and it is generally employed at 60° to 70°C., the time of immersion being about 1 hour.

The solution of sodium silicate is also about 12°Tw. in concentration and employed at 70°C.; if aluminium sulphate solution is utilised, then a concentration of 15°Tw. at 55°C. is suitable.

With many silk fabrics, the final washing takes place in soap baths in order to bring about some degree of softening; sulphonated oils or sulphated alcohols may be added to the soap solution if necessary. This is usually adequate for the better materials which are only loaded to gum-weight and have about 33% of weighting; with heavier loadings, such as 70%, it may be necessary to pass the fabric through a breaking machine to obtain the required handle and suppleness.

Where the silk has been weighted within reasonable limits the process may be regarded as a finish which produces a fullness and richness of feel and handle which are missing from the degummed material, which is apt to be thin and "raggy"; this improvement is not entirely due to the increase in weight, but also to the swelling of the fibre which takes place at the same time. This gives extra cover, draping ability, and freedom from slipping, so that the process brings about certain economies in the use of real silk if properly used, and enables the world supply to be distributed over a larger number of users. Unfortunately, the ease of operation and the enormous possible increase in weight and fullness have often resulted in the process being carried to extremes, and many so-called silk materials should more appropriately be termed tin goods; such excessive weighting only leads to diminished wearing ability and to degradation in presence of perspiration. With some goods which have been over-weighted or "dynamited" there is a spontaneous degradation.

The tendency for excessive loading to damage silk is well known, especially if traces of salt or iron are present. Another defect is the subsequent development of "red spots," accompanied by tendering; this appears to be due to catalytic oxidation in presence of copper or iron and sodium chloride, and impregnation with 1 to 3% of compounds such as ammonium thiocyanate, thiourea, or formaldehyde-bisulphite has been suggested to obviate its occurrence.

Attempts have been made to regulate the amount of loading by agreement within the trade, and it has been suggested that the maxima should vary from 60% above par for satins and canton crêpes to 10% above par for chiffons. The system of estimation may be appreciated from an example; assuming the weight of the silk has been doubled by weighting, and allowing for 30% loss in weight from the raw silk by degumming, the net increase is about 30 to 40%, and this is termed 30 to 40% over par, i.e. over the weight of the silk before degumming.

A method has been suggested for loading raw silk by foams produced by silkworm chrysalides or other means, and was first described by Schmid in B.P. 15,244 of 1915. According to a trade pamphlet, the raw silk is left overnight in tin chloride solution of 26° Bé, centrifuged, and then hung on reels in an apparatus, where it is first washed with water and then with a dilute solution of sodium phosphate. This dilute solution is drawn off and replaced by the real phosphating solution, which also contains the foam-producing chrysalides extract; the solution is brought to the boil, and the silk is allowed to remain in the foam for 15 minutes after the first pink bath and for 10 minutes after each of the subsequent baths. The concentrated phosphate solution is then withdrawn and the silk is washed in dilute phosphate solution, rinsed, and finally soured in hydrochloric acid. These operations take about 1 hour, during the course of which there is a partial degumming, so that after the requisite number of passages or rounds, followed by the usual treatment with sodium silicate solution, a final boil for 30 minutes in 6 to 10% soap solution (calculated on the silk) is sufficient to remove the remaining gum.

OTHER METHODS

Although tin salts remain the commonest for loading silk, many other compounds have been suggested. For example, U.S.P. 2,025,072 and 2,034,696 describe the use of 35% antimony trichloride in a suitable solvent such as carbon tetrachloride, followed by centrifuging, drying at a low temperature, and immersing in an aqueous solution (5%) of sodium dihydrogen phosphate.

20

Zinc salts have also been suggested, and the use of zinc acetate permits the weighting of silk to be increased very considerably; for instance, 75 lb. of degummed silk, when soaked for an hour at room temperatures in 30°Tw. stannic chloride solution, rinsed in cold water, and immersed at 75°C. for an hour in 9°Tw. disodium phosphate solution gains in weight so that it becomes 86 lb., and by repeating the process it is possible to reach a weight of 102 lb.

A similar weight (75 lb.) of degummed silk may be immersed in 60°Tw. zinc acetate solution for an hour, washed, and then treated for an hour at 60°C. in 9°Tw. sodium phosphate solution, when the weight reaches 120 lb.; a repetition of the process enables a weight of 139 lb. to be obtained and several treatments are capable of establishing a weight of 169 lb. The silk is still supple and of good colour in spite of this large increase in weight.

In a modification of the process, the silk is weighted with sodium silicate also. For example, 75 lb. of boiled-off silk is treated twice with stannic chloride and disodium phosphate so that it reaches a weight of 102 lb., and it is then treated for 30 minutes at 60°C. in 4°Tw. sodium silicate solution whereby the weight becomes 116 lb.; soaking this material for an hour at 60°C. in an ammoniacal solution of zinc acetate, followed by sodium silicate, brings about a final weight of 170 lb. Another treatment with ammoniacal zinc acetate may bring the weight to 195 lb. The ammoniacal solution is prepared by adding ammonia (0·92) to a concentrated solution of zinc acetate until the white precipitate which first forms is completely dissolved; the product is then diluted to 4°Tw. with water, but a small excess of ammonia may be necessary to maintain solubility.

It may be remarked that not only is the weight of the silk improved by the use of zinc acetate, but the volume of the fibres also increases as if tin phosphate alone had been used. The alkaline solution of zinc acetate brings about an increase in weight more quickly than neutral solutions of zinc salts.

It is also interesting to note that tin-weighted silk can also absorb lead salts such as lead acetate; mixtures of lead and zinc salts in conjunction with sodium silicate are capable of increasing the weight of 75 lb. of degummed silk to 237 lb.

The modification of the final loading may also be effected by the introduction of aluminium, and the use of aluminium sulphate is quite common in place of tin chloride in the final passage; concentrations of 12° to 16°Tw. at 60°C. are employed.

Zirconium may be introduced either with the tin salts or alone, the hydroxide being precipitated on the silk and then treated with silicate.

One-bath methods have been suggested whereby the stannic chloride, sodium phosphate, and sodium silicate are dissolved in formic acid solution which prevents precipitation; the impregnated silk is then passed through a weak solution of ammonium carbonate and dried, when the insoluble metallic salts form in the silk. The presence of glue may protect the silk from the effects of the acid, and also act as a colloid and result in the weighting being deposited in amorphous rather than a crystalline form with less likelihood of physical damage to the silk.

A continuous method for the loading of silk has been devised by Clavel, as described in B.P. 303,129, and is particularly directed to the treatment of fabrics. The cloth is first passed through 10% monochloracetic acid solution and then washed and squeezed before passing into stannic chloride solution of 64° Tw. concentration, and then into a rest-pan, where it remains for the necessary period; a second impregnation in stannic chloride solution, and another rest is followed by immersion in sodium dihydrogen phosphate (10%) and a further rest. The cloth is then passed through disodium phosphate solution containing a little sodium carbonate. A final treatment with sodium silicate solution of 2° Tw. at 60°C., with washing before and after, completes the loading process.

Clavel has also modified the usual weighting processes for silk to render them suitable for rayons, but this type of finish is not widely adopted, probably on account of there being no necessity as rayon is much cheaper than silk. The processes are outlined in B.P. 266,640, 277,602, and 280,094.

One method of treatment consists in impregnating with a solution containing 500 parts of albumen or other protective colloid, 50 parts of ammonium carbonate, and 5,000 parts of water; the fabric is then squeezed and passed through a bath containing 4 parts of stannic chloride, 10 parts of orthophosphoric acid, and 100 parts of water, followed by washing and drying.

CHAPTER XIII
DELUSTRING

Most forms of rayon possess a bright metallic lustre, unless special precautions are taken, and whereas the early demand for delustred rayon was to provide material of subdued lustre approximating to that of natural silk, dull rayons are now utilised for a variety of purposes, some of which require a strong matt effect.

There are many methods of reducing the lustre of rayon, but they all depend on the scattering of the incident light; the lustre of a surface may be defined as the ratio of the light which is reflected specularly or regularly to that which is reflected diffusely or irregularly. Most surfaces give rise to both types of reflection, but with a mirror there is a very high proportion of specular reflection. Now fabric surfaces may be regarded as a system of layers of cylindrical filaments, in the simplest case, arranged in parallel formation; any deviation from the cylindrical shape or parallel array causes a variation in the lustre; that is, in the specular/diffuse ratio. Hence, high lustre is seen with yarns of minimum twist which present a smooth homogeneous surface, but if the surface is rendered irregular then the lustre falls. In addition to the light which is reflected from the external surface, some rays penetrate the fibres and are reflected from the internal surface, and are presumed to bring about a rich and subdued lustre which is partly diffuse and partly specular. Hence, for delustring it is necessary not only to scatter the light from the external surface, but also to reflect in a diffuse manner those rays which penetrate into the interior of the material.

As diffuse reflection from an interface depends on the difference between the refractive indices of the two media, delustring may be achieved by producing a degree of heterogeneity in the fibre, as well as causing irregularities in the surface.

These two points form the basis of modern delustring which may be classified as Spun-delustring and After-treatments, corresponding broadly to internal and external delustring.

INTERNAL DELUSTRING

The methods of internal delustring depend on the addition of various substances to the spinning solutions from which the filaments are extruded; if regarded as finishing processes, then it may be said that the fibre is finished before it is formed, but as the manufacture of delustred filaments is not generally carried out by the finisher, it will only receive a brief discussion.

This type of delustring dates from D.R.P. 137,255 of Wagner in 1901, when fine iridescent powders were incorporated in solutions of cellulose nitrate with a view to the formation of opaque filaments. The most efficient delustring agents have been found to be those whose refractive index is widely different from that of the filament; some refractive indices are given in the following table:

REFRACTIVE INDICES

Viscose rayon .	.	. 1·536	Titanium dioxide	.	. 2·71
Acetate rayon .	.	. 1·477	Barium sulphate	.	. 1·637
Zinc oxide	.	. 2·04	Talc .	.	. 1·589
Zinc sulphide .	.	. 2·37	Methylene urea	.	. 1·55

On account of its high refractive index, titanium dioxide is greatly valued as a delustring agent; it was first added to spinning solutions in 1921, but its true value was realised by Singmaster in 1929. B.P. 339,603 states that various amounts of pigments are required to give similar delustring effects, as follows:

EFFICIENCY OF DELUSTRING AGENTS

Titanium dioxide	.	. 0·5%	Zirconium oxide	.	. 3%
Zinc sulphide .	.	. 1·0%	Barium sulphate	.	. 4%
Lithopone	.	. 1·5%	Aluminium oxide	.	. 4%

Titanium oxide is also valuable because it may be produced in small particles of average size 0·75μ which will not block the spinnerets.

Numerous other substances have also been suggested as additions to the viscose solution; indeed, it is difficult to think of compounds which have not been suggested, but titanium dioxide remains the chief. Many pigments reduce the tenacity of the filaments, but the high efficiency of titanium dioxide enables small amounts to be utilised with success. In some cases, the fastness to light of dyed delustred filaments was adversely affected, but this has been obviated by the methods of the I.C.I., described in B.P. 430,976, 448,262, 449,543, and 455,642.

The chief alternatives to titanium dioxide are: (a) other white inorganic pigments, (b) organic compounds such as oils, fats, waxes, soaps, hydrocarbons, and resins (1 to 5%), and (c) gas-forming compounds, or finely-divided substances which may be removed later to leave hollow spaces in the filaments.

In the spinning of viscose rayon, the yarn is first of a dull fawn colour, the lack of lustre being due to the presence of precipitated sulphur. Sunderland (J.S.D.C., 1923, *39*, 342) suggested making use of this effect in 1918; two ideas were put forward, the first of which was merely to weave a fabric of sulphur-viscose and then print with a paste containing sodium sulphide which would remove the sulphur and so produce a bright lustrous figure on a white opaque ground when the material had been bleached. The second method of producing a contrast of matt and lustrous effects was to weave a mixture of sulphur-viscose and desulphurised viscose; after bleaching and dyeing, an interesting fabric was obtained.

This printing method is almost impracticable on account of the action of sodium sulphide on the copper printing rollers. Scholefield and Denver, in B.P. 261,099, overcome the difficulty by using compounds such as sodium sulphite, potassium sulphite, ammonium sulphite, or calcium sulphite, which not only are without detrimental effect on the printing roller, but also enable many colours to be incorporated in the printing paste, and so produce coloured lustrous patterns on a dull ground. A typical printing paste may be formed by 15 lb. of Duranthrene Orange RRT, 10 lb. of sodium sulphite, 4 lb. of glycerol, 3 lb. of caustic soda, 76°Tw., 5 lb. of potassium carbonate, 2·5 lb. of sodium benzyl sulphanilate, 4 lb. of Formosol and sufficient British gum to ensure the correct viscosity. After printing, the fabric is dried, steamed for 10 minutes, soaped, and dried.

Although the modern tendency is towards the production of viscose containing the minimum amount of sulphur, U.S.P. 2,034,711 describes the use of an excess of sulphur to give a delustred material. Sodium hyposulphite is added to viscose and the solution "spun" into an acid bath so that sulphur is precipitated into the filaments as they are extruded.

EXTERNAL DELUSTRING

The after-treatment of rayon filaments results in the external application of white pigments of various types. The question of refractive index is of less importance than in spun-delustring, for the diffuse reflection is determined by the air/pigment difference in refractive index; hence any white pigment whose refractive index is sufficiently different from that of air (1·0) will give a result.

Many of the processes fall into two groups: (a) two-bath, and (b) one-bath methods.

Two-bath methods

Numerous processes have been devised to operate by the two-bath method, the principle of which is to impregnate the textile material in the separate solutions of two salts which produce an insoluble precipitate on the fibre by double decomposition. The commonest compound used in this manner is barium sulphate, but barium stannate, tungstate, and molybdate have also been used, as have zinc phosphate and tungstate. Some insoluble aluminium soaps and metallic salts of sulphated fatty alcohols have also been suggested.

Although barium sulphate was probably the first pigment to be used for delustring, and is still utilised in the hosiery trade, it suffers from certain disadvantages, one of which is the size of the particles in the irregular coarse deposit varying from 10μ to 50μ; these particles possess poor absorptive and adhesive powers for other substances. Hence the pigment is apt to "dust-off", and numerous attempts have been made to remedy these defects. It has been stated that the use of sodium sulphate in the first bath, followed by barium chloride in the second, is better than the reverse order. There appears to be some advantage in the use of barium hydroxide instead of the chloride, for the former has a greater affinity for most textile fibres. It has also been suggested to follow the barium hydroxide with aluminium sulphate as the aluminium hydroxide formed exerted a beneficial action in fixing the barium sulphate.

Many other binding media have been suggested, including cellulose ethers and synthetic resins, both of which, however, affect the handle of the product. Less drastic binding reagents are those with a fatty basis, but their effect is not pronounced.

Certain compounds which have a definite affinity for the fibre may be utilised; for example, stearamidine $(C_{17}H_{35}C:NH.NH_2)$ may be added to the bath of barium chloride in which the rayon is impregnated, followed by a treatment with sodium sulphate solution. This process is described in B.P. 446,976 of the I.G. The well-known cation-active agents are strongly absorbed by textile fibres, and their use has been outlined for delustring in B.P. 443,758 of Bohme Fettchemie; the first bath contains colophony, barium chloride, and lauryl pyridinium bromide, followed by a resin soap. The cation-active idea is also seen in B.P. 503,548 of the I.G.; rayon is impregnated with a solution of stearyl-biguanide sulphate, followed by barium chloride solution. These methods combine the principle of substantive delustring, to be discussed later, and the ordinary barium sulphate method.

Barium tungstate, formed from sodium tungstate and barium chloride, appears to be precipitated in more regular particles and more evenly distributed on the fibre than the sulphate, according to B.P. 415,822 of Sandoz. It is believed to form the basis of such preparations as Delustran ST and Visco-Mattyl N150. Titanium dioxide probably forms the chief component of Delustran SB New, together with a soap or the sodium salt of a sulphated fatty alcohol. The original Visco-Mattyl seems to have been either titanium dioxide or bentonite with the pyridinium salt of sulphated lauryl alcohol.

The production of insoluble salts by a process of double decomposition, as with barium sulphate, has certain disadvantages; some of these are inherent in the fact that neither barium chloride nor sodium sulphate are absorbed substantively by cellulose.

Viscose rayon absorbs alkaline substances preferentially, but most of the common compounds of sodium and potassium are readily soluble in water; barium hydroxide, however, may be absorbed by the rayon and then transformed into the stannate by treatment with sodium stannate solution which exerts a beneficial swelling action at the same time. Good delustring effects may thus be obtained by barium stannate formed according to B.P. 408,240 of the I.G. Rayon material may be steeped for 30 minutes at 20° to 30°C. in 0·1% barium hydroxide solution, followed by rinsing in cold water, and a further treatment in 0·5% sodium stannate solution for 30 minutes, during which the temperature is raised to 60°C.; the rayon is then washed and dried. It is interesting to note that the process may be reversed, and the rayon steeped in sodium stannate solution at 60°C., followed by barium hydroxide solution with an intermediate rinsing. Although calcium hydroxide may be used, it must be remembered that its solubility is only about 0·75%, whereas that of barium hydroxide is about 4%; actually, 1% solution, followed by sodium stannate solution, is adequate for a high degree of delustring.

Barium stannate may be applied as a one-bath process by utilising the fact that its precipitation from barium hydroxide and sodium stannate solutions may be hindered in presence of glycerol or cane sugar. If 1 part of barium hydroxide, 3 parts of sodium stannate, and 5 parts of cane sugar are finely ground together and the mixture dissolved in water, a clear solution is formed, in which viscose rayon may be worked for 30 minutes at 50° to 60°C. to give a matt effect.

A modification of this type of delustring has been outlined in B.P. 455,209 by Whinfield of the Calico Printers' Association. Viscose rayon is steeped in sodium stannate solution containing 0·5% stannic oxide, and then rinsed with a solution of a calcium salt; even water sufficiently hard to contain not less than 3 parts of calcium oxide per 100,000 is adequate to produce matt effects. Pattern effects may be created by relustring in selected areas by treating with dilute acid. An alternative method of relustring is by treating with a thickened solution of sodium hexametaphosphate, followed by steaming, as described in B.P. 486,334.

An I.G. process, described in B.P. 478,327, depends on the use of the stannates of organic bases containing long-chain groups whereby a soft effect may be obtained as well as a matt appearance.

The use of sulphur for delustring has been outlined in B.P. 245,407. Viscose rayon is dipped into a solution of an alkaline polysulphide and then treated with acid to precipitate the sulphur; alternatively, the yarn or fabric may be soaked in a solution of sulphur in an organic solvent which is then evaporated. This method may be employed to give pattern effects by application in selected areas, or by local removal from material which has received a complete treatment; different colours may be produced with various metallic salts.

A great difficulty with spun-delustred yarns lies in the production of black and other dark shades; part of the delustring effect appears to be lost because with the darker shades the ratio between the amount of light diffused and the amount regularly reflected is altered in favour of the latter, since the dark dyeing only permits a small amount of the light to pass into the pigment-holding diffusing layers. Diazo-Radium Mattine of Bohme Fettchemie has been produced to overcome this defect; it obviates loss of lustre on black-dyeing a delustred yarn and eliminates alteration in shade when delustring a fabric which has already been dyed black. The method is to adopt a two-stage process which deposits on and in the fibre a dark shaded pigment. According to B.P. 445,145, a cation-active substance, such as dodecyl pyridinium sulphate, together with ferric chloride, is used to impregnate the material, which is then treated with a solution of a tannin material or a dyewood extract. The process may also be applied in the reverse order, by using tannic acid first; this is strongly absorbed by the fibres and may be fixed with iron alum solution without the use of a cation-active substance.

One-bath methods

One-bath processes have been developed for the after-treatment methods of delustring rayon; they generally depend on the use of a dispersion of the white pigment, or the impregnation with a solution of a substance which may be decomposed to leave an insoluble deposit on the fibre.

In general, the two-bath processes for delustring are relatively expensive on account of manipulation difficulties, and the precipitated product adheres only moderately to the fibre. Attempts have therefore been made to prepare the matting agent beforehand and bring about better attachment to the fibre by certain chemical compounds, such as cation-active compounds, sulphonated oils, and sulphated fatty alcohols. The chief pigments are China clay, fuller's earth, lithopone, aluminium oxide, zinc oxide, titanium oxide, and barium sulphate. A number of commercial products are available which are based on the above ideas, and may be applied either by adsorption from dilute colloidal dispersions or by padding with more concentrated baths. For the former method, about 2 to 4% of the pigment may be adsorbed together with up to 5% of the softening agent; with the latter process, a suspension of 30% of pigment and 15% of surface-active compound may be employed.

Cation-active dispersing agents impart a positive charge to the suspended particles which are thus strongly adsorbed by the negatively charged fibres. Although dispersions of this type were first described in B.P. 391,214 by Dunbar and Lawrie of the I.C.I., their application to delustring appears to have been exploited mainly by Bohme, as in B.P. 424,672. A pigment suspension may be made with the aid of a fatty alcohol sulphate to which is added a cation-active compound; precipitation of the electro-neutral salt-like compound of the two dispersing agents takes place and surrounds the pigment particles, which are then re-peptised with an excess of the cation-active compound. This suspension is adsorbed by the textile fibres similarly to the substantive dyes, and is believed to form the basis of Radium Mattine T53.

Fractol A of the I.C.I. also appears to be a suspension containing cation-active compounds, and must not, therefore, be used in an alkaline bath or in presence of soaps or the sodium salts of fatty alcohol sulphates, otherwise aggregation of the dispersion will take place. With the padding method, the cloth may be impregnated with 1 to 2% dispersion, or, if wet fabric is used, then the concentration of the dispersion should be 5 to 10%. For working on the wince machine, a concentration of 1 to 2% is adequate, i.e. 1 to 2 lb. per 10 gallons of water. It is often advisable to pass the delustred goods through an alkaline bath containing about 1 pint of ammonia and 1 lb. of Lissapol C paste per 100 gallons of liquor; this gives an attractive soft handle and also removes any loose pigment.

Substantive delustring processes of this type are of interest and importance; the dispersions may be "exhausted," as in dyeing.

The parallel between dyeing and substantive delustring is very interesting; the effect is not removed by washing with hot water. Although the presence of sodium sulphate in a dyebath is of great assistance, its use in substantive delustring is not so efficacious, but nevertheless is quite definite. The extent of delustring is directly dependent on the temperature of the bath, as shown in the table, where lustre has been evaluated in terms of Klughardt's lustre number, G.

EFFECT OF TEMPERATURE ON DELUSTRING

Temp. °C.	Time mins.	Concn. g./l. T53	G
2	10	2	6·4
10	10	2	5·9
20	10	2	5·6
30	10	2	4·8
40	10	2	4·6
50	10	2	3·8
60	10	2	3·8
20–100	30	6	2·8
Original material			40·3

A fine degree of control may thus be exercised by temperature alone.

One of the early methods of one-bath delustring by decomposition may be seen in B.P. 264,559 by Foulds of the Tootal Broadhurst Lee Co.; the fabric may be treated with a solution of antimony or bismuth chloride and then passed into water, where the corresponding oxide is formed and deposited on the fibre. Moderately concentrated solutions of the chlorides may be prepared in presence of hydrochloric acid. (This is a one-bath two-stage process.)

B.P. 290,263, by Gardner, describes the treatment of textiles with a solution of titanium sulphate or titanium potassium oxalate, followed by heating to 100°C. to deposit a white titanium compound.

An interesting one-bath process relies on the fact that aluminium phthalate solution is stable at ordinary temperatures, but decomposes on heating to 80°C. with the formation of a basic aluminium compound. This is believed to form the basis of the Dullit process of the I.G. As the fibres are first impregnated with a true solution, the salt penetrates to the inside of the material, where the insoluble basic aluminium phthalate is formed on heating; the matt finish is not destroyed by washing, but the handle is rather unpleasant and needs correction with softening agents.

A somewhat similar idea is utilised in the Delustran method, where the material is impregnated with a cold aqueous solution of sodium stannate, which swells the cellulose and so penetrates to the interior of the fibre. Insoluble stannic acid is formed on drying, and the shade of the fibres is not greatly affected as the pigment is not characterised by a strong whiteness. It has also been suggested to use silicofluorides to form silicic acid.

Solutions of titanium salts and of tin salts which may be decomposed by heat can be used in a similar manner, according to B.P. 454,968 of Dreyfus. The textile material may be impregnated with a double salt of a weak polybasic acid with a volatile base and one of the metals, followed by decomposition of the double salt. Titanium carbonate is mentioned for use with viscose rayon.

There are many other inventions based on this idea, but it must be pointed out that the effect is not obtained with colloidal solutions instead of ionic solutions.

METHYLENE UREA

Although the pigments previously considered are mainly white inorganic compounds, some organic products have also attracted attention, such as methylene urea, which is a condensation product of urea and formaldehyde. This should not be confused with urea-formaldehyde resins, which have been known since 1918, whereas the white amorphous product which exists as small discrete particles was known thirty years previously.

Methylene urea is deposited at room temperatures from slightly acidified solutions of urea and formaldehyde, whereas, broadly speaking, the formation of the resin requires the evaporation of water, followed by heat; methylene urea formation necessitates the presence of water. The chemistry of the reaction has not yet been clarified, but it is generally agreed that in neutral or alkaline solution, urea and formaldehyde combine to form mono- or dimethylol ureas, according to the molecular proportions of the reagents.

$$\begin{array}{ccccc} NH_2 & & NH.CH_2OH & & NH.CH_2OH \\ | & & | & & | \\ CO & + CH_2O \longrightarrow & CO & or & CO \\ | & & | & & | \\ NH_2 & & NH_2 & & NH.CH_2OH \end{array}$$

When these solutions are acidified, methylene urea is deposited after a time-reaction; it may also be formed directly from the uncondensed reagents in presence of water and acid. According to Walter (Trans. Farad. Soc., 1936, *32*, 377) two forms of methylene urea are possible, the *A* form from monomethylol urea, and the *B* form from dimethylol urea; but this is by no means proved.

$$NH_2.CO.N : CH_2 \qquad H_2N.CO.N \underset{CH_2OCH_2}{\overset{CH_2}{\big\langle}} N.CO.NH_2$$

methylene urea *A*   methylene urea *B*

Foulds and Marsh, of the Tootal Broadhurst Lee Co., have utilised methylene urea for delustring as described in B.P. 467,480. The process differs from that employed for the production of crease-resisting fabrics (see page 390) in that precipitation of an insoluble compound is designedly brought about by the use of acid at room temperatures, and a final heating is not employed. The textile material may be treated with the components of the methylene urea separately and in any desired sequence, or with urea and formaldehyde simultaneously. There are three components in the system: urea, formaldehyde, and the precipitant. The fabric may be treated with a mixture of any two, and then with the third. For example, 60 g. of urea, 100 c.c. of 40% formaldehyde solution, and 100 c.c. of water are mixed together and used for impregnating the textile material, which is then squeezed and immersed in 2% hydrochloric acid solution until delustring takes place. Alternatively, it is possible to use acid vapours to produce the methylene urea. In another example, 100 g. of urea are mixed with 200 c.c. of neutralised 40%

formaldehyde solution and refluxed with 3% NH_4OH for 3 minutes, followed by rapid cooling; 300 c.c. of water are then added and the mixture acidified with 0·5 to 1% tartaric acid. The textile material is impregnated with the solution and then allowed to stand until delustring occurs. The process is completed by washing and drying.

Excellent pattern effects may be obtained by impregnating a fabric with urea solution, drying, and then printing with a vat colour containing sufficient alkali to withstand the subsequent acid treatment; after ageing, the fabric is run through acidified formaldehyde solution and allowed to stand in the damp state until delustring takes place. Bright-coloured effects may thus be obtained on a matt ground.

An improvement of the general method may be seen in B.P. 499,207 of Foulds and Marsh, whereby the mixture of urea, formaldehyde, and acid is utilised to impregnate the fabric and allowed to stand until delustring takes place; the impregnated material is then dried and heated for 2 minutes at 170°C. in order to produce a crease-resisting effect, which may be due to resinification of the residual urea-formaldehyde which has not formed methylene urea— the proportions of the reagents should be adjusted with this end in view. Alternatively, the delustring process may be followed by a treatment with acidified formaldehyde for 2 minutes at 170°C.

A further modification of the process is seen in B.P. 528,358 of Butterworth, Neary, Foulds, and Marsh. The textile material is treated with resin-forming solutions of urea-formaldehyde, and then heated to a high temperature to develop crease-resisting effects, after which the unwashed fabric is treated with an acid precipitant to convert the uncondensed components into the insoluble methylene urea and so delustre the material.

It may be mentioned that the methylene ureas formed *in situ* give delustring ranging from opalescence to a strong matt effect of excellent fastness to washing.

Dispersions of methylene urea may be formed separately and then utilised for delustring in the processes due to Johnson, Marsh, Roscoe, and Wood (B.P. 484,901). Urea, formaldehyde, and dilute acid are mixed in presence of a dispersing agent, such as lauryl sodium sulphate; the cooled solution is continually agitated until a finely divided dispersion of methylene urea is formed. The reaction takes place slowly, and immediately the product forms, it is dispersed in very fine particles. This dispersion may be used in two ways: first, as an addition to the viscose solution for internal delustring, and, secondly, the alternative application to textile yarns and fabrics in presence of a fixing agent. The dispersion may be formed from 5 to 20 parts of monomethylol urea and 1 part of lauryl sodium sulphate in 100 parts of water, to which are added 1 part of tartaric acid in 3 parts of water.

The Society of Chemical Industry at Basle has also made use of urea-formaldehyde condensation products for delustring rayon. According to B.P. 469,688, urea and formaldehyde are heated together in an autoclave for 6 to 8 hours at 100°C. to give a viscous but water-soluble product, which is dried at a low temperature in a good vacuum and sintered for 4 hours at 130°C.; this compound is pulverised and dissolved in formic acid or hydrochloric acid, after which the solution is poured into a large volume of water, when an aqueous colloidal suspension slowly forms and may be taken up by rayon yarns or fabrics, which thereby acquire a delustred appearance. This is believed to form the basis of Uromatt I, a white powder insoluble in water but soluble in formic acid. The Uromatt I solution is added to the delustring bath after being allowed to stand for a predetermined time, and during the delustring operation it is essential to maintain an accurate salt concentration; about 5% of Uromatt I, calculated on the weight of the goods, is required for a good matt effect.

The dissolving time is the period during which the Uromatt I is in contact with the formic acid and it depends on the temperature; the time varies from 35 minutes at 15°C. to 8 minutes at 30°C., after which the acid solution may be added to the bath in which the rayon has previously been wetted. As the precipitate forms in a finely-divided state, it is taken up by the viscose. The salt content of the water must be ascertained previously by experiment with concentrations of 0·125, 0·25, 0·375, and 0·5 g. of common salt per litre added to the delustring bath; the most intense delustring effect denotes the optimum salt concentration. If the salt concentration is too high, the Uromatt will be precipitated rapidly; again, the ratio of liquor to cloth should be about 30 : 1, and shorter baths also cause premature separation. The temperature of the delustring bath should be maintained at 35° to 40°C.; the average time for delustring is 30 to 45 minutes.

B.P. 478,998 states that the initial insoluble condensation product of urea and formaldehyde may be rendered more easily soluble in formic acid by soaking in water overnight.

A simpler process, also by Ciba, has been described in B.P. 528,686. Urea and formaldehyde, in equimolecular ratio, either uncondensed or in the form of monomethylol urea, are dissolved in water in which the rayon is worked; the controlled addition of acid brings about the deposition of methylene urea which is taken up by the fabric as it forms. The ratio of liquor to cloth should not exceed 15 : 1. According to B.P. 537,467 of Ciba, the bath may be used repeatedly and its concentration maintained by replacing the reagents which have been absorbed. The last-mentioned specification gives very full details which are believed to form the basis of delustring with Uromatt II. The material is delustred by a precipitate from the acidified solution of urea and formaldehyde, monomethylol urea, or dimethylol urea, formed under controlled conditions of concentration, time, temperature, liquor ratio, and acid concentration. A fast-running wince machine is advised for this process.

DELUSTRING

Liquor ratio	Uromatt II	HCl conc.	Time
	Amounts per litre		
1 : 10	7.0 g.	10. c.c.	1 hour
1 : 15	6·2 g.	9·5 c.c.	—
1 : 20	5·8 g.	9·0 c.c.	—
1 : 30	5·5 g.	8·0 c.c.	—
1 : 30	4·3 g.	6·4 c.c.	3 hours
1 : 40	4·0 g.	6·0 c.c.	—
1 : 50	3·8 g.	5·7 c.c.	—
1 : 60	3·7 g.	5·5 c.c.	—
1 : 70	3·6 g.	5·4 c.c.	—
1 : 80	3·5 g.	5·2 c.c.	—

Apart from the fact that Ciba appear to prefer the exhaustion method, whereas Foulds and Marsh seem to utilise the padding method, it is interesting to note that the later processes of Ciba seem to favour the use of uncondensed reagents or the water-soluble methylol ureas originally proposed by Foulds and Marsh. The first patent of Ciba, although using a methylene urea, was concerned with an insoluble far-condensed product which was previously prepared, dissolved in acid, and thrown out of solution by dilution in the matting bath; on the other hand, Foulds and Marsh use uncondensed reagents or water-soluble substances of crystalloid rather than colloid nature and of a low degree of condensation.

As previously indicated, the chemistry of methylene urea is still rather obscure, but it seems likely that the Ciba process gives a polymeric product, whereas that of Foulds and Marsh is monomeric.

Before passing to the consideration of cellulose acetate, attention may be drawn to a scheme for the determination of delustring treatments (Kunstseide u. Zellwolle, 1940, *22*, 80).

ACETATE RAYON

Owing to the peculiar character of cellulose acetate, many of the above delustring processes are not suited to this type of rayon. The internal delustring methods may be applied with titanium dioxide as for viscose, but external pigmentation is replaced by physico-chemical methods which depend on the alteration of the surface of the filaments when treated with hot aqueous liquors.

The first of these processes appears in B.P. 165,164 of Dreyfus, Briggs, and Clotworthy, who found that the acetate rayon could be delustred by hot water, boiling water, or steam. A matt effect could also be produced at room temperatures with 20 to 35% acetic acid solution or 15 to 30% aqueous solutions of ammonium, potassium, or calcium sulphocyanides. A disadvantage of the early process was that the lustre could be restored by a dry heat treatment, such as ironing. Pattern effects were produced by the local application of substances which modified the action of steam; for instance, the acetate could be printed with phenol, or with solvents for acetate, or substances which dissolve in the acetate, followed by treatment with steam, as outlined by Ellis in B.P. 266,777.

The use of phenols was taken a stage further in B.P. 358,574 by Ellis and Storey, who suggested their application in hot aqueous solutions for all-over delustring. The conditions of treatment were with 0.1 N phenol at $75°$ to $95°$C., but lower concentrations may be used if less delustring is required; preferred concentrations are from 3 to 10 g. of phenol per litre.

The process permits a very good control of the degree of delustring as compared with the use of a simple soap solution. Alkaline soap solutions, employed at pH 10 to 10.5, were suggested in B.P. 306,067 for degumming mixtures of silk and acetate rayon, but if utilised at temperatures in excess of $80°$C., then the acetate is delustred.

The above comments merely apply to those acetates containing about 53% of acetic acid; more highly acetylated yarns have higher softening points and are much more difficult to delustre. Above 60% combined acetic acid, the acetate cannot be delustred by boiling water or steam, and only slightly by dilute solutions of phenol. It is also stated in B.P. 478,937 that acetates containing 56 to 59% of combined acetic acid resist delustring. The usual acetates, of course, cannot be wet-processed above $80°$C. without some loss of lustre.

A somewhat favourite explanation of the delustring of cellulose acetate rayon by hot liquids is that of saponification in which some acetic acid is split off; in actual fact, acetate rayon may be saponified without loss of lustre, and the common delustring processes do not involve any chemical change. This phenomenon was examined by Stahl (Textilber., 1932, 4, 200), who found that delustred fibres are pitted with numerous crevices and cracks which are responsible for the loss of lustre. It appears that the acetate absorbs a little water and undergoes some softening on heating whereby miniature disruptions are caused by the water vapour; these hollow spaces persist on cooling.

The softening action does not occur with regenerated cellulose. Other interesting differences are that whereas the swelling of viscose

rayon in water is increased by the presence of certain salts, that of
acetate rayon is decreased with some exceptions; hence, it is possible
to boil acetate rayon in salt solutions without delustring taking place.

The physico-chemical explanation of the delustring of acetate
rayon is also in accordance with the fact that the steaming methods
do not give a permanent result, but one which may be removed by
hot ironing; it is also in agreement with the fact that it is difficult
to delustre acetate rayon in the stretched state and that for the
best results the fabrics should be treated in book-fold or on star
frames, as in crêping (see page 96).

Delustred acetate rayon may be relustred by treatment with
solvents or swelling agents for the acetate (B.P. 259,265), such as
acetic acid of 40 to 50% strength, or with 1 to 5% aqueous solution
of salts, such as the sulphates, chlorides and chromates of ammonium,
sodium, potassium, or aluminium (B.P. 259,266). Delustred and
relustred acetate rayon is capable of being delustred again under
milder conditions than those originally necessary.

The common method of delustring acetate rayon is by means of
soap and phenol, and better results are obtained by treating the
goods for 30 minutes at 100°C. than for 2 hours at 98°C. Atkinson
(J.S.D.C., 1931, 47, 5) has found that for semi-delustred finishes
with soap alone, a pH value of 10 to 11 gives the best results, but
where phenol is employed also, a pH value of 8·5 to 9 gives the
dullest results. The pH value of the water supply should be taken
into account, for otherwise a difference in dullness may result from
apparently identical treatments. Olive oil soap has been found to
give the best results, but even here the temperature is of the utmost
importance. Below 100°C. the degree of dullness is about the same,
apart from questions of levelness. It is interesting to note that
excessive alkalinity retards the delustring action.

INFLUENCE OF pH ON DELUSTRING ACETATE RAYON
(2% soap solution for 30 minutes)

Temperature	pH	Effect	
85°C.	8·0	Full lustre	
90°C.	8·0	Slightly opaque	Previously
95°C.	8·0	Semi-delustred	scoured
100°C.	8·0	Three-quarter delustred	
90°C.	8·0	Full lustre	Unscoured
95°C.	8·0	Slightly opaque	
90°C.	10·0	Slightly opaque	Unscoured
100°C.	11·0	Completely delustred	
100°C.	10·0	Almost delustred	
100°C.	9·0	—	
100°C.	8·0	Three-quarter delustred	
100°C.	7·0	Semi-delustred	
100°C.	6·0	Slightly delustred	

Treatment with soap solution usually requires from 2 to 20 g. of soap per litre at a pH of 10·1 to 10·3 and a temperature of 90° to 95°C.

In some cases it is possible to obtain fairly satisfactory results by crêping, desizing, scouring, and dulling in one operation on the winch, but it is not possible to obtain as dull an effect as when the goods are treated in book-form, possibly on account of the cooling action to which the pieces are subjected on the winch.

Considerable care must be taken to maintain the correct concentration of phenol; 0·5% of phenol reduces the wet tenacity (grams per denier) from 0·77 to 0·62 at 90°C. and to 0·47 at 100°C., whilst 0·25% of phenol only reduces it to 0·61 at 100°C. These data show that temperature, too, is an important factor.

A special type of semi-delustred acetate yarn called Opaceta was marketed by Courtaulds, and this retains its dullness even after ironing; it should not be delustred with phenol. If further dullness is required, it may be achieved by treatment in soap solutions at temperatures between 80° and 100°C., the maximum effect being obtained at the latter temperature.

It may be remarked that, in general, satisfactory delustring cannot be obtained at 80° to 90°C., and there is no alternative to the use of soap, or soap and phenol, at 100°C. In most wince machines, the highest convenient temperature is 95°C., as boiling water causes splashing; a further disadvantage of the wince is that some tension is inevitable, which renders the acetate rayon less susceptible to delustring, presumably because the swelling is reduced. Similar disadvantages obtain when the goods are treated on jigs; hence, as previously mentioned, the best method of manipulation is that used for crêping.

Attention may be drawn to a delustring process (B.P. 309,194 of the I.G.) in which the acetate is printed with 20 to 30% urea solution, dried and steamed for 5 to 10 minutes. This is believed to be the basis of the Opalogen process.

Numerous additions have been suggested to the bath in which delustring occurs; sulphonamides, diphenyl, camphor (B.P. 409,275), cation-active compounds such as cetyl pyridinium bromide (B.P. 391,847, 412,929), and emulsified pine oil (B.P. 393,985).

It may be remarked that the general theories of lustre have been discussed by Preston (J.S.D.C., 1931, 47, 136), and an account of the various methods of measuring lustre has been given by Marsh (Mercerising, Chapman and Hall, London, 1941).

CHAPTER XIV

CELLULOSE DERIVATIVES

IT is now well established that cellulose is a polysaccharide composed of long chain-molecules of β-glucose residues united in the $1:4$ positions. Now β-glucose contains three hydroxyl groups, which are alcoholic in nature; the hydroxyl groups in the 2 and 3 positions belong to secondary alcohols and that in the 6 position to a primary alcohol.

The formation of cellulose derivatives depends on these three alcoholic groups and is largely a matter of substitution, as in ordinary organic chemistry. The chemistry of the cellulose derivatives may be made a little clearer by regarding the unit parent material not as $C_6H_{10}O_5$, but as $C_6H_7O_2(OH)_3$.

The two great classes of cellulose derivatives are the esters and the ethers; e.g. cellulose nitrate is very well known and the trinitrate may be regarded as $C_6H_7O_2(ONO_2)_3$. Cellulose trimethyl ether, on the other hand, may be written $C_6H_7O_2(OCH_3)_3$.

Both the esters and ethers of cellulose have been used in the finishing of textile materials in two ways; first, they may be utilised from solution or dispersion as coating agents to give a variety of finishes; and, secondly, the actual reaction of esterification or etherification may be carried out under controlled conditions, on the textile material itself. Broadly, these two methods may be regarded as finishing by physical application of the cellulose derivative, on the one hand, and the chemical formation of esters and ethers *in situ* on the other; the latter must not be confused with the manufacture of rayons.

CELLULOSE ESTERS

CELLULOSE NITRATE is probably the best-known ester of cellulose and it may be formed by treating cellulose with a mixture of nitric and sulphuric acids. Actually the reaction results in the production of a series of nitrates according to the experimental conditions; the nitrogen content of the esters may be varied by suitable alteration of the conditions of nitration, most products being a mixture of rather indefinite chemical compounds. The trinitrate of cellulose should contain 14·2% of nitrogen, and the dinitrate and mononitrate 11·1 and 6·8% of nitrogen respectively.

The cellulose nitrates used in explosives (gun-cotton) generally contain more than 12% of nitrogen, but there is a range of nitrates containing 12·5 to 10·5% of nitrogen which is used industrially; celluloid, photographic films, lacquers, enamels, artificial leather, and rayon all provided an outlet for cellulose nitrate, but the manufacture of rayon from this product is now almost obsolete. Cellulose nitrates containing 11·5 to 12·5% of nitrogen are used for the preparation of films, whilst compounds with 10·5 to 11% nitrogen are mixed with camphor or camphor substitutes for the manufacture of celluloid.

Gun-cotton is soluble in acetone, ethyl acetate, and partly soluble in amyl acetate; it is insoluble in alcohol and ether/alcohol. The industrial cellulose nitrates, with their lower nitrogen contents, dissolve in ethyl or amyl acetate, acetone, methyl alcohol, and ether/alcohol; the solution is sometimes termed collodion, and it leaves a thin waterproof film on any surface to which it is applied. The term "pyroxylin" may be applied to all cellulose nitrates soluble in methyl alcohol or in ether/alcohol.

Although the discovery of gun-cotton is associated with the work of Schonbein in 1846, the commercial application of cellulose nitrate films deposited from solutions originated in 1881, when Stevens patented the use of amyl acetate as a solvent. The cellulose nitrate finishing industry was limited in its scope by the high viscosities of the solutions rendering numerous applications necessary to produce a film of reasonable thickness. The advent of butyl acetate and the production of low-viscosity cellulose nitrates after the 1914–18 war enabled spray-gun methods to be used.

Cellulose nitrate is widely used for waterproofing draperies, shower-bath curtains, garden furniture, suitcase and hatbox covers, etc.

The general method of preparation of the nitrate is to treat cotton with 20 to 50 times its weight of a mixture of 2 to 3 parts of sulphuric acid per part of nitric acid to which 15 to 20% of water has been added. The reaction may take 15 to 60 minutes, but the temperature should not rise above 40°C. The crude nitrate is contaminated with some cellulose sulphate, which may be removed by prolonged boiling in weak acid solution, followed by shorter treatments in calcareous water. The low-viscosity nitrates are obtained from cellulose which has been subjected to a pre-treatment such as mercerisation or slight degradation by acid hydrolysis, heat, or oxidation.

As used by the lacquer manufacturer, cellulose nitrate is supplied moistened with 25 to 30% of industrial spirit, when it is no more dangerous than any other inflammable material provided reasonable precautions are taken. If the nitrate becomes dry, it is very dusty and settles in niches and accumulates; the dry nitrate is easily ignited by sparks, friction, flame, or static electricity, and burns rapidly with intense heat.

The cellulose nitrate lacquer usually consists of a mixture of cellulose nitrate, solvents, diluents, a plasticiser, and a resin. The solvents are conveniently classified according to their boiling range, but this is not necessarily an indication of how they will behave in the lacquer; low-boiling solvents are acetone, methyl, and ethyl acetate, methyl alcohol, etc., medium-boiling solvents include butyl and amyl acetate, whereas high-boiling solvents are cyclohexanone, ethyl lactate, diacetone alcohol, glycol monobutyl ether, etc. The diluents, such as ethyl, ispropyl, butyl and amyl alcohols, benzene, toluol, xylol, and ligroin, not only act as solvents for the resins, but although non-solvents for the nitrate, increase the solvent power of the true solvents. Plasticisers endow the nitrate film with elasticity and influence lustre and adhesion; dibutyl phthalate and tricresyl phosphate plasticise in virtue of gelatinisation and are non-volatile solvents, but a softener such as castor oil has no such effect. Some of the oil-modified alkyd resins can act as plasticisers and film-forming material at the same time. Solid plasticisers such as camphor and triphenyl phosphate are apt to crystallise from the film on ageing and produce brittleness. Blown castor oil is largely used in the production of "leather cloth."

Many resins are apt to reduce the strength of the resultant film and need balancing by a plasticiser. In addition to the natural resins, such as shellac, dammar, and mastic, many of the synthetic resins of the alkyd type find extensive application in cellulose nitrate lacquers, giving a high gloss, toughness, and durability. Ester gums are almost universally used, as they are cheap and blend well with other gums.

There are two broad methods of classifying the cellulose nitrates; the first depends on the nitrogen content, and the second on the viscosity of the solution. The percentage of nitrogen may vary considerably and is a valuable indication of the behaviour of the nitrate in various solutions.

The I.C.I. method of distinguishing the various grades unites both classifications, and indicates both the nitrogen content and the viscosity of the solution in acetone. Two letters and a numeral are used. The first letter indicates the nitrogen content as follows: H refers to high nitrogen (i.e. 11·8 to 12·3%), M relates to medium nitrogen (11·2 to 11·8%), and L to low nitrogen (10·5 to 11·2%). The second letter refers to viscosity and its significance is the same as before; H is high viscosity in 3% solution, M is medium viscosity measurable in 10% solution, and *L* refers to low viscosities measurable in 20% solutions. *X* relates to an extra low viscosity product measured in 40% solutions. The numeral which follows the two letters indicates the viscosity of the solution in absolute (C.G.S.) units. Hence *HX 45* relates to cellulose nitrate of nitrogen content between 11·8 and 12·3% and of extra low viscosity which is 45 C.G.S. units when estimated in a solution containing 40 g. of nitrate in 100 c.c. of 95% acetone. *HL 140* is used for aeroplane dope, *HX 45* for brushing enamels, and both *MM 25* and *LM 10* find an outlet in the manufacture of artificial leather.

Cellulose nitrates containing 10·7 to 11·2% nitrogen are soluble in ethyl alcohol and used for plastics, nitrates ranging from 11·2 to 11·7% of nitrogen are soluble in methyl alcohol, ethyl alcohol, ethyl acetate, and other solvents, and are used as lacquers; nitrates containing 11·8 to 12·3% of nitrogen are soluble in ester solvents such as ethyl, butyl and amyl acetate, methyl alcohol and acetone, as well as in a mixture of ether and alcohol; but they are insoluble in ethyl alcohol. They are used for lacquers and for artificial leather. Nitrates containing 12·4 to 13% of nitrogen are insoluble in the usual solvents, but dissolve in acetone; they are used for explosives.

Highly volatile solvents for cellulose nitrate do not give clear films unless the atmospheric humidity is low or the rate of evaporation is decreased; butyl or amyl acetate are often used as their low vapour pressure retards the rate of evaporation, and hence the absorption of moisture on the film. A further disadvantage of rapid evaporation is the formation of "pin-holes."

When cellulose nitrate produces clear transparent films, they are apt to be stiff, so that plasticisers are added, the upper limit being three times that of the dry weight of the film; castor oil is apt to "sweat" from the film and give a greasy effect.

Some very interesting information on industrial cellulose nitrates may be obtained from an I.C.I. booklet on the subject.

COMPARISON OF INDUSTRIAL CELLULOSE NITRATES

Hercules	I.G.	I.C.I.
0·25 sec.	E 400	HX 10
	E 510	HX 20
0·5 sec.		HX 45
	E 620	HX 60
4·6 sec.		HL 30
15–20 sec.	E 950	HL 140
35–40 sec.	E 1160	HM 15–20
70 sec.		HM 30–40
200 sec.		HM 100

Some viscosity data on the American cellulose nitrates have been given by Dorée (Methods of Cellulose Chemistry, Chapman and Hall,

London, 1933, 224). The American nitrates are characterised on a viscosity basis, by the time of fall of a steel ball, 0·25 inches in diameter, between two marks 10 inches apart in a glass tube at 25°C.; times vary from 0·5 to 200 seconds. For most textile purposes, the range of 0·5 to 25 seconds is adequate with concentrations of 25%; the nitrate with lower viscosities is fairly liquid and penetrates between the yarns, but the product of higher viscosity is a paste when cold and may be used for surface effects.

In Dorée's data, viscosity by the Ostwald viscometer has been compared with that given by a falling sphere method, using a steel ball 2 mm. in diameter passing through 25 c.c. of nitrate (5 to 25 g. per 100 g. of solution) in 99 to 100% butyl acetate. The results are shown in the table.

VISCOSITY OF CELLULOSE NITRATES

Type of cellulose nitrate	Dry cellulose nitrate in solution %	Solvent	Time limit in seconds		Viscosity according to the American method, seconds
			Minimum	Maximum	
5	25		35	60	$\frac{1}{4}$
6	25		90	120	$\frac{1}{3}$
6A	22		90	120	$\frac{1}{2}$
7	15		75	120	2
8	13	Butyl acetate	60	100	4
120	11		80	100	
8A normal	9		80	100	20–30
8A extra thick	7		80	100	250–400
17	5		80	120	60–80

COATING AND SPREADING

Coating preparations often include pigments which not only colour the film, but are used as "extenders"; talc is used to load and cheapen the film-forming mixture.

The pigments are generally ground with the castor oil and added to the nitrate, together with solvents and plasticiser; the temperature may be raised to a moderate extent depending on the solvent used. For the treatment of curtains for kitchens, bathrooms, and similar purposes, the following mixture has been suggested: 12·5 parts of nitrate (25 seconds), 16 parts of alcohol, 16 parts of toluene, 31 parts of ethyl acetate, and 25 parts of dibutyl phthalate for the first application, and 20 parts of nitrate, 16 parts of alcohol, 8 parts of toluene, 34 parts of ethyl acetate, 20 parts of dibutyl phthalate, and

2 parts of talc mixture (66% talc, 33% castor oil) for the second application.

The simplest method of coating fabrics is to pass the cloth over two rollers situated several inches apart and under a blade or doctor; the knife is caused to press on the cloth and spreads the coating preparation evenly over the surface of the material. The method is illustrated in Fig. 140.

The doctor-knives are made to treat fabrics up to 72 inches in width; they are generally about 80 inches long, 8 inches wide, and vary in thickness from 0·125 to 1 inch. In general the thicker blades apply a greater amount of the coating preparation than the thinner

FIG. 140.—Diagram of spreading with doctor-knife depressing the fabric.

blades. The doctor-knife is usually rigidly carried in a support which can be swivelled to enable the angle between the blade and the fabric to be varied from a right angle to an acute angle; a second adjustment controls the height of the blade, which may merely touch the fabric or may depress it to form an acute angle. The pressure of the knife on the cloth is determined by the tension on the fabric, which is regulated by the pressure on the let-off roller; this is generally equipped with a variable-tension device which automatically regulates the tension as the roll of fabric decreases in diameter.

Several types of doctor-knife are available for different purposes, and the five commonest are illustrated in section in Fig. 141.

For a light surface coating, type A is employed as its sharp edge removes most of the coating, leaving only a thin film. A heavier coating may be applied by the use of the blade illustrated as B, where the angle of the edge of the knife is less. The type of knife illustrated in C has a curved edge which leaves a heavy coating and tends to force some of the preparation into the fabric. Type E gives the heaviest coating, and also forces the material into the cloth. The knife illustrated in D is mainly employed for the final coating, which is of lower viscosity than the previous applications.

For obvious reasons, it is desirable to apply as much of the coating product as possible in one operation, provided that a smooth even product is obtained when the fabric is dried. One difficulty in the application of heavy layers is that the solvent vapours from the interior are apt to make pin-holes in the surface; these may be removed by embossing or calendering, but where these mechanical finishes do not form part of the normal process, it is usual to avoid pin-holes by building up the surface coating in a multiplicity of thin layers. Where thin layers are deposited on the fabric, it is possible

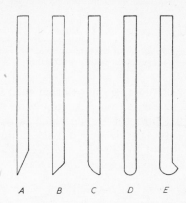

A   B   C   D   E

FIG. 141.—Diagram of various types of doctor-knife.

to obtain better bonding between the various layers than when thick coatings are applied.

Some coating preparations may contain from 40 to 50% solid matter and from 4 to 8 oz. of the solution or dough may be applied per yard of fabric in one run.

It is very important to keep the back of the doctor-knife sharp, for if its edge is irregular, then lines will appear on the fabric. Further, there is a tendency for round globules of the coating preparation to cling to the back of the knife and build up until they drop on to the fabric as heavy spots or doctor drops; this defect may be obviated by a sharp doctor-blade.

Where the method of spreading or coating is that illustrated in Fig. 140, the dope is fed into the depression formed by the cloth itself and prevented from running off at the selvedges by end-plates which form a dam. Actually, a small amount is apt to drip from the edges, but this may be collected easily, dissolved, and used again.

Another method of applying a light surface coating is shown in Fig. 142; in this case, low-viscosity solutions are applied to give a final coating which forms a hard lustrous surface.

The coating preparation is picked up from the trough by the

bottom roller and applied to the upper roller; the adjustable doctor-knife regulates the thickness of the coating applied to the fabric, which runs in part contact with the upper roller.

The method of coating fabrics with rubber, shown in Fig. 155 on page 441, is also suitable for the application of cellulose nitrate dopes.

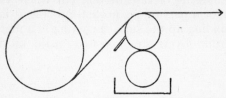

FIG. 142.—Diagram of coating by roller spreading in conjunction with doctor-knife.

Another coating machine is similar to that used for starch preparations, as illustrated in Fig. 24 on page 36. The cloth passes round a large roller or bowl into the dope, which is thus applied to one side of the fabric only—the so-called back-filling. A doctor-knife presses against the fabric and bowl, governing the weight of coating applied. A second doctor keeps the bowl clean.

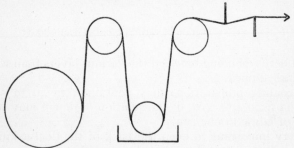

FIG. 143.—Diagram of spreading by roller impregnation followed by two doctor-knives.

It is also possible to coat both sides of a fabric at the same time, as shown in Fig. 143.

The trough or box is filled with dope so that the lower roller is partly covered; the fabric passes around the guide-roller into the trough and round the submerged roller, emerging over a second guide-roller to pass between two doctor-blades which regulate the amount of dope applied to the cloth.

The drying of coated fabrics is a relatively simple matter involving the removal of the solvents in the dope; temperatures of 60° to 80°C. are generally adequate. If excessive heat is applied, then pin-holes may be formed, but rapid evaporation of the solvent is also apt to cause "blushing" due to deposition of moisture on the newly formed surface of the dope.

It is possible to dry the coated fabric by passing over steam coils or through a festoon chamber, but the commonest method appears to utilise a "box" or chamber about 30 to 90 feet in length and sufficiently wide to accommodate the cloth. Where the fabric is only coated on one side some form of moving carrier or conveyor may be used, but if the coating is on both sides of the cloth it must be carried through the chamber free from contact until dry. Where numerous coatings are given to one side of the fabric, it is possible to arrange for a continuous treatment; after drying, the cloth drops on to a conveyor of sufficient length to bring the fabric to the front of the machine for another treatment just as the end of the cloth is leaving the doctor-knife.

As some of the dopes and many of the solvents used in coating fabrics are inflammable, certain precautions are necessary. Vapours must be removed from the impregnating room and drying boxes so that an explosive mixture cannot be formed. All motors must be of the special type devised for use in such circumstances, tools should be of brass to avoid sparks and the operatives' shoes should not be nailed or they may produce sparks from the concrete floors.

Some interesting information on the coating of fabrics generally has been given by Gibbons (Textile World, 1936, *86*, 1470, 2316).

Although cellulose nitrate is generally applied from a solution in a mixture of solvents, it is also possible to make use of aqueous dispersions. The typical product consists of two phases, cellulose nitrate dissolved in a suitable solvent and containing some castor oil, and the aqueous phase containing a mildly alkaline stabiliser and a dispersing agent; these two phases may be incorporated to form a stable aqueous emulsion of cellulose nitrate, which may be used for various purposes. An interesting glazed chintz effect may be produced by several applications of a suitably plasticised emulsion followed by calendering in the usual manner. The glazed appearance is fast to sponging and cleaning, but not to washing with soap and soda. These dispersions have also found application to rayons as a non-slip finish, when present in amounts of the order of 10%. Stiff finishes may also be obtained by the use of these dispersions, particularly with spun rayons, and interesting transparent effects have been realised on silk.

IMITATION LEATHER

IMITATION LEATHER manufacture is a separate industry and is not normally the function of a finishing works. The process was originated in 1884 by Wilson and Story, the general method being to coat the fabric with cellulose nitrate in amyl acetate solution; castor oil is added as a softening agent.

The basic cloth is generally a cotton canvas which is passed under a slot device adjusted to allow the necessary amount of cellulose nitrate to flow on to the fabric;

the number of coatings applied to the fabric may vary from three to thirty, according to the required effect. The first coating contains little oil, in order to get good adhesion; the intermediate layers contain castor oil, but the final coating contains neither oil nor pigment. After each coating the material must be dried before application of the next layer.

The solvents employed for this process include acetone and ethyl acetate, which may be diluted with alcohol, benzene, or petrol; castor oil is used to impart pliability to the cellulose nitrate.

The final treatment is to emboss the product with a design simulating the grain of leather, and rub with a pad soaked in a solvent containing a slightly darker pigment than that originally employed; this renders the grain more prominent.

Artificial leather may be manufactured in various ways, from superimposed webs of fibres, from fabric, from felted and bonded material, or by rolling sheets of nitrate and fibres.

Lace Effects

Chemical etching processes have been utilised for many years as a means of producing imitation lace effects; in some methods a woven fabric has been embroidered and the fabric base removed to leave the embroidery, whereas in other processes, the woven fabric may be treated so as to remove certain portions of it. The general object is to produce effects more cheaply than can be obtained by the ordinary methods of lace manufacture. One such method has been described in B.P. 10,867 of 1914, which depends on carbonisation for its effect.

It is possible to embroider a wool or silk fabric with cotton and then remove the animal fibres with a warm dilute solution of caustic soda, leaving a cotton embroidery with a lace appearance. Such processes are rather wasteful on account of the more expensive animal fibres being destroyed. The converse process consists in replacing the groundwork of wool with cotton and then embroidering with wool or silk, after which the cotton is removed by carbonising.

Another method was to use a groundwork of cotton treated in such a manner as to be readily removable. The pre-treatments were of various types, such as soaking in sulphuric acid solution and drying, when baking at 120° to 140°C. formed hydrocellulose which readily dusted out leaving the embroidery. The acid in the cotton was found to be a disadvantage as it produced rusting of the embroidery needles. Substances such as aluminium chloride and barium chlorate were found to be more satisfactory.

The newer manufactured fibres offer a greater scope than the older native fibres on account of their solubility in various solvents; alginate fibres, for example, dissolve in warm dilute alkali. The use of cellulose derivatives widens the scope of the finisher, and cellulose nitrate has been employed with some success.

The formation of cellulose nitrate is not accompanied by dissolution of the cellulose during esterification; it is possible to treat cotton fibres or yarns with the so-called nitrating mixture without loss of fibrous structure. Cotton treated in this manner, however, is sensitive to alkali, but this defect may be remedied by denitration in the usual manner with solutions of the sulphides or hydrosulphides of alkalis, alkaline earths, or ammonia. The two properties of alkali-sensitivity and denitrification have been utilised by Heberlein in B.P. 258,598 and 262,477 for the production of lace effects, and probably form the basis of the "Hetex" products.

A woven fabric is constructed in which the ground is formed with normal cotton material, but mixed with nitrated fibres or yarns; for instance, the nitrated fibres or yarns alternate with the ordinary cotton either singly or in pairs, or are twisted with it. The local action of alkali on such a material brings about destruction of those nitrated fibres with which it comes into contact, so that they can easily be removed by simple washing. The alkali may be applied in various ways, either directly printed on the fabric or the latter may be printed with a resist and then passed through an alkaline solution. An indirect process is to print the cloth with a denitrating agent, or to apply a local resist and pass through a denitrating bath; in subsequent treatment with alkali, in the latter case, after removal of the resist, the denitrated parts are not dissolved, whereas the areas where no denitration occurred are destroyed.

In the direct method of treatment, after the selected regions of cellulose nitrate have been destroyed, the remainder of the ester is denitrated so that the whole of the product becomes insensitive to alkali. Some interesting and spectacular effects have been produced in this manner.

A further development has been described in B.P. 537,519. Yarns or fabrics of regenerated cellulose, or mixed fabrics woven with natural and regenerated cellulose are nitrated with HNO_3 (d 1·5), diluted with acetic acid or a substituted fatty acid which is miscible with nitric acid, but not attacked at room temperatures; the special mixture nitrates the regenerated cellulose but not the native cellulose. Hence, part of the fabric becomes soluble in alkali and may be removed by that reagent, the local application of which produces etched effects. When the treatment is complete, a denitrification process renders the remaining material insensitive to alkali.

VISCOSE

VISCOSE finds its main outlet in the manufacture of rayon or artificial silk as it used to be called, but the viscose solution has been used to impart a linen-like finish to cotton. The preparation of viscose solutions has been described on many occasions, and the product used as a finishing agent is made in the same manner as for rayon manufacture. For instance, 150 lb. of cellulose in the form of wood pulp may be mixed with 68 gallons of 42° Tw. NaOH solution and macerated for 90 minutes at 20°C.; the soda cellulose is then pressed to about 425 lb., shredded, and allowed to age for about 72 hours at 20°C. The product is mixed with 37 lb. of carbon disulphide, which is added gradually with constant rotation of the product at about 25°C.; the orange-coloured crumby mass is dissolved in caustic soda solution to give a product generally containing 7% of cellulose. The viscose solution may be used immediately, but it is better to allow it to ripen for 72 hours or so; the ripening number is the volume of 10% ammonium chloride solution required to coagulate the solution of 20 g. of viscose in 30 c.c. of water. Many rayons are spun from viscose solutions whose ripening numbers lie between 8 and 10.

The action of carbon disulphide on alcohols in presence of sodium hydroxide had been known for many years before the discovery of viscose, and the general reaction may be illustrated in the following manner:

$$R.ONa + CS_2 \longrightarrow R.O.CS.SNa$$

With cellulose, the xanthate or dithiocarbonate may be regarded as an ester from the standpoint of chemical classification.

The relation to other compounds may be illustrated by the following formulae:

$$S:C \begin{cases} OH \\ OH \end{cases} \qquad S:C \begin{cases} OH \\ SH \end{cases}$$

| Thiocarbonic acid | Dithiocarbonic acid |

$$S:C \begin{cases} OX \\ SH \end{cases} \qquad S:C \begin{cases} OCell. \\ SNa \end{cases}$$

| Xanthic acid or ester of dithiocarbonic acid | Xanthate or cellulose sodium xanthate |

Interest was aroused in the possible use of viscose solutions for finishing purposes comparatively early in the history of this product; coated and printed fabrics were shown at the Paris Exhibition of 1900, but interest waned possibly on account of the poor technical and scientific development of viscose generally. Renewed activity occurred in 1920, when various organdie finishes were developed, and also methods of utilising viscose as a filling material alone and with inorganic substances such as zinc oxide and China clay; printed damask effects provided a further outlet for viscose as a finishing agent.

The viscose solution may be applied to the fabric in various ways, some of which are determined by the type of finish required. The simplest method for the thinner coatings or lighter applications is to use the padding mangle with the fabric passing directly into the nip, the bottom bowl of which furnishes the solution; alternatively, the cloth may pass through a trough containing viscose solution, and then through the mangle. A third method for thick coatings is to use the spreading method where excess of viscose is removed with a doctor-knife or scraper.

As previously mentioned, the viscose solution consists of cellulose sodium xanthate and contains free alkali; regeneration of the cellulose may be accomplished by passing the impregnated material through a bath containing 6% H_2SO_4 and 25% Na_2SO_4, when the free alkali is also neutralised. The use of this method necessitates a lead-lined tank and acid-resisting rollers. The fabric is then washed with warm water, neutralised, and rinsed.

An alternative method of regeneration is by steaming, but before this step the fabric should be dried by heating in an air-drier at a temperature of 55° to 70°C., when the cloth becomes harsh and stiff, acquiring a light-brown colour; regeneration is completed by the steaming process proper.

A two-stage method may be found useful where heavy applications of the viscose solutions have been given, and this depends on the coagulation of the viscose with ammonium sulphate or ammonium chloride solution at room temperature, followed by regeneration of the cellulose in 5% sulphuric acid solution, with or without sodium sulphate.

In all cases, the fabrics must be thoroughly washed and then the sulphur is removed in the ordinary manner with ammonium sulphide or sodium sulphite solution. The slight colour of the goods may be bleached with dilute sodium hypochlorite solution.

A special feature of viscose finishes is the shrinkage which occurs during regeneration of the cellulose, and it is essential that the goods should be maintained under tension if the steaming method is adopted, or during the drying if acid baths are employed; otherwise the coagulated mass will shrink to a hard and horny product which distorts and wrinkles the fabric. Once the fabric has been dried under tension, there is no danger of distortion through shrinkage on re-wetting. If, however, the regenerated cellulose gel is first allowed to form without restraint, then the cockled state of the cloth is permanent and the goods are useless.

The treated material may be calendered or schreinered to improve the lustre if required.

Finishing with viscose solutions presents certain drawbacks which are associated with the viscose solution itself. In the first place, it is not generally possible to have access to a commercial supply of viscose, and many finishers are not equipped or desirous of making their own solutions; the manufacture of viscose is not easy. Secondly, the viscose solution is not stable, and for uniform results must be used at the same ripening number every time. This means that unless large quantities of fabric have to be treated, innumerable difficulties occur for the viscose must be used within a certain period or it will coagulate; no means have been devised as yet for keeping viscose solutions in such a condition that they may be used with success. Not only is the "finish" different from viscose solutions of various ripeness numbers, but the affinity for dyestuffs also varies. It is, of course, possible to store the viscose for a limited time at low temperatures, but this is not generally convenient.

Apart from the general method, as already described, some more specialised applications have been outlined in patent specifications. B.P. 366,351 of Kilner outlines a process in which the fabric is impregnated with the viscose solution and, whilst stretched laterally, is then drawn immediately through a precipitating bath; the fabric may be impregnated *in vacuo* or, alternatively, the air may be removed by prior heating. Precipitation of the cellulose may be brought about by solutions of ammonium, magnesium, or alkali-metal salts, after which the material is washed free from acid, desulphurised, bleached, and dried in the stretched state.

Raduner, in B.P. 474,419 and 489,651, suggested the use of viscose solutions for impregnating, followed by coagulation and mercerising. The effect may be enhanced by treatment with sulphuric acid of less than 108°Tw. and repeated alternate treatments with acid and alkali may be given if required.

U.S.P. 2,104,748 outlines the application of regenerated cellulose to cotton fabrics or yarns, followed by mercerising under tension. A light-weight cotton lawn is impregnated with a viscose solution containing 6% of cellulose and 8% NaOH, dried and passed into a solution of 5% H_2SO_4, after which it is washed and then mercerised under tension with 60°Tw. NaOH. The fabric is finally bleached, washed, and dried under tension.

A linen-like finish may be given to cotton by treating with viscose solution of low alkalinity according to the method described by Clark in U.S.P. 1,564,943; not more than two molecular proportions of caustic soda are used to one proportion of cellulose, and this is stated to avoid discoloration on drying. The general method is first to singe and desize the cloth and then impregnate on a padding mangle with a solution of viscose containing from 5 to 10% of cellulose; the expression of the mangle is regulated so that the final increase in weight is from 2·5 to 5%, according to the degree of stiffness required. The fabric is then stentered and dried at 50°C., followed by calendering, after which it is passed through sulphuric acid solution of 5 to 10% concentration, washed, and bleached. This method is stated to give a soft and pliable finish as the use of excess alkali and high temperatures is avoided.

Lilienfeld has suggested the use of the esters of cellulose xanthic acid; applied normally, they are apt to give a stiff and papery handle which can be removed by shrinking the yarn or fabric with sodium hydroxide solution; these processes are revealed in B.P. 357,120 and 357,190.

ACETATE

CELLULOSE ACETATE is probably the best-known ester of cellulose and an organic acid. Although cellulose nitrate has been known since about 1845, and the acetate since 1866, the use of the latter developed much later. This was due to two main factors, the first of which being the slowness of the reaction in absence of catalysts, and the second the danger of degradation in presence of catalysts. The general method of preparation is to treat cellulose with acetic anhydride, acetic acid, and a catalyst such as zinc chloride, phosphoric acid, or sulphuric acid.

The second retarding factor in commercial development was the weakness and brittleness of the films made from the acetate, which was mainly the triacetate, soluble in chloroform but insoluble in acetone. The chloroform-soluble product is also known as the primary acetate. A considerable technical advance was made in 1904 by Miles, who found that partial hydrolysis of the primary acetate resulted in the formation of a secondary acetate which was soluble in acetone and other solvents; the secondary acetate has a lower acetyl content than the primary acetate. H. and C. Dreyfus became interested in the preparation of acetate about 1908, and were able to manufacture products which were suitable for films and sheets, and these were of some value on account of their non-inflammable nature as compared with cellulose nitrate. The war of 1914–18 caused a huge demand for cellulose acetate to be used for tautening and waterproofing the fabric coverings of aircraft wings, and a factory was established at Spondon; it was not until peace was established that attention was turned to the production of acetate rayon.

The general method of preparing cellulose acetate has been described by Lipscomb (Cellulose Acetate, Benn, London, 1933). Cotton linters are conditioned to contain 2 to 3% of moisture and 80 Kg. of linters are gradually added to an acetylating mixture consisting of 195 Kg. of acetic anhydride, 325 Kg. of acetic acid, and 10 Kg. of sulphuric acid; the mixture is cooled to 5°C. The reaction is exothermic and the temperature rises about 1°C. every 15 minutes for the first 2 hours; at this stage the reaction is apt to become vigorous and must be controlled so that the temperature rise does not exceed 2 to 2·5°C. per 15 minutes. At the end of a further period of 2 hours, the temperature has generally reached its maximum, which should not exceed 35°C., and then starts to fall slowly. After 90 minutes, test samples should be withdrawn to ensure that there are no unacetylated fibres and the solution is quite clear.

The next stage is to "ripen" the cellulose acetate by adding 18 litres of water and allowing the mixture to stand for 65 to 75 hours at 21°C. The course of the ripening is followed by withdrawing samples, which are tested by observing whether the material dissolves in 5 c.c. of a warm mixture of equal parts of alcohol and benzene, to which 2 or 3 drops of water are added; when ripe, the acetate is insoluble in warm chloroform, but becomes plastic.

After the ripening process, the sulphuric acid is neutralised with 17 Kg. of sodium acetate, and the cellulose acetate is precipitated by the addition of 400 litres of water, followed by washing, hydroextraction, and drying.

During the course of the reaction, some cellulose sulphate is formed, and must be removed or it will hydrolyse the acetate in presence of water; the usual method is to boil the acetate with 0·02% sulphuric acid solution for 1 to 2 hours, and then wash, hydroextract, and dry.

Cellulose acetate is usually sold in the form of white flakes. For application to textiles, it is usually compounded with various plasticisers and dissolved in a suitable solvent. It is possible to incorporate certain resins in the acetate for special purposes, and phenol-formaldehyde may be used, but the application is limited on account of the colour.

Where clear films are required, it is sometimes found that difficulty is experienced in avoiding a whitening or "blushing"; this is generally due to the use of a solvent which is miscible with water and has a high rate of evaporation, but may also be caused by precipitation of the acetate through the use of a non-solvent. The rate of evaporation is most important in deciding the choice of solvents.

As previously explained, the acetyl content of the acetate has an important bearing on its solubility, and also on the resistance to water. Cellulose acetate with a high acetyl content (40 to 42%) is resistant to moisture and has a low tolerance for non-solvents, but the use of acetates of lower acetyl content reduces the resistance to water even if the material may be dissolved in a larger number of solvents. The usual commercial products contain 36 to 42% acetyl, and are available with viscosities ranging from 2 to 120 seconds, as measured by the fall-ball method in 25% solution in acetone at 20°C. (see also page 327).

There are two methods of describing the amount of combined acetic acid, the acetyl value above-mentioned, and also the same value estimated as acetic acid. The triacetate contains 62·5% of combined acetic acid, and the diacetate 48·8%; commercial acetates range from 51 to 58% of combined acetic acid.

The viscosity of cellulose acetates may be estimated by the Ostwald viscometer, or the fall-ball method; the latter includes the time of fall of a steel ball $\frac{1}{16}$ inch diameter, through 15 cm. of liquid in a tube 28·5 cm. long and 2 cm. in internal diameter. Where the viscosity in C.G.S. units lies below 300, the acetates are regarded as low viscosity products, 300 to 400 denotes medium viscosity, and 400 to 500 high viscosities. Products of 100 and 500 C.G.S. units are extreme. As with the cellulose nitrates, the solutions of high viscosity give thin films, whereas those of low viscosity give thicker films and necessitate fewer applications.

Cellulose acetate is not compatible with plasticisers such as castor oil and linseed oil; phthalates, however, are often utilised, in particular the dimethyl, diethyl, and dibutyl compounds. Phosphates such as tributyl phosphate, triphenyl phosphate, and tricresyl phosphates are commonly used, as also are triacetin, ethyl-phthalyl-glycollate, and methyl-phthalyl-ethyl-glycollate.

The actual prescription of cellulose acetate mixtures depends to a large extent on their application; two interesting recipes representing American practice have been given by Lepperhoff (Textile World, 1937, 87, 1586). The first formula comprises 10 parts by weight of cellulose acetate of low acetyl value and viscosity of 2 to 5 seconds, 49 parts of acetone, 11 parts of methyl cellosolve, 10 parts of toluol, and 20 parts of methyl-phthalyl-ethyl-glycollate. The second mixture includes 10 parts of cellulose acetate of high acetyl value and viscosity of 15 to 30 seconds, 72 parts of acetone, 10 parts of ethyl acetate, 8 parts of methyl cellosolve, and 20 parts of butyl-phthalyl-butyl-glycollate.

It is not generally practicable to accomplish the coating with one application of the acetate solution and the common practice is to apply a number of coatings, the first of which are with low-viscosity solutions, whereas the later coatings are made with cellulose acetate of higher viscosity. The first coating usually applies about 3 to 5% of acetate to the fabric, subsequent coatings may impart a greater amount.

Cellulose acetate has also been utilised as a finishing material for special fabrics to replace windows as a war-time measure. The most suitable fabric is that in which the interstices are large, as in net constructions and similar weaves.

B.P. 543,206, by Ward, Parkes, and Coombes of Ericsson Telephones, Ltd., may be taken as an illustration of one method of this type of finish. The fabric is drawn through a bath in which the interstices are bridged by liquid, and then through a drying chamber of the tower variety through which a continuous current of warm air is passed to remove the solvent for the cellulose acetate. The drying tower is somewhat similar to that used for the production of oiled silks (see page 461), but possesses certain refinements in that it is built up of sections which differ in their degree of heat insulation. The simplest arrangement is merely to divide the drying tower by a vertical partition; the impregnated fabric passes up a well-insulated channel, around guide-rollers, and down a second channel, which is less well-insulated, so that the cloth does not emerge suddenly from a heated chamber into the outer air.

There appear to be no patent rights in the product, and British Government Civil Defence Handbooks in 1942 gave the names of numerous firms who supplied netting and similar material treated with cellulose acetate to replace window glass.

Yarsley, in B.P. 444,902, has described a process for impregnating fabric with a solution of cellulose acetate containing zinc chloride in suspension; the fibre swells and thus facilitates adhesion of the acetate. U.S.P. 2,047,919 of Du Pont, uses cellulose acetate, not in solution, but as a syrupy suspension with formamide and casein.

Mixed esters of cellulose have attracted great attention in the U.S.A., and it seems that cellulose acetopropionate and cellulose acetobutyrate will offer great scope to the finisher.

Laminated Fabric

The TRUBENISING process represents one of the most interesting and important developments in the use of cellulose acetate as a finishing agent for textiles, and its origin may be seen in B.P. 248,147; 249,946, and 419,208. Fundamentally, the process utilises the thermoplastic nature of cellulose acetate as a bonding medium in certain defined circumstances, and hence it is possible to subject a mixture of ordinary and thermoplastic fibres to heat and pressure, causing them to unite together. In this way fabrics may be united and a composite material produced. A simple illustration would be the union or bonding of a fabric composed of cellulose acetate with a cloth made from cotton; alternatively, a fabric of thermoplastic yarns may be placed between two fabrics of cotton or other fibres, and numerous other variations are possible. The extent of the softening or melting effect may vary with the degree and duration of heat and pressure so that the interstices of the fabrics become more or less closed; indeed, it is possible to produce a gasproof or impermeable effect if required. The associated fabrics may be passed through heated rollers at temperatures between 100° and 180°C. under pressures of 300 to 600 lb. per square inch, according to the effect required.

The degree of melting and the ease of bonding may be increased or accentuated by a previous application of plasticisers or solvents for the cellulose acetate; triacetin, paratoluene-sulphonamide, diethylphthalate or monomethyl xylene sulphonamide have been suggested, for application from benzene solution.

Instead of utilising complete fabrics of thermoplastic fibres with fabrics of cotton, silk, or linen, a "mixed" fabric may be used where thermoplastic yarns are intermingled with non-melting yarns of native or regenerated fibres, but these do not give such complete resistance to penetration by water or gases.

This basic idea has been carried a stage further in B.P. 419,208, to produce semi-stiff fabrics which remain permeable to air and moisture. Two or more layers of fabric may be secured together by solid fibres of the thermoplastic cellulose derivative which are so spaced that the permeability is not greatly affected. In this way, the cellulose derivative acts as an adhesive and not as a stiffening material so that the composite fabric is not brittle. With cellulose acetate, the fabric may be washed and ironed in the usual manner without difficulty, for cellulose acetate is not generally affected by ordinary careful laundering.

In composing the structure, it is preferable that the distance between the strands of cellulose derivatives should be greater than the thickness of the strands themselves, and also that the strands should be fine so that they do not show through the composite material. One of the commonest methods of composition is to inter-weave filaments of cellulose acetate in the interlayer which is later employed to bond two fabrics of cotton or linen; this is utilised in the manufacture of the modern semi-stiff collar, where the cellulose derivative is woven into the intermediate lining or interlayer of the collar.

Although this simple and highly successful treatment has reached its height in the production of collars, the same method has been used for stiffening neckbands, cuffs, and shirt-fronts.

According to the composition of the interlining, various degrees of stiffness may be produced, and at the same time the collars soften sufficiently during laundering to be freed from dirt in the ordinary manner; on ironing, they stiffen again without the use of starch.

The "Trubenising" process originated in the U.S.A. in the patents of Liebowitz (U.S.P. 1,968,409–10) which were assigned to the Trubenising Process Co., but a somewhat similar method had also been described in U.S.P. 1,903,960 of Dreyfus, whilst the use of solvents or softening agents partially to effect coalescence of the fibres had been disclosed in U.S.P. 1,828,397; the application of heat and pressure to bring about a glazing of fabrics containing thermoplastic derivatives of cellulose was protected in U.S.P. 1,716,255. The patent position was therefore rather complicated, but agreement has been reached between the various parties interested in the production of these semi-stiff or non-wilting collars whose development has been an interesting and successful technical achievement.

Instead of spacing the bonding threads of thermoplastic material in such a manner that a bonded but permeable result is obtained, it is also possible to distribute the thermoplastic substance during the actual bonding process. B.P. 497,568 of Koves utilises steam to influence the distribution of the bonding substance. The stiffened compounded fabrics are made by subjecting an assembly of two outer layers of non-thermoplastic fabric and an intervening layer of fabric containing thermoplastic threads, after treatment with a low-boiling solvent, to pressure between an upper heated surface and a lower cold surface which contains water. The upper layer of fabric becomes intimately united to the interlayer, the porosity of which is maintained or even increased by the rising water vapour. The solvent used in this process may be acetone, ethyl or butyl acetate or ethyl lactate.

B.P. 524,191 of Interfix Ltd., describes an interlayer in which some or all of the threads are composed of strands of thermoplastic and non-thermoplastic material twisted together; for example, the yarns may be made from cotton thread with cellulose acetate thread helically wrapped around the cotton. When this interlayer is placed between two non-thermoplastic fabrics, the assembly may be bonded without destroying the permeability or porosity of the composite material; the layers may be treated with a swelling or softening agent for the thermoplastic material and then placed on a cold water-absorbent surface, such as wet cotton fabric, when heat and pressure are applied to the upper surface. Here again the rising steam influences the manner of bonding and distribution of the thermoplastic material to give a composite material which retains a large proportion of its flexibility and porosity.

The two processes described above firmly unite the upper fabric to the interlayer, but the lower fabric only adheres sufficiently to the interlayer to make a bond which is reasonably permanent in wear.

The helical disposition of a thermoplastic yarn around non-thermoplastic threads has been utilised by Brew in B.P. 538,865 for the production of non-ladder stockings. The degree of twist in the composite yarn is such that there are sufficient points of contact of the adhesive parts with one another to prevent laddering, but there is also sufficient relative freedom between the component filaments to preserve elasticity; the nature of the treatment is such, that while the mutually-contacting adhesive parts unite, the adhesive part will not be united throughout its length with the inert filament. The adhesive state may be brought about by the application of a gelatinising agent or solvent for the thermoplastic material, but controlled by a diluent; in order to avoid fusion of, say, cellulose acetate to viscose, solvents such as acetone or acetic acid must not be used, but dimethyl phthalate has been found satisfactory. For example, suitably constructed hosiery may be immersed for 30 seconds in a bath consisting of 4 to 6 parts by volume of dimethyl phthalate and 96 to 94 parts by volume of benzene and then dried. The hosiery should then be hot-pressed for 15 seconds at 135° C., soaped, and dried.

This " spot-welding " process not only provides excellent resistance to laddering, but also prevents distortion, curling, and fraying of the treated goods.

Although cellulose acetate yarns are largely used in the production of semi-stiff and laminated articles of clothing, other materials have been suggested from time to time. For example, in U.S.P. 2,170,416, mixed esters of cellulose are mentioned as retaining their resiliency and adhesion after repeated laundering to a greater extent than cellulose acetate itself; cellulose acetopropionate and acetobutyrate appear to have advantages in this respect. Ethyl cellulose has been suggested in B.P. 473,961 on account of its higher melting-point (200° to 210°C.), greater flexibility and superior resistance to acid and alkali. Cellulose nitrate, in the form of an aqueous emulsion, may be used as a bonding medium according to B.P. 477,997, alone or in conjunction with an equal quantity of cellulose acetate dissolved in acetone and plasticised with a suitable plasticiser.

Now the general idea of protecting certain parts of our clothing, such as collars and cuffs, from soiling and wear was the subject of U.S.P. 1,668,744 and 5, where selected areas were impregnated with a waterproof and cementitious substance. It is only to be expected that many suggestions have been made to utilise synthetic resins in this respect and in the production of semi-stiff collars, but they do not seem to have been so successful as the cellulose esters. An interesting method may be seen in U.S.P. 2,009,139 and 2,045,963 by Redman, whereby the interlayer is first made unshrinkable by impregnation with viscose followed by a precipitation of the cellulose around the fibres; the material is then coated with a mixture of vinyl chloride and acetate in acetone, the mixture of resins being chosen to give a suitable melting-point without separation of the fused material at the boiling-point of water. Coatings of this type give an impermeable effect, but the mechanical action of the first laundering process causes the coating to crack at the interstices and so imparts some permeability.

Where resins are used, they must be capable of fusing at temperatures well below that at which the fabric will scorch, but they must remain set at the temperature of boiling water; the resins must be colourless and sufficiently flexible to withstand the mechanical processes of collar manufacture, which involves assembly inside out and then turning before stitching the final seam. Some resinous compositions have a tendency to crystallise and these should be avoided.

The co-polymer of vinyl acetate and chloride has been suggested in B.P. 473,478, and a plasticised polystyrene is also mentioned consisting of 8·5 parts of polystyrene, 1·5 parts of diethyl phthalate, 85 parts of benzene and 5 parts of xylene.

The polyisobutylenes may be utilised in the production of laminated fabrics according to B.P. 479,478, and good results may result from a polymer with molecular weight of 200,000, together with a small amount of rubber in a suitable solvent.

The methacrylate resins have also been suggested for finishes of this type, but methyl methacrylate is apt to be too harsh and brittle when used alone; various plasticisers have been put forward, such as dibutyl phthalate (U.S.P. 2,120,054) and tricresyl phosphate or dicyclohexyl phthalate (B.P. 473,961).

The disadvantages of methyl methacrylate polymers may also be overcome by either blending or co-polymerising with softer esters such as the higher methacrylates or the acrylates (B.P. 473,159).

It will be realised that there are many thermoplastic resins (see p. 360), the various combinations of which afford numerous preparations for laminating cloth, and the few which have been mentioned above merely illustrate what may be done without attempting to give a complete account of the hundreds of suggestions on these lines.

Lace Effects

Reference has been made on page 332 to the production of lace effects and embroidery by chemical methods.

Cellulose acetate has also been used in finishing processes for the production of pattern effects which simulate lace; the finishing treatment depends on differential solubility for its effect, like many others of this type (see page 332).

One of the early methods has been described by Heberlein in B.P. 237,909; a fabric is first made in which threads of cellulose acetate are distributed among the cotton threads, and subsequently printed with a resist. The cloth is then passed through a solvent which removes the unreserved cellulose acetate. Suitable resists may include solutions of glue, or an alcoholic solution of shellac; alkaline resists may also be employed, and bring about saponification of the ester as well as resisting the action of the solvent. Another method is first to effect local saponification and then pass the mixed fabric through a solvent which removes the unchanged acetate rayon. The effects may be further multiplied by utilising animal fibres together with the acetate rayon and the vegetable fibres.

A process of this type may be carried out quite economically, as it is possible to recover both the acetone and the dissolved acetate; but unfortunately even dilute solutions of acetate are viscous, so that it is necessary to employ comparatively large volumes of acetone to free the fabric from the acetate. A further difficulty is that the solution of cellulose acetate tends to adhere somewhat tenaciously to the fabric and produce an unwelcome stiffness.

B.P. 439,124 departs from the principle of simple dissolution and returns to the older method of chemical disintegration as used in carbonisation. When acetate rayon is subjected to the action of a suitable peroxide, and heated, it is readily disintegrated into a powdery form, whereas the fibres of viscose or cotton are unaffected.

Although organic peroxides have been used, it appears better to employ a mixture of an inorganic peroxide and an organic acid chloride which produces the organic peroxide by double decomposition; if a water-soluble inorganic peroxide is used in the mixture, it is possible to effect better control of the process.

A suitable recipe containing an organic peroxide is 200 g. of benzoyl peroxide, 75 g. of thickening, and 775 g. of water; this may be applied locally to a fabric containing cotton, silk, and acetate rayon, which is then dried and finally heated to a comparatively low temperature with mechanical agitation or beating, when the acetate is removed, leaving the other fibres to form a network or lace whose pattern is determined by the original arrangement of the different textile fibres.

In another example, a velvet fabric with acetate pile and silk or cotton back was printed with a mixture consisting of 254 g. of acetic anhydride, 286 g. of barium peroxide, 200 g. of benzyl acetate, 50 g. of Turkey red oil, and 210 g. of British gum thickening. The cloth was dried, and steamed with dry steam for 20 minutes, when disintegration of the acetate rayon was so complete that it was readily removed by beating, leaving a figured acetate pile fabric. Imitation lace may be obtained in a similar manner by treating a crêpe mousse fabric comprising yarns of acetate and viscose rayons.

This method may also be combined with the older "acid cut back" to produce interesting effects. For example, a velvet fabric with a silk back and a pile consisting of acetate and viscose rayons may be printed with three separate printing pastes; the first is prepared from 200 g. of benzoyl peroxide, 200 g. of benzyl acetate, 50 g. of Turkey red oil, and 550 g. of British gum thickening; the second from 10 g. of aluminium chloride, 5 g. of British gum thickening, and 90 g. of water; whilst the third includes an emulsion of 200 g. of benzoyl peroxide and 200 g. of benzyl acetate, to which is added 325 g. of British gum thickening, 75 g. of aluminium chloride (52° Tw.), and 200 g. of Turkey red oil. The fabric is then dried and heated at 120°C.; after beating and washing, a pattern effect is formed by local removal of acetate rayon by the first mixture, viscose rayon by the second preparation, and of both acetate and viscose with the third paste.

Immunised Cotton

The esterification of cellulose for the production of immunised yarn has been the subject of considerable attention; the treated material resists or is passive to the action of those colouring matters which normally dye cellulose, hence valuable coloured effects may be obtained by weaving these yarns with untreated material and then submitting the fabric to the ordinary process of piece-dyeing.

The first work on this subject was due to Cross and Bevan (Researches on Cellulose, 1901, *1*, 35), when bleached cotton was treated with boiling acetic anhydride in presence of anhydrous sodium acetate. The product was insoluble in all the usual solvents for cellulose and for the higher acetates of cellulose also; the fibrous nature of the cellulose was retained, but the product was weak and brittle. It was also established that the hygroscopic capacity of the fibres was reduced by the treatment.

The process was modified by Cross and Briggs (B.P. 5,016 of 1907) when fibres were immersed in acetic anhydride, acetic acid and a catalyst, followed by squeezing to leave a definite amount of the acetylating agent on the yarns which were then heated in a closed chamber. This process did not achieve any technical or commercial importance, as uneven results were obtained. Numerous other processes were attempted, utilising acetic anhydride vapour and weak catalysts with a view to preventing the formation of the higher acetates of cellulose which dissolve in the esterification mixture; the early work has been reviewed in detail by Rheiner (T.I.B.A., 1933, *11*, 567) and by Chippendale (J.S.D.C., 1934, *50*, 142).

It appears to have been generally assumed that the course of acetylation was first to transform the surface of the cellulose into the triacetate leaving the interior of the material unaltered; after swelling and solution of this surface layer, fresh surfaces of cellulose were exposed to the reagents and esterification continued. Rheiner and his colleagues of the Sandoz Company found that this was not necessarily the case, and were able to transform cellulose into the mono or diacetate directly by choosing an acetylating mixture of moderate activity which reacted so slowly that acetylation even to the monoacetate took 20 hours or even longer. In these circumstances it was found that the lower acetates are insoluble in the acetylation mixture. The regularity of treatment was demonstrated by examination of cross-sections of acetylated cotton which had been dyed with acetate dyes; the new product dyed evenly throughout, whereas the previous fibrous esters had shown the ester-layer in a ring surrounding the unchanged cellulose.

The low-acetylated fibres were found to possess the same strength and elasticity as the untreated material, but a somewhat firmer handle. The fibres are permanently swollen as a result of the treatment and show an increase in weight of about 20%. Like cellulose acetate rayon, however, the immunised yarn should not be subjected to treatment with hot alkali, but it will withstand the action of cold concentrated caustic soda of mercerising strength for a limited time and can be mercerised; unlike acetate rayon, the immunised yarn is not thermoplastic and can be calendered or ironed without injury.

Immunised yarn of this type is prepared according to B.P. 280,493; 314,913; 323,500; 323,515; 323,548 and 324,680.

Cotton yarn prepared according to these specifications is termed Cotopa, but when the treatment is applied to mercerised cotton, the product is called Crestol.

It is essential that the cotton yarn should be well prepared; kier-boiling for 9 to 10 hours in 2° to 3°Tw. NaOH solution at 20 lb. pressure is followed by washing and bleaching in hypochlorite solution containing not more than 2 to 3 g. of available chlorine per litre. For mercerised yarn, the kier-boiling should follow the mercerising process.

With scoured material, 1 Kg. of loose cotton is placed in an acetylating mixture of 3 Kg. of acetic anhydride, 5 Kg. of glacial acetic acid and 2·5 g. of sulphuric acid; acetylation proceeds at 15°C., and may take two days. Alternatively, 1 Kg. of yarn may be acetylated in 20 hours at 25°C. in a mixture of 4 Kg. of acetic anhydride, 4 Kg. glacial acetic acid, and 0·8 Kg. of zinc chloride. With mercerised cotton, the reaction is slower, so that it is necessary to raise the temperature above 40°C.; in an example, 100 g. of mercerised cotton is treated for 6 to 7 hours at 60°C. in a mixture consisting of 20 g. of zinc chloride, 100 g. of acetic anhydride, and 880 g. of glacial acetic acid.

If it should be required to use temperatures higher than 25°C. for the treatment of unmercerised cotton, then the amount of catalyst should be reduced; for instance, 100 parts of bleached cotton yarn may be treated for 30 to 45 minutes at 80°C. in 1,000 parts of a mixture comprising 30 parts of zinc chloride, 250 parts of acetic anhydride, and 720 parts of glacial acetic acid in a closed vessel.

It is important to realise that the immunity to dyestuffs is not complete immediately after acetylation, but is actually completed by the drying process; after acetylation and before drying, the fibres are very highly swollen, but the dried fibres do not swell again to the same extent when wetted with water. An effective method of preventing subsequent swelling is to steam the treated fibres under high pressure, according to B.P. 318,366; in these circumstances, the treated yarn may be rendered immune to cotton dyes even before the cellulose has been entirely esterified to the monoacetate stage.

Although even boiling water is incapable of reactivating the acetylated yarn when once it has been dried, yet it is possible to restore the dyeing properties by treatment with strong swelling agents, such as solutions of aliphatic carboxylic acids, particularly aqueous solutions of formic or acetic acid, as disclosed in B.P. 323,011.

Although part of the immunity to cotton dyes and the affinity for acetate colours is due to the acetylation of the cellulose, some of the resist effect is associated with decreased swelling in water; it is surprising to find the low acetylated fibres behave like cellulose in respect of solubility in organic solvents.

These acetylation processes may also be applied to viscose rayon, but have not achieved commercial importance as compared with acetylated cotton in view of the availability of acetate rayon; nevertheless, monoacetylated rayon only suffers a loss of 5% in tensile strength on wetting, compared with 45% for acetate rayon.

During the acetylation process, the affinity of the treated material for cotton dyes gradually diminishes until the monoacetate state is reached, when there is complete immunity to the cotton colouring matters.

It might be considered that these immunised yarns offer no advantage over acetate rayon, but it must be remembered that they may be dealt with on ordinary cotton machinery whereas rayon requires special winding machines and special looms; in many circumstances the high lustre of rayon is not required as shown by the numerous delustring processes. Other advantages are associated with the physical and chemical stability of immunised cotton as compared with acetate rayon.

In addition to the original Cotopa *30*, which contains 30% combined acetic acid, there is now available Cotopa *60* with 60% combined acetic acid; this triacetylated cotton is harder than the original material, but retains most of the strength and extension. It is interesting to note that the moisture regain of acetylated cotton steadily decreases with the increasing degree of acetylation up to 30% and then remains constant. The electrical properties of these materials are of interest, as shown in data provided by Standard Telephones and Cables Ltd. (see J.S.D.C., 1941, 57, 197). The d.c. insulation resistance of Cotopa *30* is 500,000 times that of ordinary grey cotton and about 25,000 times that of scoured cotton; Cotopa *60* has insulation resistance values about seventy times these figures. The Cotopas are much more resistant to heat and oxidation than cotton, silk, or acetate rayon.

Fibrous esters have also been made from alkali-cellulose, and a general account of these has been given by Marsh and Wood (Introduction to Cellulose Chemistry, London, Chapman and Hall, 1942).

Some interest has been paid to the special properties of the ester from *p*-toluene-sulphochloride which is a by-product from the manufacture of saccharin. The general work on the esterification of cellulose with aromatic chlorides in inert solvents gave products which resisted cotton dyes but were apt to be unstable; sulphochlorides were found to be more promising.

According to B.P. 195,619 of Textilwerk Horn A.G., bleached cotton is dried and immersed for an hour in warm alcoholic sodium hydroxide solution to form alkali-cellulose, which is centrifuged and placed in paratoluenesulphochloride solution in carbon tetrachloride at 15° to 20°C. The temperature rises with the course of the reaction and is then allowed to fall, after which it is raised to near the boiling-point; the material is extracted, soaped, washed, and dried. Toluene may also be used as a solvent for the sulphochloride, the amount of which should be three times that of the cotton; the ratio of solvent to cotton is about 40 : 1. The treatment causes a considerable shrinkage of the cotton with almost complete disappearance of the lumen or central canal; the weight of the cotton may be increased up to 40% without appreciable reduction in tensile strength, although the handle is somewhat harsh. These methods may also be used for pattern effects on fabric according to B.P. 233,704 of the Sandoz Company.

The immunised cotton produced from alkali-cellulose is not homogeneous, as may be shown by dyeing cross-sections of the fibres; further, it is possible to remove the esterified layer with pyridine, leaving a thin core of unesterified cellulose, or, alternatively, it is possible to remove the cellulose with cuprammonia when the esterified layer is burst by the swelling pressure of the cellulose, but remains as a spiral band.

Some special properties of this type of immunised yarn are due to the fact that whereas the esters of carboxylic acids are decomposed by ammonia and amines into acid amides and alcohols, the esters of mono- and di-sulphonic acids behave differently and form amines and the ammonium salt of the sulphonic acid. Hence, by treatment of the cellulose toluene sulphonate with ammonia or amines, it is possible to form nitrogenous derivatives of cellulose. Karrer and Wehr (Helv. Chim. Acta, 1926, 9, 592) found that the reaction proceeded readily at 100°C. in 60 minutes. The immunised cotton before treatment contained 1·9% of sulphur, which was reduced to 1·3%; there was a total loss in weight of 7·6% and about 0·8% of nitrogen was combined with the cellulose. Dyeing tests revealed that the amidated cotton had a very strong affinity for the basic colours, and this suggested the term "animalised" cotton; in point of fact, the affinity for this class of colour is stronger than that exhibited by wool itself, for in certain circumstances the amidated cellulose will strip the colour from dyed wool if heated with it in water.

Some further information on immunised and amidated cottons has been given by Marsh (Industrial Chemist, 1928, 4, 75).

CELLULOSE ETHERS

Whereas the esters of cellulose have been known for one hundred years, it was not until 1905 that attention was devoted to the cellulose ethers, but the original work was of an academic nature concerned with the properties of various colouring matters in relation to carbohydrate structure. In 1912, however, independent work from three separate sources, by Leuchs, Lilienfeld, and Dreyfus, described the formation of the methyl and ethyl ethers of cellulose; the Lilienfeld master patent is B.P. 12,854 of 1912.

Methyl cellulose is generally prepared by the action of methyl sulphate or chloride on soda cellulose; three types of product may be manufactured differing in solubility according to the degree of methylation. Methyl cellulose with the highest degree of substitution is soluble in organic solvents and often exhibits plastic and thermoplastic properties; good films may be formed from these derivatives with satisfactory resistance to water, but they have found little application in the textile industry. Ethers with a lower degree of substitution are soluble in cold water and have found an outlet as pastes in printing; they are precipitated from their aqueous solutions on warming. These products are probably the best-known methyl celluloses, and are available under trade names such as Colloresin, Tylose, or Glutoline; the methoxyl content varies from 22 to 26%, corresponding to the substitution of 1·5 hydroxyl-hydrogens per glucose residue. The alkali-soluble methyl celluloses only dissolve in a limited range of aqueous alkali such as 5 to 12% NaOH solution, and the extent of substitution of these products is approximately 5% methoxyl.

More recently, the manufacture of methyl cellulose has been subject to some variation by replacing all or part of the caustic alkali with quaternary ammonium hydroxide solutions which dissolve cellulose and promote a more even reaction. A further development of a somewhat unique nature is to treat the soda cellulose with a copper salt to form a cellulose-copper complex and then methylate with dimethyl sulphate to give a methyl cellulose which is soluble in both hot and cold water, as distinct from the methyl cellulose prepared in the normal manner which dissolves in cold water, but is insoluble in hot water. Water-solubility is exhibited at a methoxyl content of 14 to 15%, as compared with 20 to 25% in the case of the ordinary product.

Ethyl cellulose has been prepared in a somewhat similar manner to methyl cellulose, but does not appear to have been developed commercially.

Benzyl cellulose may be made by the action of benzyl chloride on soda cellulose.

The diethyl and dibenzyl ethers of cellulose are soluble in aromatic hydrocarbons and many other organic solvents; their film-forming properties are good and have found application as lacquers or coatings in a somewhat similar manner to cellulose nitrate, although to a much smaller extent; however, the flexibility and extensibility of the films may be of value for certain finishes, particularly in view of the impermeability to water exhibited by benzyl cellulose. In emulsion form, these ethers may yet find considerable outlet in the textile field.

HYDROXYETHERS OF CELLULOSE

Great interest has been aroused within recent times by the use of HYDROXYETHYL CELLULOSE as a finishing agent. This product may be made by treating soda-cellulose with ethylene oxide or with ethylene chlorhydrin.

It is important to appreciate that the action of ethylene oxide or ethylene chlorhydrin is capable of producing three classes of hydroxyethyl or glycol cellulose. If conditions are chosen so that rather less than one hydroxyl group per four glucose residues is etherified, then the resulting ether is insoluble in water and will not even dissolve in dilute sodium hydroxide solution unless cooled until ice crystals are formed; when the mass is allowed to thaw, however, the cellulose ether remains in solution. The second class of hydroxyethyl cellulose has a slightly higher degree of substitution corresponding to one etherified hydroxyl group per two glucose residues; this ether is soluble in dilute sodium hydroxide solution of about 10% concentration. As the extent of substitution is increased further, products are obtained which dissolve in lower concentrations of sodium hydroxide solution, until when about two hydroxyl groups per glucose residue have been etherified the resulting ether dissolves in hot and in cold water.

Compared with the methyl celluloses, it will be remembered that these are soluble in water at an earlier stage of substitution, but the water-soluble methyl cellulose, although dissolving in cold water, is insoluble in hot water.

Another product which is of interest, and commercially available, is cellulose glycollic acid, which may be manufactured to give somewhat corresponding solubilities in alkali and water. It is made by the action of monochloracetic acid on soda cellulose, and the substituent radical is —OCH_2COOH, whereas in glycol cellulose the substituent radical is —OCH_2CH_2OH. The water-soluble sodium cellulose glycollate has a greater binding power for pigments than methyl cellulose, but is not fast to washing when applied to cloth.

Glycol cellulose may be made in two ways, the first of which depends on the treatment of soda-cellulose with ethylene chlorhydrin

$$\text{Cell.ONa} + \text{ClCH}_2.\text{CH}_2\text{OH} \longrightarrow \text{Cell.OCH}_2.\text{CH}_2\text{OH}.$$

This reaction appears to be due to Dreyfus, as outlined in B.P. 166,767.

A somewhat unusual method, however, depends on the use of ethylene oxide, which is a gas; this method has been described in various patent specifications, including B.P. 231,807, 359,618, and 463,317. The reaction occurs as follows:

$$\text{Cell.ONa} + \underset{\text{O}}{\overset{\text{CH}_2\text{—CH}_2}{\diagdown\ \diagup}} \longrightarrow \text{Cell.OCH}_2.\text{CH}_2\text{OH.}$$

The ratio of cellulose to caustic soda to water is of the utmost importance as it regulates the speed of the reaction and the degree of substitution of the cellulose. The reaction is generally carried out in closed jacketed vessels fitted with stirrers, and the alkali-cellulose is allowed to react with the ethylene oxide, chlorhydrin, or monochloracetic acid, as the case may be, for 1 to 2 hours with stirring, after which the mixture is allowed to stand for from 10 to 70 hours, during which time the temperature is carefully controlled.

The method of purification varies according to the solubility, the lower ethers being precipitated from alkaline solution by acid, whereas extraction with alcohol may be employed for the water-soluble ethers.

The technique of manufacture has been described in detail by Schorger and Shoemaker (Ind. Eng. Chem., 1937, *29*, 114), with particular reference to those ethers containing less than one sub-stituent per four glucose residues, and soluble in alkali only on cooling.

As marketed, these hydroxyethers of cellulose retain the physical form of the material from which they were derived, and are light and fluffy in appearance; they are less soluble in potassium hydroxide solutions than in those of sodium hydroxide. The greatest solubility appears to be in 10% solutions of NaOH, and there is a marked diminution in solubility at 20% NaOH or over.

The preparation of these cellulose ethers seems to be covered in U.S.P. 1,941,276 to 8, 1,598,606, 1,722,927 and 8.

It might seem that the difficulty in dissolving the hydroxyethyl ethers, substituted in less than one hydroxyl group per four glucose residues, would militate against their use as textile finishing agents, for, as previously mentioned, it is necessary to cool the alkali to obtain dissolution. However, it must be realised that the ethers which dissolve in alkali without cooling, and which are substituted to the extent of one hydroxyl group per two glucose residues, cannot be regarded in the same class as finishing agents which are fast to washing; the difficulty in dissolution is counterbalanced by the fastness of the product on the fabric.

For textile finishes the ethers may be applied from alkaline solution in 5 to 10% NaOH; the ether itself may dissolve up to a maximum of about 7%, but when once dissolved may be diluted with water to give a stable solution. The type of finish to which these products are best suited is the crisp stiffening usually associated with a linen finish, but softer effects may be obtained with more dilute solutions or by dispersing waxes in the alkaline solution of the ether.

The application of the alkali-soluble cellulose ethers to fabrics requires two stages: first, the padding of the alkaline solution, and secondly, the coagulation of the ether; the fabric is then washed, dried, and finished in the normal manner.

The alkaline nature of the solution makes it advisable to take certain precautions; the use of brass, copper, and other metals which are affected by alkali should be avoided, as the ether coagulates on these metals. The slippery nature of the solution may make it necessary to have a positive drive for both bowls of the padding mangle.

The type of cellulose ether under consideration is only soluble in a limited range of concentrations of sodium hydroxide, and advantage may be taken of this property, to coagulate the ether during the mercerising process; this method has been shown to have considerable promise according to Clark (Am. Dyes. Rep., 1942, *31*, 110), and a large quantity of shirtings has been finished in this manner. In general, the cloth is singed and then saturated in a 2% solution of the alkali-soluble cellulose ether which may be applied from the first trough of a mercerising range. Following a heavy squeeze in the mangle, the cloth then passes into the sodium hydroxide of mercerising strength in the second mangle-box after which the normal mercerising process is applied, but care is taken to avoid the use of cold water until the alkali has been washed from the cloth. In this method, the cellulose ether must be one whose alkali-solubility is sharply defined.

The simplest method of coagulation, however, is merely to neutralise the alkali after the solution of cellulose ether has been applied to the cloth; dilute acid may be used. In certain circumstances the cloth may be partially dried by stentering, after which the alkali can be removed by washing with hot water, thus coagulating the ether.

An interesting development has been seen in the treatment of sheetings which are first kier-boiled and then padded with a 4% solution of the cellulose ether; the cloth is then passed through a J-box or Gantt piler and drawn through a horizontal trough containing acid which coagulates the ether. Finally, the cloth may be washed, bleached, and finished as usual. It would appear that U.S.A. methods seem to favour treatment of the grey cloth, and it is interesting to note that either peroxide or hypochlorite bleaching may be employed.

The application of the alkali-soluble cellulose ethers to damask and jacquard weaves is of particular interest, not only for the linen effect, but also on account of the non-linting qualities. Solutions containing about 5% of the cellulose ether may be applied to the fabric either before or after bleaching, but it is preferable to coagulate the ether with the cloth at full width.

With prints and other cloths of a plain weave it is often better to impregnate with the ether solution before bleaching in order that the mechanical treatment of the cloth in the subsequent processing will break down what would normally be a somewhat wiry, hard finish to give a full, soft handle; a satisfactory concentration of solution appears to be 2 to 2·5%.

Filled cloths may be prepared on the mangle or back-filling machine; it is possible to pad the cloth with 2 to 4% solution of the cellulose ether, apply the mixture of China clay or other filler on the back-filling machine, and then coagulate the cellulose ether.

Spun-rayon fabrics may also be treated with cellulose ethers to give a full mellow effect, utilising concentrations of 1·5 to 2%. According to Clark (Am. Dyes. Rep., 1940, 29, 549) spun-rayon gaberdines and twills which normally show shrinkages of 13 to 17% in use and laundering, may have this shrinkage reduced to 5% after a suitable treatment with an alkali-soluble cellulose ether.

Golrick (Text. World, 1940, 90, 55) has given full details of large-scale practice in the treatment of cotton sheetings with an alkali-soluble hydroxyethyl cellulose known as Ceglin. The process includes continuous scouring, bleaching, and finishing; the sequence of operations is scouring, washing, grey souring, washing, scutching, water mangling, drying, padding with the cellulose ether in alkaline solution, coagulating in rope form with dilute acid, and piling for 5 minutes, followed by washing, bleaching, etc. The concentration of cellulose ether employed was 4 to 4·5% in 8% NaOH solution, and this was later coagulated by 5% sulphuric acid solution. If the semi-drying method of coagulation is desired, then the impregnated cloth may be passed over a series of steam-heated cylinders, the first four of which are wrapped with cotton cloth; approximately 50 to 70% water is removed, and the final finish possesses a linen-like effect with an open appearance. Coagulation by souring gives a less "sheer" effect, and if boiling water containing a little acetic acid is used, then a much softer finish is obtained.

It must not be assumed that the application of these cellulose ethers, simple as it may appear, is entirely devoid of precautions. Lawrie (J.S.D.C., 1941, 57, 180) has drawn attention to the fact that the alkali-soluble varieties are applied from relatively concentrated alkali solution, so that, in certain circumstances, the action on the fibre may cause difficulties; with dyed goods it may affect the shade, and in piece-dyed fabrics the action of the alkali may cause the yarns to swell and untwist and show a speckled effect if the penetration of the dyestuff has not been extremely thorough.

Even with white goods, certain precautions are necessary on account of the fact that the cloth, whilst impregnated with glycol cellulose solution, is very sensitive to crease-marks; if these appear, they are apt to persist throughout the finishing operations, but may be removed to a certain extent by calendering. This defect, however, is not present after the ether has been coagulated and the cloth dried.

The pieces should preferably be treated in open width, and care taken to avoid any mechanical marking; for instance, the use of ridged expander rollers may produce a "tram-line" effect which is very difficult to remove. If these points are kept in mind, then the application of solutions of cellulose ethers should present little difficulty.

Craik and Davis (J.S.D.C., 1939, 55, 597) have given some details of tests on fabrics which have been finished with solutions of hydroxy-ethyl ethers of cellulose; the increase in weight of the calico material as a result of the finish was approximately 7%, and after five extremely severe launderings only 10% of this added material had been removed. Merely boiling in 1% soap and 1% soda solution produced a negligible loss in weight, although there was a slight softening of the finish. Further, whereas a fabric filled with starch and China clay lost 88% of the finish on boiling for 1 hour in 1% soap solution, a similar finish with 3% cellulose ether and China clay (3 parts of filler to 1 of ether) showed no loss after a similar boiling treatment.

Tensile strength estimations showed an improvement as a result of finishing with cellulose ethers.

EFFECT OF CELLULOSE ETHER ON BREAKING LOAD

Treatment	Breaking load in lb. Before	After
Padded with 5% glycol cellulose	130	135
Padded with 7% glycol cellulose	105	130
Padded with 7% glycol cellulose	100	136
Padded with 5% glycol cellulose	157	170

These results refer to four different fabrics.

The superior wearing properties of the treated fabrics are shown in the following table:

ABRASION TESTS ON TREATED FABRICS

Material	Strokes of rubbing machine to produce abrasion
Untreated calico	308
Treated 4% cellulose ether	920
Treated 7% cellulose ether	1,100
Untreated viscose staple fibre	470
Treated with 4% cellulose ether	945
Treated with 7% cellulose ether	990

CELLOFAS

CELLOFAS TWL of the I.C.I. is an improved finishing agent which is normally sold in the form of white flocks; it dissolves in cold water to form viscous solutions of neutral reaction. The binding properties of these solutions are superior to those of starch, so that the cellulose ether is capable of carrying a greater proportion of filler than can be held in a starch mixing; the protective colloid action of the cellulose ether solution is such that the separation of the fillers is retarded. Cellofas TWL in solution seems to be immune to mildew and fungoid growth.

Solutions of Cellofas TWL, when used alone, are capable of imparting a full supple handle to cloth, and this finish is also tough and resistant to abrasion. The solution may be applied by a padding mangle or from the back-filling machine; drying may be carried out on stenter or cylinders in the usual manner.

For most purposes it is best to start with a 5% solution of Cellofas TWL; this may be made by adding 5 parts of the flakes to a suitable vessel into which is poured 45 parts of water which is near to boiling-point and the mixture is stirred until the Cellofas is thoroughly soaked. The mixture is allowed to stand until cool, when 50 parts of cold water is added with stirring; where a double-walled vessel has been used it is advantageous to circulate cold water. Slow, steady stirring is recommended for these viscous solutions as rapid agitation causes frothing. For the best results, the cooling should be as efficient as possible, and ice is useful in this respect. The uniform viscous solution may be diluted to any required extent before use, but must not be heated above 40°C. in any circumstances.

An alternative method of making the initial solution is to dissolve 100 parts of Cellofas TWL in 1,300 parts of water, as outlined above, to give a 7% solution; 5 parts of sodium hydroxide previously dissolved in 80 parts of water are added to this solution, and the whole allowed to stand overnight. A solution of 14 parts of concentrated HCl (31·5%) in 500 parts of water is then added, to give a neutral solution containing 5% of Cellofas.

For finishing cotton, linen, or rayon piece goods, Cellofas TWL may be used in concentrations varying from 0·5 to 5%, according to the desired degree of stiffness; excellent effects may be obtained on shirtings, poplins, and muslins by padding in 0·5 to 1% solutions. If softer results are required, then substances such as Lissapol C, Cirrasol LC, or Velan PF may be added, using from 1 to 5 lb. of these products per 100 gallons of Cellofas solution, according to the degree of softening required.

If a lustrous finish is required, then the cloth may be treated with about 0·25% solution of Cellofas TWL on the dewing or damping machine before calendering. A non-slip effect may be obtained by padding at room temperatures in a solution of 0·5 to 1% of Cellofas TWL, followed by drying in the usual manner.

CELLOFAS TWF of I.C.I. is the sodium salt of carboxymethyl-cellulose; the free acid is prepared by impregnating cellulose with caustic soda solution of mercerising strength, in presence or absence of alcohol, and then etherifying with sodium monochloracetate, followed by acidification. Although generally termed cellulose-glycollic acid, the product is methyl-cellulose, which is substituted in the methyl group with a carboxyl group. The solubility of the acid, and its sodium salt, depends on the degree of substitution, and when this is very low, the sodium salt only dissolves in certain concentrations of alkali at low temperatures; but as the degree of substitution increases, the sodium salt becomes soluble in alkali at ordinary temperatures. With substitution corresponding to 0·3 carboxymethyl groups per glucose residue, the sodium salt is soluble in both hot and cold water, but the free acid remains insoluble; this sodium salt is the product sold as Cellofas TWF. Higher degrees of substitution render both the acid and the sodium salt soluble in water. CELLOFAS TAF is less substituted than the TWF variety.

The fluffy, hygroscopic, white solid dissolves in water at all temperatures, and is manufactured to give three viscosities; the viscosity of the solutions is affected by pH and reaches a maximum around pH 6 to 9. In all cases, the viscosity rises rapidly with concentration, but when heated and then cooled, the solutions show a distinct fall in viscosity; this deterioration starts at 40° to 50°C., and is fairly rapid at 100°C.

Although the sodium salt is insoluble in organic solvents, it will tolerate up to 45% of alcohol or 40% of acetone. The ammonium salt is unstable and decomposes at 50° to 60°C.; the lead, silver, mercury, aluminium, copper, nickel, and ferric salts are insoluble in water.

According to Brown and Houghton (J.S.C.I., 1941, 60, 254) carboxymethylcellulose has a dissociation constant of $5 \cdot 0 \times 10^{-5}$ and is comparable with acetic acid in strength. The sodium salt is hygroscopic and normally contains 11% of moisture, but in a saturated atmosphere this may reach 200%.

The water-soluble and the alkali-soluble cellulose ethers are valuable finishing agents as superior replacements of starch. Whereas most of the filler, such as China clay, which is bound to the fabric by starch, may be removed in one washing operation, the binding effect of the cellulose ethers is such that a heavily filled finish may be produced which is reasonably fast to washing, although by no means permanent. A high ratio of filler to cellulose ether may be employed, 4 : 1 with China clay and 2 : 1 with talc; with starch it is not wise to exceed the ratio of 2 : 1 for China clay.

These new finishing agents appear to possess five main advantages: (*a*) a stiffening effect which is reasonably fast to washing, (*b*) excellent binding action on fillers, (*c*) improved tensile strength, (*d*) improved resistance to abrasion, and (*e*) reduced tendency to shrink. Subsidiary advantages are the non-slip and non-linting effect.

Treatment with Ethylene Oxide

As already stated, it is possible to prepare hydroxyethyl cellulose by treating soda cellulose with ethylene oxide, but this reaction may also be applied to woven cloth under carefully controlled conditions in such a manner that the textile character of the material is preserved; formation of glycol cellulose *in situ* imparts novel effects to the cloth, and these effects are as permanent as the material itself.

The reaction is essentially one between soda-cellulose and ethylene oxide, and the presence of moisture is essential.

The process has been protected by B.P. 439,880, 482,942, 475,906, and 481,191; the methods have been described in an interesting paper by Lawrie, Reynolds, and Ward (J.S.D.C., 1940, *56*, 6).

Two broad variations are possible, in the first of which the stiffening action is such that organdie effects are produced; the second, and milder process, creates linen-like finishes. For the organdie effects, the degree of treatment is advanced as far as possible consistent with retention of the physical properties of the fabric, and this is brought about by a preliminary treatment with relatively concentrated sodium hydroxide solution (approximately 23% NaOH) followed by high concentrations of ethylene oxide (about 40%, calculated on the weight of the cloth) applied from solution in carbon tetrachloride. The milder process which gives linen-like effects depends on the use of weaker NaOH solutions (about 11%) and lower concentrations of ethylene oxide (about 10% on the weight of the cloth).

Concentrations of at least 9·5% NaOH are necessary for the reaction to occur, and the reactivity increases up to a concentration of 22·5% NaOH, above which there is no further increase. Concentrations of 9% NaOH or thereabouts mark the onset of mercerisation, which is accompanied by shrinkage, hence during the process there is some shrinkage of the fabric, but after the complete treatment the material is still sufficiently plastic to be stretched during the final drying operation. Naturally the amount of stretching depends on the nature of the cloth; with muslins and an energetic treatment, it is possible to recover 90% of the original width, but milder treatments on many cloths enables the full width to be recovered.

The cloth must not be dried after the initial treatment with alkali, but excess of liquid may be removed in the ordinary manner by squeezing in a mangle or by hydroextraction; with prints, the pressure of the roller controls the amount of caustic soda solution applied.

It is possible to apply the ethylene oxide in the gaseous form or from solution in carbon tetrachloride or in brine; the gaseous application appears to offer certain advantages where large-scale continuous processes are required, but necessitates special plant. For many purposes, the use of solutions in carbon tetrachloride appears most convenient, the highest concentration of ethylene oxide being 5%. The use of brine is not so simple, but it has been found possible to print the cloth with concentrated solutions of NaOH of the order of 40%, in the form of a paste with British gum, and then apply the ethylene oxide in brine. With this method, however, it is necessary to use more ethylene oxide than when solutions in carbon tetrachloride are employed.

The use of solutions of ethylene oxide in carbon tetrachloride solution necessitates a closed vessel, for ethylene oxide is extremely volatile even in dilute solution. It is also advisable to provide movement of the liquor and avoid irregularity of treatment. Some apparatus, such as an Obermaier dyeing machine, may be used when the cloth is treated in semi-rope form, but there seems to be no reason why the cloth should not be treated in an open-width kier.

In order to maintain a given effect, the concentration of ethylene oxide must be increased when the volume of the solvent is increased, or the time of reaction may need to be prolonged. With carbon tetrachloride solutions, when the volume of liquor is doubled, then the amount of ethylene oxide must be increased by 5 : 4; alternatively, if the ethylene oxide concentration is halved, then the time of reaction must be increased 2·5 times.

Normally, for both organdie and linen effects it is necessary to allow a time of reaction of about 18 hours at 20° to 25°C.; the first signs of the alteration of the cloth appear after 4 hours. The reaction may be carried out in 2 hours at a temperature of 50°C.

When the process is complete, the cloth is still alkaline and also wet with the solvent; the latter may be removed by extraction, and recovered. Alkali is removed by souring, and this part of the treatment requires care and control according to the intensity of the original reaction. If an energetic treatment has been given, then acidification may be effected with either 10% H_2SO_4 or with 10% brine containing 1% H_2SO_4 in order to produce a coagulating effect; otherwise the rate of neutralisation is so slow that NaOH of solubilising strength is formed locally with dissolution of the cloth. Actually, 5% NaOH is capable of dissolving the treated cloth, and this action may be utilised for figured and lace effects.

The neutralised and washed fabric possesses a pink colour varying in depth according to the intensity of the original treatment, but the colour may be removed quite readily by bleaching in weak hypochlorite solutions at pH 4·5; with the usual alkaline hypochlorite liquors, the bleaching is slow and incomplete. Chlorine concentrations of 0·5 g. per litre appear adequate.

Subject to the main effect, the finish of the cloth may be affected by the final drying conditions. Stenter drying gives a stiffer result than drying on cylinders, which tends to produce a leathery but less wiry handle. For the best organdie effects, stenter drying with jigging is preferred, or the cloth will be rather flabby. With linenised effects, the stenter drying may be followed by beetling or other forms of lustring; calendering produces a soft parchment-like transparent effect, and on certain cloths a highly transparent effect may result from damping heavily and calendering. Schreiner finishes enable material similar to tracing cloth to be produced.

The ethylene oxide finish may be carried out without serious effect on the tensile strength of the cloth within about 5%; the treated material has an enhanced affinity for many dyestuffs, but the colour tends to concentrate on the surface.

Broadly, the all-over effects produced by ethylene oxide include organdie, linen, and parchmentised finishes which mainly depend on varying the alkali and ethylene oxide. The organdie effect may be produced by impregnating the cloth in 50° to 60°Tw. NaOH, and expressing to contain 200% liquor; the cloth is then treated with 35 to 37% of ethylene oxide on the weight of the fabric, using 45 g. of cloth per litre of carbon tetrachloride. A stiff, wiry, and transparent finish is obtained.

The linen effect may be obtained from a preliminary treatment with 11% NaOH solution, expressed to 100% and followed by 10% ethylene oxide on the weight of the cloth, using 56 g. of fabric per litre of carbon tetrachloride. For parchmentising effects, the cloth is immersed in alkali of mercerising strength, expressed to 150%, and treated with 40% ethylene oxide on the weight of the fabric, using 56 g. of cloth per litre of solution. After this treatment, the cloth is soured as usual, and damped to 50% moisture content and calendered or damped to 30% moisture content and friction calendered.

In addition to the all-over effects, it is possible to utilise the ethylene oxide reaction for the production of patterns such as damask and window-pane effects. For instance, for the window-pane effect, selected areas may be printed with 39% NaOH in British gum and then treated with 60% ethylene oxide on the weight of the printed area, using 35 g. printed cloth per litre of carbon tetrachloride solution; the excellence of the final result depends on adequate calendering after souring, washing, and drying. Damask effects are produced by a less drastic action; the cloth may be printed with 39% NaOH in British gum and then treated with 20 to 60% of ethylene oxide, according to the intensity of action required, the ethylene oxide being calculated on the weight of the printed area of cotton and using 25 g. printed area per litre of carbon tetrachloride.

Etched pattern effects or chemical embroidery (?) may also be produced by ethylene oxide. For a lace effect, the cloth may be printed with 39% NaOH in British gum and then treated with 125% ethylene oxide on the weight of the printed areas, using 35 g. of printed area per litre of solvent. After treatment, the cloth is washed in 5% NaOH solution, which removes the printed areas, giving a lace effect; souring, washing, and drying complete the process.

Figured velveteens may be prepared by printing the pile only with 39% NaOH in British gum, taking care that the alkali does not penetrate to the back of the fabric. The cloth is then treated with 60% ethylene oxide on the weight of the printed areas, using 35 g. of printed cloth per litre of solvent. After treatment, the cloth is washed in water to dissolve the printed pile before souring in 1° to 2°Tw. sulphuric acid.

The ethylene oxide process seems particularly suited to cotton, for although it may be applied to jute and linen, there is little point in so doing; the treatment is not applicable to viscose rayon as the material becomes very harsh and fragile.

It appears that the ethylene oxide process is capable of a very wide range of effects which normally would entail the use of many and varied reagents; the degree of treatment is also easily controlled, so that the process is very flexible and capable of wide application.

CELLULOSE

The regeneration of cellulose on cotton as a finishing process is not limited to the use of viscose; B.P. 462,824 of the Bleachers' Association makes use of solutions of modified cellulose in caustic soda solution, to produce effects varying from the opal or organdie finish to linen-like products. U.S.P. 2,009,015 of Rohm and Haas utilises solutions of cellulose in the newer organic solvents such as quaternary benzyl ammonium hydroxide, followed by precipitation by acid solutions in the ordinary manner.

Solutions of cellulose in cuprammonium may also be applied to fabric to give transparent finishes, and some interesting pattern effects have been described by Hubner in B.P. 227,370 and 227,480. The fabric is printed with a cuprammonium solution of cellulose and then mercerised before removal of the metallic residues with acid.

It is difficult to dissolve cellulose in any of the common reagents, but if the cellulose is first modified then it becomes soluble in alkali because of the diminution in molecular weight and in the chain length of the parent material. One of the simplest methods is slightly to degrade the cellulose with acid until it becomes soluble in cold sodium zincate solution (prepared from sodium hydroxide and zinc oxide) which is a more powerful swelling agent and solvent than sodium hydroxide alone. The highly viscous solution may then be diluted to some extent with water alone, and applied to the cotton cloth by the usual methods of impregnation; the cellulose may be regenerated from solution by neutralising with acid, or by the action of hot water, or even by treatment with mercerising concentrations of alkali.

The earliest disclosure of this type of finish was given by Lilienfeld in B.P. 212,864; cellulose may be degraded short of complete solubility in alkali, to give solutions in cold alkali. Solutions of 4 to 10% NaOH were preferred at temperatures of —5° to —10°C. After dissolution, the temperature may be raised to normal, and the fabric impregnated in the usual manner. The finished solution may be coagulated by salts, acid, heat, etc., and utilised for coating and filling fabrics.

Solutions of modified cellulose in sodium zincate solution are popular as finishing preparations in the U.S.A., and are used to increase the bulk of the fabric or to stiffen it; additions of China clay may be used as fillers. The result is reasonably durable and exerts a valuable effect on the shrinkage potential of the treated fabric. Many sheetings are treated in the grey state, and the modified cellulose is regenerated on the cloth during the scouring or kiering operation. It is possible to calender the fabric before drying and so obtain a smooth finish.

Typical products are sold under names of Kopan and Celfon; they contain 5 to 7% of cellulose in 8 to 10% of NaOH containing 2·7% of ZnO. These solutions may be diluted with 6% NaOH solution without precipitation, provided the original solution is made at zero or below.

CHAPTER XV

THE EXTERNAL APPLICATION OF SYNTHETIC RESINS

SYNTHETIC resins are complex organic products of high molecular weight whose main outlet has been the plastics industry and the electrical field; considerable amounts have been used as paints and varnishes. The term "resin" has been employed on account of their superficial resemblance in physical properties to the natural resins.

The pioneer work of Foulds, Marsh, and Wood of the Tootal Broadhurst Lee Company, Limited, was so strikingly successful in a special method of forming synthetic resins inside the textile fibre that great attention has naturally been devoted to numerous applications of the many different products; there seems little doubt that a new range of permanent finishes has been established.

The types of synthetic resins used for surface coatings include the following:

(a) Phenol-formaldehyde resins or phenoplasts.
(b) Glyptals or alkyd resins.
(c) Urea-formaldehyde resins or aminoplasts.
(d) Ketone resins.
(e) Vinyl polymers.
(f) Coumarone and indene polymers.

The English resin industry is mainly concerned with the alkyd resins and the phenolic products for surface coatings, but the use of urea resins is rapidly increasing. The U.S.A. appears to favour the coumarone and indene polymers to a much greater extent than England.

The general use of resins for coatings includes their application as the whole of the film-forming material, and also as a reinforcement for other materials. For the former application, the alkyd resins (oil-modified) possess great speed of drying and high durability, and so have certain advantages as substitutes for the older varnishes.

The formation of synthetic resins may be divided into two main types: (a) condensation, and (b) polymerisation. There is an unfortunate tendency to group all resins under the term "polymer," and it should be realised that synthetic resins of the phenoplast, aminoplast, and alkyd types are not true polymers, but super-condensation products. It may also be remarked, in parenthesis, that the term "plastic" is unfortunate, and for some products the term "brittlic" would be more applicable.

The best-known types of super-condensation products are the phenoplasts and aminoplasts of phenol-formaldehyde and urea-formaldehyde respectively. The first reaction is to form the phenol alcohol (or methylol urea), followed by further condensation with the elimination of water to build up a three-dimensional network of interlinked molecular chains. It is possible to arrest the reaction at various stages with the production of water-soluble products which may be crystalloid or colloid according to the degree of condensation.

The phenol-formaldehyde resins are most often applied as spirit varnishes, the acid-condensed or Novolak type being used as a shellac substitute, and the alkaline or "resole" modification for laminated paper and plastic work in which a baking process is involved. The resole may be treated with rosin and esterified with glycerol to give an oil-soluble product which may replace some of the natural resins and gums.

The Novolaks, produced under acid conditions, are straight-chain condensation products which are soluble, fusible, and fairly stable to heat, in that they remain of fairly low molecular weight. Their structure is probably a chain of phenol groups connected by methylene linkages to form a diphenylol-methane type of compound.

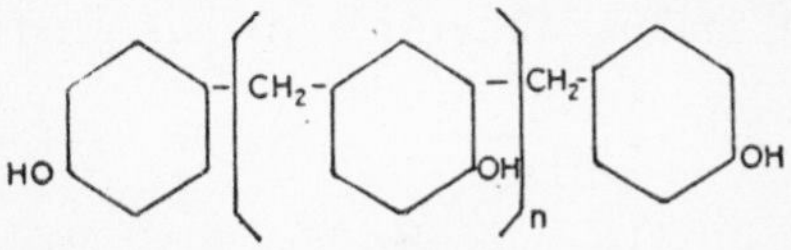

Novolak

The resoles are related to the phenol alcohols and are produced under alkaline conditions; as a result of cross-linkage formation on heating, they are converted by heat into a very complex arrangement which finally imparts insolubility and infusibility (see page 391).

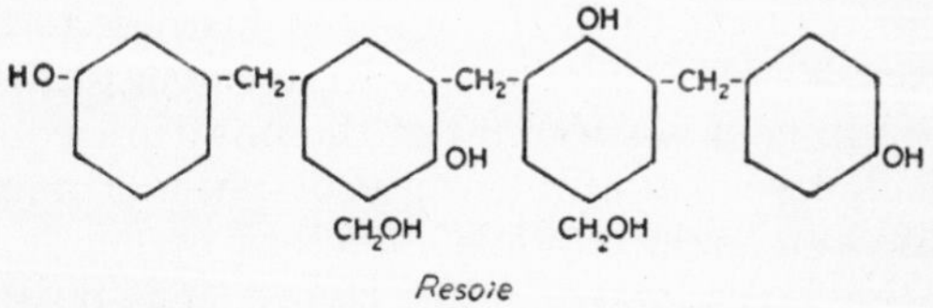

Resole

The colour of phenol-formaldehyde resins, and their further discoloration on exposure to light, limits their usefulness in textile finishing.

The urea-formaldehyde resins are water-white and fast to light, and therefore find a greater application for many purposes. Their chemistry and application is discussed in greater detail on page 379, and page 392.

The more recent developments in urea-formaldehyde manufacture include the etherification of dimethylol urea with a monohydric alcohol; the product is compatible with the hydrocarbon solvents, and may therefore be employed in conjunction with the oil-modified alkyd resins.

Some interesting work has also been done by replacing urea with melamine, or 2 : 4 : 6 triamine, 1 : 3 : 5 triazine, which is made from dicyandiamide (see page 404). The melamine-formaldehyde resins are stated to harden more rapidly at lower temperatures than the urea-formaldehyde products, and to be more resistant to heat, water, and to chemical attack.

The glyptals or alkyd resins are formed by the condensation of polybasic acids and polyhydric alcohols, as, for example, phthalic acid anhydride and glycerol (see page 374). The modern tendency is to replace part of the polybasic acid with an unsaturated monobasic acid so that the condensation product may form films which harden by oxidation. These resins may be used as an adjunct to other film-forming materials, such as cellulose nitrate, cellulose acetate, and with chlorinated rubber.

The most recent developments in the field of alkyd resins are concerned with maleic anhydride as an alternative to phthalic anhydride.

$$
\begin{array}{cc}
\diagdown\mathrm{CO} & \mathrm{CH-CO} \\
\diagup\mathrm{O} & \diagup\mathrm{O} \\
\diagup\mathrm{CO} & \mathrm{CH-CO}
\end{array}
$$

(Phthalic anhydride)   (Maleic anhydride)

The combination of maleic anhydride with rosin gives a new polybasic acid which can be esterified with glycerol to give an oil-soluble resin, capable of replacing phenol-formaldehyde in varnishes to some extent on account of the superior fastness to light.

Maleic anhydride also offers an advantage over phthalic anhydride in the alkyd resin field, on account of the unsaturated linkage. With a dihydric alcohol, such as ethylene glycol, phthalic anhydride gives a long-chain thermoplastic polymer, whereas maleic anhydride gives a thermo-setting cross-linked resin. Hence, it is possible to replace part of the phthalic anhydride with maleic anhydride in the manufacture of the drying-oil-modified type of alkyd resin and form a product of improved durability and resistance to water. It also forms the basis of a possible synthetic drying-oil.

As a general rule, the super-condensation resinous products are thermo-setting. On the other hand, resins formed by polymerisation in the true sense are thermoplastic. The best-known products of this type are the vinyl polymers (see below), under which term are included the acrylates and methacrylates.

Thermoplastic resins are believed to exist in the form of chain-molecules which are not connected by cross-linkages; on this account it is possible to "plasticise" the product by the addition of suitable reagents which find their way between the separate molecular chains. This is not possible with the thermo-setting resins because of the cross-linkages which bind the molecular structure into a more rigid three-dimensional network.

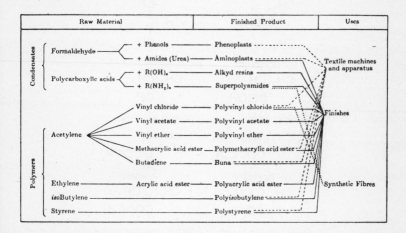

The external application of synthetic resins to textile materials is mainly devoted to fabrics from the vegetable fibres. The chief interest seems to have centred around the following:

(a) Vinyl resins.
(b) Alkyd resins.
(c) Urea-formaldehyde resins.

VINYL POLYMERS

One of the simplest cases of polymerisation by addition is seen in the formation of benzene from acetylene by heating. The monomer must be unsaturated for polymerisation of this type.

The chief commercial resins in this class form long chain-molecules of high molecular weight by the addition of the simple compound or *monomer* to form the long chain or *polymer* of the same empirical formula. Most of them are derived from ethylenic compounds of the type $CH_2 : CHR$ where R is a negative group, as in the following table.

Monomers of the Vinyl Series

$$CH_2:CH_2 \qquad\qquad CH_2:CH$$
$$\qquad\qquad\qquad\qquad\qquad\quad |$$
$$\qquad\qquad\qquad\qquad\qquad\quad Cl$$

Ethylene   *Vinyl chloride*

$$CH_2:CH \qquad\qquad CH_2:CH$$
$$\qquad\quad | \qquad\qquad\qquad\qquad |$$
$$\qquad\quad C_6H_5 \qquad\qquad\qquad\quad CN$$

Styrene   *Acrylic nitrile*

$$CH_3$$
$$\quad \diagdown$$
$$\qquad C:CH_2 \qquad\qquad CH_2:C$$
$$\quad \diagup \qquad\qquad\qquad\qquad\quad |$$
$$CH_3 \qquad\qquad\qquad\qquad\quad Cl$$

(with Cl above $CH_2:C$)

Isobutylene   *Vinylidene chloride*

$$CH_2:CH \qquad\qquad CH_2:CH$$
$$\qquad\quad | \qquad\qquad\qquad\qquad\quad |$$
$$\qquad\quad COOH \qquad\qquad\qquad OH$$

Acrylic acid   *Vinyl alcohol*

$$CH_2:CH \qquad\qquad CH_2:CH$$
$$\qquad\quad | \qquad\qquad\qquad\qquad\quad |$$
$$\qquad\quad COOC_2H_5 \qquad\qquad OCOCH_3$$

Ethyl acrylate   *Vinyl acetate*

$$CH_2:C.CH_3 \qquad\qquad CH_2:C.CH_3$$
$$\qquad\quad | \qquad\qquad\qquad\qquad\qquad |$$
$$\qquad\quad COOH \qquad\qquad\qquad\quad COOCH_3$$

Methacrylic acid   *Methyl methacrylate*

The monomeric vinyl compounds all contain the grouping $CH_2:CH-$, and styrene is actually vinyl benzene.

The fundamental facts about the growth of the molecular chains have been established by Staudinger and his collaborators, by Zeigler, Ostromislensky, Rohm and Haas, and the I.G.

Taking styrene as an illustration, the chain is formed as follows:

$$-CH_2-CH-CH_2-CH-CH_2-CH-CH_2-$$
$$\qquad\quad | \qquad\qquad\quad | \qquad\qquad\quad |$$
$$\qquad\quad C_6H_5 \qquad\quad C_6H_5 \qquad\quad C_6H_5$$

The easy solubility and thermoplastic nature of polystyrene of high molecular weight (600,000) point to the absence of linkages between the molecular chains. This is supported by the effect of interlinking with *p*-divinyl-benzene (Ber., 1934, 67, 1164), a very small amount of which produces an insoluble, infusible product. It would appear that the absence of interlinks accounts for the thermoplastic nature of the vinyl resins as a whole.

From the standpoint of textile technology, considerable attention has recently been devoted to the application of these thermoplastic resins in finishing processes. The property of softening on heating and hardening again on cooling has been utilised in many directions, such as stiffening and bonding.

With the exception of polyvinyl alcohol, the polymers are insoluble in water, but dissolve in certain organic solvents.

The properties of the final resin are dependent to some extent on the chain-length or molecular weight, but it must be remembered that the polymeric product is not a single molecular species; it is rather a mixture of molecules whose average molecular size depends largely upon the conditions of polymerisation.

The properties of the final resin are also dependent on the chemical nature of the monomer employed, but may be varied by co-polymerisation; that is, by mixing two monomers and polymerising them together. In these circumstances, a product is obtained whose properties are often quite different from those of a mixture of polymers. A well-known co-polymer is formed from vinyl chloride and vinyl acetate; polyvinyl chloride is hard and brittle, but the co-polymer with vinyl acetate in various proportions enables resins to be obtained of various degrees of flexibility and hardness. Heteropolymers are also possible, and are of great interest, so that a very wide range of products is available. Vinylite is a co-polymer of vinyl acetate and chloride, and has been made into synthetic fibres —Vinyon.

Polystyrene is thermoplastic, hard and tough; the higher polymers are apt to be brittle. This fact, together with the poor resistance of styrene finishes to washing, limits its textile application.

Other hydrocarbon polymers have been made from isobutylene and marketed as Oppanols and Vistanex (see page 445). According to the molecular weight, the product may vary from a heavy oily mass to a hard waxy solid; the rubbery resin is an intermediate product. One of the latest of these hydrocarbon polymers is Polythene of the I.C.I.; it is obtained by the polymerisation of ethylene under high pressure. These hydrocarbon polymers are only soluble in the hydrocarbon solvents, and Polythene does not dissolve below 60° to 70°C. The saturated hydrocarbon polymers are chemically inert and do not wet; they may therefore be used for waterproof finishes. Their thermoplastic and adhesive nature enables them to be used for laminated or bonded fabrics, whilst their strong film-forming property finds an outlet in the production of glazed chintz.

Some of these polymers may be applied in the solid form to textile material, in a similar manner to rubber, by making use of the pressure from a hot calender. With Polythene, a new method is possible, in that a thin film of the polymer may be directly applied

THERMOPLASTIC RESINS

$CH_2:CH_2 \longrightarrow -CH_2\text{-}CH_2\text{-}CH_2\text{-}CH_2\text{-}CH_2\text{-}CH_2\text{-}CH_2\text{-}CH_2\text{-}CH_2-$

Ethylene   *Polythene*

$$CH_2:CH\text{-}C_6H_5$$

$$-CH_2\text{-}\underset{C_6H_5}{CH}\text{-}CH_2\text{-}\underset{C_6H_5}{CH}\text{-}CH_2\text{-}\underset{C_6H_5}{CH}\text{-}CH_2\text{-}\underset{C_6H_5}{CH}\text{-}CH_2-$$

Styrene   *Polystyrene*

$$CH_2:CH\text{-}OH$$

$$-CH_2\text{-}\underset{OH}{CH}\text{-}CH_2\text{-}\underset{OH}{CH}\text{-}CH_2\text{-}\underset{OH}{CH}\text{-}CH_2\text{-}\underset{OH}{CH}\text{-}CH_2-$$

Vinyl alcohol   *Polyvinylalcohol*

$$-CH_2\text{-}CH\text{-}CH_2\text{-}CH\text{-}CH_2\text{-}CH\text{-}CH_2\text{-}CH\text{-}CH_2-$$
$$\underset{O\text{-}CH_2\text{-}O}{\quad} \quad \underset{O\text{-}CH_2\text{-}O}{\quad}$$

Polyvinylformal

$$CH_2:CH\text{-}Cl \longrightarrow CH_2\underset{}{CH}\,CH_2\underset{Cl}{CH}\,CH_2\underset{Cl}{CH}\,CH_2\underset{Cl}{CH}\,CH_2\underset{Cl}{CH}\cdots$$

Vinyl chloride   *Polyvinylchloride*

$$CH_2:CH\text{-}OCOCH_3 \longrightarrow$$
$$-CH_2\text{-}\underset{OCOCH_3}{CH}\text{-}CH_2\text{-}\underset{OCOCH_3}{CH}\text{-}CH_2\text{-}\underset{OCOCH_3}{CH}\text{-}CH_2\text{-}\underset{OCOCH_3}{CH}\text{-}CH_2-$$

Vinyl acetate   *Polyvinylacetate*

$$-CH_2\text{-}\underset{OCOCH_3}{CH}\text{-}CH_2\text{-}\underset{Cl}{CH}\text{-}CH_2\text{-}\underset{OCOCH_3}{CH}\text{-}CH_2\text{-}\underset{Cl}{CH}\text{-}CH_2-$$

Co-polymer of vinyl acetate & chloride

$$CH_2\!:\!CH\text{-}COOC_2H_5 \longrightarrow -CH_2\text{-}\underset{COOC_2H_5}{CH}\text{-}CH_2\text{-}\underset{COOC_2H_5}{CH}\text{-}CH_2\text{-}\underset{COOC_2H_5}{CH}\text{-}CH_2\text{-}\underset{COOC_2H_5}{CH}\text{-}CH_2-$$

Ethyl acrylate   *Polyethylacrylate*

$$CH_2\!:\!\underset{COOCH_3}{\overset{CH_3}{C}} \longrightarrow -CH_2\text{-}\underset{COOCH_3}{\overset{CH_3}{C}}\text{-}CH_2\text{-}\underset{COOCH_3}{\overset{CH_3}{C}}\text{-}CH_2\text{-}\underset{COOCH_3}{\overset{CH_3}{C}}\text{-}CH_2\text{-}\underset{COOCH_3}{\overset{CH_3}{C}}\text{-}CH_2-$$

Methyl methacrylate   *Polymethylmethacrylate*

$$\underset{CH_3}{\overset{CH_3}{>}}C\!:\!CH_2 \longrightarrow -CH_2\text{-}\underset{CH_3}{\overset{CH_3}{C}}\text{-}CH_2\text{-}\underset{CH_3}{\overset{CH_3}{C}}\text{-}CH_2\text{-}\underset{CH_3}{\overset{CH_3}{C}}\text{-}CH_2\text{-}\underset{CH_3}{\overset{CH_3}{C}}\text{-}CH_2-$$

Isobutylene   *Polyisobutylene*

$$CH_2\!:\!\underset{Cl}{\overset{Cl}{C}} \longrightarrow -CH_2\text{-}\underset{Cl}{\overset{Cl}{C}}\text{-}CH_2\text{-}\underset{Cl}{\overset{Cl}{C}}\text{-}CH_2\text{-}\underset{Cl}{\overset{Cl}{C}}\text{-}CH_2\text{-}\underset{Cl}{\overset{Cl}{C}}\text{-}CH_2-$$

Vinylidene chloride   *Polyvinylidenechloride*

by ironing or by passing film and fabric together through heated rollers. Attractive transparent silk materials may be made in this manner. Application from solvents is not easy and should be limited to dilute solutions, because the Polythene tends to solidify in a very viscous state so that a mass of sticky polymer may be pulled from the solution. Lawrie (J.S.D.C., 1941, *57*, 180) has given an account of these and other polymeric finishing agents.

The use of aqueous dispersions of ethylene polymerides (Polythene) as textile finishing agents has been protected in B.P. 518,917; plasticisers or fillers may be added to the emulsion before application to the cloth by the usual methods of impregnation, after which it is dried and heated to a temperature slightly in excess of the softening point of the polymeride.

Many of the resin polymers have been applied to textiles from solution in organic solvents; they may be utilised in the production of artificial leather, imitation suède, oil cloth, book-cloth, and for the special fabrics used in the shoe trade. Another common outlet is as stiffening agents in dry cleaning, to overcome the limpness which is sometimes occasioned by that process.

As stiffeners, they are more expensive than the common starch or casein preparations, but are much more durable and permanent. Small quantities of these resins may be employed in conjunction with large amounts of the cheaper filling agents; a number of polymers have been used as binding agents for pigments, but the conditions of drying play an important part in fixing the incorporated pigment. An extension of this application may be seen in pigment printing methods.

A certain degree of non-slip may also be realised with rayon goods in particular, and the same principle may be employed in treating the backs of carpets and rugs.

Considerable quantities of these vinyl resins have been used, again from organic solvents, as sizing agents mainly for rayon. The water-soluble polyvinylalcohol is also used for sizing.

Acrylates

Of all the vinyl polymers, most attention appears to have been devoted to the acrylates and methacrylates, which possess exceptional properties.

$$CH_2 : C.COOH \qquad\qquad CH_2 : C.COOH$$
$$H \qquad\qquad\qquad\qquad CH_3$$

Acrylic acid   Methacrylic acid

These substances were examined extensively by Rohm (Ber., 1901, *34*, 573), and more recent accounts of their properties have been given by Neher (Ind. Eng. Chem., 1936, *28*, 269) and by Klein and Pearce (ibid., 635). Polymethylacrylate is a tough, pliable, elastic solid; polyethylacrylate is softer, less tough, but more elastic, whereas *n*-butyl acrylates are soft and sticky in the polymeric form. Polyisobutylacrylate is harder than the *n*-butyl polymer and resembles polymerised *n*-propyl acrylate. The tertiary butyl acrylate when polymerised is not pliable, but almost brittle. Passing further up the series, it was found that the octyl and lauryl derivatives were semi-liquid even in the polymerised form. In the same series, therefore, there is considerable choice of physical effect by varying the alcohol from which the polyester is made; cyclohexyl acrylate gives hard and tough polymers, but the normal hexyl derivative forms a soft and sticky product.

The methacrylates as a class are harder than the acrylates. Polymethylacrylate is soft, elastic, and rubber-like, but the methyl methacrylate polymer is so hard that it can be machined. Passing up the series, however, the polymerised esters become softer so that polymerised n-amyl methacrylate is approximately as tough and elastic as polymethylacrylate.

Acrylates and methacrylates have aroused most interest, for the ethacrylates and propacrylates are not only difficult to make, but their polymerised esters are semi-liquid compounds.

The formulae for methyl acrylate and methyl methacrylate are

$$CH_2 : C.COOCH_3 \qquad CH_2 : C.COOCH_3$$
$$H \qquad\qquad\qquad CH_3$$

Methyl acrylate   Methyl methacrylate

Polymethylmethacrylate is a transparent, colourless, glass-like substance which is very tough and finds considerable application in windows for aircraft. It softens under heat and pressure, and has been used for bonding fabrics, to which it may be applied from solution in organic solvents. A typical method may be seen in B.P. 503,536. The textile material is coated with a solution of 30 parts of polymerised methyl methacrylate, 10 parts of polymerised isobutyl methacrylate, and 60 parts of toluene, utilising any of the suitable methods of application, such as spray, padding mangle, or roller and doctor knife. The material is then dried, and may be rolled or stored in layers until required without danger of mutual adhesion or sticking together. The fabric may later be cut into suitable shapes, as, for example, in the manufacture of collars, or may be utilised in the piece. Layers of fabric may thus be superimposed, with the coated layer between the others, and on the application of heat and pressure the materials become bonded firmly together in a permanent manner (see page 340). Methyl methacrylate polymers soften under heat and pressure; the pressure may vary from a few lb. per square inch to 1,000 lb. per square inch, and the temperature from 130° to 180°C. Without pressure, the softening point of polymethylmethacrylate is 125°C.; polymerised esters containing other ester groups have a lower softening point, with the exception of n-cyclohexylphenyl derivatives (145°C.). Highly polymerised methyl methacrylate is still rubber-like at 200°C.

The acrylates are extremely stable in the chemical sense, and in this respect are among the best of the synthetic polymers; they are stable to the effects of light, air, and weathering. The stability is probably due to the absence of unsaturated linkages in the polymers, for, in general, the presence of such linkages is a point of attack for chemical reagents. Now the resistance to water and to alkali are important features of any preparations which are applied to textile materials, and the polymerised acrylates and methacrylates are very satisfactory in this respect also. Polyacrylic esters may be hydrolysed by strong alkalis, but the attack is slow; the esters of polymethacrylic acid, on the other hand, are even more stable to alkali —polymerised methyl methacrylate can be boiled with 35% KOH solution without hydrolysis taking place. The difference may be due to the fact that in the polymerised methacrylic esters, the carboxyl group is bound to a ternary carbon atom, whereas in the acrylates it is bound to a secondary carbon atom.

$$\begin{array}{cccc} CH_3 & CH_3 & & \\ | & | & & \\ -C-CH_2-C-CH_2- & & \\ | & | & & \\ COOR & COOR & \end{array} \qquad \begin{array}{cccc} H & H & \\ | & | & \\ -C-CH_2-C-CH_2- & \\ | & | & \\ COOR & COOR & \end{array}$$

The esters of polyacrylic acid absorb very small amounts of water, polymethylacrylate absorbing the highest amount, which is only 1·5%. The methacrylates absorb less water than the acrylates.

The behaviour of these polymerised esters with organic solvents is also interesting. With the polymerised methyl and ethyl esters, the effect of the ester is seen in that the polymers are insoluble in benzine, mineral oil, etc., but they are soluble in esters, ketones, and in benzene. Polymers of the higher esters, especially butyl methacrylate, exhibit the influence of the hydrocarbon to a greater extent and dissolve in mineral oil and in benzine.

An application of the acrylic polymers is seen in B.P. 414,040 (U.S.P. 2,071,419), particular reference being made to "Plextol A," which is dissolved in a mixture of benzene, toluene, and acetone to form a 10% solution, anid then applied to cloth. Alternatively, trichlorethylene may be utilised as a solvent. The method of application is determined to some extent by the result which is required; hence, padding mangles may be used for impregnating both surfaces of the fabric, but if it is desired to coat one surface only, then the application may be effected by spraying, or by rollers, or by spreading with a doctor-blade. Local effect may be obtained by printing or stencilling, or by use of the spray-gun. Dyestuffs, coloured pigments, and various metallic powders may be incorporated in the compositions or may be applied afterwards before the coating has dried. The drying takes place at a moderate temperature of 50° to 80°C.

24

The range of effects is decided, not only by the amount of the polymer applied, but also by certain additions which may be made to the solution; these include plasticisers of various types, natural resins, synthetic resins, and cellulose derivatives.

Small amounts of the polymer impart a slight stiffening effect without destroying the flexibility of the textile material. The tensile strength and resistance to abrasion are improved as a result of the treatment, which is stated to be particularly applicable to shoe cloths and furnishing fabrics. Larger amounts of the thermoplastic preparation are capable of producing waterproof and gas-tight effects.

EMULSION-POLYMERS

The use of expensive and inflammable organic solvents is not viewed with great favour in textile finishing operations, so that the production of acrylate polymers in emulsion form may be regarded as a very important advance. It must be realised, however, that these emulsions are not made by preparing the polymer and then the emulsion, but by emulsifying the monomer and then carrying out the polymerisation; the manufacture of these EMULSION-POLYMERS is described in B.P. 358,534.

The monomers are slowly introduced into aqueous solutions of emulsifying agents containing accelerators for polymerisation, and vigorously stirred during the heating or irradiation to effect polymerisation. Suitable accelerators are hydrogen peroxide, benzoyl peroxide, and so forth. The same technique may be utilised for the production of co-polymers and hetero-polymers.

The method of emulsion-polymerisation results in products which resemble rubber latex, and may be coagulated to give rubber-like masses by the addition of hydrochloric acid to the creamy liquid. These polymerisation products are actually superior to those prepared in the non-emulsified state, in that they are much more homogeneous, probably because polymerisation proceeds regularly on account of the dispersed state of the product throughout the reaction. Further, the emulsion does not become very viscous during the reaction, as in other methods of polymerisation, so that it is possible to bring about a higher degree of polymerisation (five times) without special and costly apparatus; the products may be freed from monomers by blowing in steam until they are odourless, and are also readily removed from the reaction vessels.

There is ample evidence that widespread use of these emulsion-polymers in the textile industry was only prevented by the outbreak of war in 1939; most of the large chemical manufacturers were in the course of bringing various products to the finishing section of the industry; as, for example, the Plextols of Rohm and Haas (Darmstadt), the Rhoplexes of Rohm and Haas (Philadelphia), Bedafin D and Bedafin CM of the I.C.I., various Igeplasts of the I.G., the Methacrols of Du Pont, and so on.

It is not always possible to be certain about the chemical nature of many commercial preparations which are sold under trade names, but Methacrol M and Bedafin D appear to consist of methyl methacrylate, Methacrol B of butyl methacrylate, and Bedafin CM of Cellosolve methacrylate (Cellosolve is the mono-ethyl ether of ethylene glycol).

The emulsion polymers, which resemble rubber latex, do not need vulcanising, and on account of their saturated character are immune from attack by chemical reagents and also to the effects of light and air. The average particle size of the dispersion is about 0.2μ, and the emulsions seem quite stable. The trade products generally contain about 25% solid matter, and are of low viscosity. With solutions of similar polymers, the viscosity depends to some extent on the solvent used, and rises rapidly with concentration; with aqueous dispersions there seems to be no increase in viscosity with concentration until dispersions of about 50% are reached.

Applications of emulsion polymers are very simple, as they dry to form transparent films which are insoluble in water and have good adhesive powers for textile materials. From the chemical nature of the products, it will be understood that there is a large range of available polymers, co-polymers, and hetero-polymers which may be made in the form of emulsion polymers; these may be mixed with one another for special purposes and are also compatible with natural rubber latex.

The use of emulsion polymers appears to be the simplest method of applying synthetic polymers to textile materials, merely necessitating common apparatus such as padding mangles, jigs, or other dye-vessels. The impregnated material may then be dried on a stenter or other form of air-drier; the general effect is broadly similar to that obtained when similar chemical products are applied from solution in organic solvents. The impregnated goods may be given further treatments, such as calendering, friction-calendering, and hot-calendering if required, for smooth finishes. Plain or friction calendering does not make the resin spread. The range of available products enables a series of effects to be obtained, from a stiff and papery handle to a soft pliable finish. For general purposes the dispersions are applied in concentrations of from 3 to 5%, and there seems to be complete freedom of the individual fibres in the yarn although they are uniformly coated with resin. Larger quantities give stiffer results, and the threads are apt to adhere when concentrations of 15% and over are employed. The lower concentrations seem to exert practically no stiffening action, which is rather remarkable in view of the external deposition of the resin.

These emulsion polymers have been utilised in continental Europe for the treatment of shirtings to a large extent and also for the production of "down-proof" cloths. In England, the method is in its infancy, but has been applied to some extent as an alternative to starch as a permanent smooth filling; in this connection they are particularly suited to the finishing of spun-rayon goods which are notoriously difficult to finish with starch. A smooth, full handle may thus be given to spun-rayon cloths and impart the "character" which they generally lack. In the U.S.A. similar products have been used to replace starch in finishing; the ease of preparation and the simple cleansing of the machines largely compensate for the increased chemical cost.

Unless high concentrations of the emulsion polymers are employed, it would seem that the dried resin film is discontinuous, which may possibly account for the particular nature of this type of finish on fabrics.

The application of emulsion polymers of methyl methacrylate to textile materials has been described by Strain in U.S.P. 2,046,885.

Applications of certain emulsion polymers of acrylates and methacrylates in concentrations of approximately 3% are capable of improving the resistance to wear of textile materials, as disclosed in B.P. 527,762, by Battye, Corteen, Foulds, and Potter of the Tootal Broadhurst Lee Company. The wear resistance may be even further improved by subjecting the impregnated and dried material to a very thorough scouring operation, as, for instance, with 0·5% soap and 0·5% sodium carbonate. The resistance to abrasion is increased by 50 to 500%, as measured on the "Ring Wear" testing machine (J.T.I., 1935, 26, 101P).

This process may be applied during or after the crease-resisting process, with good effect on the wearing properties of the treated cloth.

Some interesting data regarding the effect of dispersions of acrylates have been provided by Powers (Ind. Eng. Chem., 1940, 32, 1543); the results on cotton are quite different from those on rayon. A series of impregnations was given under such conditions that the same amount of the various resins was deposited on the fabrics from emulsions containing between 2 and 3% of the polyacrylate.

EFFECT OF EMULSION-POLYMERS

	Tensile strength		Abrasion test		Stiffness	
	Cotton	Rayon	Cotton	Rayon	Cotton	Rayon
Untreated . . .	131	121	3,000	2,000	2·0	2·0
Soft acrylate . .	121	134	15,000	4,000	2·3	2·1
Medium acrylate . .	130	141	9,000	5,000	2·8	3·6
Hard acrylate . .	132	128	10,000	3,000	4·0	4·0

The stiffness of the samples is calculated on the basis of the original fabric having a value of 2·0 (1·0 in the warp and 1·0 in the weft). The values are $I \times 4/t$ ratios compared with the $I \times 4/t$ ratio of the original material, where I is the distance between the supports and t is the amount of sag in the sample. (Differences in stiffness amounting to 0·2 are readily detected by manual examination.)

The finish is resistant to washing, as shown by Walter (Textilber., 1938, *19*, 376), who utilised the Plextols of Rohm and Haas of Darmstadt which are very similar to the Rhoplexes of Rohm and Haas of Philadelphia. Printed rayon fabrics were boiled for twenty-minute periods in a solution containing 5 g. of soap and 3 g. of sodium carbonate per litre. The finished goods lost 4·3% in weight after five washes, whereas the unfinished cloth lost 4·1%. The fastness to washing and the resistance to abrasion have also been examined by Walter and Schwenk (Zellwolle-Kunstseide-Seide, 1939, *44*, 425), who confirmed the benefits of this type of finish, and commented on the improved extension at break.

The thermoplastic nature of many of the vinyl resins is somewhat apt to limit their usefulness in textile finishing; although the emulsion polymers are simple to apply, yet the finished product is apt to pick up dust and dirt rather easily and retain it during laundering processes. Again, the tacky effect produced when hot-ironing meets with some objections. The thermoplastic effect may be suppressed by providing a number of bridges or cross-linkages during the emulsion-polymerisation, according to B.P. 557,067 of Battye, Lawton, Marsh, and Wood.

ALKYD RESINS

The alkyd resins are condensation products of polybasic acids and polyhydric alcohols; great attention has been devoted to the condensation of glycerol and phthalic anhydride in particular, and the term "Glyptal" has been coined as an incomplete anagram for this product by the General Electric Company. It is becoming common to refer to those resins which give insoluble infusible products as glyptals, but the term "alkyd" is preferable as it avoids interference with trade names.

Although this type of resinification takes place through condensation, it is possible to form linear condensates which are soluble and thermoplastic, and then later to bring about further condensation to an infusible insoluble mass. The product of reaction between glycols and dibasic acids only gives the simple thermoplastic chain-molecule, but when glycerol is used in place of a glycol there are further reactive groups available to link the chains and produce a compact three-dimensional molecule.

The chemistry of the reaction is still rather obscure, but it probably proceeds in two stages.

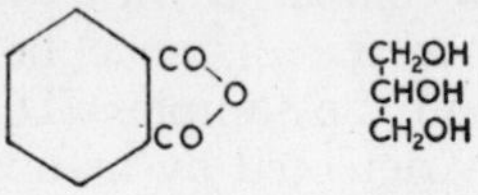

Phthalic anhydride   *Glycerol*

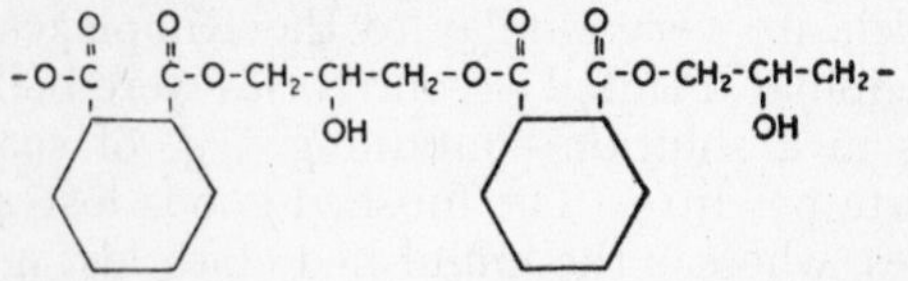

With glycerol and phthalic anhydride, as shown above, the condensation then proceeds to the second stage by interlinking of the chains.

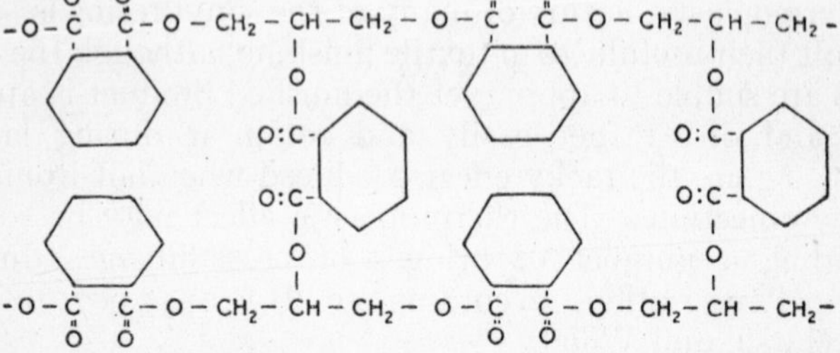

The general reaction is capable of modification in three broad ways. First, it is possible to incorporate monobasic acids which have the effect of imparting solubility to the product; acids from the non-drying oils are commonly used, such as stearic, oleic, or ricinoleic acid, but castor oil and certain natural resins may also be utilised. Secondly, a special class of monobasic acid may be employed; these are obtained from the drying-oils and linoleic acid is a well-known example. Thirdly, it is possible to incorporate synthetic resins of the phenol-formaldehyde or urea-formaldehyde type, and in this way the flexible nature of the alkyd resin helps to compensate for the brittle nature of the formaldehyde type.

It will appear, therefore, that a wide range of products is available having diverse properties. The stearic-acid-alkyd-resins are waxy solids of poor film strength, but the oleic acid-modified resins are elastic and flexible; those containing linseed oil are capable of hardening by oxidation.

From the standpoint of textile application, the alkyd resins are applied from solution—in some cases from organic solvents, in other cases from alkaline solution.

The solubility in many organic solvents is often a question of mutual compatibility rather than solubility in the usual sense; sometimes it is not possible to obtain low concentrations of the resin in the solvent—although it may be possible to produce solutions of, say, 20% and over, of a given resin in a certain solvent, it may not be possible to get solutions of less than 20%. Quite often, the problem of solution resolves itself into the amount of the solvent that the resin will take up, rather than the reverse. This phenomenon is encountered with many polymeric substances.

With certain solvents, such as a mixture of methylated spirits and toluene, the chief alkyd resins are compatible in all proportions.

The classification of the alkyd resins for textile purposes may be under three heads: (a) air-oxidising alkyd resins, (b) thermo-setting alkyd resins, and (c) miscellaneous resins.

The air-oxidising alkyd resins are mainly glycerol-phthalic anhydride condensates modified with drying oils; they are completely soluble in such organic solvents as benzene, solvent naphtha, and a mixture of toluene and methylated spirits. When applied to textiles, they tend to give limp, oily finishes of little resistance to washing; after stoving or oxidation by ageing for 24 hours at room temperature, a flexible, transparent and "non-tacky" finish is obtained similar to that given by linseed oil, including the yellow colour.

The alkyd resins which have been modified with non-drying oils give limp to stiff finishes of poor fastness to washing, although this may be improved to some extent by baking.

The Bedafin range of the I.C.I. includes a number of alkyd resins; Bedafin 20 oxidises in the air, being modified with drying oils, whereas Bedafin 285X appears to be modified with a non-drying oil.

Sometimes it is possible to make this type of alkyd resin polymerise further by heating at 180° to 210°C. for prolonged periods, but the conditions of heating are too drastic for textiles. The hardened products are soluble in alkali in certain cases, and have found application in the stiffening of hats. Bedafin 20, for example, is soluble in ammonia.

From the general textile standpoint, probably the most interesting alkyd resins are the thermo-setting type, of which the urea-formaldehyde-castor-oil-modified-glycerol-phthalic-anhydride resin is typical; apparently Bedafin 2001 of the I.C.I. belongs to this class. It is soluble in a mixture of equal parts of methylated spirits and toluene, but is more commonly used when dissolved in water with the assistance of ammonia, sodium carbonate, or triethanolamine. For example, 10 lb. of Bedafin 2001 is stirred into a solution of half a pint of ammonia (sp. gr. 0·910) in 2 to 3 gallons of water to make a smooth paste which may then be dissolved to the required volume by mixing with water. When applied to textiles, the finish would readily be removed by washing, but when the treated fabric is heated for a few minutes, further condensation occurs to give a water-resistant product. The duration and temperature are determined by the particular resin, but for Bedafin 2001, 10 minutes at 100°C. or 3 to 4 minutes at 120°C. appears adequate. The heating may take place on cylinders, but hot-air drying is better as the finish is somewhat softer. The infusible, insoluble resin film gives a colourless, flexible finish which is fast to wetting and to washing.

Concentrated solutions of Bedafin 2001 in ammonia are viscous and may therefore be spread on the surface of cloths to give a continuous film, which, on drying and heating, produces a glazed effect. Cloths of compact structure are usually employed for this purpose and may be calendered before treatment on a back-filling plant. Alternatively, the interstices of the material may be filled with starch to prevent penetration of the Bedafin 2001. B.P. 521,906 describes the pre-treatment of fabrics with a thermoplastic resin, followed by a coating of a thermo-setting resin; a similar process is covered in B.P. 523,731.

Transparent impermeable fabrics may be prepared according to the methods of B.P. 520,579, utilising a resinous composition of modified-polyhydric-alcohol-polybasic-acid resin in which part of the polybasic acid is replaced by monobasic acids from non-drying oils and in union with 7 to 12% of urea-formaldehyde condensate by weight. The composition is applied from solution in volatile organic solvents.

Bedafin 2001 is of value as a fixing agent for pigments, and has been employed in pigment printing with China clay, titanium dioxide, barytes, and the colour lakes. Delustred prints which are fast to washing may be obtained on viscose rayon, for example, and after printing the resin is fixed by steaming for 1 hour. The coloured delustred print has an attractive appearance against a lustrous background.

This type of resin may also be utilised for preserving mechanical finishes, such as embossing; they have also been suggested for preventing shrinkage on laundering, but the urea-formaldehyde resins are better for anti-shrink finishes.

The water-soluble preparations, such as Bedafin H and Bedafin HN, may be used as stiffening agents, but are more expensive than starch or glue; nevertheless they have special applications, for Bedafin HN may be used in conjunction with water-repellents without lowering their efficiency, and can also be employed for the stiffening of felts before dyeing, as it withstands the boiling acid dyebath.

Some of the alkyd resins are mainly of value as plasticisers for others in the range; for instance, Bedafin 685 is a plasticiser for Bedafin 2001, but when applied alone from aqueous ammonia imparts a limp finish which is not fast to washing. Bedafin 285X is another example which can plasticise the thermo-setting alkyd resins. The plasticising influence of the soft non-hardening alkyd resins has been extended by Rohm and Haas, as shown in B.P. 527,520, where it is applied to cellulose ether finishes, and also to the aqueous solutions of lightly condensed resins which are later hardened on the textile material; it may also be used with dispersions of thermo-plastic resins (see page 370), and dispersions of urea-formaldehyde condensates (see page 382).

Many of these dispersions, mainly commercial preparations, impart a slight stiffness and sandy handle which are undesirable, and it is usual to add a softener, such as a sulphonated oil, to the impregnating bath. When this addition is really effective, however, it is apt to weaken the resin film and reduce the fastness to washing. Rohm and Haas make use of the non-hardening alkyd resins prepared from long-chain aliphatic polycarboxylic acids, such as sebacic acid, which form soft and rubbery products; these are made as aqueous suspensions whose particle size is less than 0.5μ. At the neutral point, this dispersion of soft resin is miscible with the usual dispersions of the harder resins, and the mixture gives very satisfactory results in concentrations of about 5%, or less. With hard films from urea-formaldehyde condensates, the non-hardening resin may be present in twice the quantity of the hard resin; with softer resins, like acrylates, an addition of one-third is adequate. For urea-formaldehyde condensates intended for crease-resisting finishes, the total resin content should range between 25 and 30%, made up of 96 parts of a 25% urea-formaldehyde condensate and 4 parts of a castor-oil-glycerol-sebacic-acid resin emulsion. Sodium di-isobutyl phenoxyethyl sulphate is recommended as an emulsifying agent for the plasticising resin, which is claimed to be fast to washing when incorporated as above.

Ester Gums

ESTER GUMS are related to the alkyd resins and are obtained by the interaction of glycerol with rosin acid. They have been used for stiffening garments during the dry-cleaning process, and also to give a firm handle to spun-rayon materials. Care is needed with this type of finish as cases of dermatitis have been reported from the U.S.A.

UREA-FORMALDEHYDE CONDENSATES

The urea-formaldehyde resins are of most textile importance when produced inside the fibres of the material to which they are applied for the purpose of imparting resistance to and recovery from creasing (see page 390). Nevertheless some external applications of this resin are of interest in textile technology.

The resinification of urea and formaldehyde was discovered in 1918 by Hanns John and described in U.S.P. 1,355,834 and B.P. 151,016. One part of urea (or thiourea) was dissolved in 5 to 6 parts of commercial formaldehyde solution, and heated to drive off the water. According to time of heating, three stages were observed; first, a glue-like syrup which was soluble in water and could be used as an adhesive; secondly, a gelatinous mass; and, lastly, a hard transparent colourless resin. The initial product of resinous condensation which is soluble in water dries to form a clear, colourless, insoluble, infusible film which resembles a lacquer. John suggested that this colloidal solution could be utilised for impregnating fabrics, especially the wings of flying-machines.

The principal defects of John's resin, according to Pollak and Ripper (Chem. Zeit., 1924, *48*, 569), were the presence of free formaldehyde in the final product, and the instability of the liquid forming the first stage of condensation. Pollak, in particular, carried out a series of researches on this type of resin, as shown in B.P. 157,416, 171,094, 181,014, 193,420, 201,906, 206,512, 213,567, and many others. The first of these specifications has a textile application of John's resin, in its initial stage, for replacing the solution of shellac in borax as a stiffening agent for hats; a solution of 5 to 10% was suggested for this purpose.

The subsequent patents, however, were concerned with definite improvements in the preparation of the resin, the first of which was to reduce the proportion of formaldehyde to three molecules of formaldehyde to one of urea. In this manner, the gummy product of the first phase of resinification only had a slight odour of formaldehyde, and was a colourless limpid liquid readily soluble in water. It is prepared by refluxing the reagents until the mass no longer becomes turbid on cooling, and then distilling *in vacuo* on the water bath until the residue has a syrupy consistency. This viscous condensation product resembled other colloidal solutions in that it was capable of gelatinisation on standing; heating, however, did not reverse the process, but produced a hard glass-like mass which was resistant to most chemical reagents. The instability of this initial condensation product could be overcome, and the solution stabilised, by the addition of the alkali salts of weak acids (excepting ammonium salts); the stabilised solutions may be resinified in the cold by the addition of ammonium salts of strong or weak acids, and so may the unstabilised solutions be converted to the solid resin state. Resinification by heating is effective in presence or absence of the retarding salts.

The effect of salts of strong acids with strong bases is to accelerate gelatinisation accompanied by syneresis.

The knowledge of colloid chemistry was not particularly far advanced at the time of these observations and little was known of the chemistry of resinification. It is clear, however, that Pollak was concerned with a colloidal solution, even when discussing this "first stage" of condensation, for he states that most likely dimethylol urea is formed as an intermediate product during the reaction.

Now dimethylol urea is a well-defined crystalline compound which was known in 1897, and its solutions do not undergo gelatinisation or exhibit other colloidal properties. We now know that dimethylol urea (or monomethylol urea) is the first stage of chemical combination between urea and formaldehyde, but it does not necessarily lead to a resin if further condensed (see page 315); the "initial stage of condensation" in resinification, as described by Pollak, is colloidal and therefore far-condensed.

The first reaction is to form mono- or dimethylol urea

$$\begin{array}{ccccc}
NH_2 & & NHCH_2OH & & NHCH_2OH \\
| & & | & & | \\
CO + CH_2O & \longrightarrow & CO & \text{or} & CO \\
| & & | & & | \\
NH_2 & & NH_2 & & NHCH_2OH
\end{array}$$

Condensation takes place to a three-dimensional molecule, one formula for which may be represented by

$$\begin{array}{c}
HN-CH_2-N-CH_2-N-CH_2-N-CH_2-N-CH_2-N\cdot CH_2OH \\
| \quad\quad | \quad\quad | \quad\quad | \quad\quad | \quad\quad | \\
CO \quad CO \quad CO \quad CO \quad CO \quad CO \\
| \quad\quad | \quad\quad | \quad\quad | \quad\quad | \quad\quad | \\
HN-CH_2\cdot N-CH_2-N-CH_2-N-CH_2-N-CH_2-N\cdot CH_2OH
\end{array}$$

The methylol ureas are easily formed at room temperatures, but the solution of Pollak requires considerable heat under slightly acid conditions.

This colloidal solution was termed "Schellan," and various textile applications were suggested for it, such as a linen-finish for cotton goods. This finish was stated to resist hot water, and exhibited the strong adhesion to the fibre now known to be characteristic of urea-formaldehyde resins.

Resin solutions of urea-formaldehyde type, which rapidly pass to the final stage in presence of acid salts, particularly on warming, may be employed on textiles in conjunction with the usual fillers, such as starch, China clay, gums, etc. These fillers are not resistant to washing, but their filling or stiffening effect may be made permanent if they are applied in admixture with thiourea-formaldehyde resins in particular, according to B.P. 258,357 of British Cyanides. The first stage of condensation is not only water-soluble, but may be further diluted by the addition of water, and on account of this miscibility, it is possible to add to the dilute solution or suspension of the resinous product, aqueous solutions of starch for example. The impregnating bath may be prepared by mixing together an aqueous solution containing not more than 8% of the synthetic resin and an aqueous solution of starch at room temperature; a small amount of potassium tetroxalate solution is added before the textile goods are impregnated by means of a mangle. The resin is rendered insoluble by passing the cloth through rollers heated to 120° to 140°C. A permanent starch finish appears to be the main object.

A somewhat different application of urea-formaldehyde resin to textiles was developed by British Bead Printers in B.P. 247,001 and 277,091. The ornamentation of gauze, silk, and similar structures by drops of gum arabic is quite well known for the production of pattern effects, and a viscous aqueous solution of urea-formaldehyde resin in the early stages of condensation may be utilised for similar ornamentation of textiles. A needle-like apparatus is pushed through the cloth where ornamentation is required, into a trough or tray of the urea-formaldehyde condensate; when the needles dip into the liquid, some of the viscous condensates adheres to them, but is stripped and deposited on the fabric when the needles withdraw. The fabric should be dried in a horizontal position, so that the drops on the under-side preserve their spherical form as they are hardened into beads. B.P. 277,091 carries the idea a stage further by the use of powdered glass, metal dust, pearl dust, mica, and even loose fibrous material, which may be sprinkled on the deposited resin while it is still in the plastic state. The deposits of urea-formaldehyde may be coloured if desired. A variation of the process is to mix the condensation product with the powdered material before their joint application to the cloth.

The difference between the lightly-condensed and far-condensed solutions of urea-formaldehyde is referred to in B.P. 517,011. Urea (60 parts) and 40% formaldehyde solution (150 parts) were mixed with hexamethylene tetramine (6 parts) and heated on a water-bath until a test sample exhibited no turbidity on cooling; this took longer than the time necessary for the preparation of crease-resisting mixtures, which may be prepared by heating for 3 minutes or on prolonged standing at room temperatures (see page 394) to give a viscosity of from 3 to 5 centipoises, whereas the far-condensed solution required from 30 to 120 minutes and gave a solution of 40 centipoises for the same density. Heating until the sample no longer exhibits turbidity on cooling is frequently mentioned in the preparation of far-condensed urea-formaldehyde solutions which do not crystallise but gelatinise; disappearance of turbidity apparently denotes the point of transition from the crystalloid state to the colloid state. These far-condensed mixtures may be used in conjunction with the newer types of water-repellents, which also have excellent softening properties, to give a variety of effects.

An interesting surface application of urea-formaldehyde resin is seen in B.P. 501,442 of Arnold Print Works, which describes the preparation of glazed chintz. The fabric is first filled with an inert filler, such as starch, which may be easily removed at a later stage, and then calendered once or twice to produce a smooth, glossy surface and fill the interstices of the material; this prevents any penetration by the resin solution, which is applied in the form of a thin layer with the aid of a doctor knife. The dried surface layer is later hardened and smoothed by passing the goods through a heated calender, after which the cloth is definitely stiff. The filler is then removed by any of the known enzymes which convert starch to sugar, and after washing, the cloth is in a much softer condition. Mechanical "breaking" processes destroy the continuity of the film and produce a soft flexible fabric with a high surface gloss on one side. The cloth is not waterproof, but is sufficiently water-repellent for the glazed effect to withstand wetting and drying, unlike ordinary glazed chintz. The resin solution may be prepared by boiling 120 g. of urea, 324 c.c. of 40% formaldehyde solution, and 10 c.c. of NH_4OH for 30 minutes to form a thin syrup on cooling. The catalyst for the final hardening may be applied at the same time as the filler, as its addition to the resin solution would produce gelatinisation before application to the cloth.

Glazed chintz has also been prepared by the co-application of urea-formaldehyde resinous condensation products and casein solution. The fabric is impregnated, dried, and heated in a glazing calender to harden the resin and coagulate the casein-formaldehyde produced. The effect is stated to be flexible and spotproof; ammonium salts are used to catalyse the resin and ethyl cellulose may be used for softening purposes if desired. (U.S.P. 2,103,293, B.P. 503,414.) The above process of Bancroft appears to rely on calendering for the glaze, and is therefore fundamentally different from that of the Arnold Print Works, in which the surface effect is due to preventing the penetration of the resin by a starch film which is later removed.

Glazed chintz may also be produced by the method outlined in B.P. 523,731 of Corteen, Foulds, and Wood. The fabric is first coated with an emulsion polymer, such as polymethylmethacrylate, or with a film of a polyisobutylene, and then a further thin coating of a urea-formaldehyde resinous condensation product, modified with an alkyd resin, may be applied. The polymer should be of such a viscosity as to avoid penetration into the fabric.

The glazed chintz finish with urea-formaldehyde resins is quite popular in the U.S.A. and some finishers use a mixture of condensation products of crystalloid and colloid types; the former penetrates the fabric and stabilises it against shrinkage, whereas the latter remains in the surface and may be glazed. The proper finishing of these fabrics demands a high degree of experience and skill; for example, when the impregnated goods are dried on the stenter, it is important that they should not be over-dried, and they should be allowed to retain about 10% of moisture. Friction calendering takes place with the correct amount of moisture present; a three-bowl calender is preferred with the two lower bowls running at the same superficial speed, but the upper bowl may have from 2 to 4 times the peripheral speed of the other bowls. Two passages may be necessary, after which the goods are heated to complete the condensation of the resin. A washing process follows, after which it may be well to calender again.

Glazed chintz of this type is stated to be wash-fast; that is, the effect is not spoiled by laundering, and can be ironed without becoming "tacky."

Another process of interest in this connection has been described in B.P. 545,468 by Evans and Smith of the I.C.I., but related to the treatment of mesh fabrics to render them suitable for window-replacement material. For example, a cotton mesh fabric is impregnated with cold aqueous aluminium acetate solution (d 1·01) and dried; the net is then drawn through a solution containing, in parts by weight, farina (10), Turkey red oil (2), and water (100) at 60°C., after which the excess is removed by a doctor-blade. The net is dried, and padded or coated with a solution in ethylene glycol monoethyl ether (Cellosolve) of a urea-formaldehyde intermediate condensate modified with a castor-oil modified polyhydric alcohol—polybasic acid resin. The solvent is removed by drying, and the condensation of the resin coating is completed by heating the fabric at 150°C. for 3 minutes.

DISPERSIONS

The difficulties of an adequate control of the condensation of urea-formaldehyde to produce the far-condensed or colloidal soluble stage have led to proposals to carry out the condensation in non-aqueous solvents, such as alcohols, and to neutralise the catalyst when the desired stage of condensation has been reached. In most cases, such solutions are not stable, but continue to react in the cold with decreasing solubility and increase in viscosity. The instability depends to some extent on the ratio of urea to formaldehyde, but to a greater extent on the presence of water formed during the condensation. B.P. 498,043 describes the production of urea-formaldehyde condensates which are soluble in hydrocarbon solvents; paraform is dissolved in butyl alcohol containing a little ammonia, and urea is added to the warm solution, which on further heating becomes turbid and then clears. When the second clear stage is reached a volatile catalyst is added and the mixture distilled to remove the water formed during the condensation, but the distilled alcohol is replaced by anhydrous solvent. The reaction is complete in 10 to 15 hours, when about 2 mols. of water have been removed for 1 mol. of reacting urea. The clear product contains about 56% of resin and is completely stable; it is miscible with hydrocarbon solvents and may be used as a coating composition, alone or in conjunction with alkyd resins. The resin film hardens slowly at room temperatures, and rapidly at elevated temperatures. A modification of this process in which aqueous formaldehyde may be used is seen in B.P. 511,087.

Resins of the above type are in an advanced state of condensation, but are not fully hardened; being normally prepared in alcoholic solution, they may be used to form aqueous dispersions, as they have passed the water-soluble stage. This is protected in B.P. 512,187. The best dispersing agents appear to be a combination of a water-soluble cellulose ether and a long-chain quaternary ammonium salt; good results are obtained by using 2 parts of methyl cellulose and 3 parts of the ammonium salt per 100 parts of resin solution. Suitable salts are dimethyl cetyl benzyl ammonium chloride or sulphate, and the corresponding oleyl, or lauryl compounds.

The alcoholic solution of the resin is added slowly while the mixture is vigorously beaten, so that the resin is emulsified as rapidly as it is added; the resin must not be thrown out of solution during emulsification. Dispersions containing 25% of resin may be made. They form good finishing agents for textiles, imparting a soft and leathery feel which is quite different from that obtained with solutions, probably because the resin particles, although on the surface of the textile material, do not form a continuous film; they are very useful for back-filling finishes as they impart a sense of bulk and increased thickness.

The resin emulsion is usually diluted with 5 to 20 parts of water before application to the cloth, and as the resin is not fully condensed, an acid condensing agent is also added before use. After impregnation and drying, the goods may be heated for 2 minutes at 135°C. or 10 minutes at 115°C., according to the type of material.

These emulsions impart a certain degree of resistance to shrinkage and also to "slipping"; they may be used to fix pigments, fillers, and delustrants. They do not give resistance to creasing. Emulsions of urea-formaldehyde condensates must not be confused with emulsion polymers of the thermoplastic resins; they are emulsions of condensates and not emulsion condensates—condensation precedes emulsification, whereas with emulsion polymers, emulsification and polymerisation occur simultaneously (see page 370).

Before heating, the condensate is insoluble in water, but dissolves in organic solvents.

(Rhonite W250, of Rohm and Haas, is probably a resin-emulsion of this type.)

Interesting effects may be obtained by the application of mixtures of the emulsions of condensates and emulsion polymers, which are miscible in all proportions.

The results obtained by the external deposition of far-condensed urea-formaldehyde products in the dispersed form are quite different from the effect of a high concentration of a lightly condensed product applied from aqueous solution under such conditions that surface resin is formed on the cloth; the results are also distinct from the effect of treatment with an aqueous solution of a far-condensed product. There is no stiffening and no embrittlement of the fibres, probably on account of the discontinuity of the external resin formed; on the contrary, the resistance to abrasion is actually increased, as shown by Powers (Ind. Eng. Chem., 1940, *32*, 1543).

Effect of Resin Treatment on Wear

| | Abrasion resistance | |
	Cotton	Spun rayon
Untreated material	3,000	2,300
True aqueous solution	3,500	2,200
Intermediate polymer in true solution . .	2,200	2,700
Intermediate polymer in colloidal solution .	1,000	4,100
Higher polymer in colloidal dispersion . .	7,000	3,100
Very high polymer in dispersion . . .	14,000	2,800

The table shows the effect of applying identical resin concentrations, but varying the physical form of the resin and consequently the location and distribution of the resin; other properties of the fabric also change, but the relative resistance to abrasion is most remarkable.

In view of these effects, it is interesting to compare the results of applications of the same quantities of the different types of the commoner resins.

Effect of Resin Treatment

	Stiffness	Resilience	Durability	Tensile strength
Untreated material . . .	2·0	2·3	10	51
Urea-formaldehyde solution .	2·4	3·2	11	47
Urea-formaldehyde dispersion .	4·0	2·7	45	61
Hard acrylate dispersion .	11·7	2·6	36	62
Soft acrylate dispersion .	2·3	2·7	48	64
Hard alkyd dispersion .	2·2	2·5	42	61

CHAPTER XVI

THE INTERNAL APPLICATION OF SYNTHETIC RESINS

THE chief process in which resins are synthesised inside the textile fibre is the crease-resisting process produced by Foulds, Marsh, and Wood of Tootal Broadhurst Lee Company, Limited.

As will appear later, resistance to creasing is only one of the many improvements which are due to this type of process, and most of these improvements will be discussed under the heading of resistance to creasing. However, there have been suggestions to utilise resins as mordants in dyeing (see page 434), and also to produce non-felting wool by resin treatments (see page 236).

RESISTANCE TO CREASING

The crease-resisting finish is chiefly applied to rayon, cotton, and linen fabrics, but it may also be used on some types of woollens and worsteds; as will appear later, crease-resistance is only one of many improvements which are the outcome of the successful internal application of synthetic resins, and although its novelty and importance have been greatly appreciated, it must not be overlooked that the accompanying advantages are also of no small moment.

Cellulosic materials are notoriously susceptible to creasing, and the removal of this defect may perhaps be regarded as one of the greatest achievements in the history of textile finishing.

The definition of the improved product is obviously one which has exercised the minds of those associated with it, for various terms have been suggested at different times—non-crush, anti-crease, and crease-resisting; it may be that none of these is completely satisfactory, but nevertheless some popular and simple terms had to be evolved in order to explain or define the new product to the general public. It may be remarked that before the advent of these products, terms such as *knitterfest*, *infroissable*, and *anti-piega* were unknown in textile terminology.

The new property imparted to cellulosic fibres is a combination of resistance to and recovery from creasing, but much greater emphasis must be placed on the recovery; many materials resist creasing, which means they resist deformation and are therefore rigid, but what is required is a product which can be deformed but rapidly recovers from deformation—there must be a resilience which includes some resistance to creasing, but also a powerful and rapid recovery therefrom. There is perhaps a *nuance* about "crease-repellent" which infers a slight yielding followed by a strong rejection, which is missing in crease-resistance.

It may be that new words, such as *piezophobic*, *kamptophobic*, or *angofuge*, may be considered better to define the product than the older terms. If one assumes that the crease-resisting property is part of the decreased form-changing effect, to copy a German omnibus term, then the word "stabilisation" has much to commend it; concomitant with the crease-resisting effect are found other valuable properties, such as decreased laundry shrinkage, improved fastness of certain dyestuffs, increased strength of rayons, and other features to be discussed later.

Wool, of course, is famous for its elastic recovery, and is greatly prized for its powers of resistance to and recovery from creasing; these properties, however, are affected to a large extent by the type of woven structure in which the wool is employed—where the fibres are parallel and highly twisted, the elastic recovery or crease-resistance is much less rapid and powerful than in the typical woollen construction with its random arrangement of the fibres and the open construction of the fabric.

Silk is also prized for its crease-resisting properties, which are not quite so good as those of wool; this difference is accentuated by the fact that most silk cloths are much thinner than fabrics of wool, and therefore in actual usage there is greater pressure brought to bear on the thinner material.

From various data, it has been concluded that the extension of fibres consists of two components—an elastic extension and a plastic extension; animal fibres have a high elastic extension, but the vegetable fibres have a relatively small extension, most of which is plastic. It has also been concluded that the two types of extension are due to the heterogeneous nature of the fibre.

Modern views of fibre structure throw some light on the reasons for this heterogeneity. For example, with cellulose it is now generally accepted that the fibres consist of long chain-molecules, which in certain areas lie parallel and are packed in such a close and regular formation that crystal properties result. In other regions, however, the orientation of the chain-molecules is very poor and the state of disorder is such that the material may be regarded as amorphous. Hence, the fibre consists of alternating regions of amorphous and crystalline structure, but with certain of the molecular chains running through both regions to give an irregular flexible network.

Within the crystallites, the chain-molecules of β-glucose residues are probably fully extended, but this is not necessarily so in the amorphous regions, where the chains may be more or less crumpled.

With disorientated fibres, the effect of stretching is to bring about some orientation, but when the strain is released there is a tendency to revert to the original position; with orientated fibres, however, a relatively small amount of extension will cause the micelles to slip on each other so that the extension becomes plastic, for when the strain is released, the micelles do not return to their original position, i.e. the fibre is deformed or creased.

The crushing or creasing of textile material is a complex effect involving tensile, flexing, compressive, and torsional stresses. The tensile extension plays a relatively small part in elastic recovery, and measurements of the modulus of elasticity are little guide to the creasability of the various fibres, for the most "elastic" materials in the engineering sense are apt to crease most readily. Torsional elasticity does not appear to have received the attention which it merits, possibly because the imparted twist in the yarn is intended to be permanent and bind the fibres or filaments into a compact yarn without a high degree of torsional resistance. With yarns of "hard-twist" a substantial degree of torsional elasticity is often observed, and this is sufficient to give the fabric a certain amount of springiness or spurious recovery from creasing; when sufficient pressure is exerted to overcome the torsional resistance, the springiness disappears.

The bending elasticity seems to be of the greatest importance in the phenomenon of creasing; creases appear when the material is distorted in such a manner that part of it is stretched beyond its small powers of elastic recovery. The bending of the fibres or filaments which takes place during creasing leads to an extension of the cellulose on the upper surface, and a compression on the under surface.

The external layers of the fibre are already orientated, and therefore possess little power of elastic recovery, which is never very high in cellulose. The external crystallites slide on one another to establish plastic extension (or compression) and form creases.

It is common experience that the animal fibres possess a greater elasticity than the vegetable fibres; this is manifest in respect of recovery from creasing. Indeed, it may be stated that the great defect of fabrics from vegetable fibres is the ease with which they crease and retain the creases. Amongst the common textile materials the order of diminishing crease-resistance is wool, silk, acetate rayon, viscose rayon, cuprammonium rayon, cotton, flax.

Uncreasing Tests

Many attempts have been made to measure the recovery from creasing of various textile fibres, and probably the earliest is that of Krais (Textile Forschung, 1919, *1*, 71). Various fibres were attached to a small frame of cardboard which was pushed beneath a stretched silver wire; the sides of the frame were then cut away and the cardboard bent around the silver wire so that the fibres are folded and may be compressed between the cards by a weight of 1 Kg. for 24 hours. The fibres were then cut from one side of the cardboard and freely suspended in order to observe their creasing angles; the best recovery from creasing was seen with wool and silk, and the worst with rayon and cotton. It is also interesting to note that Krais observed a rapid recovery in a moist atmosphere with wool, silk, and viscose rayon, but not with cotton.

A somewhat similar test was given by Hall (J.S.D.C., 1930, *46*, 267) whereby viscose and acetate rayon yarns were wound around a strip of cardboard and subjected to a pressure of 20 lb. for 5 minutes, after which the card was removed and the yarn examined for its "crease-trace," allowing 5 minutes for any linear contraction to occur.

This type of yarn-testing has been elaborated and a recent method is to use a strip of card 2 cm. in width and 0·6 mm. in thickness, around which the yarn is wound under a constant tension of 10 g. and then allowed to remain creased for 10 minutes before cutting longitudinally through yarn and card, and so forming a number of yarn fragments in the shape of the letter "*V*." These fragments are allowed to fall on to a surface of mercury, where they remain for 10 minutes before measuring the angle of the "*V*."

Methods of this type are open to several objections; they are not sufficiently accurate with lower angular recoveries, and show little or no correlation between yarn recovery and measurements of creasability of the same yarns when measured in fabric form. Another difficulty is that of dealing with yarns of different deniers and counts, as in most of these tests the applied load is constant, but the pressure in Kg. per sq. mm. must vary with the type of yarn. Elöd (Angew. Chem., 1938, *51*, 45) has employed a load of 20 g. per 100 denier.

Angular recovery of yarns may be of value in some technical investigations, but for the evaluation of the crease-resistance of fabrics it is best to measure the effect on the fabric itself. A simple test, suggested by Willows, is to cut a strip of fabric 4 cm. by 1 cm. along the warp or weft of the fabric, taking care that a yarn forms the edge, and then carefully fold the strip in half so that it measures 2 cm. by 1 cm.; this strip is placed under a thin strip of spring steel and weighted with 500 g. for a period of 5 minutes, after which it is removed with forceps and suspended on a wire for 3 minutes before measuring the distance between the extremities as seen on a mirror scale engraved in mm. Separate determinations are made of both warp and weft strips. This simple method has been used with satisfaction for many years, but the original apparatus has been modified and elaborated by Tankard.

PLATE **XXV**

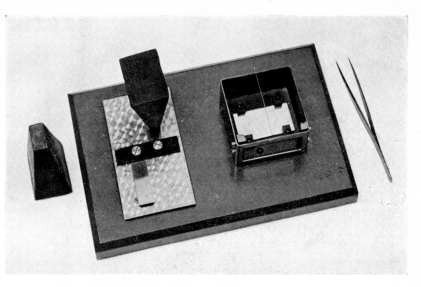

FIG. 144. Apparatus for measuring recovery from creasing.
(The strip of fabric is under the weighted strip of steel.)

FIG. 145. Measurement of recovery from creasing.
(The strip of creased fabric is placed on the wire over the
engraved mirror.)

Courtesy of Mr. J. Tankard, M.Sc., F.Inst.P., F.T.I.

To face page 388,

PLATE XXVI

FIG. 146. Measurement of recovery from creasing.
(The strip of creased fabric has uncreased and its length
may be measured on the engraved mirror.)

FIG. 147. Apparatus for measuring pile recovery.

Courtesy of Mr. J. Tankard, M.Sc., F.Inst.P., F.T.I.

In theory a perfectly uncreasable piece of fabric would give a recovery figure of 40 mm., but such fabrics do not exist, and if they did, they would have no textile value on account of the lack of draping abilities. Laboratory samples of crease-resisting fabrics have been prepared with recovery figures of 38 mm., utilising the methods described on page 394, which depend on synthetic resins; but years of experience have shown that it is unwise to exceed the recovery figure of good-quality wool or worsted (about 33 to 35 mm.), and that it is essential to preserve the other textile qualities of the fabric.

It has been stated that the above test measures draping as well as crease-resistance, and to some extent the criticism is justified. Draping effects may be obviated by measuring the angle of the strip of fabric placed edgewise on a surface of mercury; the effect of gravity is thus avoided, but the mercury surface must be cleaned frequently, and certain fabrics with a "lazy" recovery give fictitious results. Alternatively, a skilful manipulator may balance an unfolded strip of fabric 4 cm. by 1 cm. on the wire of the standard apparatus and so measure the draping effect—a somewhat difficult, but not impossible, feat.

The recovery of pile fabrics may be measured by a modified dial gauge of the type used for measuring the thickness of paper and fabrics; this method was suggested by Marsh and established by Tankard. After adjusting the dial gauge, the spindle is raised and a small sample is placed under the foot with the pile uppermost; the foot is slowly lowered and the thickness of the pile fabric (A) is estimated. The pile is then compressed by loading with 750 g. on the top of the spindle, and the sample allowed to remain under load for 5 minutes, when the thickness (B) is measured again. The weight is then removed and the spindle raised so that the pile of the fabric is allowed to recover free from pressure for 3 minutes, after which the height of the pile (C) is measured again. The pile recovery may be calculated from the following formula and expressed as a percentage:

$$\text{Pile recovery} = \frac{C-B}{A-B} \times \frac{100}{1}$$

Examination of many warp pile velvet fabrics with rayon piles showed a recovery of 60 to 70% in the untreated state; similar fabrics with a real silk pile gave a figure of 90 to 95%, and the crease-resisting treatment applied to the rayon pile velvets enabled them to reach a recovery figure fully equal to that of the real silk constructions. It may be remarked that pile fabrics whose recovery lies below 80% may be regarded as poor.

Recovery measurements should obviously be made under controlled and standardised conditions of temperature and humidity.

THE CREASE-RESISTING PROCESS

The original patents of the Tootal Broadhurst Lee Co., Ltd., which describe the production of crease-resisting textile materials, are B.P. 291,473 and 291,474, with the corresponding U.S.P. 1,734,516. According to Foulds, Marsh, and Wood, the result of the treatment is to produce a non-crush effect on the fabric without undue tendering, stiffening, or interference with the suppleness of a woven or knitted fabric; the material should be capable of use as dress goods, and able to be "draped about the human body and fall in graceful folds." The crease-resisting effect is also substantially fast to washing.

It is particularly important that the product used for imparting this effect should be situated within the fibre of the textile material, for in so far as it merely adheres to the surface, without penetration, the result is disadvantageous, because the suppleness of the fabric is diminished without imparting crease-resistance. Although various synthetic resins may be used for these finishes, most commercial results being obtained with urea-formaldehyde resins, yet the patent protection is not limited to these; indeed, U.S.P. 1,734,516 of Foulds, Marsh, and Wood claims a fabric in which "so much of an impregnating agent, solidified from a liquid, is contained within but not substantially between the individual fibres, that the material shows a substantially lessened tendency to crease or crumple while retaining its suppleness."

The two chief types of resins mentioned in the specifications are those from phenol-formaldehyde and from urea-formaldehyde; obviously substances which behave in a similar manner may also be utilised, but in general, all the phenoplasts are coloured, which is a serious disadvantage for many purposes, so that the practical application is invariably with amino-plasts.

B.P. 291,474, by Foulds, Marsh, and Wood, refers to the treatment of cellulosic fabrics with synthetic resins mainly of the phenol-formaldehyde type; the treatment of all textile fabrics with other synthetic resins, such as urea-formaldehyde, is discussed in B.P. 291,473 of Foulds, Marsh, Wood, Boffey, and Tankard.

Before considering the application of these resinous condensation products to textile materials, it might be well to comment that neither the structure of textile fibres nor of synthetic resins was clear at the time of the crease-resisting invention.

It is now known that the thermoplastic resins, such as polystyrene, methyl methacrylate, and so forth, exist in the form of chain-molecules which are not attached to one another by primary valency forces, but that the thermo-setting resins, such as phenol-formaldehyde and urea-formaldehyde, form three-dimensional networks in which the chains are united by primary valencies. The syntheses of these resins take place by the condensation of phenol (or urea) with formaldehyde to form small molecules, which are then caused to condense further and form the large molecule, i.e. the resin. Foulds, Marsh, and Wood made use of this phenomenon to impregnate the fibres with the small molecules which were found to penetrate the cellulose, and then bring about resinification *in situ*.

The process of resinification has been discussed on page 360, but a few comments on phenoplasts and aminoplasts may be useful here.

Although the chemistry of resin formation is most complex, yet a simple picture of the phenol-formaldehyde reaction may be obtained by following the alkaline condensation of the reagents to form a simple water-soluble phenol-alcohol.

The phenol-alcohol may condense with more phenol to give a product of the dihydroxydiphenylmethane type.

The actual structure of the complete resin may be represented in several ways, but perhaps the following formula (shown on page 392) may be taken as typical.

The condensation and resinification of phenol-formaldehyde takes place under alkaline conditions.

As previously mentioned, the phenoplasts are coloured, but the aminoplasts are colourless; the commonest type of the latter product is formed from urea and formaldehyde.

Under neutral or slightly alkaline conditions, urea and formaldehyde condense to give either mono- or dimethylol urea, according to the molecular proportions of the reagents. Both of these compounds are crystalline substances, with well-defined melting-points (110° and 126°C. respectively), readily soluble in water, and of low molecular weight.

When heated under acid conditions, these products form the well-known urea-formaldehyde synthetic resin, one formula for which has been given on page 379, and another is given below.

It will be noticed that the resinification of urea-formaldehyde has been separated into two stages, first under neutral or slightly alkaline conditions, and later by heating under slightly acid conditions.

Turning to consideration of the types of fabric to which the process is best applied, it may be stated that one criterion is that the fabric should be constructed so as to be as supple as possible; that is, the fibres or filaments should be able to move readily on one another. This does not necessarily limit the process to yarns and fabrics of loose construction, for hard-twist yarns are not a disadvantage if the reed and pick of the cloth are suitable; this is shown by the fact that cotton voiles have been successfully treated in substantial quantities.

The success of the process is largely dependent on the distribution of the resin throughout the cellulose; hence, steps must be taken during the preparation of the fabric to ensure that its absorbency is of the highest possible order. The crease-resist finish is a final finish and therefore applied not only to white goods, but also to dyed and printed material; the purity of most bleached goods may be good, but as many heavy shades of dyed fabrics do not require a thorough preliminary bleaching treatment before dyeing, and are therefore less absorbent, special care should be taken to improve their absorbency. This is also necessary on account of the fact that rapid and thorough penetration of the cellulose by the pre-condensate of urea-formaldehyde is hindered by the presence of large amounts of colouring matter already within the fibre.

In addition to impurities, a poor absorbency may be a reflection of the history of the cellulose itself, in that over-drying or baking may have brought about an excessive amount of mutual satisfaction of the hydroxyl groups. Foulds and Marsh have dealt with this aspect of the problem in B.P. 304,900 by suggesting that the cellulose be dispersed or swollen beforehand; suitable swelling agents include caustic soda solutions and, if necessary, the fabric may be treated in the wet swollen state after removal of the swelling agent. Mechanical treatment, such as repeated impregnation with squeezing rollers, is beneficial in assisting the penetration of the fibre by the reaction mixture.

As viscose rayon is already a dispersed cellulose, it presents less difficulty than native cellulose, provided the temperature of drying has been kept reasonably low, but it is sometimes advisable to pass the fabric through dilute alkali (about 6 to 7% NaOH), which not only swells the cellulose but breaks down the film or surface of orientated cellulose produced during extrusion of the filaments. After such an alkaline treatment, the NaOH should be removed by washing with cold water, and the fabric dried at the lowest practicable temperature.

The aim of this book is not to give a highly detailed account of one particular process, but rather to survey Finishing as a whole. As with most textile operations, the use of the process over many years has resulted in the finisher accumulating a large amount of practical experience which forms the craft, rather than the theory, of the crease-resisting finish.

THE REACTION MIXTURE

Consideration of the various patents shows that the urea and formaldehyde may be employed in two ways:

(a) Uncondensed reagents.

(b) A pre-condensate.

There can be no doubt that the use of the uncondensed reagents possesses certain disadvantages, although at first sight it would appear that they offer a means of utilising the products with the lowest possible molecular weight; formaldehyde, however, is both reactive and volatile, hence uncondensed reagents when applied in bulk are rapidly reacting and increasing in molecular weight; and, moreover, the formaldehyde is continually evaporating, particularly during the drying of the impregnated material. It is therefore preferable on economic grounds to attach the formaldehyde to the urea and so use it in a non-volatile form; a stable pre-condensate also helps in the production of consistent results. Now, when the urea-formaldehyde is applied to the fabric it must be catalysed with an acid substance, and it has been found that with the uncondensed reagents, the acidified aqueous solution is apt to deposit an amorphous methylene urea in white discrete particles which "foul" the bath, and do not give rise to crease-resisting effects, although they may be used for delustring effects, as discussed on page 315. The pre-condensates are more stable even in acidified solution.

These pre-condensates are probably methanol ureas which may be formed by condensing urea and formaldehyde either at room temperatures or by refluxing for a short time.

Experience has shown that the best results are generally obtained by using a molecular ratio of formaldehyde to urea of 1·6 : 1. This does not mean that the process is limited to this ratio, for various other ratios have been given in the T.B.L. patents, ranging in general from 1 : 1 to 2 : 1, sometimes with a slight excess of formaldehyde. The "best" results are not necessarily those which exhibit the highest degree of crease-resistance; it is common experience that any particular textile property when pressed to the extreme, often interferes with other desirable textile characteristics. The somewhat indefinite textile merits of a fabric are an integration of many different qualities; as previously mentioned, the highest possible degree of crease-resistance interferes with handle, draping, softness, and other textile properties, and for this reason it may be stated that careful experience has shown that a ratio of 1·6 : 1 represents the optimum effect rather than the maximum. It may perhaps be remarked that an increase in formaldehyde gives greater springiness to the fabric, but more firmness, whereas an increase in urea imparts a softer effect which is, however, slightly less resistant to washing.

The preparation of the pre-condensate may be effected in either of two ways: (a) by boiling under a reflux condenser, or (b) by allowing the mixture to react at room temperatures. In both cases, a slightly alkaline mixture of urea and formaldehyde is utilised. With laboratory quantities, boiling may be prolonged to 3 minutes as it is possible to cool quickly, but with larger amounts it is advisable to cool as rapidly as possible after the mixture has reached boiling-point.

Similar mixtures may be allowed to stand at room temperatures until the viscosity has reached a value between 5 and 7 centipoises (water value 1).

The control of the condensation process is of great importance as it is essential to use condensation products of low molecular weight and to avoid the formation of products of higher molecular weight which will not penetrate the fibres. The viscosity of the reaction mixture is generally found to lie between 5 and 7 centipoises at 20°C.; lower values may be used with satisfactory results, but there is a tendency for the formaldehyde to escape on account of its volatility. A very low viscosity indicates that the formaldehyde has not combined with the urea; the viscosity of the uncondensed mixture is about 3 to 4 centipoises. The density of the condensate also increases during the initial reaction, rising from 1·15 to about 1·17 (34°Tw.).

Where the reaction mixture is prepared at room temperatures, it is not possible to obtain colloidal products of high viscosity, so that this method is both safer and more reliable, even if it requires longer than the reflux method. If the mixture is allowed to stand too long, crystallisation of the methanol ureas takes place, but solution may be effected either by gentle warming or by adding more water. The solid content of the mixtures as prepared is about 60%, and as this is generally reduced to about 30% before catalysing and impregnation, followed by drying and baking, there is no reason why water should not be added after the initial condensation has taken place; as will appear later, the stability of the initial solution is improved by dilution.

MIXTURES PREPARED AT ROOM TEMPERATURES.

Urea: formaldehyde : : 1 : 1·6

	30% formaldehyde		40% formaldehyde	
	Density	Viscosity	Density	Viscosity
Before condensation	1·125	2·9	1·15	4·3
After condensation	1·15	4·05	1·17	6·5

When urea is dissolved in formaldehyde solution there is a fall in temperature, but the addition of ammonia is attended by the development of heat; the solution should be stirred periodically, and its temperature should not be allowed to rise above 35°C. About 4 to 6 hours is the minimum time for the formation of the pre-condensate at room temperatures; completion of the reaction is accompanied by crystallisation of the methylol ureas from super-saturated solution, as remarked above; but, if necessary, the crystalline materials may be collected, dried, and re-dissolved as required for use.

In some countries 40% formaldehyde solution is not commercially available, and 30% solutions must be used.

Where the reflux method of preparing the reaction mixture is employed, it is possible to exceed the viscosities of 5 to 7 and form products of high molecular weight which are still soluble in water; these are colloidal solutions of the type mentioned on page 378. Such solutions will not penetrate the fibre, even when diluted with water to diminish their apparent viscosity, for dilution only increases the space between the molecules and does not alter their size—a point which is not always understood. Further, the far-condensed solutions are colloidal, and slowly form a gel even without heat, whereas the reaction mixture of low viscosity is crystalloid in nature, being a supersaturated solution of a mixture of mono- and dimethylol ureas, together with some uncondensed reagents, so that on standing for some time, it does not gel, but forms a crystalline sludge. This may be obviated by diluting the reaction mixture with about 25% of water, should it be necessary to keep it for some days before use.

The crystalline products may be purchased, ready for use, from some chemical manufacturers; these products are all substantially methanol ureas, sometimes with additions of surface-active chemicals, softeners, sucrose, ammonium sulphide, or other compounds. These must not be confused with the urea-formaldehyde syrups or glues, which, as previously mentioned, do not penetrate textile fibres.

A recent product, Aerotex M3 of the Calco Chemical Division of the American Cyanamid Co., may be a melamine-formaldehyde product in about 80% concentration.

IMPREGNATION

The reaction mixtures, prepared as described on page 395, contain approximately 60% of solid matter and would give very stiff results if applied without dilution; for most purposes the concentrated mixture may be diluted with water to about 45 to 50% of the original strength; that is, to a solid content of 27 to 30%. It is not wise to be dogmatic on this point, for the dilution is determined to some extent by the type of fabric to which the solution is applied, and also by the expression of the mangle used for impregnation. It is necessary to add an acid catalyst to the diluted mixture in order to effect resinification during the heating of the dried fabric. In the earlier days of the process, it was customary to utilise organic acids because the addition of mineral acids caused precipitation of methylene ureas and rendered truly continuous impregnation impossible. Even with free organic acids, the stability of the impregnating bath is only moderate at room temperatures, and therefore of limited convenience from the standpoint of works' practice.

However, this difficulty was overcome by the work of Battye, Marsh, Tankard, Watson, and Wood, as shown in B.P. 449,243; the catalyst may be added in such a form that the correct acidity is not developed until the drying process. The ammonium salts of strong acids may thus be used, and these permit the impregnating solution to be used over a long period of time without fear of instability. Such catalysed solutions are highly satisfactory in practice; a very convenient catalyst is ammonium dihydrogen phosphate, but ammonium chloride or sulphate may also be used. With any catalyst, however, there is an optimum concentration, calculated on the solid content of the mixture employed.

As will appear later, the use of weak organic acids which was essential for reasonable minimum stability, necessitated curing temperatures of the order of 180°C., but with the stronger mineral acids a final temperature of 120°C. is adequate. It may be remarked that the employment of the ammonium salts of mineral acids is modern practice, with pre-condensates of urea-formaldehyde. With uncondensed urea and formaldehyde, these potential acid catalysts have no real advantage over the free acid, for the free formaldehyde reacts with the ammonium salt to give a hexamine salt of the strong acid; this salt is largely hydrolysed in water on account of the weakness of hexamine as a base in comparison with ammonia. The solution becomes highly acid very quickly and rapidly gives a precipitate of methylene urea.

Whatever catalyst is employed, the amount is critical for the best effects; if too much is utilised there is a danger of the resin being hydrolysed by the excess of acid, and even of some hydrolytic attack on the cellulose itself, whereas if too little catalyst is used the condensate is not properly resinified and is soluble in mild alkali.

The impregnating solution may also contain a suitable wetting agent, but care must be taken to ensure that it is not only stable in the impregnating liquor, but does not interfere with the stability of the solution.

The fabric is generally impregnated by the usual trough and mangle arrangement; any good padding mangle is capable of giving good results if used with intelligence. The lowest possible expression should be achieved, and every attempt should be made to ensure that the fabric is evenly impregnated across its width. Some finishers prefer to use a two-bowl mangle, both bowls being rubber-covered; others prefer a three-bowl mangle in which the middle bowl is made of brass, and the upper and lower bowls are rubber-covered.

The hydraulic mangle has certain advantages over the system of weights and levers. These mangles are often more robust than the non-hydraulic types, and it is sometimes possible to procure a better expression of the fabric and, hence, a superior penetration of the reagents.

The suction type of hydroextractor may be suitable for certain fabrics, such as fine rayons and crêpes; cotton voiles with their hard-twisted yarns may be impregnated on a mangle whose bowls have been wrapped with a fine cloth.

During the impregnation of fabrics dyed with aniline black and other oxidised amines, the bath becomes contaminated with soluble basic colouring matter, but this may be obviated by a preliminary diazotisation of the fabric, followed by soaping.

It may be of interest to remark that there is no exhaustion of the liquor by the fabric; urea-formaldehyde solutions do not possess substantive properties and there is no preferential absorption by the cellulose.

DRYING

The drying of the impregnated fabric must be so conducted as to avoid the formation of interstitial and superficial resin. It does not appear to be sufficiently appreciated that there are essential differences between simple solutions which deposit solids when the water is evaporated, and a resin-forming liquid.

With some fabrics, such as crêpes, it is possible to carry out the drying process in a festoon chamber or an Air-Lay drying machine, and then produce the correct dimensions of the fabric on a stenter equipped with a steam-box. In general, however, most fabrics are stenter-dried; pin-stenters are preferred and care should be taken to ensure that the fabric is not unduly stretched during the stentering but dried under minimum tension.

An important point in the drying process arises from the modern use of ammonium salts of strong acids as catalysts for the final resinification; these salts must be converted to the free acid during the passage of the impregnated fabric through the stenter, and a pH below 4·5 should be realised before the final heating process.

If may be remarked that with stenters operating in an efficient manner and at high temperatures, the drying and subsequent resinification may take place in one passage through the stenter, some of which have been suitably "zoned" for this purpose. In general, however, it is important to avoid high temperatures in the initial stages of drying because this brings about a migration of resin to the surface of the fabric, and surface-resin is undesirable. This migration may be demonstrated by a staining test devised by Courtaulds; the fabric is treated with 4% Naphthol AS at room temperatures for 15 minutes, coupled with 20% Fast Red Salt 3GL, washed and soaped. The heavier stain indicates smaller amounts of resin.

If special effects, such as embossing or calendering for a smooth finish, are required, they should be applied after drying and before baking; as will appear later, the crease-resisting process itself imparts a considerable degree of resistance to shrinkage, but if controlled compressive shrinkage methods are required, these, too, may be applied after drying and before heating.

HEATING

The impregnated and dried material must be heated to transform the methylol ureas into the synthetic resin, and for the best effects, this heating step needs careful control. It may be remarked that a melt of methylol ureas within the fibres is sufficient to give a transient crease-resistant effect even without a catalyst, but a durable result requires more heat and a catalyst to form the resin; the Tootal Broadhurst Lee Company marketed its goods on the basis of satisfaction to the public and could not therefore sell materials whose resistance to creasing would disappear at the first wash. Apart from the commercial aspect of the product, it is difficult to appreciate the technical advance (if any) described in patent specifications which aim at low temperature curing, minimum amounts of catalyst, and so forth, at the expense of resistance to washing, for a "different" recipe may be novel without being an improvement in the art.

In general, the temperature of heating is determined by the type of catalyst employed; organic acids generally require several minutes at very high temperatures, according to the thickness of the fabric, but the mineral acids, in the form of their ammonium salts, bring about resinification at 120°C. in 2 to 3 minutes. For the same catalyst, the rate of reaction appears to double itself for each rise of 10°C., as might be expected.

Various machines are available for the final condensation of the resin; the use of a special high-temperature stenter has already been mentioned. At one time, in the early days of the process, electrically heated cylinders were employed in the final curing, but these have now given way to festoon chambers.

Wall (Text. Manuf., 1938, *64*, 164) has made reference to the evolution of formaldehyde during the final condensation, and this appears to be an integral part of the process. Wall indicates that if the partial pressure of the formaldehyde within the chamber is increased to disturb the equilibrium, this evolution is prevented, but the resin does not resist washing; further, this does not depend on the ratio of formaldehyde to urea, for at any ratio between 1 : 1 and 2 : 1, the presence of formaldehyde within the chamber prevents proper condensation of the resin. This is contrary to general experience, for results which are identical in crease-resistance and in fastness to washing may be obtained either by festoon or cylinder heating; further, many processes have been devised which make use of extra formaldehyde, and whereas these give "harder" resins, on account of the formaldehyde, the handle and other physical properties of the treated fabric are adversely affected.

Some variations on the usual heating process have been suggested; for instance, Molinari (in B.P. 452,891) describes a process for heating under pressure, whereby the fabric is heated at 10 atmospheres in an autoclave at 110°C. for 15 minutes when the pressure rises to 14 atmospheres. The results are said to be soft and contain less resin than required by the usual procedure. This discontinuous process, of course, could not compete with the normal continuous process, even if the results were as good. There are many other suggested processes in patent specifications, the novelty of which appears to lie in heating for about 2 hours at 100°C. instead of 2 minutes at 125° or 170°C. Others state that the same degree of condensation may be obtained under less drastic conditions of heating than have been established by Foulds, Marsh, and Wood; unfortunately, no indications are given as to how the degree of resinification is established, so that such statements cannot be verified. The Tebilized products are tested in various ways to ensure not only crease-resistance and fastness to washing, but freedom from the regeneration of formaldehyde and the production of methylamines with their unpleasant odours; these tests, and other methods of control, still form a valuable commercial asset and cannot be disclosed as yet.

Some alarm has been expressed at the dangers of heating cellulose to high temperatures in presence of acid catalysts, but it may be stated that with proper control, there is no damage to the cellulose, which can be recovered unchanged by hydrolysing the resin, as shown by measurements of fluidity and solubility numbers. Apparently the energy of the acid is employed in forming the resin instead of attacking the cellulose.

WASHING

Many organic reactions do not proceed to completion, and it is therefore wise to wash the treated fabric so as to remove any uncombined reagents which may give rise to unwelcome effects later; also, occasionally, a little surface resin on the fibres gives rise to a dry and "sandy" feel, and this too may be remedied by washing. The two general methods of washing are in open width or in rope-form, followed by rinsing; a dilute solution of soap and sodium carbonate is generally adequate for this purpose. The final rinsing waters may contain a softening preparation if necessary.

Mention has already been made (*supra*) of the desirability of removing the uncondensed reagents lest they should form methyl-amines with their unpleasant "fishy" odour; any methylamine salts which exist will be decomposed by the mildly alkaline wash and thorough rinsing, so that with efficient processing there is no need for complaints to arise.

It was originally feared that certain goods which had been finished with resinous preparations would give rise to dermatitis in actual wear; there have been no complaints with goods treated by the crease-resisting process. Moreover, the amount of free formaldehyde present in these goods may be estimated, and therefore controlled, by sensitive methods established by Marsh and Wood.

The drying process is usually conducted on a stenter, and care must be taken to finish the fabric at its natural dimensions which have been determined during the intermediate drying process before the final heating. Excessive stretching after heating will merely cause shrinkage during the first laundering treatment.

LINEN

Fabrics of linen are notoriously bad in respect of creasing, possibly on account of the high degree of the orientation of cellulose in this fibre. Although this may be remedied in a most remarkable manner by the standard crease-resisting process, yet there is considerable embrittlement of the flax as a result. This may be remedied by the methods of B.P. 437,361 of Corteen, Foulds, and Wood, which depend on mercerising without tension after the standard crease-resisting process; the fabric must therefore be constructed so as to permit this shrinkage and give an attractive appearance in the shrunk state. It is also necessary to insist on certain minimum standards of "solubility number" before treatment, owing to the ease with which linen is damaged.

For example, a fabric 38 inches in width is prepared so as to have a high degree of absorbency and is treated as previously described; the heated material is then impregnated with 0·25% solution of sodium carbonate and 0·25% solution of a sulphated fatty alcohol at 80°C. for 4 minutes, squeezed, and passed into sodium hydroxide solution of 50° to 60°Tw. without tension where it is allowed to lie for 3 minutes or more, when it will shrink in both warp and welt directions. When fully shrunk, the cloth is passed through the usual

26

mercerising plant and finished at about 36 inches, with the usual precautions necessary in the mercerising of piece goods.

A high degree of resistance to creasing is exhibited by the treated fabric, but the improvement in mechanical properties as a result of the "after-mercerising" process is most remarkable. The cause of this is not yet clear, but it may be associated with the disorientation of the original cellulose.

It must be remarked that the shrinkage treatment is essential for the production of strong fabrics which will give satisfaction in wear, and this is all the more remarkable in that the mercerising of untreated linen is accompanied by a decrease in breaking load of 6 to 8% when the process is effected without tension. According to B.P. 437,361, however, the breaking load of a crease-resisting linen fabric was increased from 17·3 lb. to over 30 lb. as a result of "after-mercerising" accompanied by about 12% shrinkage. There was also a manifold improvement in the resistance to wear as measured by rubbing tests.

CREASE-RESISTING AND SHOWER-PROOF

Some years after the appearance of the original patents by Foulds, Marsh, and Wood, with the insistence of resinification within the fibre, attention was drawn to a process by Zanker, patented by Heberlein in B.P. 413,328, and which referred to methods of preventing the resin penetrating unfavourably into the fibre. In point of fact, when the Zanker process is followed and samples examined, it can be demonstrated that the resin is inside the fibre; according to a private communication, Zanker was of the opinion that as the process rendered normal dyeing operations rather difficult, then the resin must be outside the fibre, but the same argument holds for resins inside the fibre where they may prevent penetration by dyestuffs.

The Zanker process actually combines resin-treatment with the deposition of metallic oxides from the salts of di- and trivalent metals; suitable metallic salts are those of aluminium, zirconium, tin, and zinc. For example, the usual mixture of uncondensed reagents or the solution of the pre-condensate follows the treatment of a textile fabric with 2% aluminium acetate and steaming for 30 minutes at 105°C. Presumably the acetate is decomposed into the basic acetate or oxide, and imparts spotproofing properties. Although Zanker prefers treatments with 0·1 to 0·001% solutions of metallic salts, it has been found that the "spotproof" effect is not very marked until 0·2 to 2% solutions are used.

It is also possible to vary the order of treatment to some extent; for instance, a viscose rayon material may be treated for 15 minutes at 70°C. in a solution containing 200 g. of urea and 2 g. of aluminium acetate per litre, squeezed, and then passed through 40%

formaldehyde solution, after which it is allowed to stand for $2\frac{1}{2}$ hours, followed by drying at 80°C.

It may be mentioned in passing that a later patent of Zanker, B.P. 450,225, suggests that the final hardening of the resin in the impregnated fabric may be effected by salt solutions at temperatures exceeding 100°C.; suitable salts include sodium sulphate, magnesium sulphate, magnesium chloride, and calcium chloride.

The combined crease-resisting and spotproof effect does not appear to have been adequately recognised, and many writers in technical publications have fastened on the "unfavourable penetration" of the resin as the main feature of this process, which is based on the salt decomposing in such a manner that the metallic constituent imparts spotproofing, and the acid liberated acts as a catalyst for the resin.

Some later processes, however, have emphasised the combination of hydrophobic and crease-resisting effects; it is not possible to give an exhaustive account of the various suggestions, but some of the methods are interesting.

B.P. 451,082 of the I.G. refers to a preliminary treatment of the fabric with a wax emulsion expressed to 100%, followed by treatment with 20% dimethylol urea solution containing 6 g. per litre of mono- and disodium phosphates, drying and heating in the usual manner. B.P. 466,535 by Heberlein,, suggests the addition of emulsions of paraffin or the anhydrides of the higher fatty acids. For example, a fabric may be impregnated with a solution containing 3 Kg. of urea, 7·5 litres of 40% formaldehyde solution, 400 c.c. of ammonia, 500 g. of paraffin emulsion, and 45 litres of water; the fabric is expressed to 90%, and then passed through a bath of 13·5 litres of 30% formaldehyde solution, and 100 g. of aluminium sulphate in 40 litres of water. The fabric is then dried and heated at 130°C., followed by soaping, rinsing, and drying in the usual manner.

A later specification of the I.G., B.P. 495,714, covers the use of stearic acid methylol amide in conjunction with an acidified solution of dimethylol urea; B.P. 495,645 of the same combine suggests the use of octadecyl isocyanate in conjunction with or followed by an acidified solution of dimethylol urea (100 g. dimethylol urea and 1 g. of tartaric acid per litre), drying and heating for 10 to 15 minutes at 130°C. Other processes are outlined in B.P. 495,829 and 495,830.

The use of products of the "Velan" type in conjunction with crease-resisting mixtures has been suggested by Evans of the I.C.I. in B.P. 501,288, and also by Battye, Candlin, Tankard, Corteen, and Wood of Tootal Broadhurst Lee Co., in B.P. 506,721.

A solution is made by dissolving 100 parts of urea in 200 parts of neutralised formaldehyde (40%), to which is added 7·5 parts of ammonia (0·88); the mixture is boiled for a few minutes and rapidly cooled to room temperature. An addition is then made of 8 parts of octadecyloxymethylpyridinium chloride and 6 parts of ammonium dihydrogen phosphate in 50 parts of cold water, and the whole diluted to a total volume of 400 parts with water. The fabric is impregnated in this solution, squeezed, and dried in a current of air at 40°C., followed by heating at 140°C. for 3 minutes; the usual soaping, rinsing, and drying operations complete the process. Stearamidomethylpyridinium chloride may also be utilised.

ALTERNATIVES TO UREA

Some interest has been shown in the melamine-formaldehyde resins as alternatives to urea-formaldehyde. The use of these products for crease-resisting effects appears to have been first suggested by the I.G. in B.P. 458,877, but various Ciba processes have also been outlined in B.P. 466,015, 468,677, 468,746, 486,519, and 486,577.

The chemistry of the process is very similar to that of urea-formaldehyde, but the urea is replaced by an amino-derivative of 1 : 3 : 5-triazine or its substitution product.

Melamine   Formoguanamine

According to B.P. 458,877 of the I.G., 20 parts of melamine may be dissolved in hot water and 60 parts of 40% formaldehyde solution added, after which the solution may be made up to 200 parts with water. Fabric may be impregnated with the liquor, dried, and heated for 40 minutes at 140° to 150°C. to develop the crease-resisting effect.

In B.P. 456,015 of Ciba, it is stated that the melamine-formaldehyde condensation is slow in neutral or feebly alkaline solutions, but is accelerated in feebly acid solutions. Hence, it is possible to mix 63 parts of melamine with 300 parts of neutral formaldehyde solution (30%) and boil for 10 minutes; a white paste separates on cooling, and 96 parts of the paste may be mixed with 100 parts of hot water, cooled, and made up to 190 parts with water. The fabric may be impregnated in a slightly acidified solution, prepared as above, dried, and then heated at 150°C. for 4 minutes. The process is completed by soaping, rinsing, and drying.

Other urea-like compounds have been suggested as alternatives in the reaction with formaldehyde; both the I.G. (B.P. 424,076) and Pollak (B.P. 441,038) have drawn attention to hydrazine dicarboxyl-diamide, whose formula is $NH_2.CO.NH.NH.CO.NH_2$.

Some interesting diethers of dimethylol urea may be prepared according to the methods of Du Pont described in B.P. 522,643. Their application to fabric for crease-resisting effects is outlined in B.P. 537,971. For instance, 70 parts of dimethylol urea, 150 parts of methyl alcohol, and 30 parts of anhydrous magnesium sulphate are mixed and refluxed for an hour, followed by removal of the insoluble magnesium sulphate. The solution is diluted with water to the required concentration and employed for the impregnation of fabric which is dried and then heated for 6 minutes at 170°C.

In view of the success attending the treatment of fabrics with condensation products which are transformed into synthetic resins inside the fibres, it was only to be expected that experiments should be made with various inorganic salts capable of forming translucent colloids under certain conditions. Compounds such as borates, silicates, and stannates were examined by Marsh and Battye in 1929, and although it was established that they were capable of giving crease-resisting effects with cotton and rayon, the treated fabrics had two disadvantages compared with those containing urea-formal-dehyde resins. First, the crease-resisting effect was broken down by repeated crumpling or squeezing and finally became very slight; and, secondly, the effect was not sufficiently fast to washing.

It was noticed the best results gave rather poor recovery figures when tested by the apparatus described on page 388, although the treated fabrics exhibited plenty of spring. The effect of sodium stannate was quite good with an increase in weight of about 20%, but the crease-resistance appeared to diminish on ageing in contrast to that obtained with resins. It was also observed that the break-down of the effect on repeated squeezing could be obviated by the presence of about 3% urea-formaldehyde resin which presumably binds the salt into a continuous medium of greater elasticity.

More recently, inorganic salts have been suggested for producing crease-resistance. In 1935, Pomphrey outlined a process for deposit-ing within the cellulose a metallic compound in vitreous, transparent form in a state of continuity; suitable compounds may be salts of inorganic or organic acids, and as an assistant to the retention of the vitreous state, there may be added glycol, glycerol, or other polyhydric alcohol. For example, a rayon fabric may be treated with a 5% solution of calcium acetate containing 0·5 to 1% of glycerol, squeezed, and dried in warm air; the fabric is then impreg-nated with a 5 to 10% solution of sodium silicate (Na_2SiO_3 or $Na_2Si_2O_5$) containing 0·5 to 1% of glycerol, squeezed to remove excess liquor, dried, and heated at 100° to 150°C. Other substances mentioned by Pomphrey in B.P. 457,659 are borates, boro-silicates, and phosphates.

The J. B. Martin Company of Connecticut made use of the complex of the soluble salts of boric and salicylic acids; these acids were dissolved in the theoretical amount of ammonia and applied as a finishing preparation, followed by drying and heating to 80° to 100°C., according to B.P. 458,979.

The later processes of Rotta and Quehl, as outlined in B.P. 504,273, 504,343, and 505,970, also utilise water-soluble borates and stannates, mixed if required with sodium-potassium tartrate. Precautions are taken to prevent the formation of coarse crystals which do not give crease-resisting effects. In B.P. 504,273, for example, it is suggested to impregnate rayon with a solution containing 8% of sodium borate and 1·5% of an alkaline olive-oil emulsion; in other examples, the fabric undergoes an increase in weight of 10 to 15%. Other water-soluble salts, such as sodium sulphate, are mentioned in B.P. 504,343, deposited from solutions containing colloidal substances or emulsions of fats, oils, or waxes which prevent crystallisation of the salt inside the fibre. Again, B.P. 505,970 mentions that a solution of a borate or stannate with sodium or potassium tartrate, if required, is capable of giving crease-resisting effects even in absence of colloidal dispersions or fatty emulsions; the increase in weight of the treated material is from 5 to 10%. It is believed that these specifications cover the "Preska" process.

Morton and Boulton of Courtaulds have also suggested the use of a salt of boric acid together with a fatty lubricant, followed by drying and heating; no tendency to crystallise was observed, and good results were obtained with 10 to 15% solutions of borax, containing 1 to 2% of a sulphated fatty alcohol or a soap-stabilised emulsion of vegetable oils (B.P. 492,449).

It has, of course, been known for many years that polymeric substances of high molecular weight can be formed from glycerol and boric anhydride, as well as from glycerol and orthosilicic acid esters; the vitreous masses have been described by Schiff and Bechi (Z. Chem., 1866, 9, 147).

Borates, silicates, and stannates are also capable of forming polymers which may consist of a three-dimensional network of a type which bears some resemblance to the molecular architecture of the thermo-setting resins.

THE CREASE-RESISTING PRODUCT

As previously mentioned, the crease-resisting property is one which is not easy to define; further, this property is only one of the many effects which are associated with the internal deposition of suitable resinous substances within the textile fibre. Resistance to and recovery from creasing are only examples of a decreased response to forces which tend to change the form of the treated material; in most cases, the fabrics are manipulated so as to preserve the flat state, and the recovery from creasing is merely the return to the flat state. If, however, the goods are creased, pleated, embossed, or otherwise distorted before the final heating stage of the process, then the methods previously outlined are capable of producing permanent creases or a crease-restoring effect. The decreased response to various forces is evident in the resistance to distortion or permanent extension to which many textile materials are prone, the reduced tendency to shrink on laundering, and the decreased swelling in water with many products; these examples of dimensional stability are of some consequence, and, indeed, of great consequence with fibres of regenerated cellulose, whose low wet-strength is a serious defect, but one which is remedied by the crease-resisting process.

In addition to these "stabilised" properties, the application of the resin adds to the weight of the fabric, and in the special case of spun rayon, brings about such an improvement in handle, feel, draping, and textile character that the general effect alone is a valuable finish without the more striking properties mentioned above.

The resin treatment also improves the fastness properties of many dyestuffs and protects the cellulose itself against degradation by light.

Many of these improvements are associated with a decreased swelling capacity of the treated product, from which it has been assumed, and wrongly, as will appear later, that the anti-crease effect and the anti-swelling property were one and the same. Numerous applications of the stabilising effect of the resin have been mentioned in different patent specifications, too numerous to discuss, but the *novelty* of the process, the *new* method of manufacture, and the *invention* that recovery from strain is manifest in different directions are not immediately obvious to the writer.

The manifold utility of the treated product is such, however, that there can be little doubt that Foulds, Marsh, and Wood have produced a general-purpose finishing process, which is perhaps at its best on spun-rayon materials, which can be treated to give a range of products varying from a sheer linen finish to a soft woollen effect. A minor improvement lies in the freedom from slipping or fraying of many rayon fabrics.

Summarising the chief advantages of the product, the following list shows:

(*a*) Improved resistance to and recovery from creasing.
(*b*) Increase in weight.

(c) Improved resilience, handle and draping properties.
(d) Increased strength of rayons, in both dry and wet state.
(e) Decreased extension of rayon with freedom from distortion.
(f) Decreased water imbibition with quicker drying properties.
(g) Decreased shrinkage on laundering.
(h) Improved fastness of many dyestuffs.
(i) Resistance to degradation by light.
(j) Decreased slip and fraying.
(k) Rotproofing.

The manifold advantages of crease-resisting goods are shown by the action of the Board of Trade of the United Kingdom, in the manner of dealing with "Utility Fabrics"; in 1942, 16 out of the 20 spun-rayon fabrics were specified as having to be "crease-resisting," and in January 1945 the specification was revised stipulating that 26 out of 32 of these Utility Fabrics must be "crease-resisting."

Many crease-resisting materials are sold under the registered trade mark "Tebilized," which indicates that such goods have been treated by certain methods so as to conform with specified standards established by Tootal Broadhurst Lee Co. Ltd., Tebilized fabrics irrespective of their producers are not only tested for crease-resistance, but have to satisfy additional requirements. The Tebilized plan was launched in the U.S.A. in the spring of 1939, and in the United Kingdom in the spring of 1943.

CREASE-RESISTANCE

Some typical results of the process are shown in the following table, referring to four different fabrics. The test of recovery is that mentioned on page 388, referring to the distance between the extremities of a folded strip originally 4 cm. by 1 cm.:

RECOVERY FROM CREASING

Fabric	Untreated		Treated	
	Warp	Weft	Warp	Weft
Cotton/rayon . . .	17 mm.	22 mm.	33 mm.	33 mm.
	15 ,,	19 ,,	28 ,,	37 ,,
	17 ,,	13 ,,	29 ,,	38 ,,
100% spun rayon . .	24 ,,	26 ,,	33 ,,	35 ,,
Viscose-cotton mixture .	12 ,,	12 ,,	33 ,,	31 ,,
100% viscose crêpe . .	11 ,,	20 ,,	28 ,,	30 ,,

The results are expressed in mm., and it will be remembered that good-quality woollen material would give a recovery figure of 33 to 35 mm.

It is possible, of course, to multiply such examples of the recovery from creasing of treated and untreated materials, but the above data

are sufficient to indicate the type of effect which can be obtained;
as stated elsewhere, it is possible to exceed these recovery figures,
but a very high recovery from creasing is apt to interfere with the
draping and other desirable textile characteristics.

The treated fabric is usually washed directly after the condensation
process, which takes place by heating under acid conditions, and it
is rather interesting to note that the full recovery from creasing
does not develop for a few days. Although the washed and dried
material is better than the original, yet the recovery improves rapidly
for the first two days and slowly for another four or five, after which

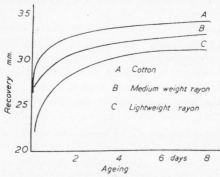

FIG. 148.—Initial improvement in recovery from
creasing on ageing.

there is a slight improvement. This effect is shown in Fig. 148, from
which it appears that the improvement in recovery is rather more
rapid with cotton than with rayon; the actual recovery figures, both
initial and final, are of no significance in these curves, and it is only
the shape of the curve which matters. To a less degree, there is also
a delay in regaining the full power of recovery from creasing with
goods which have just been washed.

As with most tests on textile materials, the physical properties are
measured under standardised conditions of temperature and humidity.

The resistance to creasing of treated fabrics varies somewhat
according to the relative humidity of the atmosphere; the following
table gives the means of measurements taken at 25°C. in atmospheres
of different relative humidities:

RECOVERY AND RELATIVE HUMIDITY

Sample	Thickness	30% R.H.	45% R.H.	60% R.H.	75% R.H.	90% R.H.
(a)	0·35 mm.	35·5 mm.	34·5 mm.	33·5 mm.	31·5 mm.	22·5 mm.
(b)	0·363 ,,	35·0 ,,	34·5 ,,	32·5 ,,	32·25 ,,	22·75 ,,
(c)	0·395 ,,	37·75 ,,	37·5 ,,	35·5 ,,	34·5 ,,	18·75 ,,
(d)	0·420 ,,	38·25 ,,	37·75 ,,	35·75 ,,	32·0 ,,	23·25 ,,
(e)	0·640 ,,	38·5 ,,	37·75 ,,	34·5 ,,	32·5 ,,	18·75 ,,

In the series of samples examined, the textile material was spun viscose rayon. Accordingly, the moisture absorption curve of viscose rayon as established by the B.C.I.R.A. was examined for correlation with recovery from creasing; the average values of the fabrics were found to lie on approximately the same curve. It appears, therefore, that with treated rayon fabrics the recovery from creasing is a linear function of their moisture content.

As the criterion of success in the crease-resisting finish is to form the resin within the textile fibre, the distribution of the resin is of greater importance than the quantity. Nevertheless, there seem to be certain average quantities which have been reached after years of experience, but not solely determined by recovery from creasing. It may be remarked that substantial recovery effects of the same order may be realised with less resin in cotton than in rayon; in general, it does not appear customary to use less than 5% of resin with cottons and about 10% with rayon, but these figures are by no means critical. Many treated cotton goods contain between 6 and 10% of resin, excellent finishes on voiles being obtained with the lower amounts; linen often appears to contain 10 to 12% of resin, filament rayon about 10 to 15%, and spun rayon 15 to 20%, estimated on the weight of the untreated material. It is, of course, possible to exceed these figures and commercial crease-resisting spun-rayon fabrics are sometimes encountered with 25% of resin and more. Even with cotton goods, by special methods of manipulation, it has been possible to obtain samples containing as much as 40% of resin within the fibre, leaving the fabric soft, flexible, and supple, but with a formidable recovery from creasing and no draping properties.

It has been stated that the resin lies within the textile fibre and the production of a supple product containing 40% of resin demonstrates this point, but a special staining method devised by Battye and utilised as a microscopic technique by Miss Alexander made it quite apparent that stiff, brittle, and readily-creasing products could be formed with a very little resin *outside* the fibre, whereas soft, supple, and resilient samples with a greater amount of resin had the urea-formaldehyde deposited *within* the fibre.

For many years the declared object of the research work was to obtain crease-resistance by synthesising resins within the textile fibre, and after its successful accomplishment, the staining technique afforded a neat confirmation of the soundness of the original hypothesis.

Some of these photomicrographs are illustrated in Figs. 149 and 150; the cellulose nitrate in which the section is mounted was stained red to afford a visual contrast to the blue stain which coloured the resin, but had no affinity for the cellulose.

PLATE XXVII

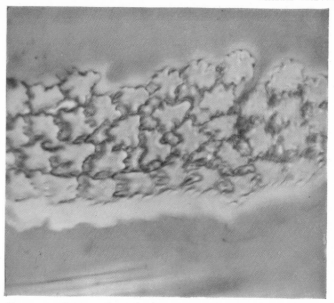

FIG. 149.—Cross-section of viscose rayon fabric treated with a colloidal solution of urea-formaldehyde which does not penetrate the fibre. It gives stiff and brittle effects.

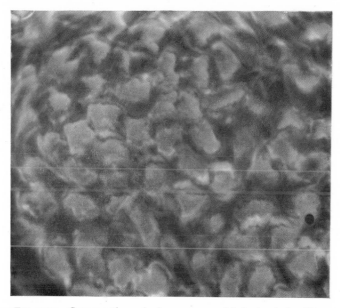

FIG. 150.—Cross-section of viscose rayon fabric treated with a crystalloidal solution of urea-formaldehyde which penetrates the fibre. It gives supple, crease-resisting effects.

Courtesy of Miss Alexander.

To face page 410

It will be noted that in the crease-resisting products, the fibres are distinct and separate, and, indeed, the absence of superficial cementation may be demonstrated by the ease with which the fibres or individual filaments may be separated from the yarn of a crease-resisting fabric.

X-ray photographs have demonstrated that the resin is not situated within the micelle and must therefore lie between the crystallites; this is only to be expected, for as water does not penetrate into the micelle, it is not to be expected that an aqueous solution of a pre-condensate of urea-formaldehyde will find its way where water does not go.

There are certain properties which assist in the determination of textile character or merit which are generally assessed in a subjective manner, although within recent years objective tests have been devised. One of these properties is the elusive draping ability of fabrics; most cotton, linen, and rayon goods are improved in this respect by the crease-resisting process, quite apart from the property of crease-resisting. Dresses and frocks of treated material can often be recognised at a glance from the way they "hang" or drape. Substantial quantities of lightweight curtain material have been successfully treated solely for the purpose of improving their draping properties. The improvement does not appear to be due to the slight increase in weight.

The handle and feel of the goods are also improved as a result of the process, and without loss of softness and suppleness. A certain indefinable type of resilience, which is not necessarily synonymous with crease-resistance, gives a sensation of robustness which adds to the textile merits of the material; this is particularly striking with fabrics of spun rayon, as these are apt to be somewhat lifeless and characterless in the untreated state.

The presence of the resin within the fibre does not cause the treated goods to attract dirt and dust; indeed, it has been found that the crease-resisting fabrics soil less easily than untreated goods, although part of this improvement may be due to the crease-resisting property itself, for if there is freedom from wrinkles and creases, then the dust and dirt have less opportunity of establishing themselves.

Although the resistance to washing cannot be regarded as absolute in the scientific sense, yet it is quite adequate. Careful measures of control have been developed to ensure this.

The chemical constitution of the resin is such that it could not be expected to resist boiling alkaline liquors (and nor can wool). When washed with the reasonable precautions which are taken with wool, silk, or rayon, then the crease-resisting property will last as long as the useful life of the material itself. The effect of washing will be discussed again on page 425, but this may be a convenient opportunity of stating that the effect is not removed by dry-cleaning, or with any common solvent with which the goods are likely to come into contact.

BREAKING LOAD AND EXTENSION

The improvement in the breaking loads of rayon goods is a characteristic and noteworthy feature of the crease-resisting material. Some typical results are given in the following table:

IMPROVEMENT IN BREAKING LOAD

		Dry		Wet	
		Warp	Weft	Warp	Weft
Spun rayon, untreated.	.	49 lb.	59 lb.	19 lb.	28 lb.
treated	.	66 lb.	97 lb.	37 lb.	57 lb.
Viscose voile, untreated	.	24·6 lb.	21·5 lb.	—	—
treated	.	33·0 lb.	23·8 lb.	22 lb.	16·8 lb.

Some further data on "war-time" fabrics are perhaps of interest.

IMPROVEMENT IN BREAKING LOAD

	Breaking Load			
	Dry		Wet	
	Warp	Weft	Warp	Weft
Spun rayon Angora, untreated.	60 lb.	46 lb.	30 lb.	19 lb.
treated .	65 lb.	63 lb.	42 lb.	38 lb.
Spun rayon dress goods, untreated	46 lb.	34 lb.	20 lb.	16 lb.
treated	64 lb.	43 lb.	36 lb.	25 lb.
Spun rayon yarn-dyed, untreated	70 lb.	60 lb.	29 lb.	26 lb.
treated .	89 lb.	71 lb.	52 lb.	38 lb.

The wet tensile strength of rayons relative to the dry tensile strength has often been measured and has frequently been assumed to have some significance. It is interesting, therefore, to examine the relationship between wet and dry tensile strengths of the treated and untreated materials.

WET TENSILE STRENGTH AS PERCENTAGE OF DRY TENSILE STRENGTH

Filament Viscose		Spun Viscose A		Spun Viscose B	
Resin	Wet/Dry	Resin	Wet/Dry	Resin	Wet/Dry
0%	31%	0%	41%	0%	46%
3·3%	47·5%	2%	50%	2%	54%
6%	50%	5·3%	55%	4·4%	56%
9%	58%	8·8%	58%	6·6%	62%
12	63%	10·2%	64%	9·0%	64%
16%	65%	16·2%	69%	14·4%	70%
23%	59%	21·3%	66%	19·2%	74%

These results are plotted in Fig. 151; the differences between fabrics *A* and *B* is mainly that of weight (120 and 180 g. per square metre respectively in the untreated state).

The results are so substantial that were it not for the great novelty of resistance to creasing, the treated goods might, in the writer's opinion, be termed Reinforced Rayons.

It is interesting to note that the improvement in wet strength by the incorporation of urea-formaldehyde resin in rayon is also seen in paper.

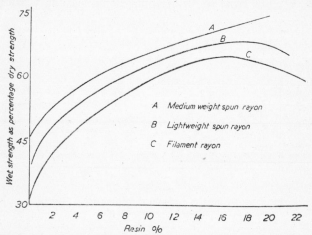

A   Medium weight spun rayon

B   Lightweight spun rayon

C   Filament rayon

FIG. 151.—Effect of resin content on ratio of wet strength and dry strength of rayon.

The properties of various treated fabrics have been described by Molinari (Materie Plastiche, 1936, *3*, 11) and some of the results are shown in the following table:

EFFECT OF CREASE-RESISTING PROCESS

Material	Increase in wt. %	Washing loss %	Breaking Load			
			Warp		Weft	
			Original	Treated	Original	Treated
100% spun rayon .	15·5	2·15	27 kg.	41·6 kg.	30·2 kg.	40 kg.
	22·8	2·5	33 ,,	48 ,,	30 ,,	44 ,,
Cotton/rayon .	14·7	1·5	23 ,,	21·8 ,,	23 ,,	28 ,,
Spun rayon/rayon .	21	3·0	32·4,,	48·6 ,,	35·8 ,,	45 ,,
Wool/spun rayon .	17	2·15	50·2,,	67 ,,	30·6 ,,	43 ,,
100% spun rayon .	16·5	1·5	33 ,,	48·4 ,,	31 ,,	42 ,,

It will be noted from these figures that the breaking load of the rayon is increased from 20 to 53% in the dry state; the breaking load of wool is also increased, but that of cotton has fallen by 5%.

In general, it may be stated that the effect of the process on viscose rayon is to increase the dry strength from between 30 and 50%; the wet strength may be increased up to 100%.

With cotton, the position is somewhat different, and there is often a decrease in apparent breaking load which may vary from 5% to as much as 15%. This apparent decrease usually occurs in the weft and not in the warp; it does not seem to be associated solely with the count or twist of the yarn, but also with the method of impregnation. It is interesting to note that fabrics composed of cotton yarns of very low twist show an apparent increase in breaking load.

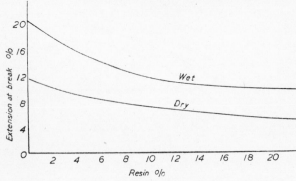

FIG. 152.—Effect of resin on the extension at break of filament viscose rayon.

The apparent decrease in breaking load of treated cotton goods, except those of low-twist yarns, is not accompanied by true tendering or degradation of the cellulose, in spite of the fact that the goods have been heated to a temperature above 100°C. under acid conditions. Removal of the urea-formaldehyde resin by suitable methods of hydrolysis, even acid hydrolysis, brings about a restoration of the original physical properties of the material. More precise tests of chemical damage, such as Fluidity or Solubility Number, show that there is no difference between the original material and treated goods from which the resin has been removed; hence there has been no degradation of the cellulose.

With untreated rayon, the extension is apt to be very high; more important, however, is that the extension is plastic and the filaments show little power of recovery from extension. This property is responsible for many forms of distortion to which rayon is prone, and, in particular, the stretching, sagging, and ballooning of knitwear. The extension at break of regenerated cellulose is reduced as a result of the crease-resisting process, but not to a harmful extent. Many rayons produced during the period 1920–30 showed an extension at break of about 33%, and this was reduced to the order of 20%

by the crease-resisting process. Later productions (1935–40) showed
lower extensions at break, amounting to about 12% in the dry state
and 20% in the wet state; these figures may be reduced by 50% as
a result of the crease-resisting process. A typical series of extensions
at break, plotted against the amount of resin in the fabric, is shown
in Fig. 152.

The stabilising action of the resin is also to be seen in the reduced
tendency of knitwear to roll or turn in at the edges.

VARIATION OF PROPERTIES WITH RESIN CONTENT
Filament Viscose Rayon (1930)

Resin %	Dry Load lb.	Dry Extn. %	Wet Load lb.	Wet Extn. %	Recovery mm.
None	38	33	12	33	24
3·3	42	29	20	30	28
6	46	26	23	30	29
9	46	26	27	29	31
12	46	24	29	27	33
16	46	23	30	25	35
23	39	18	23	21	37

Filament Viscose Rayon (1940)

Resin %	Dry Load lb.	Dry Extn. %	Wet Load lb.	Wet Extn. %
0	46	11·4	24	20·4
2	46	10·3	26	17·7
6	47	8·3	29	13·6
9	48	7·1	32	13·0
12	50	7·0	32	11·7
15	52	6·6	35	10·4
18	62	5·9	35	9·7
23	56	4·7	36	9·4

MOISTURE ABSORPTION

The absorption of moisture may be considered under two headings:
first, the absorption of water vapour, and, secondly, the imbibition
of liquid water.

Crease-resisting materials, whether of cotton or rayon, show the
same moisture regain at equilibrium as untreated goods in atmospheres of various relative humidities up to about 75% R.H.,
provided the calculations are correctly made with reference to the
cellulose, and *not* with reference to the gross weight of cellulose and
resin. Considerable misconception appears to exist on this simple
matter. At higher relative humidities, such as 90 or 95% R.H., the
treated materials exhibit a slightly lower regain of the order of 1%;

VARIATION OF PROPERTIES WITH RESIN CONTENT
Lightweight Spun Rayon

Resin %	WARP				WEFT				Water Imbibition %	Recovery	
	Dry		Wet		Dry		Wet			Warp mm.	Weft mm.
	Load lb.	Extn. %	Load lb.	Extn. %	Load lb.	Extn. %	Load lb.	Extn. %			
None	48·6	15·3	20·4	23	38	20	17	24	82	23	22
2·0	52·4	16·7	26	21	39	22	19	23	69	27	25
5·3	54·1	14·1	30	20	44	19	25	22	55	28	27
8·8	54·5	15·0	32	20	43	18	25	21	48	30	29
10·2	54·4	13·0	35	18	45	17	27	21	45	31	30
16·2	55·0	12·5	38	17	45	15	30	20	40	33	32
21·3	59·0	11·6	39	16	45	14	30	19	37	35	34

The weight of the cloth is 120 g./m.² (Utility 1006.)

TREATMENT OF SPUN RAYON WITH U/F RESIN

| | Resin Content | Warp Dry | | Weft Dry | | Warp Wet | | Weft Wet | | Water Imbibition | Recovery Tests | |
| | | Load | Extn. | Load | Extn. | Load | Extn. | Load | Extn. | | Warp | Weft |
	% —	lb.	%	lb.	%	lb.	%	lb.	%	%	cm.	cm.
Blank	—	60·8	14·7	53·0	18·4	28·1	21·1	25·2	22·2	78·5	2·5	2·15
A	1·9	63·3	16·7	60·0	16·6	34·6	23·4	33·7	20·5	66·3	2·6	2·5
B	4·4	68·5	16·1	61·4	15·2	38·5	20·8	37·0	20·0	56·1	2·75	2·65
C	6·6	71·0	15·0	64·7	14·4	44·4	20·0	42·6	19·6	49·1	2·85	2·9
D	9·2	71·5	14·5	65·6	13·9	45·7	18·9	41·6	18·3	45·6	3·0	3·0
E	14·4	68·0	13·9	68·2	13·6	48·2	17·9	48·0	17·8	39·1	3·2	3·1
F	19·2	69·0	13·3	66·3	13·0	51·2	16·6	47·5	16·1	36·9	3·4	3·2

The weight of the fabric before treatment was 180 g./m.^{2} (Utility 1010.)

this may be due in part to a true hysteresis effect caused by the temperature of final condensation of the urea-formaldehyde resin.

The velocity of water-vapour absorption is slower with treated cellulosic materials than with untreated goods.

Water-imbibition, by which is meant liquid water, is lower with crease-resisting goods than untreated materials; the implications of this interesting fact are very important. Estimations of water-imbibition with a centrifuge whose acceleration is 1,500 G., show that many crease-resisting rayons have about one-half of the water-imbibition of the untreated materials; cotton shows a 40% reduction. Now the water-imbibition of viscose rayon is generally admitted to be excessive, and it is interesting to note that the resin treatment reduces the value to approximately the same as that of untreated cotton. The crease-resisting treatment reduces the speed of wetting, but the actual rate of drying is the same for both treated and untreated material, although the former will dry more quickly because it contains less water.

Most viscose rayon shows a water-imbibition of 85 to 90%, and many cottons provide a figure around 45%, based on the dry untreated material.

It seems to be a popular fallacy that anti-swelling and anti-crease always go together; in addition to the data given on page 427, it is interesting to note that when crease-resisting goods are mercerised their water-imbibition is increased without substantial effect on the crease-resisting property. For example, it is well known that crease-resisting linen has been mercerised after the final condensation of the resin; the water-imbibition of the final product is *greater* than that of the original material.

WATER-IMBIBITION OF LINEN

	Fabric A	Fabric B
Untreated	63·5 %	54·5 %
Treated and mercerised . . .	69·6 %	62·0 %

As a first approximation, the imbibition of water may be regarded as a measure of the volume-swelling, provided that all possible surface liquor is removed, and that the measurements are confined to materials of the same history and origin.

Returning to consideration of viscose rayon, it seems very probable that the high wet-strength of the treated material is due to the decreased water-imbibition, and similarly with the decrease in extension at break in the wet state. The reinforcement of the rayon by resin is obviously a property of great importance where any wet treatments are concerned, such as laundering; the useful life of the material is prolonged by the resin process.

Most shrinkage difficulties are now known to be due fundamentally to the swelling of the weft of the fabric (see page 242); hence, it is only to be expected that the crease-resisting product will exhibit a reduced tendency to shrink on laundering.

The lower water-imbibition and reduced swelling are probably due to the mechanical constraint exercised by the internal resin; there is no evidence of the formation of a compound between the

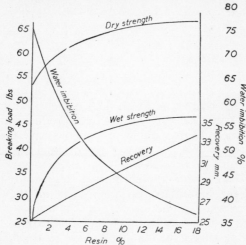

FIG. 153.—Effect of resin on some physical properties of viscose rayon.

resin and the cellulose, either with urea-formaldehyde or phenol-formaldehyde, nor is there any evidence of the chemical blocking of hydroxyl groups by these resins.

SHRINKAGE

Another useful feature of the crease-resisting product lies in its reduced tendency to shrink during laundering. The shrinkage phenomenon has been discussed on page 240.

The warp-shrinkage is generally the more serious, and it may be controlled by mechanical methods of compressive shrinkage, but these are of comparatively little value with rayon, which merely extends after the compressive process. The following data represent results with four different rayon materials, before and after the crease-resisting process:

CREASE-RESISTANT FINISH AND SHRINKAGE

	Warp shrinkage %			
Standard finish .	6·1	5·5	3·0	1·2
Crease-resist . .	1·5	1·4	0·5	0·6

The shrinkage potential of fabrics is determined by many factors, including the type of fibre, spinning and weaving conditions, the woven structure, and also the extension applied during bleaching, dyeing, or printing, and often varies from fabric to fabric of the same structure according to the conditions under which weaving occurred. The following results represent effects on three plain-dyed fabrics:

SHRINKAGE OF CREASE-RESISTING RAYON

	Standard	Crease-resist
Filament rayon . . .	3·9%	0·7%
Heavy spun rayon . .	12·0%	4·7%
Light spun rayon . .	7·9%	3·1%

Although the crease-resisting finish does not entirely eliminate the shrinkage of rayons, yet in the treated products the potential shrinkage is reduced to reasonable proportions, and the goods may be finished within a few per cent of the original yardage, whereas compressive shrinkage processes rely on a loss in yardage by warp compression. Where very low shrinkages are required with spun-rayon fabrics, the best plan appears to rely on the "stabilising" action of the resin in conjunction with mechanical methods.

The following results may be taken as an indication of the manner in which the resin affects the laundry shrinkage; the figures relate to two different stenters used for the intermediate drying.

LAUNDRY SHRINKAGE OF SPUN RAYONS

Resin	Fabric A Pin stenter	Fabric B Clip stenter	Pin stenter
20%	—	1·7%	0·5%
10%	4%	2·4%	0·7%
7·5%	5%	2·4%	0·7%
5%	5%	4·8%	0·6%
2·5%	6%	7·0%	1·4%
0%	12%	10·0%	6·0%

The pin stenter was hand-fed, but the clip machine had an automatic feed attachment.

The same difficulties of laundry shrinkage are not encountered with cotton goods, and the crease-resisted product is satisfactory in this respect. It may be remarked, however, that some of the above data were published in the technical magazines in 1932; a patent by Raduner (B.P. 445,891) of later date claiming the hardening of the resin on the fabric in a tensioned state gives the following example of "the extraordinary advance in the art":

WARP SHRINKAGE OF COTTON VOILE

Before treatment	.	.	.	.	7 to 9%
After treatment	.	.	.	.	0·09 to 1·8%

The laundry shrinkage of the "war-time" fabrics, mentioned on page 412, is also of interest.

LAUNDRY SHRINKAGE

	Warp	Weft
Spun rayon Angora, untreated . . .	7·2%	1·6%
treated . . .	0·4%	2·8%
Spun rayon dress goods, untreated . .	7·4%	1·8%
treated . .	2·0%	1·8%
Spun rayon yarn-dyed, untreated . .	11·2%	3·8%
treated . . .	4·0%	1·6%

FASTNESS OF DYESTUFFS

It has been found that, in numerous instances, the fastness of dyestuffs is improved as a result of the crease-resisting process. This phenomenon should properly be discussed in text-books of dyeing rather than finishing; however, a brief account of the subject may be of interest.

Some dyeings alter slightly in shade as a result of the finish, often on account of the temperature of final condensation of the resin; the alteration in shade is not usually appreciable and is of little consequence as few goods are sold in both ordinary and crease-resisting finishes, for the former do not bear comparison with the latter. Changes in shade are of more importance where pale shades are used, and perhaps browns require special care; with heavy shades, however, difficulties are not apt to arise.

Where direct dyes are used, unless data are available from the dyestuffs manufacturer, it is wise to choose those of the highest fastness to light. With the crease-resisting process, the fastness to light of many direct colours is improved, others are unaffected, but some are reduced; hence it is important to appreciate this point and avoid using those susceptible colours whose light-fastness will be reduced, for if the degree of fastness to light is already low, the final effect may be disappointing. On the other hand, the great majority of direct dyes are improved in respect of fastness to washing; some are unaffected but none is impaired. The extent of improvement in fastness to washing is similar or even superior to that given by diazotisation or treatment with formaldehyde where this is possible.

Provided the colour is sufficiently fast to withstand the simple impregnation process during the crease-resisting treatment without appreciable bleeding, the initial fastness to washing is of small moment, for it will be greatly improved in the vast majority of colours.

With the azoic colours, there is little evidence of change in shade on account of the process. There is, however, a general improvement in fastness to light, and this may be of considerable importance for the few azoic combinations which are deficient in light-fastness. No azoic colours appear to be impaired in fastness to light or washing as a result of the crease-resisting process.

Vat dyes again are unaffected in respect of shade by the treatment. The fastness to light and to washing, already of a high order, are not impaired by the process and, indeed, are often improved.

Sulphur colours are not extensively utilised on rayon goods as they are apt to be somewhat dull; some of them alter in shade as a result of the process. There is no evidence of deterioration in fastness to light or to washing, and in many instances these two properties are improved by the treatment.

It appears to be a safe generalisation that the most important effect on the colours of goods which have been crease-resisted is the improvement in fastness to washing.

PHOTO-HYDROLYSIS

It is well known that many of the regenerated cellulose rayons are photo-sensitive, more particularly in presence of certain dyestuffs, such as the vat yellows and oranges, but nevertheless some tendering occurs even in absence of dyestuffs. When rayon has been given the crease-resisting finish, however, a considerable measure of protection is afforded, as shown by the following data due to Wood:

PHOTO DEGRADATION OF VISCOSE RAYON

	Breaking Load of 2-in. strip	
	Dry	Wet
Untreated and unexposed	63 lb.	31 lb.
Untreated and exposed	30 lb.	nil
Treated, but unexposed	83 lb.	63 lb.
Treated and exposed	80 lb.	57 lb.

In the above tests, the rayon was exposed to ultra-violet light for 44 hours. The resin content was approximately 15% estimated on the cellulose; some similar results were obtained by the writer on rayon treated so as to contain approximately 7·5% of resin.

PHOTO DEGRADATION OF VISCOSE RAYON

	Breaking Load of 2-in. strip	
	Dry	Wet
Untreated and unexposed	60 lb.	30 lb.
Untreated and exposed	20 lb.	nil
Treated and unexposed	74 lb.	39 lb.
Treated and exposed	59 lb.	21 lb.

Better results appear to be obtained where the full amount of resin has been applied; hence, resistance to photo-degradation is an inevitable accompaniment of resistance to creasing with urea-formaldehyde resins.

The above results refer to rayon exposed under an ultra-violet lamp, but the writer has obtained similar effects when the material was exposed to sunlight.

PHOTO DEGRADATION OF RAYON BY SUNLIGHT

	Blue		Yellow		Green	
	Dry	Wet	Dry	Wet	Dry	Wet
Untreated and unexposed .	60 lb.	27 lb.	98 lb.	42 lb.	60 lb.	30 lb.
Untreated and exposed .	47 ,,	19 ,,	46 ,,	nil	47 ,,	12 ,,
Treated and unexposed .	80 ,,	35 ,,	120 ,,	52 ,,	84 ,,	48 ,,
Treated and exposed . .	53 ,,	24 ,,	91 ,,	38 ,,	65 ,,	33 ,,

The above samples contained between 8 and 10% of resin, and the time of exposure was such that the yellow rayon was degraded until the wet-strength of the untreated material was less than 5 lb. It will be noted that the resin exerts a protective influence even with those dyes whose presence accelerates photo-degradation.

The rate of photo-degradation of rayon may be seen from the following experiment.

A fabric composed of filament rayon was treated so as to contain 12·5% of urea-formaldehyde resin and then exposed to ultra-violet light with the following results:

PHOTO DEGRADATION OF VISCOSE RAYON

	Breaking load in lb. of 2-in. strip after various hours' exposure				
	0	10	20	30	40
Untreated, dry strength .	55·0	51·5	43·5	37·5	33·5
wet strength .	27·0	14·0	5·0	—	—
Treated, dry strength . .	77·0	77·5	76·5	74·0	71·5
wet strength . .	55·0	52·5	48·5	47·5	46·0

NON-SLIP

Crease-resisting rayon fabrics show a reduced tendency to slip, that is, the yarns do not slide over one another very readily; many fabrics which "slip" exhibit a distortion of the woven structure and the spacing between the yarns is uneven. Fabrics which are easily distorted in this manner are apt to fray at the edges when made into garments.

Tests on two typical fabrics containing filament viscose rayon, made in 1932, gave the following results, under a load of 25 lb. on a 2-inch strip:

SLIPPING OF RAYON FILAMENT FABRICS

Fabric A			Fabric B		
Untreated	.	. 0·9 cm.	Untreated	.	. 0·52 cm.
			3·5% resin	.	. 0·4 cm.
			5·5% ,,	.	. 0·36 cm.
7·0% resin	.	. 0·4 cm.	7·0% ,,	.	. 0·31 cm.
14·0% ,,	.	. 0·4 cm.	13·0% ,,	.	. 0·29 cm.
16·0% ,,	.	. 0·35 cm.	16·0% ,,	.	. 0·28 cm.

Instead of measuring the slippage produced by a given load, a modern alternative test is to measure the load required to effect a given degree of slip in the fabric. In these circumstances, it has been found that for the same degree of slip, 1·6 times the force is necessary for the crease-resisting fabric compared with the same fabric in the ordinary finish.

It will be seen, therefore, that a greater effort is required to produce a given degree of slip on crease-resisting goods. The tendency to slip, of course, depends to a large extent on the fabric structure, and many goods are satisfactory in this respect.

The decreased tendency to slippage does not seem to be due to any roughening of the surface of the rayon, for the resin is inside and not outside the fibre. However, it has been noted that the formation of synthetic resins within the cellulose brings about a permanent distension of the material; the increase in the diameter of the fibres may cause a greater cohesion of the warp and weft with a reduction in tendency to slip.

Sommer and Viertal (Klepzig's Textil-Z., 1941, *44*, 637), in their review of German crease-resisting fabrics, comment on the behaviour in actual use of jackets made from spun rayon, both ordinary and crease-resisting; after the third wash, the seams of the garment of ordinary rayon tore apart comparatively easily, and as the number of washes increased, so did the tearing of the seams, particularly at the pockets, whereas no such defect was observed with the crease-resisting material.

ROT-PROOFING

Experience has shown that crease-resisting cotton and rayon goods are less susceptible to zymolysis than is the case with the untreated material. Most dress goods, however, are rarely kept under conditions where attack by mildew, for example, is likely to be encountered; nevertheless, this comparative immunity is of interest. It has also been found that crease-resisting cotton and rayon are less sensitive to bacterial decay or rotting; this may be due, in part, to the reduced capacity for imbibing water compared with the same goods in the ordinary finish. (See also Ind. Eng. Chem., 1947, *39*, 1628.)

Crease-resisting materials are also less susceptible than the untreated cellulose to attack by perspiration.

They also exhibit considerable resistance to those reagents and influences which are apt to modify cellulose and bring about damage; for example, the presence of the resin gives the treated material a considerable measure of immunity to oxidation and to acid hydrolysis (naturally they cannot be termed acid-proof). Again, although cotton is resistant to alkali, yet viscose rayon is readily affected and may dissolve; crease-resisting rayon, on the other hand, is relatively insensitive to caustic alkali, and may even be mercerised with sodium hydroxide solutions.

WASH AND WEAR

Laboratory evaluation of textile finishes has not yet reached the stage when it can be regarded as completely replacing an examination of the behaviour in wear; the only satisfactory criterion of textile merit is the performance in actual use.

It has already been stated that the urea-formaldehyde resin is not fast to boiling alkaline liquors, but if the treated fabric is washed at a lower temperature of 50° to 60°C., then the effects persist for 25 or more launderings. This is no great restriction, for it merely limits the severity of the laundering to that normally used for wool, silk, or rayon. Many rayons would be substantially deteriorated by 25 launderings, whereas the crease-resisted products after a similar number of launderings are often as sound mechanically as the untreated, unwashed material.

Any slight amount of "loose" resin in the crease-resisting fabrics is generally removed in the first two or three washes (say, 0.25% Na_2CO_3 at 60°C.), but even after 25 washings, there is still evidence of the presence of resin.

After numerous launderings, the dry strength of treated rayon is still greater than that of untreated laundered materials; the relative wet strength of the crease-resisting goods is better than that of the untreated material throughout the whole series of washings. Both relatively and absolutely, the wet strength of the treated goods after 25 washes is better than that of the untreated rayon which has also been washed. The dimensional change on washing is also much less with crease-resisting rayon than with ordinary goods. The water-imbibition of the treated material after 25 washes is less than that of the untreated goods.

Untreated rayons tend to become still more limp and flabby on washing, but the crease-resisting material exhibits excellent handle, draping and appearance, as well as a lack of flabbiness as washing proceeds.

The resistance to abrasion as measured by various mechanical devices (on the merits of which there is considerable disagreement) indicates that the treated rayon is rather more susceptible than the untreated; the resistance to abrasion is generally improved at the first wash and after further launderings is only slightly less than that of the untreated material. Goods which are dry-cleaned or seldom washed, may perhaps be expected to show signs of slightly premature wear, but actual experience of wear and wash shows that, provided they are washed during their life, the treated rayons have greater durability and a better utility performance. The treatment actually increases the useful life of fabrics which are frequently washed. In point of fact, very little personal wearing apparel *wears* into holes, it mostly *breaks* into holes, the ease of break being assisted by abrasion previously; very often these holes appear after laundering. Hence the improvement in breaking load, both wet and dry, of the crease-resisting rayons can hardly be over-estimated.

Theoretical and Speculative

Many specious reasons have been advanced to account for the property of recovery from creasing shown by cellulosic materials treated according to the methods of Foulds, Marsh, and Wood; some suggestions will not withstand critical examination. For instance, it has been stated that recovery from creasing is associated with the permanence of the wavy form of the fibres, and that the resin fixes the fibres in the undulating position. In nearly all fabrics, the weft is much straighter than the warp, which is caused to take up an undulating path, yet measurements of recovery in the treated fabrics show that the weft recovery is very frequently superior. The permanent-wave theory is difficult to reconcile with the good recovery from creasing possessed by the pile of treated rayon velvets. The correlation between waviness and resilience may be high in wool fibres, but it is difficult to differentiate between the resilient filaments of silk and nylon, for example, and the readily deformable filaments of regenerated cellulose on the basis of external form. Nevertheless, waviness may be a contributory factor.

A more popular theory is that which associates recovery from creasing with reduced swelling in water; it may be mentioned that wool swells considerably in water and yet is regarded as the standard of recovery from creasing. Cellulose acetate and nylon do not swell as much as cellulose and have better crease-resisting properties, but glass does not swell at all, yet fabrics from glass fibres have practically no recovery from creasing whatever. It is true that cellulosic material which has been crease-resisted either by resins or by the formaldehyde process shows a reduced tendency to swell in water, but the two properties do not go together, as shown by Wood (see

Fig. 154). The broad generalisation that reduced tendency to crease is accompanied by a reduced tendency to swell, even if the converse does not obtain, is not always true, for crease-resisting linen has a higher water-imbibition value and shows a greater swelling in water than the untreated product; further, it is possible to prepare some cellulose methylene ethers which are very highly swollen in water and only exhibit resistance to creasing in the wet and super-swollen state.

It is possible to suppress swelling by blocking the hydroxyl groups of the cellulose, but this does not lead to a crease-resisting product;

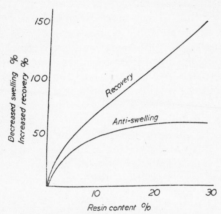

FIG. 154.—Comparison of anti-crease and anti-swelling.

for example, among the numerous derivatives of cellulose which may be made without destruction of the fibre structure, the mono-acetate has reached some commercial importance, but although its moisture absorption and swelling are low, it has never been suggested as a crease-resisting product.

Most fibres, even from crease-resisting material, show a lower recovery at high humidities; this may be accounted for by the plasticising action of the water vapour absorbed between the chains of β-glucose residues in the amorphous regions of the cellulose. In many instances, the fibres swell as they absorb atmospheric moisture, but decreased absorption of water vapour, decreased swelling, and increased recovery from creasing are not necessarily related. The moisture absorption of resin-treated crease-resisting material at equilibrium at any relative humidity is *not* less than that of the untreated cellulose, provided the calculation refers to the cellulose and not to the cellulose and resin.

Anti-swelling effects, and also considerable dimensional stability, may be obtained by the *external* application of many synthetic resins, but the treated goods exhibit increased susceptibility to creasing.

Explanations of the crease-resisting properties of the various fibrous materials have also been attempted on the basis of their fine structure. One of these hypotheses makes use of the fact that textile fibres are porous and contain a number of small cavities between the crystallites of which the fibres are composed; these cavities are assumed to act as air-cushions or air-pockets which are responsible in part for the elastic recovery of the compressed fibres. Further, when the sub-microscopic cavities are very small, they are much less susceptible to crushing, and so cause an elastic pneumatic reaction to the folding of the fibre, which behaves like a porous rubber tube of very small dimensions.

This theory appears to rely solely on some data of Frey-Wyssling (Protoplasma, 1937, *27*, 372), from which it appears that the cavities in wool and silk (50Å.) are about one-half the size of those in cellulose (100Å.), but reference to the original work shows that it depends on the impregnation of fibres with various metallic salts from aqueous solution, followed by deposition of the metal and the measurement of the metallic particles; hence the data refer to the wet and swollen state and not to the dry fibre. Even without this criticism, it will be noted that there is no correlation between cavity size and recovery from creasing—the pore sizes of rayon and silk are the same.

PORE SIZES OF TEXTILE MATERIAL
(Maximum?)

Cotton	not measured
Ramie	80 to 135Å
Viscose	50Å
Silk	50Å
Acetate	60Å
Wool	60Å

Attention has been drawn to the relation between the orientation of the chain-molecules of which fibres are composed and their powers of recovery from creasing; at first sight there appears to be some correlation in the order wool, silk, acetate rayon, viscose rayon, cotton, and flax, but reference to X-ray photographs shows that silk is more highly orientated than acetate rayon, and also that nylon is highly orientated although it possesses good elastic recovery. It may be remarked that it is also possible to show good correlation between recovery from creasing and the specific gravities of the various native fibres; in general, the lower the density, the better the elastic recovery. Returning to the question of orientation, however, Quehl (Textilber., 1939, *20*, 76) has suggested that the creasing properties of fibres are determined by the amount of crystalline material which they contain, and that by increasing the proportion of amorphous material it is possible to improve the elastic recovery. Quantitative estimations of the relative amounts of crystalline matter in the various textile fibres are on a very insecure basis and cannot be regarded as well-founded at present. Further, if the development of crease-resistance was merely a question of increasing the proportion of amorphous material in the textile fibres, then the very numerous amorphous substances would surely have been employed to good effect. Water itself is an amorphous substance, and yet there is evidence to show that many fibres exhibit greater recovery from creasing as the amorphous substance (water) is removed.

The combination of cellulose with formaldehyde is not necessarily accompanied by resistance to creasing, but Quehl himself points out that the crease-resisting product contains no deposit of amorphous material.

Condensation products of urea and formaldehyde exist in two amorphous forms—the synthetic resin and the particulate product methylene urea; the latter does not give resistance to creasing when deposited inside or outside the textile fibres, and the former does not give resistance to creasing when present as an external layer, although both increase the proportion of amorphous matter. A continuous structure appears to be important.

Further data showing the importance of a continuous structure compared with discrete particles may be taken from the work of Quehl (Textilber., 1939, *20*, 76), although it must be stated that this worker advanced the following results in support of a suggestion that crease-resisting was due to an increase in the amorphous constituent of the fibre. The recovery is expressed in terms of the "uncreasing angle."

COMPARISON OF DIFFERENT FORMS OF BORATE

	Cotton	Viscose	Viscose crêpe
Untreated . . .	98°	89°	138°
Preska finish, normal drying	128°	122°	154°
„ „ air-dried .	104°	97°	142°

According to Quehl, these figures show that the amorphous form of borate imparts crease-resistance, whereas if the crystalline form is produced by slow drying at room temperatures there is little crease-resistance; it must be remarked, however, that when the "Preska" material is dried on a warm glass plate, a film is formed thereby exhibiting continuity of form, as against the particulate deposition which results from drying at room temperatures.

RECOVERY AND OTHER PROPERTIES

Recovery		Crystallinity		Density		Moisture Regain		Increase in Sectional Area —65% RH to wet	
Wool	Very high	Wool	Low	Nylon	1·14	Nylon	4%	Nylon	5%
Silk	High	Acetate	Low	Silk	1·25	Acetate	6%	Acetate	6–9%
Nylon	High	Silk	Medium	Wool	1·32	Cotton	8·5%	Wool	25%
Acetate	Moderate	Rayon	Low to high	Acetate	1·33	Viscose	11%	Cotton	30%
Viscose	Low	Cotton	Medium	Viscose	1·52	Silk	11%	Silk	46%
Cotton	Low	Nylon	High	Cotton	1·52	Flax	12%	Viscose	35–60%
Flax	Very low	Flax	Very high	Flax	1·52	Wool	16%	—	

Although the truly thermoplastic resins have a continuity of structure they do not impart the property of crease-resistance; it appears that long unconnected chain-molecules of this type are less effective than the tri-dimensional network of aminoplasts.

The hypothesis of molecular entanglement, formulated by the writer in 1937, has some points of interest as a mechanistic basis of explanation for the crease-resisting phenomenon.

It is now generally agreed that cellulose fibres consist of a multitude of long chain-molecules which occasionally come together in an orderly manner to form crystalline regions; these areas are joined by individual molecular chains which are in random array and persist through the crystallites. The idea of sharply defined crystalline and amorphous regions has given way to that of a gradual transition from the crystalline to the amorphous state.

Extension of the fibre inevitably involves a complex system of stresses and strains among the entangled mass of molecular chains which are not in regular formation, and this region is most probably responsible for elastic after-effects or "Nachwirkung."

It is well known that highly orientated filaments exhibit a relatively small total extension compared with that of disorientated filaments; the extension of the former is mainly due to micellar slippage, and that of the latter is a type of plastic flow. If, however, suitable entanglements are established between the micelles, then slip is prevented; the strain is thrown on the entanglements, and the release of stress brings with it the release of strain.

Plasticity is probably due to the non-crystalline chains linking the crystallites; the greater the distance between the chains the greater the plasticity, for plasticising agents are mainly compounds which keep the "free" molecular chains apart.

Within recent years, great attention has been focused on the crystalline nature of cellulose, to the comparative neglect of the regions of low cohesion within the fibre and between the micelles.

Most plastic substances are characterised by random orientation or low cohesion; with cellulose there is moderate cohesion in the crystalline regions owing to the multiplicity of weak forces of attraction between the parallel molecular chains, but in the amorphous regions the chains are not straight and therefore the forces of attraction are very slight. Some of the plasticity of cellulose is due to these crumpled chains which link the crystallites together.

The amorphous regions of cellulose are more susceptible than the crystallites to chemical attack and to penetration by water and other reagents; the swelling of cellulose with water is due to the water entering the amorphous regions and forcing the molecular chains apart. When cellulose is completely dry, however, it is almost non-plastic and exhibits moderately good recovery from creasing.

This is probably due to the crumpled and disorientated molecular chains coming close together as the water is removed, so that the cohesional forces are at a maximum; as drying proceeds, the molecular chains approach and the hydroxyl groups undergo mutual attraction, possibly with hydrogen bonding, and set up a molecular entanglement of the crumpled chain-molecules. Hence, it is possible to visualise, to a minor degree, part of the cellulose consisting of curled or crumpled chains with occasional bridges or cross-links.

The forces of association are not very strong and are few in number, for the "amorphous" chains are not straight or parallel; they are easily separated by water vapour as the dry cellulose is allowed to condition. In these circumstances, the cellulose is plasticised again by water, the molecular entanglements are broken, and the material resumes its tendency to crease.

It is interesting to record that when cotton fabric is impregnated in a boiling aqueous solution of boric acid, and dried, it acquires crease-resisting properties; the product is brittle, but on washing in water, the brittleness, the crease-resisting property, and the boric acid are all removed. Now boric acid is capable of forming a complex with certain carbohydrates, as shown by Boeseken (Configuration of the Saccharides, Sijthoff, Leyden, 1923); the work has also been discussed in the Annual Reports of the Chemical Society (1917, *14*, 64, and 1930, *27*, 97). These addition complexes appear to unite polyol molecules which contain hydroxyl groups which are close together; the transient crease-resisting effect with cellulose may therefore possibly be explained by molecular entanglement, through boron bridges.

$$\begin{array}{ccc} >C - O & & O - C< \\ | & B & | \\ >C - O & & O - C< \end{array}$$

Another type of entanglement may be established by the reaction of cellulose with formaldehyde to make methylene cellulose (see page 143); in certain circumstances, a non-swelling product is obtained, and this, according to the extent of methylenation, may exhibit crease-resistance. It appears that the particular type of cellulose methylene ether owes its properties to the methylene bridges between the chain-molecules of cellulose; a relatively low degree of methylenation is sufficient to suppress the swelling in water and dissolution in the usual solvents for cellulose, whereas a higher degree produces a brittle crease-resistant product. These facts may be explained by molecular entanglement through methylene bridges.

Molecular entanglements may also be established by the condensation of synthetic resins within the fibre. There is no need to postulate chemical combination, which would include the blocking of hydroxyl groups; the reduced swelling in liquid water and lower water-imbibition may be due to mechanical constraint. It is interesting to note that not all resins are capable of producing crease-resistance, and the truly thermoplastic products seem of little value in this respect. Continuity of structure seems essential and lack of this property may account for certain transient crease-resistant effects; a tri-dimensional network generally accompanies those products which impart crease-resistance, whether they are of the aminoplast and phenoplast type, or the inorganic products to which reference has already been made. From this it may be postulated that the resinous product itself must have a certain macromolecular elasticity based on a tri-dimensional network of crumpled molecular chains.

Knowledge of the properties of thermo-setting resins has usually been gained by examination of these materials in the mass; inside the textile fibres, however, they are probably filamentary and so behave differently. The composite material is a synthetic fibre inside a native or regenerated fibre. Plastic resins inside textile fibres are apt to be displaced on compression and therefore do not impart resistance to creasing.

Consideration of the crease-resisting properties of textile fibres would be incomplete without reference to rubber. Raw and unvul-canised rubber possesses a high degree of extensibility, but little elastic recovery; the elastic properties of rubber do not develop until the product has been vulcanised. It is now fairly generally assumed that the vulcanisation of rubber involves the formation of numerous cross-linkages or molecular entanglements even if precise knowledge of their chemical structure is lacking. The work of Meyer (Natural and Synthetic High Polymers, Interscience Publishers, New York, 1942), Houwink (Elasticity, Plasticity and Structure of Matter, Cambridge University Press, 1937), and of Davies and Blake (Chemistry and Technology of Rubber, Reinhold Publishing Co., New York, 1937) may be consulted in this connection.

The elastic properties of wool are due in some measure to the folded nature of the main polypeptide chains, but the cross-linkages also play a part; they not only strengthen the fibre and suppress plastic flow, but assist in restoring deformed fibres to their original state. Strain is thrown on the cross-linkages and the release of stress brings about the release of strain. It is well known that setting processes depend on the breakage and reformation of new linkages in different positions.

For high elasticity, a coiled chain structure is preferable, but it is necessary to have long chain-molecules with free rotating links; the glucose residues in the molecular chain of cellulose do not facilitate free rotation. Another requirement for high elasticity is weak

28

secondary forces, but in cellulose the secondary forces are relatively
strong because of their multiplicity. The third requirement, that
of a network structure by interlocking of the molecular chains, is
not normally present, but may be provided by cross-linkages or by
purely physical entanglement. It is well known that anhydrous
cotton and linen are temporarily resistant to creasing, and also that
transient effects may be produced with certain water-soluble
resinous materials, both organic and inorganic. Permanent effects
may result by combining formaldehyde with cellulose, or better still,
by synthesising tri-dimensional resinous condensation products
inside the fibre; similar resins outside the fibre do *not* impart recovery
from creasing.

It seems clear that an orderly and regular arrangement of long
molecules, micelles, fibres, or yarns will not be able to resist or
recover from the distortions of bending or folding; on the other hand,
a thoroughly random arrangement of similar molecules, micelles,
fibres, and yarns cannot be subjected, in the small area undergoing
distortion, to such a high pressure when the same force is applied
to the oriented material.

Further, when, in addition, some lateral cohesion is obtained by
actual chemical cross-linkages, or by physico-chemical association,
or even by thoroughly random entanglement, conditions exist for
relatively small distortions in the particular area under pressure.
The available experimental information indicates a general conclusion that uncreasing appears when the component parts of the
structure are thoroughly entangled by the natural coiled character
of that structure, or by physical, chemical, or physico-chemical
means; the effect is more durable where these imparted conditions
are stabilised.

RESIN MORDANTS

The fundamental idea of resin mordants may be seen in the
suggestion of Zundel of Moscow about 1912 (D.R.P. 264,137) that
phenol-formaldehyde resins could be used not only for the mechanical
fixation of powders and pigments, but also for the chemical fixation
of the wool colours on vegetable fibres. The stiffening produced by
the final condensation was a great disadvantage. Attention may
also be drawn to the previous unsuccessful work of Favre (Rev.
Gén. Mat. Col., 1901, 5, 181), who attempted to replace tannin
mordants with resorcinol and formaldehyde.

The earliest condensation products of phenol and formaldehyde
were not soluble in water, but only in dilute alkali, and this limited
their use with textiles. A definite advance was seen in the work of
Gunther in 1915 (D.R.P. 318,509) when water-soluble condensation
products of phenol and formaldehyde were formed. This process is

only of historic interest, but the neutral solution was used to impregnate fabrics, and then steamed to render the condensation product insoluble. The treated material was found to possess a definite affinity for the wool colours, particularly the basic dyes towards which the phenol formaldehyde condensation product acted as a mordant. It may be remarked that it has been shown by Wood that the treated cotton fabrics do not possess increased resistance to creasing; indeed, crease-resisting fabrics by the phenol-formaldehyde method dye less than the original fabric and are almost immune. A disadvantage of all the phenol processes is the production of a yellowish tinge which later turns purple and "saddens" even the darker colours.

The urea-formaldehyde resins, discovered in 1918, do not suffer from this defect, being perfectly water-white, transparent, and fast to light. Investigation of the crease-resisting fabrics which contain these resins showed that the treated goods had some affinity for the wool colours, but this was not sufficiently pronounced for commercial purposes. Attention was therefore turned to an examination of the various condensation products obtained by the reaction between formaldehyde and urea or its near relatives.

B.P. 433,143 discusses the fact that urea is easily and cheaply changed by heating at 160°C. for 12 to 48 hours; the technical mixture from heat-treated urea contains guanidine, biuret, cyanuric acid, guanyl-urea, and urea. This mixture may be condensed with formaldehyde and used for the impregnation of cotton and rayon fabrics; after hardening, the treated goods possess good affinity for the wool colours.

The same specification mentions dicyandiamide which is easily obtained from calcium cyanamide.

$$\begin{matrix} NH_2 \\ \\ NH \end{matrix}\!\!\!\!\!> C.NH.CN \quad \text{(dicyandiamide)}$$

Dicyandiamide may be condensed with formaldehyde under acid conditions to give a gummy product which is insoluble in alkali, but may be purified by dissolving in acetic acid and precipitating with alkali. The reaction is discussed in B.P. 520,573.

Solutions of dicyandiamide-formaldehyde of about 25% concentration may be applied to the fabric which is then dried and heated for 2 minutes at 165°C., followed by soaping, washing, and drying; the treated material shows a good affinity for Benzyl Green B, for example.

Whereas urea-formaldehyde condensation products are hardened in presence of acids, B.P. 433,210 discloses that organic bases may be used under certain conditions, and these bases increase the affinity for acid colours to a marked degree; suitable bases are ethylenediamine, ethylamine, methylamine, and so forth. Organic acids, on the other hand, give the condensation product an affinity for basic dyes. The use of organic bases is not limited to the urea-formaldehyde condensation products, but may be applied with those derived from dicyandiamide, biuret, guanidine, etc.

B.P. 506,793 is more particularly concerned with cyanamide and dicyandiamide; the solution in formaldehyde is mixed with a little ammonium chloride to act as a hardener, and then applied to the fabric, which is later heated to 140°C. for 20 minutes. The treated material dyes deeply with acid dyes. Mixtures of urea and cyanamide or dicyandiamide may also be used.

Other mixed condensation products of a somewhat similar type have been described in B.P. 510,516 and 524,511.

It is believed that Courtaulds "Rayolanda" utilises resins of the cyanamide-formaldehyde type for its affinity for the wool colours.

Many other methods have been suggested for imparting to vegetable fibres an affinity for the wool dyes, and some of these have been described by Marsh and Wood (Introduction to Cellulose Chemistry, London, Chapman & Hall, 1941).

Before leaving the discussion of the treatment of textile materials with various resins, reference may be made to their suggested use in connection with non-felting wool (see page 236).

CHAPTER XVII

RUBBER

NATURAL rubber latex is obtained from the barks of the para rubber trees (*Hevea brasiliensis*) by the process of tapping or cutting away a thin shaving to open the ends of the latex vessels. The latex gradually exudes and is collected.

The milky liquid consists of small particles of rubber dispersed in a watery serum and is almost neutral as it flows from the tree, but gradually becomes acid through the action of enzymes. The fresh latex finally coagulates on account of this acidity, but also begins to putrefy, so that anti-coagulants are necessary to stabilise it and antiseptics to preserve it. Ammonia is commonly used as an anti-coagulant.

If the latex is coagulated by acid, a coherent mass is obtained which is termed the coagulum, and this may be squeezed and dried to form a compact elastic solid. Stevens (Rubber Latex, London, 1936) has likened the three stages to milk, butter, and cheese.

Particles of rubber latex are lighter than the serum and may rise to the surface to form a cream, which may be collected and dried. Alternatively, the moisture may be evaporated from the latex to give a "whole latex" rubber which comprises both the particles originally in suspension and those dissolved in the serum.

Sheets of rubber.obtained by drying the latex are generally stronger than those formed by coagulation on account of the spongy structure of the latter; on rolling, however, the structure is broken to give a stronger and more compact mass.

The solid content of latex varies from 30 to 38%, but by careful evaporation with pyridine as a stabiliser, it may be raised to 75%, as in the case of "Revertex," for example.

The two chief forms of solid rubber prepared from the latex are crêpe rubber and smoked rubber. Crêpe rubber is made by first diluting the latex to 20% concentration and adding 1% sodium bisulphite, after which it is coagulated by acid. The coagulum is then cut and passed through the crêping machine where it is washed and at the same time masticated by grooved rollers turning in opposite directions at different speeds. When dry it has a crinkled, roughened appearance and a yellow colour. Smoked rubber is prepared from latex which has been diluted to 15% rubber content and coagulated with 1 part of 0·5% formic acid for every 10 parts of latex. Immediately before coagulation in a trough, division plates are inserted to produce slabs of the coagulum, which are later removed and machined. The slabs are passed through a series of rollers provided with water sprays for washing, and are then dried for 2 hours, after which they are smoked by means of a wood furnace for 9 or 10 days at 40° to 50°C. The sheets become translucent and amber-coloured.

Flint (Chemistry and Technology of Rubber Latex, Chapman and Hall, London, 1938, p. 117) has given a useful account of the subject.

One of the most important properties of rubber is the phenomenon of vulcanisation; it is not always appreciated that raw rubber possesses low tensile strength, limited elasticity, a permanent tackiness or thermoplasticity, together with solubility in oils and volatile hydrocarbons. Vulcanised rubber, on the other hand, possesses high tensile strength, great elasticity, an absence of thermoplasticity and tackiness, and a lack of solubility in oils and hydrocarbons. Many of the properties commonly assigned to rubber are really those of vulcanised rubber.

The chief vulcanising agent is sulphur, which is supposed to react with the rubber molecule at the double bonds to form sulphur bridges between the polymerised molecules; if all the double bonds become saturated, then a hard rubber results with almost complete loss of elasticity. Normal soft rubber contains 3 to 4% of sulphur, whereas ebonite may contain 20 to 30%.

The usual vulcanising process involves heat, but cold curing may be applied to thin goods by treatment with 3 to 5% of S_2Cl_2 in carbon disulphide.

Vulcanisation may be assisted by various accelerators, generally complex organic compounds, in addition to activators like zinc oxide; further modification may take place by incorporating colouring matter, softeners, adulterants, and anti-oxidants to improve the resistance to ageing and to retard the formation of a hard and brittle product on exposure to light and air.

The compounding of rubber is the modification of the vulcanisate to the desired extent; suitable ingredients are added as outlined above, and compounded to a homogeneous mass which can be made into a sheet on the calender or treated with a solvent to form a dough for spreading.

It may be remarked that without the process of vulcanisation, the rubber industry would only be of moderate importance.

The rubberised textile materials produced by Macintosh in 1823 by the application of rubber in naphtha were not very successful, as raw rubber possesses little strength. The vulcanisation process of Goodyear was an extremely important development, and after it had been extended to cold vulcanisation by Parkes in 1846, there was a very rapid growth in the proofing industry.

Structure

According to modern theories, rubber is composed of about 2,000 units of isoprene in the molecular aggregate; the formula for isoprene C_5H when given in detail is shown below.

The molecular structure of rubber has not yet been clearly defined, but most of the views expressed come under three categories such as: (*a*) a two-phase system, (*b*) stretched chains, possibly with fringes forming a net, or (*c*) molecular springs. The important observation of Katz (Chem. Zeit., 1925, *49*, 353) with regard to a crystalline form of rubber being produced on stretching is well known.

Mastication is generally supposed to break down the molecular aggregates to a certain extent, thus accounting for the increased solubility and decreased viscosity in solution.

The process of vulcanisation which develops the true elasticity of the rubber and reduces its solubility has been interpreted as forming a number of intermolecular bridges, as previously mentioned.

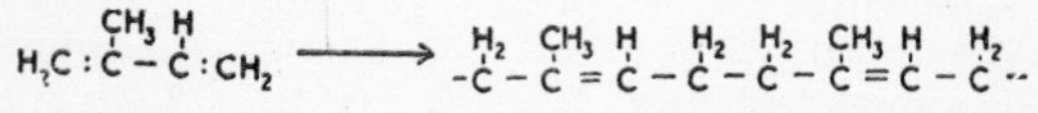

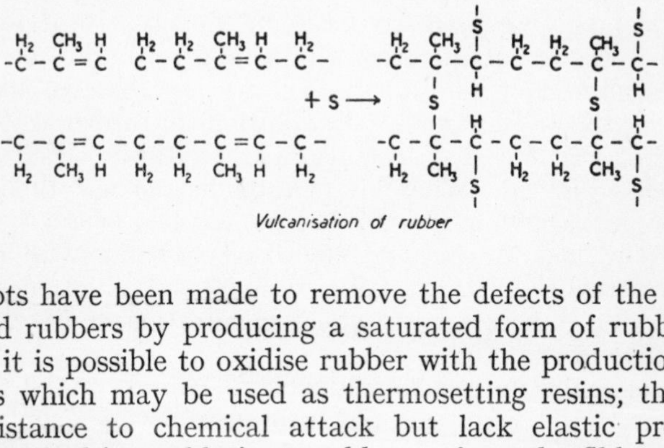

Vulcanisation of rubber

Attempts have been made to remove the defects of the resilient vulcanised rubbers by producing a saturated form of rubber. For example, it is possible to oxidise rubber with the production of the Rubbones which may be used as thermosetting resins; they have great resistance to chemical attack but lack elastic properties. Another method is to chlorinate rubber to form the Chlororubbers; these have no elasticity and are quite brittle. However, they may be plasticised and used for films and adhesives. Another well-known film is Pliofilm which is a rubber hydrochloride, formed by treating rubber with chloro-stannic acid. It is a tough resistant material with thermoplastic properties, but without the resilience of rubber.

Many of these products may be described as cyclorubbers, for the lower degree of unsaturation is due to cyclisation within the molecule. In some of these products, it has been suggested that there is only one double bond for every five isoprene units, as four of them have combined to form a ring structure within the molecular chain.

As many of the best reagents for producing cyclisation are non-metallic halides, it seems that when cold vulcanising of rubber is performed with sulphur chloride, some partial cyclisation occurs.

$$\underset{\text{CH}_3\ \ \text{H}}{\text{H}_2\text{C}-\text{C}=\text{C}-\text{CH}_2} \longrightarrow \ \ \begin{array}{c} -\text{CH}_2\text{-C-CH-CH}_2\text{-CH}_2\text{-C:CH-CH}_2- \\ -\text{CH}_2\text{-C-CH-CH}_2\text{-CH}_2\text{-C:CH-CH}_2- \end{array}$$

Cyclisation

This particular reagent gives elastic and resilient rubber, but others give products which tend to be plastic rather than elastic.

Preparation

The first process in the treatment of the raw material is to masticate it between heavy rollers which exert a disintegrating action as well as a squeezing effect; the material is washed at the same time. The next stage is to break down or plasticise the rubber by hot rollers, and when in the plastic state the "mix" is added to make a dough. The mix contains the vulcanising reagent and such ingredients as may be considered necessary to reduce the cost and alter the properties as previously mentioned. During the working of the rubber there appears to be some depolymerisation, for the mechanical treatment increases the solubility of the material and also gives a product whose solutions are less viscous than similar solutions of the original material. Solutions of rubber are extremely viscous, but the viscosity depends on the nature of the rubber and its previous history. Where it is intended to use the spreading technique for applying the rubber to textiles, then the less the rubber is worked the better, but where bonding with maximum adhesion is required, then a fairly low viscosity is essential, so that some working is necessary to effect penetration of the solution at a later stage in the process.

The usual procedure is to roll the raw rubber into sheets which are then cut into pieces and put into an iron vessel containing the solvent which is generally benzine or naphtha, and fillers, pigments, and vulcanising agents where required. The compounded mixing is agitated by a fork in presence of the solvent until sufficiently swollen when it is transferred to a kneading machine, where it encounters two powerful curved blades which rotate towards one another in a trough and knead the material until it is homogeneous. The product is the dough or rubber solution which is a highly viscous colloidal solution, and like most colloidal solutions the colloid absorbs the solvent.

The amount of benzine or naphtha used may vary within wide limits according to the type of rubber and the nature of the filling.

Treating fabrics

Fabrics to be treated with the rubber solution or dough should be free from starch, size, or filling, in order to obtain the best adhesion of the rubber to the cloth; where it is intended to use the cold method of vulcanising, it is advisable to impregnate the fabric in advance with 5% sodium carbonate solution to protect it from attack during vulcanisation.

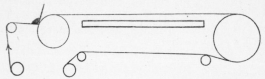

FIG. 155.—Diagram of the spreading of rubber.

In the spreading method, the cloth is passed between a rubber roller and a doctor-knife; the dough is carried forward by the cloth until it meets the doctor-blade, which is fitted with check plates to prevent the rubber overflowing at the ends. The thickness of the applied rubber is controlled by the adjustment of the knife.

The impregnated cloth then passes over a hot plate or steam chest to evaporate the solvent which may be collected and recovered. A number of treatments builds up the necessary coating, but it is usual to reverse the direction of feeding the cloth after each application.

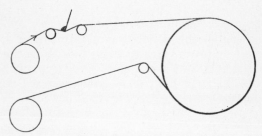

FIG. 156.—Diagram of the spreading of rubber latex.

The calendering method may be used when it is necessary to obtain thicker coatings of rubber in a single application or when the rubber mix is difficult to dissolve, as with waste rubber. In some cases there is no need to prepare a solution or dough, and it may suffice to press a calendered sheet of rubber mix on to the fabric in one operation. A three-bowl calender is usually employed, the top two bowls being heated and the bottom bowl cooled with water; for friction work, the middle roller may be driven at twice the speed of the top bowl. The mixing may be worked on warm mixing rollers of a separate machine until it is sufficiently soft and plastic, when it may be calendered to the necessary thickness. In the meantime the spreading or frictioning calender is adjusted to the approximate thickness of material, and the cloth is passed between the lower and centre bowls, and the rubber between the hot upper and centre bowls, and carried round the centre bowl to be pressed into the cloth between the lower and centre bowls. It is possible to have the cloth under considerable tension during this process. The rubber may not be so firmly fixed as by the spreading process, but it is possible to spread first and calender afterwards.

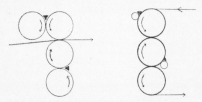

Fig. 157.—Diagram of the application of
rubber by calendering.

The adhesion or tackiness of the rubber surface may be reduced by coating with starch powder or talc and then brushing off any excess before vulcanising. With hot vulcanising it is usual to incorporate sulphur in the mix, and this may be preferable with double textures, i.e. two layers of cloth with the rubber between; cold vulcanising may be effected by sulphur chloride vapour in a special chamber or by a solution in carbon bisulphide.

The use of inflammable solvents is not particularly welcome in the textile industry for obvious reasons, and where the chlorinated hydrocarbon solvents have been tried it appears that their toxic nature presents difficulties on a large commercial scale.

The introduction of rubber latex offers definite advantages for these two standpoints, but it must not be assumed that the arguments are entirely in favour of the aqueous dispersion even from considerations of cost, for it is more expensive to evaporate one pound of water than one pound of benzine. Further, with solvents the rubber is in a molecularly dispersed form, the solvent wets the textile material, and the combination of these two factors gives a better penetration into the fibrous system than may be obtained with latex, where the large size of the molecular aggregates hinders penetration into a material which does not readily wet with water. The viscosity of latex is low, as with all aqueous dispersions compared with colloidal solutions, so that larger amounts may be spread at one operation than with solutions or dough, where even low concentrations possess high viscosities.

Comparing the various methods of applying rubber to textiles, the use of the doctor-knife is preferred for smooth thin coatings and these often form a foundation for later treatments. With roller spreading, the solution tends to penetrate the fabric and the weave is still apparent after the spreading; it is useful on fabrics which do not readily accept the coating. Both the doctor and roller spreading necessitate viscous solutions, and require the evaporation and recovery of solvents. The use of hot calender rolls, however, permits the application of thermoplastic material without solvents in many instances; thicker coatings may also be applied in one operation.

LATEX

The application of rubber latex to textiles was known to the natives of South America before the European countries were aware of the existence of rubber; the proofing of fabrics in a primitive fashion was demonstrated in 1759, when the King of Portugal was presented with a waterproof costume which had been treated by pouring latex on to the cloth which was stretched in the sun so that the latex could dry without causing irregular shrinkage.

The commercial use of rubber latex, however, was not investigated until about 1824, but it was not found possible to obtain the smooth finish on textiles which was obtained by the use of rubber solutions. A more serious difficulty, however, lay in the lack of adhesion between the cloth and the rubber, the applied coating being easily removed. A further difficulty was an adequate supply of stabilised latex.

Within more recent times the advance of science in general, and colloid chemistry in particular, revealed certain fundamental differences between the results of impregnation with rubber solutions and with latex. In the former, impregnated yarns were found to contain the rubber well within the yarn itself and surrounding the component fibres, but in the latter, the rubber latex merely coated the yarn externally and did not reach the inner fibres. It would seem that the serum penetrates between the fibres, but that the particles of rubber are too large to pass through the interfibrillar spaces. These effects have been illustrated with photomicrographs by Dieterich (Ind. Eng. Chem., Anal. Ed., 1930, 2, 102) and Grenquist (Ind. Eng. Chem., 1928, 20, 1073).

The application of latex was found to give very promising results in spite of the poor adhesion; treatment of cord and other fabrics with rubber latex showed a manifold improvement in resistance to flexing compared with similar material impregnated with rubber solutions. Numerous attempts were made to improve the penetration and adhesion by pressure, suction, repeated squeezing, and other methods of impregnation which might be considered helpful, but without great success. The use of wetting agents, however, has been much more promising, particularly as many of them are also stabilisers for the latex. In addition to the wetting agents already common in the textile industry, such as sulphated fatty alcohols, sulphonated oils, and aromatic sulphonates, other substances, such as thiourea, ammonium linoleate, *o*-toluidine, and saponin are also successful in enabling the latex to penetrate the yarn; it is preferable to add the wetting agent to the latex in most cases. Hauser and Hunemorder (Trans. Inst. Rubber Ind., 1932, *8*, 316) have described the effect on the surface tension of the rubber latex of 31 wetting agents in 5% solution calculated on the weight of the rubber.

In some particular cases, such as heavy cotton beltings, the wetting agents are only moderately successful and special methods are required; these include causing the belting to describe a sinuous path during impregnation so that the sharp bending will open the material; alternatively, high fluid pressure of 1,000 to 10,000 lb. may be utilised to force the liquid into the textile material.

It may be added that there is no evidence that rubber can be made to penetrate the cellulose itself; indeed, there is evidence to the contrary by H. P. and W. H. Stevens (Rubber Latex, London, 1936, p. 68). It would seem that the molecular aggregates of rubber are too large to pass into the pore spaces of cellulose.

An interesting development has been recorded by Bongrand in B.P. 405,311, where attention is drawn to the alkalinity of common rubber latex, about pH 10 to 11·5, as compared with the slight acidity of cellulose. It is suggested that when the acid fibres are brought into contact with the alkaline latex, a partial coagulation takes place at the point of contact with the formation of an almost invisible film which is sufficient to prevent further penetration. The pH may be adjusted by treatment of the textile material or of the latex; in the latter case, it is possible to add acidic substances in presence of a peptising agent to avoid coagulation—naphthenic acid combines both functions. Suitable peptising agents are the trade products Hygrolite, Nekal, or Saprotin, with whose assistance it is possible to bring the latex to pH 5. Alternatively, it is possible to use a latex which is naturally acidic, such as Funtumia elastica; if necessary, it may be made alkaline, in its turn, by the addition of casein. When Hevea latex is made acidic as above, it becomes more viscous, but fluidifies in contact with the alkaline fibrous mass and therefore penetrates more readily. A simple method is to boil the raw cotton for about 3 hours with 2 to 5% sodium carbonate solution, and rinse to obtain the required alkalinity and then treat with an alkaline latex.

The use of slightly alkaline fibres is not new, for Dunlop (B.P. 324,664) wetted gloves with ammonia before treatment with latex to assist penetration, and Pirelli (B.P. 347,691) has employed slightly alkaline water as a pre-treatment to avoid premature coagulation when latex is brought into contact with dry yarn or fabric. The particular method of Bongrand, however, is utilised in conjunction with other methods devised by Bongrand and Lejeune, as outlined in B.P. 338,381 and 344,414. As previously mentioned, it is possible to coat yarns with latex fairly easily, but the latex does not penetrate between the fibres in the yarn as the interspaces are so small; the serum will penetrate, however, and tends to leave the rubber particles as a cream on the surface. These difficulties have been largely overcome by treating the fibres before they are twisted into yarn. Spools of roving are placed on a spindle on a disc which revolves in a vertical plane so that any latex which would tend to drain away is absorbed again during the rotation which is prolonged in an atmosphere of ammonia to preserve the liquid state. If necessary, the impregnation may take place under pressure or *in vacuo*. After thorough impregnation the material is set aside until the rubber gelatinises on the fibres; in this state it is possible to unwind the spools as the rubber is not fully coagulated, and pass the thread through a coagulating bath to complete the operation. Each coated fibre becomes attached to another and imparts high tensile strength and resistance to abrasion. The dried thread readily absorbs more latex and may be given a second impregnation, and it is easy to produce yarns of 50% rubber and 50% cotton where both ingredients are evenly distributed throughout the mass; these form the well-known Filastic threads which may be twisted, braided, or woven to form a foundation which may be treated with masticated rubber and vulcanised to give proofed fabrics which are superior to those prepared by spreading or other methods. Filastic fabrics, when spread, have been utilised for belting and have also found an outlet, when incorporated with fillers, in the manufacture of soles for footwear.

According to Flint (loc. cit.) textile applications afford the biggest outlet in the world for rubber latex; in addition to the combining of fabrics for various purposes, latex may be spread on cloth for the manufacture of gasproof and waterproof materials for balloons and collapsible boats, and for backing rugs and carpets. An additional outlet lies in its use with semi-manufactured goods, such as the rubberised fabrics for transmission belts and conveyor bands, hose-pipes, and boots, as well as the production of cord fabrics for the tyre industry. Beltings and cords which are intended to receive very hard use are generally given a preliminary impregnation of the fibres, as previously described, before receiving the spreading or calendering treatment.

With the spreading process for rubber latex, the viscous solution of rubber is replaced by a compounded concentrated latex containing the particular additions according to the purpose of the process. The equipment is very similar to that employed for spreading rubber solutions on cloth, but the adjustment of the doctor-blade is different on account of the tendency of latex to "strike" through the cloth on the first run. In the initial stages of spreading, the doctor-blade

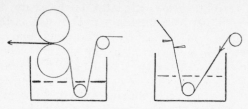

FIG. 158.—Impregnation with rubber latex.

is set to form an acute angle with the cloth, which has passed under it, and a "sharp" blade is used (i.e. a blade bevelled at an acute angle). This procedure permits of thin coatings which seal the cloth, after which the blade may be changed for the type with a rounded blunt end set perpendicular to the cloth—an arrangement which permits thicker coatings. The standard arrangement is to pass the cloth over a roller, on top of which it meets the doctor-blade; the rubber is held against the doctor by the movement of the cloth, which is pressed against the blade by the roller. With the more fluid mixes produced by latex, such as those which may be poured, two rollers are employed and the doctor blade set between them

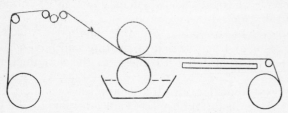

FIG. 159.—Coating with rubber latex.

and pressing on the cloth to form a trough of cloth which holds the latex; side-pieces on the doctor prevent lateral flow. The fabric is thus held against the blade by its own tension, and the absence of a support below the blade obviates the tendency to "strike" through the cloth. (See Fig. 156.)

The treated cloth in either case passes over the steam chest or drying drum, but the speed of drying with latex is less than with solvents and the output is only one-third.

The usual methods of coating textiles may also be employed, such as applying the latex to the cloth from a roller which runs in the latex dispersion and which is given an even coating by a doctor-knife and applies this coating to the cloth; alternatively, the fabric may pass over the top of the roller which picks up the latex and applies it to the cloth, the tension given to which affects the thickness of the deposit.

It is generally preferable to use concentrated latices in order to avoid the evaporation of a large excess of water. The compounded latex also contains fillers and colouring matter where required in addition to the vulcanising ingredients and anti-oxidants.

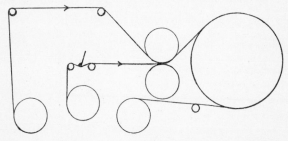

FIG. 160.—Diagram of the combining or doubling of fabrics.

A typical mixture for waterproofing cloth, according to German practice, is 130 parts of Revertex, 50 parts of chalk, 5 parts of zinc oxide, 2 parts of sulphur, 0·2 parts of an accelerator, 5 parts of 10% casein solution, and 10 parts of water. A number of recipes have also been given by Flint (loc. cit., p. 474).

After the cloth has been spread it may be "combined" with another cloth, which may or may not also be spread; it is also possible to arrange for two rubberised fabrics to be prepared on different machines, dried and bonded with a calender. Doubled waterproof fabrics have numerous advantages in that the appearance is improved, the handle is more attractive, and there is less trouble with the condensation of moisture from the body. With light doubling, it is possible to go a stage further in obviating condensation by printing or stencilling the latex, and so producing a more porous structure. The bonding of fabrics affords an important outlet for latex, particularly in the manufacture of shoe-cloths.

With light doubling, it is generally sufficient to spread one fabric only, and then bring the untreated cloth into contact with the freshly spread surface, pass the double material through rollers, and dry; vulcanisation may be brought about in a warm room where the fabric is hung on rollers in festoons. For heavier doubling, a coating of the required thickness is first built up on one or both cloths which are combined immediately after the final application of latex. Very strong bonding can only be effected where uncoagulated latex is allowed to join with unvulcanised latex; but with clothing material it is often adequate to join two dried, but unvulcanised, surfaces by passing through rollers and then curing.

Impregnation, as distinct from spreading, is utilised for the preparation of cord fabrics for tyres, and for the treatment of fabrics for beltings; the concentrated latex mixture may be forced into the textile material by calendering, but better results are obtained by impregnating, drying, and then effecting the true rubberising. Impregnation may be done by passing the material through a trough, and between two rollers or two doctor-blades to remove any

FIG. 161.—Use of mangle bowls to form
their own trough.

excess of the latex; the impregnated material is then dried. A typical mixture, according to Flint (loc. cit.), is composed of 166 parts by weight of 60% ammonia-preserved latex, 1 part of sulphur, 1·5 parts of zinc oxide, 1 part of sodium diethyldithiocarbamate, and 1 part of sodium cetyl sulphate. In this case, the impregnated material should be dried at 100°C. for 20 to 30 minutes. For the rubberising of cord fabrics, the impregnated cord threads are laid side by side to form a "fabric" which is passed through a three- or four-bowl calender to give a friction coating to both sides of the material; true textile fabrics may be similarly treated.

In some cases, the impregnated cloth may be spread with a number of coatings, and then folded to give the required thickness of material before vulcanising under a hot press. A typical spreading composition, according to Flint, is 166 parts by weight of 60% ammonia-preserved latex, 50 parts of China clay, 2 parts of zinc oxide, 2·5 parts of sulphur, 0·75 part of butyraldehyde-aniline, 1 part of sodium cetyl sulphate, and 1 part of anti-oxidant; the vulcanising conditions require 1 hour at 120°C.

Latex has also been applied to cloth by spraying under pressure in a manner similar to that used with the spray-gun; a series of jets covers the cloth with a traverse motion to give an even coating, but the spray must not be directed vertically on to the cloth.

An interesting application of latex to textile materials may be seen in the production of artificial leather. The thicker material is made by combining two pieces of cloth with sufficient latex to give the necessary thickness and flexibility, and then spreading one surface with a pigmented cellulose nitrate dope, followed by embossing. Rexine and Pegamoid are well-known products. Thinner "leathers" may be produced by impregnating a raised cotton fabric with a dilute latex mixture and then spreading both surfaces with a latex mixture; a single coating simulates the undressed side of the leather and a number of coatings the smooth, dressed side.

A further development in the use of latex is to treat the backs of carpets and rugs to anchor the pile; this has recently been extended to the treatments of very loose backings, and even to fabrics where the backing is entirely composed of latex to secure the pleated layer of fibres which is later cut or sheared to form the pile. Fabrics of this type show complete freedom from fraying and may be cut to any desired shape.

It has also been suggested to add rubber latex to the viscose spinning solution (B.P. 328,627) and to make use of the sulphur in the viscose for vulcanising the rubber. The yarn is stated to be stronger, more elastic and less lustrous, but has not yet reached commercial importance.

On the other hand, rubber threads have been produced by the extrusion of latex to give a round thread as distinct from the older square-section rubber thread which was cut from sheets of thin rubber. B.P. 205,532 and U.S.P. 1,570,895 refer to the coagulation of the extruded latex by dilute acid solutions, and a commercial process has been developed by Dunlop (B.P. 303,544 and 311,844) in which low-viscosity latex is coagulated in a dehydrating and setting bath composed of ammonium acetate and sodium chloride. Numerous other specifications have been described in the Reports of the Progress of Applied Chemistry from 1934 onwards. Flint (Chemistry and Technology of Rubber Latex, Chapman and Hall, London, 1938, p. 510) has given a good review of such processes; the patent situation is very complicated. Lactron thread is well known, and when covered with a very fine yarn of wool, cotton, or silk, is marketed as Lastex yarn (see Textile World, 1933, *83*, 50), which has found numerous applications in the manufacture of bathing costumes, corsets, surgical stockings, belts, garters, and many other articles.

The use of latex for finishing textiles may be devoted to either coatings or fillings; the first patent (B.P. 217,973) of the latter type merely claims the addition of latex to the usual fillers.

The "batting" of fibres into a sheet affords an outlet for latex in 1 to 5% concentration where cotton is required as the basis.

29

One of the disadvantages of the latex treatment of textiles compared with solvent spreadings is the unpleasant handle of the goods, which suffer from a surface drag or tackiness which is absent from the older proofings. After the application of the solvent dough, it is customary to brush fine starch powder into the surface of the material and then remove any excess; with cold curing methods the surface of the proofing is swollen by the solvent, so that the starch becomes embedded to give a soft feel which is in great demand in spite of the poor ageing qualities of cold-cured rubber. In any case, the application of the solvent dough itself gives a smoother surface. It has been suggested to add starch to the latex dispersion (B.P. 397,270), thickened with ammonia soaps and the flocculent precipitates produced by treating latex with sodium silicate and aluminium sulphate. The surface finish may also be improved by incorporating a dispersed wax in the coating for the final layer, as suggested by Stevens and Stevens (Trans. Inst. Rubber Ind., 1935, *11*, 67); the incorporation of phthalic anhydride resins has also been protected (B.P. 356,738 and 358,095). Chemical modification of the surface layer may also be brought about by treatment with 1% bromine in carbon tetrachloride, but excessive treatment produces a very brittle surface; sulphuric acid has also been used.

Unfortunately, even the feel and handle of the best rubberised textile material is not acceptable when dress goods are considered; the textile technologist still complains of "tackiness," but not in the sense of the rubber technologist, for it is the normal handle of rubber which is unpleasant. This fact has prevented the use of rubber in finishing dress goods generally, and limited its application to proofing, bonding, and other special effects.

Where latex is used for the impregnation of textile materials it is not always necessary to vulcanise; the film of rubber from latex is different from that deposited from a dough or solution in which the rubber has previously been masticated and therefore degraded. The film from latex is harder and more resistant to heat and light; in addition, the serum constituents contain anti-oxidants and preservatives. Curing is generally advisable, but it is also possible to make use of vulcanised latex (B.P. 193,451 and 208,235), such as Vultex and Revultex. The general appearance of the latex is not altered by vulcanisation of the individual particles of rubber; after the removal of moisture, the cohesion and agglomeration of the particles produce a film of vulcanised rubber.

It has been suggested to use rubber latex as a means of imparting fastness to washing to many of the ordinary finishing agents applied to textiles; for example, starch, gums, and China clay (B.P. 217,973), but without commercial success, probably on account of the unwelcome feel of the treated material, and the tendency to collect dust and dirt. Processes of this type have been examined by H. P. and W. H. Stevens (Trans. Inst. Rubber Ind., 1935, *11*, 67). Padding cotton fabrics with latex containing 40% rubber gave a full handle to the goods, but after more than one passage the effect of the rubber was obvious and objectionable as an ordinary finish for wearing apparel. It was found that part of the "tacky" feel was due to absorption of the serum constituents by the cellulose and could be removed by prolonged soaking in warm water; alternatively, vulcanisation, followed by soaping, was also efficacious. Latex does not produce a wash-fast finish when used in conjunction with starch, but is more successful in conjunction with China clay.

The wartime shortage of natural rubber led to a search for substitutes as distinct from synthetic rubbers, and the field of application to textiles was no exception. For "non-rubber" proofing, both linseed oil and gelled rape-seed oil have been applied. Considerable work was also done utilising cellulose nitrate plasticised with castor oil. The U.S.A. was better situated with regard to synthetic products, some of which were suitable for application by the calender; the co-polymer of vinyl chloride and vinyl acetate (see page 365) was used to a great extent. The polyvinylformals, particularly the acetal and butyral, were employed by the spreading technique for the production of double textures.

Wool

The treatment of wool with latex has been examined by Blow (J.S.D.C., 1939, 55, 337). Wool carries a negative charge in alkaline solutions and the latex is also negatively charged, so that there is no affinity or attraction between them, and deposition of rubber from the latex does not occur. Reversal of charge, however, may be brought about by the use of cationic soaps which are strongly adsorbed by textiles and give a positive charge to the surface. In these circumstances, definite deposition of rubber may be effected by a two-bath process, outlined in B.P. 483,496; the goods are first treated with a cationic soap such as cetyl pyridinium bromide, and then with latex from which the rubber is deposited with exhaustion of the latex bath. Alternatively, as in B.P. 497,793, the latex may be treated with the cationic soap so that the particles carry a positive charge in alkaline solution; here again exhaustion of the latex occurs when applied to textiles, in a manner somewhat analogous to a dyeing process.

TREATMENT OF WOOL

Treatment	Untreated wool	Pre-treated wool
5% latex, squeezed and dried	3 to 4%	12%
5% latex, washed and dried	0·25%	10%

Vulcanised latex may also be applied in a similar manner. Chlorinated wool possesses a higher affinity for rubber, as shown by an example where pre-treated wool and pre-treated chlorinated wool were immersed in 5% rubber latex for 30 minutes, washed, hydroextracted, and dried; unchlorinated wool absorbed 6% of rubber and 11·5% was absorbed by the chlorinated wool.

With the above process the rubber is present as a partial or discontinuous coating, and not as a continuous film on the yarn. The tensile strength and resistance to abrasion of the material is greatly improved by the Blow process, and, in addition, there is a great reduction in the tendency to "rub-up" of garments made from these treated wools, presumably on account of the better cohesion of the hairs.

Minor uses

There is another and older method of depositing rubber from latex. Owing to the electro-negative charge of the rubber particles, they may be caused to migrate by placing them in an electric field. Articles may be "rubber-plated" by making them the anode of an electric cell, when, on passing the current, the rubber particles move towards the anode where they are deposited (B.P. 245, 177, 246,532, and 257,885). This "anode-deposition" process, described by Klein, may be applied to vulcanised or unvulcanised rubber, and, like the Blow process, is peculiar to latex and has no application to rubber doughs or naphtha solutions.

The elastic nature of rubber has naturally brought it into consideration for improving the resistance to creasing of cotton, linen, and rayon, but the results are generally so disappointing that they have not been worthy of extensive patent protection or commercial exploitation. Watkins (B.P. 431,330) describes a process in which the cloth is padded with latex under such conditions as to leave 5 to 10% of rubber in the fabric, which is dried and then boiled for about 3 hours in a bath containing 24 parts of dispersed sulphur, 2 parts of zinc oxide, and 2 parts of an accelerator for every 100 parts of rubber in the material. When the bath is exhausted, the goods are rinsed, dried, and heated for 15 to 45 minutes at 115°C. In a process of Gibbons (U.S.P. 1,980,676), the cloth is impregnated in a bath of casein, trisodium phosphate, and latex compounded with sulphur, zinc oxide, and an accelerator. During the drying and curing, the fabric is jigged or otherwise flexed, to prevent adhesion of the yarns at their points of intersection; treatment with sodium oleate solution completes the process.

Rubber latex has been utilised with urea-formaldehyde resins in the well-known crease-resisting process, according to B.P. 486,926 of Battye, Tankard, and Wood of the Tootal Broadhurst Lee Co., which makes use of ammonium salts to prevent coagulation of the latex in the solution of the urea-formaldehyde condensate, which is later resinified by the acid liberated from the ammonium salts on drying and heating; the process is applicable to synthetic latices and rubber-like dispersions. A two-stage process of Botson, Perlmuteer, and Raepset (B.P. 490,135) describes treatment with rubber latex, followed by urea-formaldehyde condensates which are later resinified.

British Celanese, in B.P. 346,511, has used latex to bind dispersed pigments to the fibres of cellulose acetate fabrics, and so reduce their lustre; an added advantage of the treatment is the reduced tendency to run or ladder or slip. Teague and Brewster (B.P. 403,121 and 403,394) also claim reduced tendency to ladder and improved wear when stockings are treated with dilute latex containing relatively large amounts of casein.

Waterproof rayons are very attractive, but the adhesion of the rubber is apt to be poor on account of the smooth nature of rayon fibres; a preliminary coating with casein, ammonia, and latex is stated to overcome this difficulty (B.P. 433,777).

It is important to ensure a freedom from copper in all goods and machinery which come into contact with rubber latex.

SYNTHETIC RUBBERS

The so-called synthetic rubbers have recently come into some prominence; a good account of these substances has been given by Barron (Modern Synthetic Rubbers, Chapman and Hall, London, 1942).

In general these compounds are derived from ethylene or acetylene, or from a narrow "cut" of crude petroleum. Most of these new substances for replacing rubber may be divided into five main classes:

(a) Neoprene, which is a polymer of chloroprene.
(b) Thiokol, from aliphatic dihalides and sodium polysulphides.
(c) Bunas, which are polymers of butadiene, or co-polymers with styrene, acrylonitrile, etc.
(d) Koroseal, which is plasticised vinyl chloride.
(e) Vistanex, which is polyisobutylene.

One of the first commercial synthetic rubbers was Neoprene, which was developed by Du Pont in 1931; it is a polymer of chloroprene, which is 2 : chloro-1 : 3-butadiene, and Carothers, of nylon fame, played a large part in its synthesis from acetylene.

Monomers of the Divinyl Series

$$CH_2{:}CH{.}CH{:}CH_2$$

Butadiene

$$CH_2{:}\underset{\underset{CH_3}{|}}{C}{.}CH{:}CH_2$$

Isoprene

$$CH_2{:}\underset{\underset{CH_3}{|}}{C}{.}\underset{\underset{CH_3}{|}}{C}{:}CH_2$$

Dimethylbutadiene

$$CH_2{:}\underset{\underset{Cl}{|}}{C}{.}CH{:}CH_2$$

Chloroprene

Neoprene resists heat much better than natural rubber, and also possesses a greater resistance to oils and solvents. It can be processed on standard rubber machinery and also mixed with many of the compounding substances for rubber mixes; a metallic oxide, such as zinc oxide, is essential for vulcanisation.

$$CH_2{:}\underset{\underset{Cl}{|}}{C}{.}CH{:}CH_2 \longrightarrow -CH_2{.}\underset{\underset{Cl}{|}}{C}{:}CH{.}CH_2\left[CH_2{.}\underset{\underset{Cl}{|}}{C}{:}CH{.}CH_2\right]_n CH_2{.}\underset{\underset{Cl}{|}}{C}{:}CH \sim$$

Chloroprene   *Neoprene*

Neoprene cannot be made into a dough with solvent naphtha, and aromatic solvents are essential for this purpose. When Neoprene is polymerised in emulsion form, a Neoprene latex is obtained, which can be used in much the same way as rubber latex. The electrical properties of Neoprene are inferior to those of rubber.

The Thiokols are mainly of German origin, but on account of their characteristic and unpleasant odour, they have practically no textile applications. They are not particularly thermoplastic. Thiokol *A* is made from ethylene dichloride and sodium polysulphide, Thiokol *B* from dichloroethyl ether and sodium polysulphide, and Thiokol *F* from dichloroethyl formal.

$$Cl\,C_2H_4\,Cl + Na\,S_n\,Na \longrightarrow C_2H_4\,S_n\,C_2H_4\,S_n\,C_2H_4\,S_n \cdots \quad \text{Thiokol } A$$

Ethylene   *Sodium*   *Polyethylenesulphide*
dichloride   *polysulphide*

The Bunas originate from butadiene, on which most work seems to have been concentrated; rubbers have been made both in Germany and in the U.S.S.R. The leading German types are Perbunan, Perbunan-Extra, and Buna-S; the two best-known Russian types are S.K.A. and S.K.B. The American varieties are Perbunan, Buna-S Hycar, and Chemigum. These substances are more difficult to process than rubber itself, but with the exception of Buna-S, they may be handled on standard rubber plant. The addition of sulphur and accelerators converts them from the plastic state to the elastic condition similar to that of vulcanised rubber.

$$CH_2:CH.CH:CH_2 \rightarrow -CH_2CH:CHCH_2CH_2\ CH\cdot CH\ CH_2CH_2CH:CHCH_2-$$

Butadiene   *Buna*

Butadiene is obtained from petroleum.

Buna-S is a co-polymer of butadiene with 25% of styrene, and is claimed to be far superior to rubber in heat resistance and abrasion resistance; Perbunan is a co-polymer of butadiene and 25% acrylic nitrile. These substances may be made in the form of latices by emulsion-polymerisation, and vulcanised with sulphur. They have been used successfully for sheeting and dipped goods, such as gloves. Perbunan-Extra contains a larger proportion of acrylic nitrile and offers still greater resistance to oils and solvents; it is more readily thermoplastic, however.

Hycar is also based on butadiene and acrylic nitrile, and Chemigum is supposed to contain butadiene as the main constituent, together with polymers other than styrene and acrylic nitrile.

Koroseal, as previously mentioned, is plasticised vinyl chloride, derived from acetylene; the polymer may be produced in emulsion form. According to the degree of polymerisation, the product may vary from a rubbery plastic to a hard resin (see page 365).

Vistanex represents the class of polyisobutylenes derived from the by-products of the processing of petroleum; the low members of the series are viscous fluids, and the highest are more rubbery than rubber itself, although there is no chemical relationship. Their resistance to water is very great, and their reaction to solvents is similar to that of rubber (see page 438).

As the polyisobutylenes are completely saturated hydrocarbons, they are more inert to chemical reagents than rubber; they cannot be vulcanised, and are subject to cold flow or permanent deformation. No emulsion polymers of isobutylene appear to have been formed as yet, and this limits their application to textiles; perhaps this is due to the method of polymerisation, below $-50°C$. It may be remarked that the polyisobutylenes are less thermoplastic than rubber, but the temperature range of the elastic properties is wide. Other polyisobutylenes are the Oppanols of Germany and the Isolenes, and all of them appear to be depolymerised to some extent on prolonged exposure to sunlight.

The modern butyl rubbers are co-polymers of butadiene and

isobutylene, the controlled amount of the former being sufficient to impart the property of vulcanisation and suppress cold flow.

$$-CH_2.CH:CH.CH_2.\overset{\overset{\textstyle CH_3}{|}}{\underset{\underset{\textstyle CH_3}{|}}{C}}-CH_2-\overset{\overset{\textstyle CH_3}{|}}{\underset{\underset{\textstyle CH_3}{|}}{C}}-CH_2-\overset{\overset{\textstyle CH_3}{|}}{\underset{\underset{\textstyle CH_3}{|}}{C}}-CH_2-\qquad \text{Butyl rubber}$$

Copolymer of butadiene & isobutylene

Before leaving this subject, attention may be drawn to the absence of any sharp line of division between the so-called synthetic rubbers and some of the so-called synthetic resins obtained by true polymerisation as distinct from super-condensation (see page 360).

CHAPTER XVIII
WATERPROOFING

THE earliest known methods of rendering textile fabrics impervious to water seem to have originated in primitive treatments with vegetable exudations, of which rubber latex is perhaps the most famous; this aspect of rubberproofing is discussed on page 443.

The oldest methods of European origin were based on linseed oil and date from the fourteenth century, but by the beginning of the nineteenth century treatments with aluminium soaps had been discovered in England. The original two-bath method is still employed, but it was modified by Schmieder in 1825, utilising a single bath containing alum, soap, and gelatin or isinglass, which acted as a protective colloid; this treatment was later combined with the use of fats and waxes.

The waterproofing of fabrics may be divided into two large classes:

(a) Processes in which the interstices of the fabric, as well as the surface of the material, are covered with a film or skin in such a manner that the treated material is not only water-repellent, but impermeable to air and moisture.

(b) Processes whereby the fibres of the material are made water-repellent through coating with a hydrophobic substance or by a chemical reaction, but the fabric remains porous to air.

In general, the impermeable finishes are not very attractive for clothing as the treated material is heavy and stiff; the draping qualities are almost entirely destroyed. A further disadvantage of using impermeable material for clothing is associated with its "airproof" character, which prevents moisture escaping through the clothing from the body and is therefore unhygienic. This fact is recognised in many rubber-proofed garments by the provision of ventilation holes.

The impermeable finishes may be produced by almost any substance which will form a water-resistant film and close the interstices of the cloth and the interspaces of the yarn as well as coating the fibres; such films must be flexible, however. The chief substances which have been utilised for this purpose are rubber, drying oils, various tars and pitches, cellulose derivatives, and the more flexible synthetic resins; for economic reasons, the two last-mentioned are not often used for ordinary waterproofing, but may be employed for special purposes such as glazed chintz for bathrooms and kitchens, as well as for the so-called "American cloth." More recently, American Army raincoats have been treated with Vinylite (see page 365). As previously stated, it is very uncomfortable to have to work in these impermeable garments under moist or wet conditions, and the importance of a water-repellent fabric, as opposed to coated or waterproof cloth, does not seem to have been fully appreciated in the U.S.A.

An interesting modern development in the finishing of fabrics which will not allow water to pass, makes use of the principle that when water is transmitted through a hose there is a leakage at first, but the wet fibres swell, fill the interstices and make the fabric water-tight. Ventile fabrics of the Shirley Institute make use of mercerised cotton, low twist yarns and special weaves, but the Southern Regional Research Laboratory of the U.S.A. used a supplementary swelling material, such as 6 to 7% of cellulose-hydroxy-ethyl-ether, which dissolves in alkali but not in water.

WATERPROOF FINISHES

The rubberising of cloth has been discussed in some detail on page 441, both in respect of rubber solutions and rubber latex. The latter does not give a very satisfactory water-repellency, but improved effects may be obtained by incorporating wax, fatty acids, or soap with the latex emulsion. B.P. 445,631 of International Latex Processes describes a treatment with rubber latex containing about 25% of water-repelling substances, such as waxes, higher fatty acids, higher alcohols, or zinc or magnesium stearate. Latex and Carnauba wax are mentioned in B.P. 448,711; the treatment is followed by aluminium chloride, which coagulates the dispersion of 10% of equal parts of the latex and wax. Chlorinated rubber latex may be employed according to the methods of B.P. 442,277.

Chloroprene (Du Pont) may be applied to textiles in much the same way as rubber itself, either to close the interstices of the material and make it impermeable, or, as described above, to preserve the porous nature of the material but render it water-repellent.

Apart from the above special uses of rubber, rubberproofing is utilised generally to close the interstices of the cloth and the interspaces of the yarn.

The term "waterproof" is not strictly limited to impermeability, but there is a growing tendency to differentiate between waterproof and water-repellent.

In the U.S.A. it appears customary to grade the treatments in the following order: waterproof, rainproof, showerproof.

Heavy cotton goods are frequently required for tarpaulins, canvas roofings, wagon covers, and similar purposes. These may be impregnated with hot mixtures of solutions of pitches and waxes in petroleum naphtha coloured with various pigments and mixed substances, such as lithopone. Most of these cloths gain at least 30% in weight as a result of these processes.

A typical formula is 50 lb. of Trinidad asphalt, 200 lb. of wood tar, 100 lb. of paraffin wax, and 500 lb. of solvent naphtha. Another recipe, and for a softer finish, is 200 lb. of asphalt, 90 lb. of spindle oil, 90 lb. of paraffin wax, and 400 lb. of solvent naphtha. These solutions may be applied by impregnation from a mangle and trough, after which the goods are dried in circumstances which permit recovery of the solvent.

An economical method of heavy impregnation with this type of mixture is to omit the solvent and melt the ingredients together; the molten mass may be applied to the cloth by a spreading machine.

Oil coatings have also been applied to these heavy- and medium-weight fabrics, and usually many coatings are given with an interval for drying between each coat. For black oiled materials it is usual to mix vegetable black with the boiled linseed oil to the extent of 20 to 25%. The grey cloth is impregnated with this mixture by a mangle and then dried at room temperature for 1 to 4 days (drying may be hastened by cobalt linoleate in the mixture). The material is then re-treated either by impregnation, as before, or by brushing, and again allowed to dry; four coatings and dryings comprise a typical treatment. More recently, mixtures of boiled linseed oil with synthetic resins have been utilised.

Some interesting details of the preparation of tarpaulins from cotton canvas and duck have been given by McClain (Am. Dyes. Rep., 1938, 27, 507); the waterproofing materials are applied by various methods, such as padding, doctors, or brushes and doctor. A special font system may also be used with a sponge under the fabric beneath the slot; the sponge provides resilient pressure which prevents bleeding and absorbs any excess of the preparation. Some typical recipes are as follows: 25 lb. of neutral petroleum asphalt, 20 lb. of paraffin wax (m.p. 51°C.), 25 lb. of petroleum jelly (m.p. 57°C.), and 35 lb. of Venetian red, diluted with 50 to 100 parts of solvent naphtha; another preparation includes 15 lb. of fused lead oleate, 30 lb. of petroleum jelly (m.p. 43°C.), 50 lb. of asphalt (m.p. 88°C.), and 5 lb. of paraffin wax (m.p. 56°C.). Coating compositions for application with a doctor or spreader do not need naphtha or other volatile solvent; an example is 45 lb. of paraffin wax, 45 lb. of asphalt, 30 lb. of yellow ochre, 18 lb. of petroleum jelly, and 30 lb. of an extender such as China clay.

OILED FABRICS

OILPROOFING has been known for many years, but within recent times the heavy black or yellow material has largely been replaced by translucent lightweight cloths of a very attractive character; oiled silk in particular represents an outstanding development.

The transparent nature of many oiled textile fabrics is due to the coincidence of the refractive indices of the applied coating and the textile base.

Canvas or cotton duck formed the basis of the first "oilskins"; several coatings of linseed oil were given, each coating being allowed to dry before application of the next. Naturally this was a lengthy process and occupied at least a year. The "tacky" nature of the final coating, even when dry, was obviated by home-made recipes such as white of egg, but for the past fifty years most of the thinner oiled silks and cottons have been given a final coating with a varnish which leaves a smooth surface.

Linseed oil is still the chief finishing material for oiled silks in spite of the large number of synthetic products available; the oil is yellow and has a characteristic odour. If the raw linseed oil is heated to about 250°C. it becomes cloudy, the solid matter settles to the bottom of the vessel, and the refined oil may be drawn off or decanted, and heated further without difficulty.

Linseed oil contains the glycerides of unsaturated fatty acids with 18 carbon atoms in the chain: genuine linseed oil contains about 9·5% of oleic acid, 42·5% of linoleic acid, and 38% of linolenic acid, together with small amounts of palmitic and stearic acids; the component glycerides have not been precisely outlined. Oleic acid is $CH_3.(CH_2)_7CH : CH.(CH_2)_7.COOH$, linoleic acid is $CH_3.(CH_2)_4.-CH : CH.CH_2.CH : CH.(CH_2)_7.COOH$, and linolenic acid is $CH_3.CH_2.CH : CH.CH_2.CH : CH.CH_2.CH : CH.(CH_2)_7.COOH$.

There are two important changes which linseed oil undergoes on exposure to heat and to atmospheric oxygen; first, there is a thickening which is probably due to some sort of polymerisation of the fatty molecules, taking place on heating to 260°C. by the old fire-heating process for making boiled oil; and, secondly, there is the conversion of the oil into a solid rubbery mass or, with thin layers, into a clear, hard film, by an oxidation process without molecular disruption.

This change on oxidation accounts for the term "drying oil," but it should be realised that the rate of oxidation depends on the temperature, the atmospheric conditions, and the presence or absence of certain metallic salts called "driers." As the absorption of oxygen is accompanied by the evolution of heat, care must be taken to avoid spontaneous combustion of the impregnated fabrics.

The preliminary refining of the crude oil is generally followed by further processes which may either thicken the oil, or partially oxidise it, or incorporate metallic driers which will cause the films to oxidise and harden rapidly; these processes have been described in some detail by Hilditch (Industrial Fats and Waxes, Baillière, Tindall and Cox, London, 1941).

There are three methods of preparing the thickened, polymerised, or "stand" oils. The old process was to heat the oil in an enamelled iron pan at 260° to 280°C. until the desired consistency was reached, and this often took from 1 to 3 days. A more modern method is by the circulation of hot oil by a series of coils immersed in the linseed oil. A variation of the first method is to heat the oil in an open pan until the vapours catch fire, when the oil thickens more rapidly; this process demands considerable skill.

Boiled oil is made by heating the linseed oil with little polymerisation or marked oxidation and at the same time effecting the solution of very small amounts of metallic salts, such as the resinate or linoleate of cobalt, lead, or manganese; the modern process operates at 130° to 150°C. According to the time of heating, the oil may be pale or dark-coloured; the latter is known as double-boiled oil, and is also more viscous. It is used for the impregnation of heavy oilskins and some tarpaulins. Thorough drying after impregnation is essential as the oxidation of the oil continues and may develop sufficient heat to cause fires in storage. Goods for export must have been stoved at 60°C. for 8 hours and dried for a month before packing.

It may be remarked that the boiling process imparts body to the oil and gives a gloss to the final film; the action of the metallic driers is such that the drying time of films is reduced to 7 or 8 hours instead of 3 days.

Blown oils differ from the boiled oils in that they are oxidised by the passage of an air current at about 120°C., after the driers have been brought into solution; blown oils are used in paints or varnishes. Prolonged blowing gives a plastic mass which is utilised as a constituent of linoleum. It may be remarked that the final oxidised product of linseed oil is termed linoxyn.

The boiled oils give a hard lustrous surface on drying, but as this surface is liable to crack, the boiled oil is generally mixed with raw oil to give a more elastic product.

Varnishes are generally mixtures of boiled oils, gum resins, and turpentine; the art of preparation consists mainly in a suitable choice of the constituents. One of the commonest gum resins is colophony, or rosin; its chief constituent is abietic acid $C_{19}H_{39}COOH$, which is unsaturated and dries to give a durable glossy coating. It may also be used to form ester gums with glycerol. Most gum resins need heating to about 300°C. before they will remain dissolved in the oil.

For application to cloth, the mixture of raw oil, boiled oil, and driers is warmed to 25° to 30°C. and kept in a tank through which the cloth is drawn; the coating of oil is regulated by scrapers, spreaders, or doctors. The coated material is then drawn upwards through a "tower" or vertical trunking, usually 40 to 50 feet in height, and passes over a roller before descending to another roller, upon which it is wound. The temperature of the air in the tower is usually 70° to 95°C. and the cloth is moved through it at the rate of 6 to 10 yards per hour, depending on the textile material and the amount of oil it has acquired.

It is important that the material should be thoroughly dry after passing through the heating towers.

If a dull finish is required, then one application of the oil is usually sufficient, but for a glossy effect a second coating is usually necessary. In this case, however, the composition of the oiling mixture is somewhat different, and may include resin gums or synthetic resins. The second drying period is much slower than the first and may take four times as long.

The oiled cloth is then spread on hot plates or beds at a temperature of 30° to 40°C., and a thin coating of shellac applied from dilute ammoniacal solution in order to remove the tackiness of the treated material; four or five applications may be necessary.

A final drying completes the process, but it is important to emphasise the necessity of thorough drying; indeed, goods for export must have been stoved at 60°C. for 8 hours and dried for a month before packing.

Some interesting details of the manufacture and use of oiled fabrics have been given by Warner (Oilsilk, Harlequin Press, Manchester, 1939). American methods have been described by Le Brun (Textile World, 1938, 88, 56). The fabrics are run through troughs containing the oil mixture in a suitable solvent, any excess being removed by scrapers. The average speed of the cloth is about 30 yards per hour, and the temperature of the tower is approximately 95°C. Three applications of the oil are generally given. Vinyl resin lacquers are often applied from a suitable solvent with the oil.

LINOLEUM

Although the manufacture of linoleum hardly falls within the scope of textile finishing, it may be of interest to remark that the general method is to impregnate a strong jute canvas with a composition containing 40% of wood and cork fibres, 20% of pigments and fillers, and 40% of a cementing material made from linoxyn and rosin.

American Cloth

AMERICAN CLOTH is the well-known glossy material used for covering tables and shelves; it is generally prepared by first coating one side with a filling made by mixing China clay or lithopone with thickened linseed oil. The cloth is allowed to dry before a second coating is given, and, in the case of the better qualities, is rubbed down between the two applications, dusted with French chalk, and calendered. This process may be repeated a number of times, but the fabric is allowed to dry at a moderate temperature between each coating. The final application takes the form of a varnish which must be sufficiently elastic to prevent cracks in use; many types of American cloth are printed immediately before this final varnish coating. The varnish usually consists of an oil-soluble synthetic resin mixed with thickened linseed oil and wood oil, together with a little white spirit to bring the mixture to the desired consistency for application to the fabric; driers, in the form of oil-soluble metallic soaps, are added to all the oil coatings, cobalt linoleate being commonly used. (American cloth is also known as Lancaster cloth.)

Cellulose Derivatives

CELLULOSE DERIVATIVES, such as the nitrate and acetate, are capable of forming films and can therefore be used to coat fabrics and close the interstices of the material; in actual fact, these derivatives are rarely used for waterproofing fabrics. There are several reasons for their exclusion; the nitrate is inflammable, and the acetate is relatively expensive and apt to detract from the handle and finish of the cloth. However, it is possible to form a film of cellulosic material from the cloth itself by treatment in principle with cuprammonium hydrate, which is a solvent for cellulose; the surface solution is then squeezed into and over the fabric.

Two processes involving the use of copper compounds have been applied with considerable success. Although primarily intended for mildew resistance (see page 512), yet they also produce a very considerable degree of water-repellency, but give the cloth a characteristic green coloration. In the cuprammonium process the cloth is passed through a bath of cuprammonium hydrate solution, squeezed between rollers, and dried in hot air. The cuprammonia exerts a slight solvent action on the surface of the cotton or linen and forms a film on the cloth; this film, however, is disintegrated on prolonged exposure to sunlight. The solution may be made by allowing concentrated ammonia solution (*sp. gr.* 0·88) to trickle over copper turnings or by treating copper sulphate solution with sodium hydroxide solution and then dissolving the precipitate in concentrated ammonia; in both cases, the concentration of the solution used for impregnating the cloth should be such that it contains from 0·5 to 2% of copper.

Close chemical and physical control is necessary to achieve uniform and good results.

The copper-aluminium formate process is also of interest, but it suffers from the disadvantage of being a multi-bath process necessitating the use of three solutions. The first solution is prepared by mixing together copper sulphate and sodium carbonate solutions, and dissolving the precipitate in formic acid. The copper formate is diluted according to the quantity of copper required to be deposited on the cloth. At the same time aluminium formate may be made by precipitating alumina from aluminium sulphate and sodium carbonate and then dissolving the alumina in formic acid to give a solution of 2°Tw. These two solutions are mixed in about the proportions of 10 parts of the first (1·2% copper) to 1 part of the second, to form the first impregnating solution. The cloth is treated with this solution in an ordinary padding mangle, and then dried on steam cans, after which it is impregnated in a solution of 1 part of ammonia solution (*sp. gr.* 0·88) in 8 parts of water, and again dried on steam-heated cylinders provided with some means of collecting the ammonia vapour. The final treatment is to impregnate the cloth in a wax emulsion composed of 20 parts of paraffin wax, 6 parts of starch, and 3 parts of soap, and dry on steam-heated cylinders.

Here again a bluish-green colour is imparted to the fabric. A paler colour may be produced by incorporating a soluble chromate or bichromate in the cuprammonia; subsequent treatment with sulphides, sulphites, or sulphocyanides gives a brown coloration to the material.

SHOWERPROOF FINISHES

Water-repellent finishes which are porous to air may be produced by a variety of methods:

(1) Aluminium compounds applied alone, or with soap in order to form a hydrophobic metallic soap.

(2) Oils, fats, and waxes applied from solution in organic solvents or from aqueous emulsion.

(3) Vegetable and animal proteins.

(4) Synthetic compounds of high molecular weight.

(5) Chemical reactions produced on the fibre to give an actual compound with the textile material; the surface compound is both hydrophobic and permanent.

These methods fall into two main classes, those in which a hydrophobic substance is deposited on the surface of the fibres, and those where the fibre itself is made hydrophobic or water-repellent by chemical combination with the fatty chain. Methods *1* to *4* belong to the first class, and method *5* comprises the second class in itself. Nevertheless, they all depend on the fundamental point of applying fatty or waxy substances to the fibre either mechanically or by a true chemical reaction.

ALUMINIUM ACETATE

One of the oldest methods of waterproofing was by the ALU-MINIUM ACETATE process, chief disadvantage of which was the amount of time and labour involved. In many works it was custo-mary to prepare the aluminium acetate solution by double decom-position between a 9% solution of aluminium sulphate and a 14% solution of lead acetate; the precipitated lead sulphate is allowed to settle and the supernatant liquor drawn off and used for the im-pregnation of cloth. The general method was to run the cloth through the bath of aluminium acetate solution without squeezing and roll it into a batch; this was repeated several times, after which the cloth was plaited on a wagon and allowed to drain. The im-pregnated goods were then dried by moderate steam heat in a festoon chamber, the use of high temperatures being avoided until the cloth was dry. A slight excess of alum should be used in this process so as to avoid the presence of soluble lead salts in the liquor, as these will darken on exposure to the atmosphere by forming lead sulphide and stain the fabric.

Aluminium acetate solution may be purchased from chemical manufacturers and used in concentrations of 1° to 4°Tw., according to the effect required and the nature of the cloth. Although the method is cheap, the handle is apt to be harsh, but nevertheless may be suitable for tent-cloths. Another outlet for the aluminium acetate process is for non-absorbent finishes which are a preparation or foundation for further proofing, such as rubber and similar film-forming substances.

The ordinary commercial solutions of aluminium formate or acetate as used for impregnating cloth for water-repellent finishes do not contain the neutral salts, but monobasic salts of variable composition, as distinct from definite chemical compounds. When water is removed from the acetate or formate, part of the acetic or formic acid is also removed, so that the compound changes from a water-soluble monobasic salt to the insoluble dibasic compound. This is precipitated on the fibre, where it is tenaciously retained to impart showerproof finishes. For successful processing, it is essen-tial to give the fabric a lengthy impregnation in the solution before drying.

The normal acetate $Al_2(CH_3COO)_6$ has not been isolated in the dry state; it only exists in solution and decomposes on warming to form basic salts, $Al_2(OH)_4(CH_3COO)_2$ or $Al_2(OH)_2(CH_3COO)_4$ or $Al_2(OH)_3(CH_3COO)_3$.

Aluminium formate is sometimes preferred as it does not leave a disagreeable odour on the fabric; the neutral formate is unknown, but the basic formate can be made by dissolving the fresh hydroxide in 90% formic acid solution to give $Al(HCOO)_2(OH).H_2O$, which on heating goes to $Al(HCOO)_2(OH)$. Some crystalline triformates have been made, such as $Al(HCOO)_3.3H_2O$, which can be buffered and made stable.

ALUMINIUM SOAPS

The use of ALUMINIUM SOAPS was an almost inevitable sequence to the aluminium acetate process; as generally applied, it is a two-bath process, and although in theory it is of little consequence whether the soap or alum is applied first, in practice it is better to apply the soap first. This ensures that the sodium soap is entirely converted into the aluminium soap, for if any soluble soap remains in the proofed material, it detracts from the water-repellent effect (see also page 486).

Where woollen goods are treated, it is sometimes convenient to leave soap in the goods after milling, and convert it into an aluminium soap by treatment with aluminium acetate solution.

A typical treatment for the formation of aluminium soaps is to impregnate the goods with a soap solution containing 1·5 to 2 oz. of good-quality soap per gallon (i.e. 1 to 1·25%) and squeeze out any excess liquor, before working in aluminium acetate or formate solution in a jig or winch machine. Where aluminium acetate is utilised, a concentration of 8° to 10° Tw. is often employed. The process is completed by drying the goods.

A one-bath alternative to the above process is to impregnate the cloth with a solution of the metallic soap in a suitable organic solvent such as solvent naphtha or benzene. The aluminium soap is colourless, but although a copper soap imparts a green colour to the material, it also produces a resistance to mildew which may be of value in certain circumstances.

Solutions of aluminium soaps in gasoline may have their viscosity reduced by the addition of triethanolamine, and so penetrate more thoroughly into the fabric, according to U.S.P. 2,032,528.

The waterproofing of the heavy woollen greatcoats for Army, Navy, and Air Force is generally accomplished by aluminium soaps, and although it is possible to use wax emulsions in conjunction, the general effect would be to destroy the suppleness of these thick materials. A fatty emulsion offers a useful alternative and may be applied with aluminium sulphate or acetate.

One recipe is to dissolve about 12 lb. of lannette wax in the minimum quantity of water (lannette wax is a mixture of cetyl and stearyl alcohols), and then add 24 lb. of stearin with boiling; when a good emulsion has been obtained the liquor should be diluted to 12 gallons with constant stirring. For the waterproofing process, about 9 lb. of aluminium sulphate should be dissolved in water and

3 pints of aluminium acetate added together with 1 pint of the stock stearin emulsion. The proofing process should last for about 30 minutes, after which the pieces should be hydroextracted and stentered.

The formation of metallic soaps on the fibre need not necessarily entail a two-bath process, for the modern knowledge of emulsification has made it possible to produce emulsions of the fatty acid and the aluminium salt; when dried on the fabric the aluminium soap is formed. In U.S.P. 2,046,305, instead of the free fatty acid, an ester is emulsified; for example, diglycostearate may be emulsified in presence of aluminium stearate and applied to textile material. The formation of the metallic soap takes place under the action of heat.

Apart from the emulsification method, recent developments make it possible to replace soaps by some of the newer detergents. B.P. 354,443 claims the use of the aluminium salts of higher alkyl sulphates and sulphonates. The textile material may be treated with 1% solution of sodium cetyl sulphate, followed by 3° Tw. aluminium acetate solution.

The metallic soaps of tall oil are also very suitable for showerproof finishes; tall oil is a natural mixture of fatty and rosin acids, recovered from pine wood in the alkaline paper-pulp process.

WAX

Showerproofing with WAX in various forms has been applied to many lightweight dress materials, sometimes in conjunction with aluminium acetate; for instance, a weak solution of aluminium acetate may be applied as a preliminary treatment.

Good-quality paraffin wax of 57°C. melting-point may be employed alone or in conjunction with a softening agent; the wax may be utilised in various ways, such as from solution, by friction, by spraying in a molten condition, or from aqueous emulsion. For the solvent process, a solution of 4 to 6% of the wax in benzene or benzine may be applied from a trough in which a roller revolves and carries the solution round to the cloth which passes over its upper surface under slight tension. The cloth is then dried by any suitable means, such as cylinders, stenter, or drying chamber.

For the friction method, the wax is prepared in long bars about 4 inches thick and slightly longer than the width of the cloth, which is passed through a steam-box before it meets the bar of wax. If necessary, a number of bars may be used and the cloth is rubbed against them under slight tension, after which a warm calendering operation melts the applied wax and distributes it more evenly on the cloth.

The spraying process involves the use of a number of pipes rising from a trough of molten wax, and at the mouth of each pipe a small high-pressure steam jet sprays the molten wax on to the fabric, which passes before the apparatus. Here again the cloth is finally heated on drying cylinders, where the wax is melted and distributed evenly on the fabric.

The emulsion method is perhaps the commonest method of shower-proofing fabrics with wax, and many commercial emulsions are available.

Crude methods of emulsification do not give good results, but as a result of considerable work on emulsification by the large chemical manufacturers, it is now possible to obtain stable emulsions of paraffin wax. These emulsions have passed through three commercial stages. First, a wax emulsion was marketed which was unstable to aluminium acetate and therefore necessitated the use of the two-bath method, but this was soon superseded by wax emulsions which were stable to aluminium acetate and could be used in a one-bath process. With these emulsions of paraffin wax, fatty acid, etc., the aluminium salt could be added to the diluted emulsion immediately before use or, alternatively, the emulsion could be used alone in one bath and followed by the aluminium salt in a second bath. The third stage was an improvement on the stable dilute emulsion, and comprised a stable one-bath emulsion containing both wax and aluminium acetate ready for use when diluted. The manufacture of these stable emulsions appears to depend on careful control of pH and the use of highly efficient emulsifying agents. Trade products such as Waxol W, Ramasit KG, and Cerol T are very well known and probably belong to this third type.

It is important to remember that these emulsions are unstable in the presence of certain electrolytes, such as those with SO_4'' ions, so that the cloth should be free from these or other fillings which might interfere with the penetration of the emulsion. Certain fillings such as starch and dextrin may be added to the emulsion before application to the cloth. The material is generally worked in the dilute emulsion, say 5%, for some time, and then the excess liquor removed by any suitable means; piece goods may be impregnated by padding, and it should be realised that better results are obtained by treating dry cloth rather than the wet fabric, which may dilute the impregnating liquor. The final drying process should take place at a fairly high temperature, preferably above the melting-point of the wax.

Although there are many different emulsions, they have much in common. They generally show a slightly acid reaction (pH 3·5 to 5·5) because of the formate or acetate they contain. These salts hydrolyse but as the cloth is sometimes slightly alkaline, the pH is apt to rise, and if it reaches 6·0 or more, then the emulsion may be upset; hence it may be a wise precaution to have a little acetic acid in the bath. Some of the emulsions contain substantive products which exhaust and this may be very useful for wool goods. In general, the padding method is preferred for cotton goods, and a three-bowl mangle is advantageous; otherwise, it is well to arrange for adequate time in the liquor and between the liquor and the nip of the mangle. It is not always appreciated that many of these products are initially heat-sensitive when applied to fabric, so that batching after drying should not take place until the goods are cool.

An important property of cloths treated with these emulsions is that their finish differs only very slightly from that of the original material.

WAXOL W of the I.C.I. possesses excellent stability in hard water, mineral acid, and solutions of salts; starch, dextrin, or gum arabic may be added to the emulsion, but where gum tragacanth is used, the proofing bath should not contain less than 5% of this product. Sulphonated castor oil, or other wetting agents, should not be added to Waxol W emulsions. The stock emulsion of Waxol W may be prepared by stirring the paste with about three times its weight of water at a temperature of 40°C.; complete dispersion is readily obtained and the resulting emulsion may be diluted to the required concentration with hot or cold water. The usual range of concentrations of the impregnating bath is from 1 to 3%, that is, 1 to 3 pounds of Waxol per 10 gallons of liquor. The working temperature is generally 50° to 60°C., the lower temperature being preferred for acetate rayon. It should be noted, however, that both temperature and concentration depend on the type of cloth being treated and the machinery on which the process is carried out; on the padding mangle it may be necessary to increase the concentration to 3 or 4%. With tightly woven goods, it may be essential to increase the time of impregnation and the temperature of the bath. Grey cotton goods may require the addition of 1 pint of 16°Tw. aluminium acetate solution per 10 gallons of proofing liquor.

Drying temperatures of 110° to 120°C. are advised, and it is also pointed out that the goods should be allowed to condition in the atmosphere before testing the efficiency of the proof.

WAXOL PA of the I.C.I. is recommended for use with wool in preference to Waxol W. Where suitable machinery is available, such as a five-bowl scouring set, a continuous process may be used; alternatively, the goods may be treated in a dolly. In the former case, three baths may contain the Waxol PA emulsion, after which the fabric may be passed directly through two baths containing the aluminium acetate or formate solution. Each of the Waxol PA impregnating baths should contain a 4% Waxol PA emulsion prepared by pasting and diluting 4 lb. of Waxol PA with 10 gallons of water; the emulsion should be maintained at 45° to 50°C. The aluminium acetate or aluminium formate solution for the subsequent baths may be made by diluting 3 to 5 pints of the acetate or formate (12° to 16°Tw.) with 10 gallons of water.

With approximately 200 lb. of wool fabric (based on the dry weight) the goods may be wetted in the dolly with water at 35° to 45°C.; when thoroughly wet, the surplus liquor is removed and the wool may be treated with 8 to 10 lb. of Waxol PA (4 to 5% on the weight of the goods) which has been pasted with water at 60°C. and then diluted with 4 to 5 gallons of water at the same temperature. After running for 15 minutes, about 2 or 3 gallons of the liquor are removed and replaced by 4 to 6 pints of aluminium acetate or formate (12° to 16°Tw.), diluted to 2 to 3 gallons with cold water. At this stage, the milkiness of the Waxol emulsion gradually disappears over a period of 15 minutes; persistence of milkiness indicates the need for further additions of the aluminium salt. The process is completed by hydroextraction or mangling, followed by stentering in the usual manner.

RAMASIT KC of the I.G. was also marketed in the form of a paste which is mixed with 5 to 10 times its weight of water to form a stock emulsion which can be used at any desired strength. The temperature of the impregnating bath is usually 30° to 40°C. for light goods and 60° to 70°C. for heavier cloths. Where a short period of immersion on the padding mangle is given, an average concentration of 2 to 2·5% is adequate, but for longer treatment in the winch machine, this may be reduced to 0·5%. Drying should be above 60°C. Rayon, for umbrella cloth, may be impregnated with 0·5 to 1% solutions.

PERSISTOL was originally a continuation of the Ramasit type and consisted of wax emulsions. Zirconium oxychloride was used instead of aluminium salts, and the effect was stated to be superior in repellency and also in resistance to washing; probably the paraffin has a better affinity for the zirconium hydroxide. From 1939 to 1945, many fabrics in Germany were treated with Persistol Base (wax emulsion) and Persistol Salt (zirconium oxychloride). A one-bath process is described in U.S.P. 2,328,431; the treatment is completed by rinsing and then drying at a comparatively high temperature.

CEROL S of the Sandoz Chemical Company may be used in a one-bath process with aluminium acetate, according to the following recipe: 2% of Cerol S and 1·3% of Special Aluminium Acetate S calculated on the weight of the impregnating liquor. For heavy cloths, or special water-repellent effects, the Cerol S may be increased to 4%, but the aluminium acetate should always be 66% of the Cerol S. The impregnating temperature should be 50°C.

Cerol SNN Conc. contains both the wax emulsion and the aluminium salt; the usual concentration is 4 to 6 gallons of Cerol SNN per 100 gallons of water.

In most of these trade products, stability is assured partly by the size of the particles, but more by the nature of the protective colloid which is present. The I.C.I. in B.P. 393,276 utilise cetyl pyridinium chloride, which also confers a positive charge on the wax particles and so facilitates absorption by the fibre. The I.G. has utilised oxy-ethyl stearyl ether among other dispersing agents, as outlined in B.P.401,712.

An important advance in emulsification process has been made by Du Pont; it depends on the use of salts of partially de-acetylated chitin. B.P. 458,815 describes the use of these agents in conjunction with paraffin wax and a fixing agent such as aluminium acetate for water-repellent effects. A silk crêpe treated in this type of emulsion acquired water-repellency which persisted through 10 to 15 launderings with soap and water, as compared with 1 to 4 launderings in the case of an ordinary commercial emulsion. The superiority is attributed to the strong fixative action of the de-acetylated chitin, which binds the wax to the fibre.

PROTEIN PRODUCTS

PROTEIN PRODUCTS have also been used for the production of a water-repellent finish. A typical recipe of about thirty years ago was to dissolve 40 parts of casein in 300 parts of water and then add 1 part of slaked lime in small quantities; a solution of 20 parts of neutral soap in 240 parts of water was then added and the cloth steeped in the mixture, squeezed, and then passed through aluminium acetate solution to make the casein insoluble.

Another prescription was 100 parts of potash alum, 100 parts of glue, 5 parts of tannin, and 2 parts of sodium silicate, which were mixed with the necessary amount of water, boiled, cooled, and used for the impregnation of woollens.

Gelatin (50 parts), tallow soap (50 parts), alum (75 parts) may be mixed with water (2,000 parts), boiled, cooled, and used for water-repellent finishes. A modern recipe has been given by the Glycerin Producers' Association of New York, and involves a two-bath process for tent-cloths. The first solution is made from light glue (10 parts), water (50 parts), and glycerin (10 parts); the second solution consists of 100 parts of 40% formaldehyde solution in 900 parts of water. The cloth for treatment is impregnated in the first solution and dried, after which it is hardened by impregnation in the second solution, followed by drying.

From the above examples it will be seen that there are two main methods of rendering the protein insoluble in water: (a) treatment with aluminium salts, and (*b*) treatment with formaldehyde. The latter is apt to be obnoxious in finishing works unless special precautions are taken to deal with it; for this reason, the formation of the aluminium compound is generally preferred.

It has been suggested to treat textiles with a solution of gelatin or glue in acetic acid, to which aluminium acetate has been added; in such a mixture it is also possible to incorporate a solution of paraffin or other fatty substance in white spirit.

A special method of preparing stable emulsions is described in B.P. 380,076; the aluminium salt is first added to the aqueous solution of glue, and then the paraffin is emulsified with the resulting solution. For example, 80 parts of gelatin are dissolved in 700 parts of water and 100 parts of aluminium acetate added, after which the mixture is warmed to 60°C. until a uniform solution is obtained. This is used to emulsify 125 parts of petroleum jelly and 125 parts of paraffin. About 5 parts of this product is dissolved in hot water, and made up to 100 parts with cold water; this solution may be used for the impregnation of cloth, which, after drying, possesses water-repellency.

Higgins in B.P. 496,490 makes use of the observation that a combination of casein and amphoteric metals, such as aluminium and zinc, under controlled acid conditions gives rise to a high degree of water-repellency after dehydration. Further, as the alkaline solutions of casein are generally compatible with alkaline soaps, and are good wetting agents, they may be used to emulsify fats and waxes; sodium aluminate may also be added together with an ammonium or pyridinium salt of an organic acid. In this manner a stable concentrated emulsion is formed, which can be diluted with water and applied to cloth; on heating, however, acid conditions arise under which reaction takes place between casein and aluminium to give a strong water-repellent effect.

IMPREGNOL M is a trade product believed to contain casein, emulsified fats or waxes and an aluminium salt. The white viscous mass should be dissolved in water at 60° to 70°C. before use. For padding processes, the amount of Impregnol calculated on the weight of the liquor varies from 2 to 5%, but for exhaustion processes in winch machines, etc., the Impregnol is calculated on the weight of the goods and averages from 2 to 10%. The lower percentage is used for heavier goods, and the higher percentages for lighter material; the ratio of liquor to cloth may vary between 5 : 1 and 60 : 1, and the period of treatment should be some 30 minutes. The process is completed by drying the goods.

The Impregnol method is probably that disclosed in U.S.P. 2,015,864 and 5, by Mueller of Erba A.G.; it is possible to produce stable emulsions by changing the electric charge of the dispersion through the use of concentrated dispersions (i.e. more than 15% solid matter, such as fats, oils, waxes, and protective colloid), to which the necessary amount of concentrated aluminium acetate solution is added. The whole dispersion is diluted after the additions of the salt and the protective colloid such as glue; if the metallic salt is added to the dilute dispersion it discharges the latter and coagulation occurs. When prepared according to the new method, the dispersion is positively charged, and is capable of firm and rapid fixation to the negatively charged textile fibres.

MYSTOLENE of the Catomance Company is a protein degradation product in dispersed form, which is diluted and mixed with aluminium formate immediately prior to application to textile materials. This product is very suitable for use with wool, and a special variety termed "milling proof" is available for application during the milling of woollens with formic acid.

Mystolene KP may be applied by the padding process or by exhaustion. With the padding method, a solution should be made of such concentration that 3% of Mystolene KP will be left on the material, and to this solution should be added one-tenth of the weight of the Mystolene of aluminium triformate (48°Tw.). The ratio of liquor to goods should be about 15 : 1.

Mystolene KP is substantive to wool and may be applied by a method similar to dyeing; again 3% of the product is required, estimated on the weight of the wool. The goods are worked in the liquor and the temperature is gradually raised to about 50°C., and working continued until the liquor is clear. The appropriate amount of aluminium triformate is then added, and working continued for about 5 minutes. After hydroextraction, the goods are dried at about 60° to 70°C.

SYNTHETIC COMPOUNDS

SYNTHETIC COMPOUNDS of high molecular weight have been used as water-repellents; this is an almost inevitable outcome of their application in other branches of textile finishing. The subject has been covered by numerous patent specifications of which the following are only taken as typical of the general line of advance.

Ammonium polyacrylate and aluminium acetate have been used in a two-bath process described in B.P. 371,041, and heavy metal salts of general formula $R.OCH_2.COOH$ are mentioned in B.P. 413,728, R being a long chain radical. These are examples of metallic salts of high molecular weight.

Condensation products or polymerised compounds have also been used; the general idea is to incorporate some fatty or hydrophobic group in the reacting material. The crease-resisting finish (see page 390) is obtained by impregnating textile materials with lightly condensed solutions from formaldehyde and urea and completing the resinification in the fibre; such crease-resisting textiles are not normally water-repellent, but there are numerous processes for incorporating fatty and waxy products in the reaction mixture and so combining two effects. A different line of approach, however, is to introduce a long-chain group into the urea or phenol molecule in such a manner that the final product has water-repellent properties, but these modified products do not generally confer crease-resistance. Suitable substances are octadecyl urea or octadecyl phenol, as mentioned in B.P. 463,300 of the I.G.; these condense with formaldehyde and then, on heating, form substances of complex structure in the fibre to which they have been previously applied. Presumably the great molecular size accounts for their fixation on the fibre, which is made water-repellent by the fatty radicles incorporated in the compound. Octadecyl urea is $C_{18}H_{37}NH.CO.NH_2$ and octadecyl phenol is $C_{18}H_{37}C_6H_4OH$. For good effects the alkyl radical should contain at least 11 carbon atoms; stearyl urea $C_{17}H_{35}CO.NH.CO.NH_2$ and lauric acid amide $C_{11}H_{23}CONH_2$ are also mentioned. The process may be carried out in two ways. The solution or dispersion of the urea or amide may be applied to the textile material, which is dried and heated for several hours at 110°C. in presence of formaldehyde; alternatively, the latter may be added to the impregnating bath and the reaction completed by drying and heating. The effect is stated to be very resistant to washing.

Other compounds containing amino-groups may be applied to textile materials and then treated with formaldehyde, as shown in B.P. 467,166 of the I.G.; suitable amines are laurylamine $C_{12}H_{25}NH_2$ and oleylamine $C_{18}H_{35}NH_2$ and may be applied in the form of a salt from aqueous solution, which has certain advantages over the use of emulsions or organic solvents. Cotton cloth may be treated for 15 minutes in a solution containing 5 g. of stearylamine acetate, 2 g. melamine, and 50 c.c. of formaldehyde, centrifuged and heated for 1 hour at 100°C.

The hydrochlorides of higher alkyl imidoethers and amidines may be utilised with formaldehyde, as described in B.P. 446,976 of the I.G.

It is, of course, possible to incorporate fatty amides such as stearamide in the crease-resisting mixture of urea and formaldehyde, and so obtain a water-repellent effect in addition to crease-resistance.

Solutions of polymerised vinyl chloride have been used in substantial quantities for the production of rainproof coats, particularly for the American Army. The trade product, "Koroseal," is believed to be a plasticised polyvinylchloride, and the various "Vinylites" have also been used from solution in a mixture of butyl alcohol and the new nitroparaffin solvents. The term "Vinylite" covers many vinyl resins; for instance, Vinylite A is polyvinylacetate, Vinylite Q is polyvinylchloride, Vinylite V is a co-polymer of vinyl acetate and vinyl chloride, and Vinylite X is a vinyl alcohol butyral.

The vinyl type of polymerisation has been used in another I.G. patent (B.P. 464,860), which makes use of the fact that it is possible to produce a modified vinyl resin by polymerising in the presence of maleic anhydride. For instance, long-chain groups may be incorporated in the vinyl compound which is then reacted with maleic anhydride. Suitable vinyl compounds are vinyl stearate CH_2:- $CHOCOC_{17}H_{35}$ or vinyl stearyl ether $CH_2 : CHOC_{18}H_{37}$. Organic solutions or aqueous dispersions of the reaction product with maleic anhydride are used to impregnate textile materials, which are then dried at 100°C. for a short time. This idea may be seen in B.P. 472,613 (also by the I.G.) which utilises mixed polymerisation products.

The glycerol-phthalic anhydride type of product has been used for water-repellency, according to B.P. 419,373 of Du Pont, by esterifying the free hydroxyl groups as, for instance, with stearyl ketene $C_{17}H_{35}CH : C : O$.

Recent developments in Germany have led to the development of Persistol VS which is stated to attract dirt less readily than most products. Persistol VS is octadecyl-ethylene-urea in a dispersed form; it is used in concentrations of 5%. After impregnation, the goods are squeezed and dried at a temperature in excess of 80°C. when reaction is supposed to occur with the fibre; there is no need for subsequent rinsing or neutralising, as the product is neutral and there are no by-products. Originally, the method was to treat rayon with Persistol LA (methylolstearamide) in conjunction with Persistol VS.

HYDROPHOBIC FIBRES

The greater part of textile material which is required to be non-wetting is cellulosic, so that chemical reactions which aim at the production of hydrophobic fibres must be based chiefly on cellulose chemistry.

The two great classes of cellulose derivatives are the esters and ethers; the former are susceptible to the action of alkali, but the latter are only affected by acid under such circumstances that the cellulose itself is degraded. Hence, although suitable alkyl esters and ethers of cellulose may be made, the effect of the latter will be as permanent as the cellulose itself. Esterifying and etherifying agents containing suitable fatty groups have been reacted with cellulose for water-repellent effects.

ESTERIFICATION

The common method of preparing CELLULOSE ESTERS is to treat cellulose with the acid anhydride or chloride; with the higher fatty acids, the anhydrides are difficult to prepare and not very reactive, so that the simplest method is to use the acid chlorides. There are, however, some indirect methods of making cellulose esters.

Prior to 1928 or so, most of the fatty esters of cellulose were formed under such conditions as to give amorphous, structureless products, and little attempt was made to preserve the fibrous structure. The interest in methods of immunising cellulose against direct dyes led to methods of esterification where the fibrous structure was preserved, but apparently Heberlein (B.P. 313,616) first produced water-repellent effects by treating the cloth with alcoholic alkali, followed by stearyl or oleyl chloride in carbon tetrachloride.

The superficial esterification of cellulose with stearyl chloride has been investigated by Nathanson, and is described in B.P. 355,256 and 356,878. The reaction is slow, a typical example being the treatment of cotton with 5% stearyl chloride in benzene solution for 24 hours at 60° to 80°C.; a weak organic base such as diethylaniline is also present in amount corresponding to the chlorine of the stearyl chloride. Another example relates to treatment with 2% palmitic anhydride in boiling benzine for 6 hours.

Instead of organic solvents, the emulsion method may be used. 10 g. of the mixed anhydrides of stearic and palmitic acids are melted and mixed with 85 c.c. of 0·6% vegetable gum at 70°C., 12 c.c. of 2·2% ammonia solution being added. After stirring vigorously, the mixture is diluted to 400 c.c. with water at 70°C. Fabrics may be impregnated with this emulsion, squeezed, dried, and ironed.

B.P. 356,878 contains further examples mainly utilising stearic anhydride, which may be applied in 0·5 to 5% concentration from benzene, benzine, or carbon tetrachloride. After drying, the treated fabric should be heated for about 6 hours at 80°C.; the range of fabrics susceptible to treatment includes cotton, viscose rayon, wool, and silk.

Emulsions of anhydrides have been suggested more recently; for example, B.P. 458,805 uses soap as the emulsifying agent.

Esters of chloro-carbonic acid combine with alcohols and may therefore be utilised for the superficial esterification of cellulose, producing a mixed carbonic ester.

$$\text{Cell.OH} + \text{Cl.COOR} \longrightarrow \text{Cell.O.COOR}$$

Where the chloro-carbonic ester contains a long-chain group such as stearyl ($C_{18}H_{35}$) or cetyl ($C_{16}H_{33}$), water-repellency is obtained.

B.P. 460,602 of the I.G. describes this method; cotton is treated with 5 parts of chloro-carbonic octadecyl ester ($Cl.COOC_{18}H_{37}$) and 1 part of pyridine in 1,000 parts of carbon tetrachloride and heated for 1 hour at 90°C. The function of the pyridine is to neutralise the hydrochloric acid which is formed during the reaction and would degrade the cellulose during the drying process. The esters may also be applied in aqueous dispersion as an alternative to organic solution.

A somewhat similar process depends on the fact that the chloro-carbonic esters may first be treated with another alcohol or with an amine to give mixed carbonates or carbamates.

These alkyl carbonates or urethanes have been utilised for the production of hydrophobic fibres, as shown in B.P. 461,670 of the I.G. The general formulae are R'O.CO.OR or R'O.CO.NR''R in which R may be hydrocarbon or any desired organic radical, but R' and R'' are organic radicals of which at least one contains six or more carbon atoms. Suitable compounds are hexyl-ethyl carbonate, octadecyl-ethyl carbonate, or cetyl-ethyl carbonate and octadecyl-urethane, octadecylhydroxyethylurethane or octadecylethylurethane.

The impregnation may be effected by aqueous baths containing 1 to 10 g. per litre of the compound, together with triethanolamine or other emulsifying agent, followed by drying and heating for 1 hour at 90°C.; alternatively, the fabric may be impregnated with 1% solution of the compound in carbon tetrachloride, followed by drying and heating. Temperatures of 50° to 100°C. are advised. As there is no possibility of acid being produced in the reaction, there is less possibility of damage than where the chloro-carbonic ester is used, according to the previous method.

Isocyanates

ISOCYANATES may also be utilised in the production of cellulose esters of carbonic acids.

This interesting reaction in cellulose chemistry was discovered by Goissedet, depending on the fact that alcohols or phenols can react with aliphatic or aromatic isocyanates to produce esters of the alkyl or aryl carbamic acids.

$$R.OH + C{\overset{\displaystyle N-R'}{\underset{\displaystyle O}{\Big\langle}}} \longrightarrow RO.C{\overset{\displaystyle NH.R'}{\underset{\displaystyle O}{\Big\langle}}}$$

This reaction has been applied to cellulose or its derivatives which contain hydroxyl groups, as outlined in B.P. 130,277; cellulose may be heated with phenyl isocyanate in presence of pyridine, and the resulting phenyl carbamic ester isolated by pouring the mass into a large volume of water. The cellulose derivative will be

B.P. 317,019 of Ciba describes a surface reaction where the cellulose does not pass into solution when treated with 90 parts of phenyl isocyanate and 10 parts of pyridine.

Now cellulose alkyl urethanes with hydrophobic properties have been produced from carbimides (isocyanates) or thiocarbimides (isothiocyanates) which contain long-chain fatty radicles, and in this way a fatty hydrophobic chain becomes chemically fixed to the cellulose molecule and imparts water-repellency. B.P. 461,179 (I.G.) gives a comprehensive account of these important reactions in which, naturally, the structure of the cellulose is preserved. In one example, a cotton twill is treated with a solution of 10 g. of stearyl isocyanate per litre of carbon tetrachloride, hydroextracted, and dried at 100°C. for 1 hour. Stearyl isocyanate is $C_{17}H_{35}.N : C : O$. More complex isothiocyanates are also mentioned; for example, cotton may be steeped for 20 minutes in 1·5% octadecylphenyl isocyanate in carbon tetrachloride, hydroextracted, and the solvent evaporated at 50°C. Heating for 1 hour at 120° to 125°C. completes the process and makes the fabric water-repellent.

Another example describes the treatment of viscose rayon with 5 to 10% solutions of octadecyl isocyanate ($C_{18}H_{37}N : C : O$) in pyridine, followed by heating for 16 hours at 110°C.

Isothiocyanates (R.N : C : S) may be used in a similar manner to that employed for the isocyanates (R.N : C : O).

B.P. 474,403 of Stolte-Missy also describes various treatments with isocyanates not containing less than 10 carbon atoms in the alkyl or aryl radical. Decyl and eicosyl isocyanates are typical examples of the alkyl isocyanates, and an interesting instance of the mixed aliphatic-aromatic series is stearyl-oxyphenylene-isocyanate $C_{17}H_{35}CO.OC_6H_4.N : C : O$. Cholesterol from wool fat may be used to make cholesterol adipic acid ester isocyanate, and this may be applied to wool from 0·5% solution in benzine, followed by drying and heating for 2 minutes at 140°C. to give a good water-repellent effect.

A further development by the same inventors embraces the use of thiocyanic methyl ethers (R.O.CH$_2$.S.C : N) where the radical contains at least 10 carbon atoms. The higher thiocyanic methyl-ethers can be converted by tertiary amines into quaternary ammonium compounds which are soluble in water; for example, octadecylthiocyanicmethyl ether forms a water-soluble quaternary pyridinium salt which applied to cotton from 1·5% solution gives a good water-repellent effect after heating at 90°C. for a few hours. Further details may be seen in B.P. 494,833.

Related to the isocyanates and isothiocyanates is another type of compound described in B.P. 511,536 of Deutsche Hydrierwerke. Mono- or di-substituted carbodiimides containing at least one alkyl residue with 10 carbon atoms are believed to combine with cellulose to give water-repellent effects coupled with softness; the fibres or fabrics are preferably heated for the best result, but improvements with cellulose are achieved even without heating. As usual, cetyl or octadecyl groups exemplify the type of aliphatic residue necessary for water-repellent results. The basic structure of the carbodiimides is $R.C_6H_4N : C : N.C_6H_4.R$, and they may be made by heating an alkylated aniline with carbon disulphide to give a thiourea which is then treated with lead carbonate. This is illustrated by considering cetyl aniline.

$$2(C_{16}H_{33}.C_6H_4.NH_2) + CS_2 \rightarrow (C_{16}H_{33}.C_6H_4.NH)_2.CS$$
$$\rightarrow C_{16}H_{33}.C_6H_4.N:C:N.C_6H_4C_{16}H_{33}.$$

These compounds are applied to cellulose from organic solution, of which about 1% concentration appears adequate; the solvent is then removed by evaporation and the impregnated material heated for 1 to 2 hours at 110° to 125°C.

Ketenes

The use of KETENES of high molecular weight represents yet another method of esterification to produce hydrophobic fibres on account of the chemical fixation of a fatty radical. Ketene itself is $CH_2:C:O$, a gas which reacts directly with cellulose to form cellulose acetate. Substituted ketenes have been prepared by the methods of B.P. 522,033, which depend on the reaction between strong tertiary bases and the chlorides of aliphatic monobasic acids of high molecular weight; for instance, lauryl ketene may be made according to the following scheme:

$$C_{11}H_{23}COOH \longrightarrow C_{11}H_{23}COCl \left[+N(C_2H_5)_3 \right] \longrightarrow C_{11}H_{23} : C : O$$

Palmitic, oleic, caproic, and similar fatty acids may also be used.

In utilising these ketenes to treat cotton, wool, or rayons, the general method is merely to dissolve the ketene in an organic solvent, impregnate the material, evaporate the solvent, and heat to 110°C. For example, rayon may be soaked in 20% cetyl ketene in benzine solution for 20 to 30 minutes, expressed, dried, and heated to 110°C.; the water-repellent effect is fast to washing and dry-cleaning and, in the case of rayon, is due to the formation of cellulose oleate. Further details are given in B.P. 522,204 of Deutsche Hydrierwerke.

ETHERIFICATION

CELLULOSE ETHERS of a special type have been found to possess remarkable water-repellent properties, and as the ethers as a class are stable to alkali, the new hydrophobic fibres are permanent and the effect is fast to washing. The key substances in these reactions are α-halogen methyl compounds.

Modern methods of producing hydrophobic fibres appear to depend to some extent on a process invented by Deutsche Hydrierwerke in 1931 (B.P. 394,196). Halogen ethers of the type R—O—CHX—R' are treated with tertiary bases to form quaternary ammonium salts which are soluble in water; R may be an alkyl radical, R' a hydrogen atom or similar hydrocarbon radical, and X a halogen atom, but either R or R' must contain at least 8 carbon atoms. The preparation of the halogen ethers may be seen from an actual example in which octadecyl alcohol and formaldehyde are treated with dry hydrogen chloride in benzene at 5° to 10°C. After separating the aqueous layer, the benzene is removed *in vacuo*, and then the stearyl chlormethyl ether is distilled at 200°C. under a pressure of 2 to 3 mm. of mercury.

$$C_{18}H_{37}.OH + CH_2O + HCl \longrightarrow C_{18}H_{37}O.CH_2Cl + H_2O.$$

The new compound, a substituted methyl chloride, may be regarded as stearyl chlormethyl ether or stearoxymethyl chloride; it reacts with tertiary amines, such as triethylamine or with pyridine to give compounds which are readily soluble in water, unlike the original alkoxymethyl chloride. These quaternary ammonium salts, when in aqueous solution, foam strongly and exhibit great wetting powers.

Their first use with textiles appears to be disclosed in B.P. 426,482 by the same firm, and was mainly directed to improving the dyeing properties of cotton and other cellulosic fibres so that they could be coloured with the acid wool dyes. Butyl chlormethyl ether (1 part) and pyridine (10 parts) were heated for 4 hours with 1 part of cotton, hydroextracted, washed with alcohol, rinsed, and dried. It was also stated in the specification that the treated cotton showed water-repellent properties, but later examination and comparison revealed that the hydrophobic character of the product was only moderate; nevertheless, water-repellency was indicated. More important, however, was Schirm's suggestion that a chemical reaction had taken place with the cellulose forming an acetal Cell.O.CH$_2$.OC$_4$H$_9$.

It seems very probable that a chemical reaction of this type does in fact occur, for at a later date Bock and Houk actually prepared similar ethers of cellulose, as shown in U.S.P. 2,083,554 and 2,084,125 of Rohm and Haas. The methods disclosed depend on the treatment of cellulose *in solution* in the benzyl quaternary ammonium hydroxides. In one example, bleached sulphite pulp was dissolved in 40% benzyl triméthyl ammonium hydroxide and treated with chlormethyl lauryl ether; the reaction product contained one lauryloxymethyl group per glucose residue, and was soluble in toluene and aliphatic hydrocarbons. The formula would appear to be Cell.-$O.CH_2.OC_{12}H_{25}$; the cellulose ethers liberate formaldehyde on hydrolysis with dilute acid. As often happens in cellulose chemistry, comparison of the same reaction of cellulose in the fibrous state and in solution yields a better defined product in the latter instance.

The important feature of these new reactions was the development of chlormethyl ethers as reagents for cellulose in conjunction with a quaternary ammonium base; with pyridinium compounds, for instance, the influence of high temperatures brings about decomposition into pyridine and the chlormethyl alkyl ether which, when cellulose is present, reacts immediately to form a derivative which is fast to alkali. If the correct number of carbon atoms is present in the alkyl group, then water-repellent properties are conferred on the cellulose by actual chemical combination.

It is interesting to record that the process of Deutsche Hydrierwerke, described in B.P. 394,196, was filed on October 6, 1931, and that the Society of Chemical Industry in Basle, on October 24, 1931, filed a specification for improving the fastness to water of direct dyes in which one of the products was formed by the addition to pyridine of the compound made by passing hydrogen chloride into a mixture of cetyl alcohol and formaldehyde; B.P. 390,553, however, contains no mention of water-repellency. Improved fastness of dyeings on paper or paper pulp by treatment with aqueous solutions of the cetyl ether of N-oxymethylpyridinium chloride has also been mentioned in B.P. 396,992, and B.P. 434,911 of Deutsche Hydrierwerke claims the treatment of dyed textiles with aqueous solutions of quaternary ammonium salts containing an aliphatic radical of at least 10 carbon atoms and obtained by the treatment of α-halogenethers with tertiary amines; the softening effect of this treatment is also mentioned.

Reynolds, Walker, and Woolvin of the I.C.I. were responsible for developing the permanent water-repellent properties which can be produced by treating cellulose with substances such as octadecyloxymethylpyridinium chloride in aqueous solution under definite conditions, as outlined in B.P. 466,817. The I.C.I. process differs from its chemically similar predecessors in that particular quaternary ammonium salts are applied in aqueous solution and that a subsequent heating or baking treatment is utilised. The cellulosic material is passed through the aqueous solution, dried, and heated; the production of the desired effect is determined to a large extent by the conditions of drying and heating. Drying is carried out at a

31

relatively low temperature, determined to some extent by the speed of drying, but heating takes place at 90° to 120°C.

During the heating process, the salt decomposes, as is evidenced by the odour of pyridine when the salt is a pyridinium salt, and the chloroalkyl ether combines with the cellulose in the following manner:

$$C_5H_5N\begin{matrix}\diagup Cl\\\\\diagdown CH_2OC_{18}H_{37}\end{matrix}+Cellulose\longrightarrow Cell.O.CH_2OC_{18}H_{37}+C_5H_5N+HCl$$

If the wet material, impregnated in 1% aqueous solution of the salt, is dried on a steam-heated cylinder at 120°C. for 1 minute, no water-repellent effect is obtained, but heating for 5 minutes produces water-repellency which is sensitive to the action of solvents; more prolonged heating gives a finish which is fast to both dry-cleaning and laundering. The baking treatment is essential for the production of permanent water-repellent properties.

The treated material begins to show water-repellency after 10 minutes at 70°C., but more vigorous treatment is necessary for a permanent effect; the temperature of baking may vary from 70°C. to 200°C., but the time must be adjusted to avoid injury to the fibre.

The concentration of the reagent may vary from 0·1 to 2% in the aqueous solution, and in addition to octadecyloxymethyl-pyridinium chloride, it is also possible to employ cetyloxymethyl-pyridinium chloride, the corresponding dodecyl compound, and the ether of sperm oils (C_{10} to C_{20} alcohols) with hydroxymethyl-pyridinium chloride. It is worth noting that spermaceti may be used as a source of cetyl alcohol, as it is $C_{16}H_{33}O.OC.C_{15}H_{31}$—cetyl palmitate.

In typical examples water-repellent effects may be obtained by impregnating cellulosic material in a 2% aqueous solution of octadecyloxymethylpyridinium chloride, drying at 30°C. and heating for 30 minutes at 90°C. or even 1 hour at 100°C. when 1% solution is employed; with viscose treated in 1% oleyloxymethylpyridinium chloride and dried, 4 minutes at 120°C. seems adequate.

It may be stated in connection with B.P. 466,817 that many writers on textile technology have concluded that Velan PF (Zelan in the U.S.A.) is octadecyloxymethylpyridinium chloride, a conjecture which must be regarded with great caution.

Baldwin, Reynolds, Walker, and Woolvin of the I.C.I. have provided some further interesting information about chloromethyl octadecyl ether in B.P. 469,476; water-repellency may be conferred on cellulose or cellulose esters by treatment with the reagent in an inert organic diluent and in presence of "an acid-binding agent." Although B.P. 426,482 of Deutsche Hydrierwerke describes the treatment of cotton with butyl chlormethyl ether and pyridine, a much better water-repellent effect is obtained with longer-chain aliphatic derivatives; for instance, treatment with 2% of α-chlormethyl octadecyl ether enabled a sample of cotton to support a head of water 20 cm. high, whereas a sample treated with 100% of butyl chlormethyl ether, tested in the same apparatus, wetted rapidly and no head of water could be determined.

Examples illustrating the invention include treatment with 0·52 parts of α-chlormethyl octadecyl ether and 1·4 parts of pyridine in 250 parts of toluene at 90°C. for 30 minutes. Other inert solvents which may be used include trichlorethylene and carbon tetrachloride, as well as benzene, acetone, etc. Organic bases are more efficient than inorganic reagents as acid-binding media, as they are miscible with the diluent. It is also possible to treat cotton with 1 part of octadecyloxymethylpyridinium chloride in 146 parts of trichlorethylene at 33°C., dry in air at 30°C., and bake at 105°C. for 30 minutes.

The use of organic solvents for water-repellency instead of aqueous solutions is not necessarily a backward step, for in many cases the hydrophobic and hydrophilic properties of textiles are affected, if only to a small extent, by the liquid in which they were last immersed; again, one does not always obtain the same effect from chemical reactions in aqueous and non-aqueous media. It must be admitted, however, that aqueous solutions are preferred when possible in most finishing works for obvious reasons.

Returning to the fundamental chemistry of these new reactions, it has been found that the chloro-compound is not the only reagent which can be utilised. Baldwin and Piggott of the I.C.I. have described a number of sulphites in B.P. 475,119. These may be prepared, for instance, by refluxing a mixture of cetyl alcohol, pyridine, and paraformaldehyde, and then passing in gaseous sulphur dioxide until a test sample is readily soluble in water. The new quaternary salt appears to be a mixture of cetyloxymethylpyridinium pyridine sulphite and pyrosulphite.

$$C_{16}H_{33}.O.CH_2.NC_5H_5 \qquad\qquad C_{16}H_{33}.O.CH_2.NC_5H_5$$
$$\mid \qquad\qquad\qquad\qquad\qquad \mid$$
$$SO_3.NC_5H_5 \qquad\qquad\qquad S_2O_5.NC_5H_5$$

(Sulphite)   (Pyrosulphite)

Further, it is not necessary to use the long-chain fatty alcohols, and a considerable advance was made by Baldwin and Piggott of the I.C.I. when they discovered that carboxylic acid amides or carbamic esters of general formulae R.CONH.R' and RO.CONH.R' could be treated with hydrogen chloride in presence of formaldehyde to give new compounds which react with tertiary amines to give water-soluble quaternary ammonium salts. (B.P. 471,130.)

Suitable starting products are stearomethylamide (made from stearic acid or stearyl chloride and methylamine), methyl undecylcarbamate, methylheptadecylcarbamate, and so forth.

The general method of preparation is to suspend stearomethylamide and paraform in benzene and pass in hydrogen chloride, keeping the temperature below $10°C$. until saturation point is reached. The new product is believed to be N-methyl-stearamido-methyl chloride

$$C_{17}H_{35}.CO.N.CH_2Cl$$
$$|$$
$$CH_3$$

Methylheptadecylcarbamate may also be treated with hydrogen chloride in presence of paraform to give N-carbomethoxyheptadecyl-aminomethyl chloride

$$CH_3O.CO.N.CH_2Cl$$
$$|$$
$$C_{17}H_{35}$$

It will be noticed that in these new compounds the long fatty chain is no longer attached to oxygen, as it was in the product from the alcohols, and the fatty chain occupies a different position according to the starting product. The new compounds are also capable of forming water-soluble quaternary ammonium salts with pyridine. It is interesting to note that the I.G. in B.P. 466,853, described the treatment of amides of carboxylic acids, having at least 8 carbon atoms, with formaldehyde and sulphurous acid in presence of tertiary amines.

Baldwin and Walker of the I.C.I. have outlined in B.P. 475,170 a process for the manufacture of quaternary ammonium salts which involves reacting together, in presence of a tertiary amine, an acid amide of general formula $R.CO.NH_2$, formaldehyde, and a salt of the amine; hydroxymethylamides, prepared from formaldehyde and amides, may also be utilised. In this manner it is possible to obtain quaternary ammonium salts of general formula

$$R.CO.NH.CH_2.NC_5H_5$$
$$|$$
$$X$$

where X represents the monovalent anion of an acid. Stearamido-methylpyridinium chloride may be prepared by the reaction between stearamide, pyridine hydrochloride, pyridine, and paraform; an alternative method is by means of stearohydroxymethylamide, pyridine hydrochloride, and pyridine. The formula is given as

$$C_{17}H_{35}CO.NH.CH_2.NC_5H_5$$
$$|$$
$$Cl$$

Lauramidomethylpyridinium chloride and oleylamidopyridinium chloride are also described.

The production of water-repellent effects by means of these new quaternary ammonium salts, of general formula $R.R'N.CH_2.N$ (tert.) X, has been described by Baldwin, Evans, and Salkeld of the I.C.I. in B.P. 477,991. Seven of the nine examples relate to stearamido-methyl pyridinium chloride, and it may be remarked that there is reason to believe that this, or a closely related compound, forms the basis of Velan PF.

The impregnating solution should be maintained at temperatures below 40°C. when dilute (0·1%) aqueous solutions are used, but with more concentrated solutions (e.g. 1%) a higher temperature may be employed. When kept at temperatures above 40°C. the solution may become acid and a less satisfactory product obtained which is less resistant to organic solvents. With woven cotton fabrics, such as limbrics, the concentration may be as low as 0·05%, and with heavier fabrics 0·5% solution may be used, but this solution will become useless if maintained at 60°C. for 2 hours or at 80°C. for 1 hour. Alkali substances with a buffering action may be added to the bath; the presence of sodium acetate, for instance, assists in avoiding the tendering of the material by acid.

After the padding process, the goods are preferably, but not necessarily, dried prior to heating and decomposition of the quaternary salt; with a concentrated (0·5%) solution, it is not necessary to dry the goods, which may be heated directly to 120°C., provided that evaporation of moisture takes place within a minute or so. In general, however, it is advisable to dry before heating, and so ensure the permanence of the water-repellent effect. Optimum effects are shown when the heating takes place around 120°C. for about 2 minutes; poorer results are obtained at higher temperatures and longer times, such as 30 minutes at 150°C. It should be emphasised that a good softening effect is also produced, and this, too, is permanent.

The three types of condensation which have been considered in this section are concerned with derivatives of (a) alcohols, (b) acid amides, and (c) carbamates; in the first case, the fatty chain on which water-repellency depends is joined to pyridine (and will later be joined to cellulose) through an oxymethyl group $-OCH_2-$, whereas in the two later instances it is joined through $-N.CH_2-$, or $-CO.N.CH_2-$. This is seen by comparing the three types of compound as follows:

$$C_5H_5N \diagup^{Cl}_{\diagdown CH_2.O.R} \qquad C_5H_5N \diagup^{Cl}_{\diagdown CH_2.NH.COR} \qquad C_5H_5N \diagup^{Cl}_{\diagdown CH_2.NH.CO.OR}$$

Velan

VELAN PF (or Zelan in the U.S.A.) is marketed as a cream-coloured powder which should be stored in a cool, dry place. It dissolves in water at 35° to 40°C. to give a slightly opalescent solution, from which the Velan gradually separates as a very fine dispersion, in which condition it is usually employed, as the warm solution is somewhat unstable. An addition of 5 oz. of crystalline sodium acetate (3 oz. of anhydrous salt) per pound of Velan should be made to the final bath.

In view of its dual effect of waterproofing and softening, Velan can be used not only on gaberdines, but also on more delicate materials where handle and draping qualities are essential. The process may be applied to most textile materials, including cotton, linen, viscose and acetate rayons, jute, hemp, and sisal, as well as to animal fibres such as wool and silk; chlorinated wool in particular is not only rendered water-repellent but acquires a soft and attractive finish. An outstanding feature of the Velan finish is that the effect is resistant not only to washing, including boiling soap solutions, but also to dry-cleaning. The softening effect may be produced by impregnating and drying, but for a permanent water-repellent effect a final heat treatment is essential.

In general the concentration of Velan should not be less than 1 lb. per 10 gallons of water (i.e. 1% solution), and where highly twisted and tightly woven yarns are concerned it is preferable to use the liquor at about 35°C. The Velan solution is not very stable towards sulphates and sulphonic acids, boric acid and borates, sodium hydroxide, sodium carbonate, and various phosphates; the Velan powder already contains some sodium chloride which has a definite effect in promoting surface action.

The Velan treatment is divided into three stages—impregnation, drying, and heating. Impregnation may be carried out in a jig, winch, or padding mangle when treating fabrics, or in a dye-beck when treating yarns; the excess of liquor may be removed by squeezing or by hydroextraction. The drying step may be conducted on drying cylinders, festoon drier, or hot-air stenter; it is better to dry the goods rapidly and the higher the drying temperature, the more necessary it is to remove the resultant water vapour quickly from the vicinity of the goods. Heating is the most important part of the treatment and should be carried out in a hot-air chamber. The goods must be heated uniformly to the required temperature for a period long enough to give the required effect, and the period of heating varies inversely with the temperature; for instance, at 100°C. the time should be at least 5 minutes, at 120°C. a period of 3 minutes is required, and at 150°C. a minimum period of 1 minute is needed.

The goods should be given a light soaping with 0·2% soap and 0·1% soda ash solution at 35° to 40°C. for 1 to 2 minutes, followed by a thorough rinsing, for *any soap or other detergent left in the material will reduce its apparent water-repellency.* It is important to realise that the final drying stage of the treatment should be effected at a high temperature for the best result.

For cotton or rayon dress goods, a concentration of 2 to 3% Velan PF may be required, but this may vary with the nature of the goods; for cotton gaberdines 3 to 6% is advisable, and the impregnating solution should be lukewarm (i.e. about 35°C.). Similar concentrations are recommended for silk, wool, and worsted, but concentrations of the order of 0·5 to 1% are quite adequate for acetate rayon.

Recent Work

As would be expected, numerous variations have been executed on this theme, and it is not possible to give an account of every process which has been devised. Some of the developments, however, are of great interest as illustrating the advance of textile science, as well as effecting small but definite improvements in the technique of water-repellency.

A very interesting development has been described in B.P. 517,474 by Rogers and the I.C.I.; methylene distearamide is first prepared from stearamide and formaldehyde and the product treated with more paraformaldehyde, and also hydrogen chloride, when a product is formed containing three formaldehyde residues attached to the stearamide molecules. The reactions proceed as follows:

$$C_{17}H_{35}.CO.NH_2 \qquad\qquad C_{17}H_{35}.CO.NH$$
$$+ H.CHO \longrightarrow \qquad\qquad \overset{|}{C}H_2$$
$$C_{17}H_{35}.CO.NH_2 \qquad\qquad C_{17}H_{35}.CO.\overset{|}{N}H$$

$$\begin{array}{cc} C_{17}H_{35}.CO.NH & C_{17}H_{35}.CO.N.CH_2Cl \\ | & | \\ CH_2 + H.CHO + HCl \longrightarrow & CH_2 \\ | & | \\ C_{17}H_{35}.CO.NH & C_{17}H_{35}.CO.N.CH_2Cl \end{array}$$

This compound forms a di-pyridinium compound of formula

$$C_{17}H_{35}.CO.N.CH_2.N(C_5H_5).Cl$$
$$\overset{|}{C}H_2$$
$$\overset{|}{C_{17}H_{35}.CO.N.CH_2.N(C_5H_5).Cl}$$

and this may be applied to textiles made from vegetable fibres in the manner which has already been described for the preceding treatments; the new products are also suitable for the treatment of wool. One feature of importance is their stability to possible decomposition by hot water during the process of application, and in this respect they are superior to the simpler compounds previously described. It is also claimed that these quaternary salts may be applied in conjunction with the crease-resisting process, described on page 390, and so provide textiles which are crease-resistant and water-repellent; the two processes may be carried out simultaneously or separately, and in either order.

The use of amides and carbamates in the preparation of compounds which are capable of making cotton water-repellent suggests that a similar type of reaction might be used with urea derivatives. This has been accomplished, as described in B.P. 497,856, by Cusa, Salkeld, and Walker of the I.C.I., utilising compounds of formula R.CO.NH.CO.NH$_2$, of which lauryl urea is an example. This may be treated with paraform and hydrochloric acid in the usual manner to give a compound which forms a pyridinium salt.

$$C_5H_5N \diagup^{Cl}_{\diagdown CH_2.NH.CONH.COC_{11}H_{23}}$$

(Cf. formulae on page 485)

The cotton or wool is treated by the method already described. Another type of compound is shown by the general formula R.NH.CO.NH$_2$, of which heptadecyl urea ($C_{17}H_{35}$.NH.CO.NH$_2$) is an example.

Yet again it is possible to utilise alkyl carbamates as the starting products; these are derived from carbamic acid NH$_2$.COOH. B.P. 498,287, by the same inventors, outlines the use of carbamates of general formula RO.CO.NH$_2$ where R is the radical of an alcohol obtainable by reducing the carboxylic group of an acid made from oils and fats by saponification. The quaternary salt has the general formula

$$C_5H_5N \diagup^{Cl}_{\diagdown CH_2.NH.CO.OR}$$

of which carbo-octadecyloxyaminoethylpyridinium chloride may be taken as an illustration

$$C_5H_5N \diagup^{Cl}_{\diagdown CH_2.NH.CO.OC_{18}H_{37}}$$

Here again the same general method of application is followed; the textile material is impregnated, dried, and baked, when the fatty residue becomes chemically combined with the fibre to give a permanent water-repellent effect.

Further developments with alkyl carbamates (NH$_2$.COOR) are given in B.P. 517,632 by Baldwin, Rogers, and the I.C.I. The alkyl carbamates are treated with either formaldehyde and hydrochloric acid or with a dihalogen dimethyl ether to give a chlormethyl derivative which may be utilised in the form of its quaternary ammonium salt. Stearyl carbamate $NH_2.COOC_{17}H_{35}$ is an interesting example.

Rogers and the I.C.I., in B.P. 517,631, have described the treatment of paraphenylenediamine with stearyl chloroformate to give

$$NH.COOC_{18}H_{37}$$

$$NH.COOC_{18}H_{37}$$

which may be treated with paraform and hydrochloric acid in benzene to give a chlormethyl derivative which, in its turn, forms a dipyridinium salt of the following formula:

$$Cl.C_5H_5N.CH_2.N.COOC_{18}H_{37}$$

$$Cl.C_5H_5N.CH_2.N.COOC_{18}H_{37}$$

It is interesting to compare the above compound with that made according to B.P. 517,474 (see page 487); in this instance, however, carbamates or urethanes are the starting-point in the formation of a somewhat more complicated structure.

An ingenious method of utilising di-carbimides is seen in B.P. 521,116 of Deutsche Hydrierwerke. The di-carbimides or di-isocyanates react with a fatty alcohol to give a urethane

$$R(NCO)_2 + R'OH \longrightarrow R \begin{array}{c} NH.COOR' \\ | \\ \\ | \\ NH.COOR' \end{array}$$

which can be used to produce water-repellent effects on textile materials.

Long-chain methylolamides of general formula $R.CO.NH.CH_2OH$ have been utilised by Du Pont for water-repellent effects; compounds of this type have been known for some time, but it has now been discovered that they may be converted to less polar esters which are soluble in organic solvents. For instance, methylol stearamide may be treated with acetic anhydride to give acetoxymethyl stearamide $C_{17}H_{35}CO.NH.CH_2O.CO.CH_3$. Cotton may be made water-repellent by impregnating with 1% lactic acid solution, drying, and then treating with a 5% solution of the above ester in benzene. Drying at room temperature and baking for 10 minutes at 150°C. completes the process. Further details may be seen in B.P. 537,297.

Methylolamides have also been utilised in B.P. 524,737 of Ciba. Compounds such as methylol stearamide are dissolved in pyridine and treated with benzoic-acid-sulphochloride to give a product soluble in hot water $C_{17}H_{35}CO.NH.CH_2O.CO.C_6H_4SO_3H$. Actually, it is preferable to apply this compound from feebly acidulated aqueous solution by working for 10 minutes at 50° to 60°C., followed by drying and heating.

Further attention has recently been given to solubilising methods other than the formation of quaternary ammonium salts; the above-mentioned specification relies on the sulphonic acid group in the benzene nucleus. The same company has utilised sulphur compounds of the thiourea type to effect solubility, as outlined in B.P. 526,738; stearyl alcohol is converted to its chlormethyl ether in the usual manner, dissolved in benzene, and heated with thiourea to form

$$C_{18}H_{37}O.CH_2S.C : NH.HCl$$
$$|$$
$$NH_2$$

which separates on cooling. When a fabric is impregnated with an aqueous solution of this reagent and dried at 75°C. it acquires water-repellent properties which are fast to washing.

Another Ciba process is described in B.P. 527,012, where methylol amides are treated with thiourea in alcohol and then alcoholic hydrogen chloride is added to form compounds of the type

$$R.CO.NHCH_2S.C(:NH).NH_2.HCl$$

These compounds are applied to cotton, in presence of sodium acetate, from about 1% solution, squeezed, and dried at 75° to 100°C.

Another method of producing increased solubility in water is to form poly-quaternary ammonium salts of the chlormethyl derivatives of methylol amides of fatty acids. This new departure is due to Du Pont, and is outlined in B.P. 536,619 and 538,608. A simple polytertiary amine (an amine with more than one tertiary nitrogen atom in the molecule) is tetramethyl diaminomethane $N(CH_3)_2.$-$CH_2.N(CH_3)_2$, made from formaldehyde and dimethylamine.

It is interesting to note that the specification in question also discloses another method of converting methylolamides into the chlormethyl compounds, by dissolving in ethylene dichloride and treating with thionyl chloride

$$R.CONH.CH_2OH + SOCl_2 \longrightarrow R.CO.NH.CH_2Cl$$

These may be combined with the polytertiary amines to give poly-quaternary ammonium salts, which are very soluble in water. Solutions of these compounds, when applied to textiles, give water-repellent effects when baked at 105° to 130°C.

It is interesting to compare these compounds of Du Pont with the I.C.I. products of B.P. 517,474, as described on page 487.

$$C_{17}H_{35}CO.N.CH_2.N(C_5H_5).Cl$$
$$\mid$$
$$CH_2$$
$$\mid$$
$$C_{17}H_{35}CO.N.CH_2.N(C_5H_5).Cl$$
(I.C.I.)

$$Cl.N(CH_3)_2.CH_2.NH.COC_{17}H_{35}$$
$$\mid$$
$$CH_2$$
$$\mid$$
$$Cl.N(CH_3)_2.CH_2.NH.COC_{17}H_{35}$$
(Du Pont)

In concluding this section, it may be emphasised that most of these new compounds consist of quaternary ammonium salts of pyridine and contain a hydrophobic portion and a polar portion which is capable of forming a bond with cellulose. This polar group must be very reactive; this property is shown by the chlormethyl group, but *not* by the chlorethyl group. Zerner and Pollak (Textile Research, 1944, *14*, 242) have shown that small differences in internal molecular structure may have a great effect on water-repellency.

$$C_{17}H_{35}CO.N.CH_2.N(C_5H_5)Cl$$
$$\mid$$
$$CH_3$$
(Long chain to CO—good)

$$CH_3.CO.N.CH_2.N(C_5H_5)Cl$$
$$\mid$$
$$C_{18}H_{37}$$
(Long chain to N—bad)

Another interesting example, due to steric hindrance, may be seen in the consideration of the following compound.

$$\begin{array}{c} C_{17}H_{35}CO \\ \diagdown \\ \\ Cl.N(C_5H_5).CH_2 \diagup \end{array} N.CH_2.CH_2.N \begin{array}{c} \diagup CO.C_{17}H_{35} \\ \\ \diagdown CH_2.N(C_5H_5)Cl \end{array}$$

This compound is bad in respect of water-repellency, but a similar compound, with an odd number of methylene groups between the fatty amide radicals, gives good results.

CHAPTER XIX
MOTHPROOFING

THE ravages of the clothes moths have been known from early times; for instance, in Job xiii, 28, there is a biblical reference to "a garment that is moth-eaten." Even to-day the problem of protecting the keratin fibres from insect pests is still of general interest to housewives, retailers, wholesalers, and manufacturers. Owing to climatic conditions, and possibly the popularity of central heating, continental Europe and the U.S.A. present greater opportunities to the pests than is the case in England.

The insects which are able to destroy keratin materials, such as wool, hair, fur, feathers, etc., may be divided into two classes: (*a*) the clothes moths, and (*b*) the Dermestid beetles.

There are three common types of clothes moth—*Tineola Bissellella* Hummel, or common clothes moth; *Tinea Pellionella* L., or fur moth; and *Tricophaga Tapetiella* L., or tapestry moth; the first-named is the commonest, and is responsible for the greater part of the damage commonly attributed to insects feeding on animal fibres which Clark (J.T.I., 1928, *19*, 295) estimates to be over £1,000,000 annually in England alone and about $100,000,000 in the U.S.A. Meckbach (Textilber., 1921, *2*, 19) estimated the world's annual loss of wool due to this pest to be 22,500,000 lb. at that time.

A complete description and life-history of the various moths has been given by Austen and Hughes (Clothes Moths and House Moths, British Museum, London, 1932). The adult clothes moth is a pale buff colour with a metallic lustre; the moths vary in size, but some specimens have a wing span of 0·5 inches.

The life-history of the clothes moth is very similar to that of the other two species. The sexes mate soon after emerging from the pupal stage, and the female usually starts laying eggs within 24 hours; the life of the female is only 16 days, but eggs are laid daily, although most of them are laid in the first few days. The average number is about 150, and these are laid loosely on the material, but soon find their way into crevices on account of their smallness. The grubs hatch in 8 to 10 days, and are about 1 mm. in length; the larval stage is that during which damage to keratin fibres takes place, for this material is essential to the grubs not only as solid food, but also as a source of water of which keratin usually contains 15%. The average daily increase in weight during the feeding period of some 70 days is 550%. After reaching full growth, the larva spins

492

itself a cocoon and passes into the pupal stage, emerging as a moth in 14 to 44 days, depending on the environment.

It is interesting to note that the clothes moth does not attack the cellulose fibres or even silk; apparently the presence of sulphur in the keratin is of special significance.

The Dermestid beetles are not prominent as textile pests in England, there being only occasional damage, but they are responsible for serious destruction in the U.S.A., to which they were introduced from Europe, and where they are generally known as carpet beetles. As with the clothes moth, the damage is done by the voracious larvæ, which also consume leather and silk, as well as wool, fur, and feathers.

The beetle is about $\frac{3}{16}$ inches long, with a black and white marbled appearance; the larvæ are reddish brown in colour and covered with short hairs. Being fond of darkness, they infest carpets, particularly of the fitted type, and are often found in the crevices between floor-boards. The larva sheds its skin many times and the pupa develops in the last larval skin; the pupal stage lasts 6 to 15 days.

CONTROL

The same general methods of combating the ravages of these pests may be applied to clothes moths and carpet beetles; the latter, however, is much hardier than the former, being more catholic in feeding.

Primarily, some control may be exercised by exposure to light and air, for the pests are fond of the dark, and many of the carpet beetles require a warm atmosphere for their welfare (approximately 80°F. or 27°C.); hence their ravages in centrally heated buildings which are apt to be overheated. Exposure to sunlight is a very old method of dealing with insect pests, about 90 minutes being adequate. It has recently been suggested to expose infested material to the radiation from a resistance element heated to give a maximum emission peak between 8,000 and 10,000 Å.; the radiation is lethal to insect pests, and may be produced in a lamp containing 86% argon and 4% nitrogen, with the filament heated to 3,400°K.

Mechanical removal of eggs and larvæ by brushing and beating is largely practised in the fur trade, as well as in the household; the method is laborious and unreliable. Great attention must be paid to seams and pleats of garments, carpets must be taken up, and the whole process repeated at frequent intervals. The mechanical action which occurs during dry-cleaning also helps to remove larvæ and eggs.

Special closed packages are commonly employed when goods have to be stored, but care must be taken to ensure that the goods are not already infested, or the packing will merely provide the pests with their favourite environment. One common method is to wrap the goods in paper, and it is a popular fallacy that newspaper is particularly valuable on account of the printer's ink; any paper providing a secure package with no means of entry affords good protection. Cedarwood chests have also been used extensively in the U.S.A. on the assumption that the wood itself acts as a mothicide, but Back and Raback (U.S. Dept. Agric. Bull., No. 1051, 1922) investigated this point and concluded that chests of ordinary wood, if tightly constructed, were equally effective.

Storage *in vacuo* has been practised in the U.S.A., and this kills any insects infesting the goods, which, however, are liable to reinfection when removed from the protective chamber. The same criticism applies to the methods of cold storage, which is practised both in England and the U.S.A., particularly for furs; in addition, the cold does not kill the moth or beetle, but merely renders it dormant. Back (ibid., No. 1353) found both larvæ alive after a year at 40°F. or 4° to 5°C. It is possible, however, to kill young grubs by submitting them to sudden changes in temperature; as an example of the method, the goods may be placed in an atmosphere at −8°C. for a short time, then 10°C., and finally −8°C. The process should be repeated, after which the goods may be permanently stored at 4° to 5°C.

High temperatures may also be used to kill moths at various stages in their development; hot ironing is a household method, but superheated steam has been employed on an industrial scale. The minimum temperature for the destruction of moth larvæ by hot water is about 60°C.; the fabric should be immersed for 10 seconds and dried. It is obviously important that the fabric should wet evenly and the use of a wetting agent is advisable. This method is limited in its application on account of interference with shape, finish, and permanence of colour with many materials.

FUMIGATION

The most effective fumigants will kill both grubs and insects, but not the eggs; hence, a second application is necessary after an interval of several days. Fumigation, of course, offers no subsequent protection, and it is necessary that the fumigating agent employed should have no deleterious effect on the goods under treatment. On this account hydrogen cyanide is the best reagent, but owing to its lethal nature, it requires expert attention. Sulphur dioxide is also effective and less dangerous. The methods of application have been given by Whewell (Textile Recorder, 1941, Jan., p. 16). Carbon disulphide has been used to a large extent, but the inflammable nature of the vapour is a disadvantage. Fumigation with formaldehyde is of no value.

Numerous volatile compounds have been suggested to create an atmosphere which is obnoxious to the moth or beetle and so act as deterrents; they are less volatile than the reagents employed for fumigation, but, being volatile, cannot achieve permanent results and are often of doubtful efficiency. The most popular compound is naphthalene.

Compounds of this type are obnoxious to the female moth, and she will avoid the neighbourhood, but they are useless where eggs have already been laid. A high vapour concentration must be established, and for naphthalene it is necessary to use about 1 lb. per 6 to 10 cubic feet; this compound should be used in the form of flakes, for according to Clark (loc. cit.), balls are useless. For the most satisfactory results, the materials should be stored in closed containers, such as bags, drawers, and cupboards, and the naphthalene renewed from time to time.

Paradichlorbenzene is considered to be superior to naphthalene as a deterrent, and its odour is certainly less objectionable to human beings; some valuable data on this compound have been given by Darkis, Vermillion, and Gross (Ind. Eng. Chem., 1940, 32, 946). It appears to be effective when used in the proportion of 1 lb. per 20 cubic feet. A further point in its favour is that the smell is readily removed by airing the goods.

Camphor is another popular favourite for home use, but is less effective than naphthalene or paradichlorbenzene, and requires 1 lb. per 5 cubic feet; it is of no value against carpet beetles.

MOTHPROOF FINISHES

In view of the difficulties associated with setting up an atmosphere of obnoxious vapour, and human reaction to the malodorous preparations of camphor and moth balls, it is not surprising that attention has been devoted to a mothproof finish for keratinous textile material.

Two chief methods have been developed, and may be termed temporary and permanent. The temporary mothproofing depends on impregnating the fibres with a substance of low vapour tension and the protective agent is the toxic vapour produced. The method is actually very old, for the Greeks and Romans painted their manuscripts, made from animal skins, with cedarwood oil.

Many of the substances used as moth deterrents have been applied from organic solvents, but their use is open to the same criticism as the vapour method; indeed, more so, for in the fabric state it is often necessary to press the material during garment manufacture with unpleasant results. The organic solvents required are a disadvantage in most textile finishing works.

Permanent mothproofing consists in impregnating the fibre with non-volatile substances which render it unsuitable as food for the grubs of the clothes moth and carpet beetle. A successful preparation must also be without adverse effect on the textile character of the material to which it is applied; it must not affect handle, colour, strength, fastness of dyestuffs, nor must it be capable of irritating the human skin. Naturally, it must be cheap and capable of application from aqueous solution.

Many natural products have been suggested as permanent mothproofing agents, although they do not always fulfil the above requirements. Extracts of derris root have often been used as constituents of proprietary preparations for spraying; pyrethrum extract has also been applied, but neither of these substances can be regarded as highly efficient. Further, their potency rapidly diminishes.

Alkaloids have also been put forward for mothproofing purposes, the chief suggestions being nicotine, quinine, brucine, caffeine, and quinidine. According to Back (U.S. Dept. Agric. Bull., 1353) tobacco extracts containing nicotine, and also tobacco powder, are of no value. With regard to the other alkaloids, there is some difference of opinion, for Jackson and Wassel (Ind. Eng. Chem., 1927, *19*, 1177) consider that they are satisfactory, but Minaeff and Wright (ibid., 1929, *21*, 1187) found that although the treated fabrics were immune to attack for a little time, they were eventually damaged; the latter workers found that the sulphates, oxalates, salicylates, and sulphosalicylates of the alkaloids were of little value. It seems indicated that whereas the alkaloids have some protective action, they cannot be regarded as satisfactory mothproofing agents. The use of alkaloidal extracts has been protected in various specifications from time to time, namely, B.P. 230,203, 263,092; an Index of Mothproofing Materials has been compiled by Roark (U.S. Dept. Agric., Bureau of Entomology and Plant Quarantine, Division of Insecticide Investigation, 1931, 1933, and 1936).

ORGANIC COMPOUNDS

Synthetic organic compounds are responsible for the potency of most mothproofing preparations, and their use is based on certain discoveries in connection with dyestuffs. In 1917 or thereabouts, Meckbach of the I.G. started a series of researches into mothproofing compounds by placing 100 pieces of cloth in an infested box; each piece of cloth had received a different chemical treatment. At the end of six months, the only unattacked sample was that dyed with Martius Yellow. Many thousands of compounds were then tested during 1918 without success. Some difficulty was experienced in rearing the colonies of moths and examining their habits, so an extensive study of the clothes moth was made by Titschack (Beitrage zu einer Monographie der Kleidermotte, Leipzig, 1922). Further research by Meckbach (Textilber., 1921, 2, 19) resulted in the production of a satisfactory mothproofing compound introduced as Eulan; this name was originally applied to one compound, but now covers a whole series irrespective of chemical classification. The first Eulans were only effective against clothes moths, but the later products gave protection against dermestid attack also.

Meckbach's researches are assumed to have originated from the old wives' tale that green-coloured material never became moth-eaten; in actual fact, this only obtained with those green dyes of which Martius Yellow (2 : 4-dinitro-α-naphthol) was a component.

His great discovery, however, was that any inorganic compound containing fluorine will impart mothproofing properties to wool (e.g. B.P. 173,536), and this observation formed the basis of many preparations; the first Eulans, M and F, were not commercially successful, but Eulan Extra (an aluminium and ammonium double fluoride) had considerable application from 1924, until it was withdrawn in 1928. Eulan W Extra was then marketed and appeared to be acid potassium fluoride (potassium bifluoride).

The Eulans are protected by many patent specifications covering a wide range of substances, not all of which are organic compounds. D.R.P. 344,266 refers to the sulpho- and carboxylic acids of aromatic hydrocarbons and their substitution products excepting amino-naphthol-sulphonic acids, and D.R.P. 346,596 includes carboxylic acids with the carboxyl group in the side-chain of the aromatic or heterocyclic compound, such as phenyl-acetic acid and benzilic acid.

B.P. 238,287 claims the use of non-dyeing compounds which contain the grouping

$$-N-X=Y$$
$$\mid$$
$$R$$

where X represents nitrogen or carbon, Y represents nitrogen, carbon, or a carbon nucleus, and R represents hydrogen or a hydro-carbon radical or an acid group such as acetyl, benzoyl, and so forth; particularly applicable substances are ethylidenephenyl hydrazone, ethylidenehydrazone-phenylcarboxylic acid-ethyl ester, diazoamino-benzene, triphenylguanidine, phthalic acid-phenylhydrazide, and pyrazolone.

D.R.P. 449,126 discloses the use of aromatic sulphonic acid chlorides, such as paratoluene-sulphochloride and $1 : 5$ naphthalene disulphonic acid chloride; the corresponding fluorides form the basis of D.R.P. 450,418 and are stated to be more effective.

B.P. 274,428 describes the use of orthohydroxycarboxylic acids

32

or their derivatives, in which the para-position to the hydroxyl group
is occupied by halogen or sulphur, or in which the ortho-position
is occupied by hydroxyl, halogen, sulphur, or hydrocarbon residue;
where both ortho- and para-positions are occupied, the para-position
may also be taken by a hydrocarbon. Specified examples include
1-hydroxy-4-chloro-2-benzoic acid, 1-hydroxy-4-6-dimethyl-2-ben-
oic acid and sulphurised 2-hydroxynaphthoic acid.

Thiourea and its derivatives were mentioned in B.P. 301,421 and
developed further in B.P. 340,319 to include compounds of the
general type

$$S = C \overset{\textstyle R}{\underset{\textstyle NHR'}{<}}$$

where R is alkyl, aryl, or aralkyl and R is hydrogen or aryl; thio-
benzamide is an actual example. Thiouronium salts were suggested
later in B.P. 346,039.

The use of fluorides is taken further in B.P. 316,987 to cover
borofluor-organic compounds such as boro-trifluoro-acetic acid; the
introduction of fluorine directly attached to the carbon atom of the
molecule forms the basis of B.P. 333,863, from which it appears
that sodium-3-nitro-4-fluoro-1-benzoate confers mothproofing properties although sodium-3-nitro-1-benzoate does not.

An enormous amount of work appears to centre around the
colourless halogen-containing hydroxy di- or triarylmethane compounds originally described in B.P. 316,900, and many subsequent
specifications suggest that the mothproofing effect is due to the
phenolic residue; B.P. 333,584 utilises compounds where the phenolic
residues are directly linked, as in the hydroxydiphenyl compounds
such as 3-5-3'-5'-tetrabromo-2-2'-dihydroxydiphenyl, which may be
applied from an acid dyebath.

As an alternative to the halogens, it has also been found possible
directly to link to carbon the elements of phosphorus, arsenic,
antimony, bismuth, or tin, and provide mothproofing preparations,
according to B.P. 303,092, which mentions phenylarsenic acid and
triphenylphosphinedihydroxide. This general idea has been developed further in B.P. 312,163 and 326,137 to embrace compounds
of general formula $(HO-Ar)_2X$, where Ar represents aryl and X
represents oxygen or nitrogen attached to hydrogen or an alkyl
radical.

Arylsulphonicacidamides such as 4-chlorobenzenesulphonamide
are described as mothproofing agents in B.P. 324,962; they are
difficult to dissolve, but in conjunction with phosphoric acid esters
they may be applied from organic solvents.

Although the development of colourless dyes as mothproofing agents has been the subject of considerable work, dyestuffs themselves have also been investigated. Minaeff (Textile Colourist, 1927, *49*, 89) found that samples of wool dyed with Victoria Blue, Methyl Violet, Brilliant Green, Congo Red R, Fuchsine, Safranine, Chrysoidine, Indigo, Methylene Blue, and Auramine resisted the carpet beetle in the above order, but for the clothes moth the order was slightly different; even the best samples, however, could not be regarded as adequately mothproof. Martius Yellow and Naphthol Yellow have excellent mothproofing properties; the former is a salt of dinitro-α-naphthol and the latter of dinitro-α-naphthol-β-sulphonic acid.

Returning to the question of colourless dyes, the pentachlorodihydroxytriphenylmethane sulphonic acids are very suitable agents, for they are absorbed like acid dyes and behave like acid milling colours in respect of fastness. Herrmann (Am. Dyes. Rep., 1940, *29*, 539) suggests 2% of the reagent on the weight of the wool for protection against the carpet beetle and 1·5% where only the clothes moth has to be considered. The proofing is fast to light, washing, and dry-cleaning.

The enormous number of substances which has been patented for mothproofing renders classification difficult, but the chief lines of advance among organic compounds have been outlined above; further details have been given by Clark (J.T.I., 1928, *19*, 295P; 1936, *27*, 389P). Whewell (Textile Recorder, Dec. 1940 to June 1941) has provided a very useful review of the subject. More recent contributions have been made by Clark (J.S.D.C., 1943, *59*, 213) and by Hartley, Elsworth, and Barritt (ibid., 1943, *59*, 266).

Among the well-known commercial mothproofing preparations, Eulan *BS* or *BL* was quite popular until it was found to cause dermatitis; Eulan *B* was a waxy solid whose constitution does not appear to have been disclosed. It was withdrawn in 1927. Another preparation which was also soluble in organic solvents and therefore used by dry-cleaners was Eulan *AL*.

$$\text{Cl} \underset{\underset{\text{Eulan AL}}{}}{\overset{\overset{\text{Cl}}{}}{\big\langle\underline{\quad}\big\rangle}} SO_2.NH.CH_3$$

Eulan *RH* and *RHF* appear to be based on B.P. 274,425; the chief constituent was 1-hydroxy-4-chloro-6-methyl-2-benzoic acid. The product was sold as the water-soluble sodium salt, but it was not easy to obtain level results.

Eulan *N* was probably 2 : 2'-dihydroxy-3 : 5 : 3' : 5': tetrachlorotriphenylmethane-2''-sulphonic acid (B.P. 316,900 and 335,547);

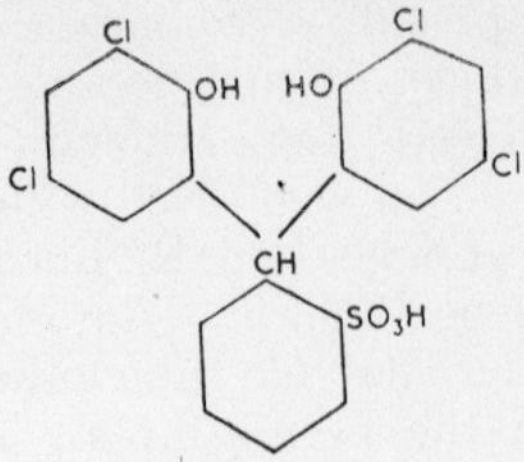

Eulan New

when applied from solution it gave level results and was fast to all circumstances with the exception of heavy milling. Eulan *CN* also exhausted completely; it was the sodium salt of 4, 3′, 5′, 3″, 5″ pentachlor - 6,6″ dihydroxy - triphenylmethane - 2 - sulphonic acid. About 2% was required on the weight of the wool, and it was best applied from a slightly acid bath.

Eulan *NK* has been stated to rely on B.P. 312,163 and appears to contain a triphenyldichlorbenzylphosphonium group as the essential component.

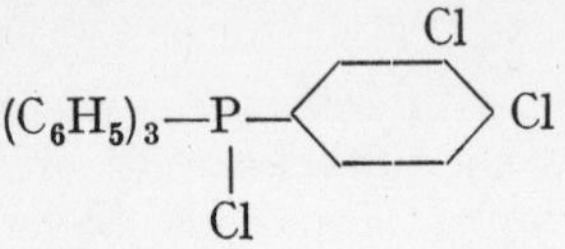

Eulan NK

More recently, the Geigy Company has marketed Mitin *FF*, whose constitution is shown below; many compounds suggested by this company are substituted ureas in which the substituents are aromatic groups with suitable solubilising groups. A typical compound is 4-trimethyl ammonium laurophenone methyl sulphate.

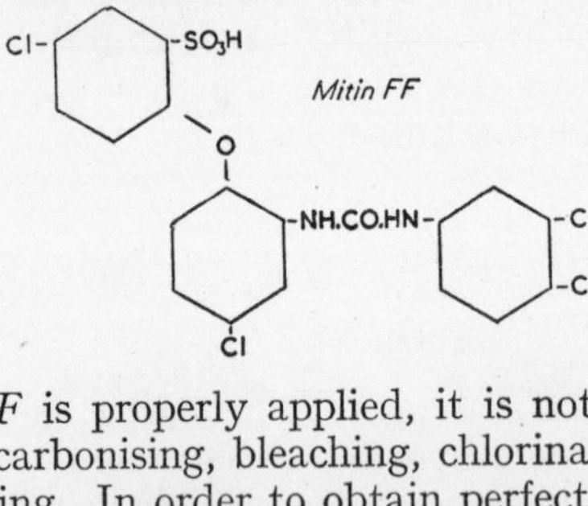

Mitin FF

When Mitin *FF* is properly applied, it is not affected by light, milling, potting, carbonising, bleaching, chlorination, or by general dyeing and finishing. In order to obtain perfect protection against moths, 3% of Mitin *FF* should be used calculated on the weight of the dry wool; the best fixation is obtained when the Mitin is applied at the boil, and it may be applied at the same time as the dyestuff.

Good protection is also obtained when Mitin *FF* is applied at 45°C., which may be necessary in the treatment of dyed goods; the bath is made up with 3% Mitin *FF*, and 0·5 to 1% of formic acid. The goods may be entered at 30°C., raised to 45°C. in 20 minutes, and maintained at that temperature for 45 minutes, followed by hydro-extraction and drying. If Mitin *FF* is applied at 25°C. it will withstand rinsing with water, but not washing. The time of treatment at 25°C. should be 1 hour.

INORGANIC SALTS

A number of INORGANIC SALTS has also been successfully utilised as mothproofing agents; indeed, up to about 1928 the chief moth-proofing agents were salts of the neutral fluoride type as compounds containing fluorine appear to be peculiarly toxic towards the carpet beetle and clothes moth. Sodium fluoride has received great attention, and materials immersed in a saturated solution of this compound, squeezed, and dried are adequately mothproofed; unfortunately the effect is removed by washing or dry-cleaning.

B.P. 173,536 disclosed the use of fluorides and silicofluorides for mothproofing. This was followed later by the use of neutral solutions of the silicofluorides of sodium, potassium, lithium, zinc, or aluminium, according to B.P. 235,914, or with a soluble sulphate in addition, as suggested in B.P. 235,915.

B.P. 173,536 actually discloses the use of many other substances, such as phosphotungstic acid, antimony tungstic acid, phospho-molybdic acid, tungstic acid, uranic acid, colloidal silicic acid, colloidal stannic acid, molybdic acid, antimonic acid, potassium silicate, ammonium molybdate, as well as hydrofluoric acid, zinc fluoride, aluminium fluoride, titanium fluoride, hydrofluosilicic acid, and the double fluoride of ammonia and titanium. In D.R.P. 347,723 it is proposed to after-treat the fibres which have already been proofed according to the above specification (B.P. 173,536) with metallic salts so as to form insoluble compounds capable of withstanding milling, acid treatment, and other finishing operations. Assistants, mordants, and acids may be added to the hydrofluosilicic acid or its salts, according to D.R.P. 347,849, and the use of wetting agents in conjunction with the main compounds is the subject of B.P. 288,825.

An important development of B.P. 173,536 may be seen in B.P. 295,742, which discloses the use of compounds of general formula $X(HF)_n$ where X indicates an inorganic or organic salt free from fluorine, or, alternatively, a metallic fluoride. An example from the specification describes the treatment of 100 kg. of wool in ten times its weight of hot or cold water containing 2 kg. of tripotassium difluorodisulphate, followed by rinsing and drying. Another example refers to monopotassium monofluorophosphate, and further substances mentioned are potassium bifluoride, polyacid fluorides such as $KF(HF)_2$, or mixtures of simple and polyacid fluorides such as $KF(HF) + KF(HF)_2$.

It is probable that Eulan Extra and Eulan W Extra of the I.G. are related to the subject-matter of the above specification, but, as previously mentioned, Eulan covers a range of compounds, the number of patents being so large that it is difficult to identify products sold under trade names.

Sodium silicofluoride has been shown to be more satisfactory than sodium fluoride as a mothproofing agent, and forms the basis of many commercial preparations of which "Larvex" is well known; both Burgess (J.S.D.C., 1935, 51, 85) and Minaeff and Wright (Ind. Eng. Chem., 1929, 21, 1187) have described its effectiveness. The most satisfactory method of application is to immerse the goods in the cold saturated solution, squeeze, and dry. For home use, a solution of 0·25 oz. of sodium silicofluoride and 0·5 oz. of a wetting agent per gallon of warm water has been advised. The result, of course, is not fast to washing, and a further disadvantage is the chalkiness produced on dark materials which have been treated and then subjected to local pressure. Minaeff and Wright (loc. cit.) found that whereas sodium fluoride is not preferentially adsorbed by wool, yet there is a definite adsorption with the silicofluoride; this adsorption is influenced by the presence of other compounds, being accelerated by aluminium compounds which may be used to ensure rapid exhaustion of the bath. Sodium sulphate and certain acids, however, bring about a reduction in the amount of silicofluoride taken up by the fibre. As "Larvex" was developed by Minaeff and Wright, it may be assumed to consist of sodium silicofluoride and aluminium compounds. The reagent is generally employed in aqueous solution containing 0·6% sodium silicofluoride, and the goods are impregnated for 10 to 20 minutes. If it is intended to spray the wool, then a concentration of 0·1% is adequate.

Chromium fluoride has also been used for mothproofing, but its efficient application requires certain well-defined conditions. B.P. 413,445, by Lowe, discloses the use of 3 lb. of chromium fluoride per 100 lb. of wool, the material being immersed in the solution for 20 minutes at 82°C. and then hydroextracted and dried at 65°C., or higher. The heat treatment is important as it fixes the chromium on the wool, and for effective mothproofing, chromium compounds equivalent to at least 0·55% of chromium fluoride must be deposited on the wool. The treatment is fast to washing, boiling in water only removing 0·1% of the deposited salts. The chief disadvantage of this method is that the goods are tinted green, which renders it unsuitable for white material and wool to be dyed in pastel shades.

This difficulty has been overcome by the use of a mixture of chromium and antimony fluorides in the ratio of 4 : 1; white materials are not stained and delicate shades may be produced without difficulty, although it is advisable to carry out a preliminary test in case the shade produced by certain dyes is altered by the mordanting action of the chromium salt. This improvement, also by Lowe, forms the basis of B.P. 413,529; the use of the double salt of chromium fluoride and sodium antimony fluoride (obtained by evaporation of the mixture) is described in B.P. 454,458.

The Kydo mothproofing process is described in B.P. 516,317, the reagent being ammonium fluorantimoniate, $(NH_4F)_2.SbF_3$, which is rather more convenient than mixtures of a fluoride and an antimony salt. In actual examples of various modifications of the process, it is possible to treat the wool with 2% of sodium antimony fluoride, calculated on the weight of the wool, or with 1·5% sodium antimony fluoride and 1·5% sodium silicofluoride at 30° C. for 30 minutes, followed by hydroextraction and drying.

Eulan W, or potassium bifluoride, was probably the best and cheapest mothproofing agent where fastness to water did not matter; being an acid salt, it was absorbed from the liquor by the wool and entered into loose chemical combination with the fibre.

MOTHPROOF FIBRES

One of the latest methods of mothproofing wool is to modify the keratin structure by chemical means. This is due to Geiger, Kobayashi, and Harris (Bur. Stand. J. Res., 1942, *29*, 381), who converted the disulphide linkages into bis-thioether linkages. The disulphide groups are first reduced to sulphydryl groups by treatment with a mercaptan under suitable conditions, such as thioglycollic acid at pH 7 and 50° C. The reduced wool is then washed and alkylated by treatment with an alkyl halide such as methylene dibromide at pH 8 for 2 hours at 50° C., using 0·0005 mol. of alkylating agent per gramme of wool.

$$R—S—S—R + HSCH_2COOH \longrightarrow RSH + HOOC.CH_2.S.S.CH_2.COOH$$
$$R—SH + (CH_2)_n Br_2 \longrightarrow R—S—(CH_2)_n—S—R$$

The mothproofing effect is not removed by laundering or dry-cleaning.

CHAPTER XX

MILDEWPROOFING

As spores and bacteria exist everywhere, the formation of moulds and mildew is possible on most textile fibres. The two essential conditions for the growth of mildew are warmth and moisture, so that where goods are stored under cool, dry, and well-ventilated conditions there is little danger of micro-organisms being formed; it must be realised, however, that a humid atmosphere is not so necessary for fungi as for bacteria. Whatever precautions may be taken in warehouses are apt to be nullified by the type of size or finishing preparation which may be present in the goods and act as a culture medium for the micro-organisms; some preparations applied to cloth contain hygroscopic compounds and these favour the production of moulds and mildew.

In very many cases it is possible to detect the presence of moulds by examining the goods in ultra-violet light which produces an intense yellow fluorescence of the infected areas.

The actual destruction of the textile material is due to enzymes which are secreted by the micro-organism. For instance, the moulds and bacteria which live on cellulose do not support themselves on the cellulose itself, but on its degradation products formed by the action of enzymes. The degradation of cellulose by enzymes is very similar to that which takes place in presence of acids with the exception that the enzyme is constantly regenerated; the production of glucose is due to the enzymes cellulase and cellobiase, and the glucose in its turn ferments under the action of zymase. Native cellulose, which is in the highest state of polymerisation, is only attacked by cellulase between 20° and 70°C.; this enzyme is chiefly found in moulds and bacteria which feed on wood. Cellobiase, on the other hand, is of much more common occurrence; its activity ceases at 67°C.

From this it appears, and is an important practical point, that resistance to the action of these enzymes is a function of the state of polymerisation of the material infected, so that regenerated cellulose is more susceptible than native cellulose; similarly, starch is more readily affected than cellulose, and yet again, the blocking of the hydroxyl groups in cellulose acetate renders it practically immune, for not only are the hydrolysis products different (no glucose is formed), but the initial moisture of the fibre is much lower.

In the destruction of wool, the active part of the micro-organism is the proteolytic enzyme which has the ability of hydrolysing the peptide linkage —CO.NH—. This hydrolysis is brought about by trypsin, which is composed of a proteinase, a polypeptidase, and a peptidase, but the tryptic enzymes are always associated with enterokinase, an activator in absence of which native proteins cannot be destroyed by trypsin. Ordinary keratin cannot be digested by the tryptic enzymes unless the disulphide group has been ruptured, as, for example, by oxidation. It is also noteworthy that the scaly layer, which is free from tyrosin, is much more resistant than the cortex or medulla.

It is common knowledge that wool which has been treated with alkali is more susceptible to attack than untreated wool, and it has been suggested that the swelling with alkali, as in vat dyeing, rendered the fibre liable to degradation. It is now known, however, that the activity of the tryptic enzyme reaches its maximum at pH 8·5, and that tests with solutions of barium and sodium hydroxides of the same pH value gave equal attack by these enzymes in spite of the difference in swelling.

Free amino-groups appear to be a prerequisite to severe attack by enzymes; this can be obviated by treatment with formaldehyde, which prevents fixation of the enzyme on the protein anions. Many dyestuffs are capable of preventing enzymatic hydrolysis; the chromed colours have this effect and methylene blue, even in an alkaline medium, also prevents destruction.

Silk appears to be much less susceptible than wool to enzymatic attack; a number of moulds which grow on raw silk only attack the gum, turning it a yellow colour, whereas attack on the silk protein is accompanied by a brown coloration and an odour of ammonia, together with the loss of tensile strength which is produced on all fibres when attacked by moulds and mildew. Bacteria do not develop very strongly on real silk.

WOOL

The factors affecting the growth of mildew on wool have been studied in some detail by Burgess (J.T.I., 1928, *19*, 315; 1929, *20*, 333; 1930, *21*, 441; J.S.D.C., 1931, *47*, 96; 1934, *50*, 138). Moisture is undoubtedly the chief factor and a scoured wool containing 0·5% alkali (estimated as sodium carbonate) will not form mildew at 23°C. unless it contains 24% of moisture; unscoured wool will form mildew at a lower moisture content, but on well-washed wool, even in a saturated atmosphere, the growth only appears slowly. Bacterial decomposition is practically limited to wool in the wet state.

A further consideration is the nature of the nutriment in the wool, and the presence of dirt, grease, and other foreign matter in raw wool promotes the formation of mildew. Increased susceptibility is produced by many detergents, such as soaps and wetting agents, but increased hygroscopicity may be a contributory factor. Some vegetable oils also assist the formation of mildew, but mineral oils tend to check the growth.

The growth of mildew is also affected by the soundness of the wool, and as all wool is more or less damaged, if only by weathering on the sheep's back, the infection rapidly passes to the sound or slightly damaged fibres. The state of the wool is apt to be aggravated by processes of a mechanical or chemical nature which tend to lower the protective value of the scales. The most seriously damaged fibres are the first to be affected by micro-organisms.

As previously stated, the presence of mildew is often due to the alkaline state of the wool, which was originally thought to cause chemical damage alone, but it is now known that it is the alkalinity which is responsible for mildew even in the absence of damage. The presence of strong acid favours the growth of moulds which, however, is checked by a slight degree of acidity, so that wool which has been dyed with acid dyes is less liable to mildew formation.

It is well known that considerable resistance to mildew results from the use of chrome in the dyebath; from 130 dyed samples exposed to infection by Burgess, 46 out of 49 which showed considerable resistance had been chromed. These results also showed that 0·5% chrome (either as CrO_3 or Cr_2O_3) imparts a definite resistance to mildew, while 1% checks the growth of mould. It is interesting to note that Thaysen and Bunker (Second Report of the Fabrics Co-ordinating Research Committee, 1930) found that a substantial resistance to mildew on cotton was obtained by dyeing with mineral khaki by the iron-chromium method; Burgess obtained similar results on wool.

It appears that the inhibitory action of chrome is due to the formation of a stable wool-chrome complex which is of no nutritional value to the mould. Conversely, the presence of alkali hydrolyses the wool substance to provide nutriment for the mildew.

The most efficient way of avoiding the growth of mildew is to provide adequate ventilation and avoid areas of stagnant air; a strongly alkaline condition of the wool must not be permitted, and the goods should be free from soaps and conditioning agents.

Treatment with antiseptics has received considerable attention, particularly for inhibiting the growth of mould fungi. Of some 150 substances examined by Burgess, sodium fluoride, sodium silico-fluoride, and Shirlan (salicylanilide) were found to be satisfactory both in effect and in suitability for commercial application. Sodium silico-fluoride (0·5%) is very suitable as it is inimical to both mould fungi and bacteria.

Harris and his co-workers (J. Res. Nat. Bur. Standard, 1941, 27, 459) have carried out some important experiments in connection with the resistance of wool to enzymes. As previously stated, wool which has not suffered mechanical or chemical damage is resistant to the action of proteolytic enzymes, but when the cuticle or scale layer is damaged mechanically the wool becomes susceptible to attack by pepsin and chymotripsin, after which the fibres are weakened and their structure partially destroyed, although only a small portion of the wool is digested. If the disulphide bonds are broken, as, for instance, by reduction or reduction followed by methylation, then the wool may be almost completely digested by pepsin and chymotripsin, but is only slightly attacked by trypsin. If, however, the reduced wool is re-oxidised, and the sulphydryl groups reconverted to disulphide groups, then the wool regains its original stability. It was further established that if the sulphydryl groups of the reduced wool are converted to *bis*-thioether groups by the action of an aliphatic dihalide, the stability of the wool to enzymes is greatly enhanced; suitable dihalides which may be used include methylene diiodide, ethylene dibromide, tetramethylene dibromide, and trimethylene dibromide (see also page 503).

CELLULOSE FIBRES

The cellulose fibres are attacked by a much larger number of different kinds of mildew than is the case with wool; further, the cellulose fibres are utilised under such conditions that exposure to mildew is almost inevitable. The high tensile strength of native cellulose, particularly in the wet state, renders it useful for many purposes to which wool is not suited, quite apart from questions of availability and expense, and in connection with such uses infection with mildew is almost inevitable.

Canvas for hosepipes, tent-cloth, awnings, screens, and many other outdoor applications is naturally subjected to conditions which favour attack, and the wartime necessity for sandbags extends the range of susceptible materials. Sailcloth and fishing-nets need special treatment to render them immune to destruction by micro-organisms. Cellulose acetate is naturally resistant.

In addition to the coarser textile materials mentioned above, large quantities of medium and fine fabrics of cotton and linen have to be stored and transported under conditions which sometimes give rise to mildew, and similar considerations apply to yarn and raw fibres. It is not possible to treat these materials with the crude but effective preparations which may be applied to covers for trucks and wagons, and this presents an added difficulty.

Mildewproofing

Mildewproofing is the protection of textile yarns and fabrics from the growth of micro-organisms, generally under tropical conditions of humidity and temperature.

The use of antiseptic materials is one of the commonest means for avoiding the growth of mildew in cotton goods, particularly cotton which contains starch or size. Substances such as phenol, cresol, salicylic acid, formaldehyde, and zinc chloride have been extensively used at various times, but suffer from certain disadvantages. For example, zinc chloride is only effective in fairly high concentrations (0·8%), and is apt to impart a damp feel to the cloth on account of its hygroscopic nature; the danger of tendering is acute on account of the ease with which acid is produced. Although salicylic acid is a good antiseptic in acid solution, its efficiency is impaired in presence of alkali. Formaldehyde and phenol are both objectionable on account of their odour and volatility.

A suitable antiseptic for general use must not be expensive; it must be colourless and odourless, unaffected by heat and readily soluble in any of the finishing preparations which may be applied to cotton. The reagent itself must be without action on cotton and inert towards the various dyestuffs or finishing agents which may be applied in the later stages of manufacture.

Fargher, Galloway, and Probert (J.T.I., 1930, 21, 245) made a comprehensive examination of a large number of antiseptic compounds, including 32 inorganic salts, 23 organo-mercury compounds, and 108 organic compounds. Previous to this work, Morris (ibid., 1927, 18, 99) had made a preliminary survey of available antiseptics and found three substances of exceptional toxicity, thallium carbonate, p-nitro-phenol, and 2 : 4 : 6-trichlorophenol. The first of these was not commonly available and was expensive, the second developed colour under neutral or alkaline conditions, and the third has a pungent odour.

The toxicity of phenol may be increased by the introduction of an alkyl, nitro, or halogen group, but is counteracted by sulphonic acid groups. Acetanilide was shown to be about half as toxic as phenol, so that its derivatives and allied substances were examined by Fargher, Galloway, and Probert. The combination of aniline with salicylic acid led to the observation that salicylanilide was as toxic as thallium carbonate, and much superior to any other salicyl derivative. When required in a soluble form, the sodium salt may be used without any loss of efficiency.

The use of salicylanilide as a mildew preservative is covered in B.P. 323,579 (U.S.P. 1,873,365), and the product is available under the registered trade name of SHIRLAN. Salicylanilide is a white, stable, odourless solid which is sparingly soluble in water; 0·005% at 25°C. and 0·08% at 100°C. Shirlan is available in three grades. Shirlan Extra is commercial salicylanilide, and its chief use lies in application to heavy cotton cloths which are subjected to weathering, and also to wool yarns and fabrics; it is applied from ammoniacal solution. A stock solution may be prepared by adding 2 parts of Shirlan Extra to 89 parts of water, heating to 70°C., and adding 9 parts of 30% ammonia solution. The stock solution may be diluted as required, with water or with dilute ammonia; the yarn or fabric is merely impregnated with the solution and dried. Shirlan D is salicylanilide in the form of a readily dispersible powder, and is about 60% as strong as Shirlan Extra; its chief use lies in the simple impregnation of yarns and fabrics, as it may be incorporated in starch sizing or finishing mixtures. For the treatment of awnings, tents, and sailcloth, a special aqueous dispersion, Shirlan A, is available for mixing with wax emulsions used for waterproofing; Shirlan A is 30% as strong as Shirlan Extra.

A survey of mildew-resistant treatments has also been made by Furry and Robinson (Am. Dyes. Rep., 1941, *30*, 504), utilising 8-oz. cotton duck material. The effectiveness of the treatment was based on the change in breaking load of the treated fabrics after inoculation and incubation with the micro-organism *Chaetomium globosum*; the incubation period was 14 days.

For convenience in discussion, the results may be arranged in three groups: (*a*) organic compounds, (*b*) organo-metallic compounds and metallic salts of organic compounds, and (*c*) inorganic compounds.

Organic compounds

The organic groups of treatment include an acetylating mixture, a resin from acetone and formalin, chlorothymol and thymol with phenyl salicylate, cutch, two chlorophenols, salicylanilide, and three quaternary ammonium compounds. The acetylation process consisted of treatment for 20 hours at 20° to 25°C. with a mixture of 33·3 g. of acetic anhydride, 27 g. of glacial acetic acid, and 3·7 g. of zinc chloride in 100 c.c. of water; very good protection against mildew was obtained, but the breaking load of the material was reduced 14% by the treatment. The acetone-formaldehyde resin could not be relied upon to give protection against mildew. Chlorothymol and its related compounds gave good protection even with 2 to 3% on the fabric, but the volatility of these compounds in steam may be a disadvantage in certain circumstances; combinations of chlorothymol with thymol or with phenyl salicylate are good mildew-resisting agents, but some 15% is required in the former case and 40% for the latter. Cutch (0·3%) used with cuprammonia (1% $CuSO_4$ solution) as a second treatment gave very good results, the cutch colouring the fabric a dark brown; the total increase in weight was 1·6%. Where cutch (1·3%) is used in conjunction with

potassium bichromate (0·3%) as a second treatment, the amount
(2·7%) on the fabric was insufficient for resistance to mildew, but,
as shown previously (Ind. Eng. Chem., 1941, *33*, 538), an increase
in weight of 3·7% makes the fabric very stiff, although it affords
excellent protection. The chlorinated phenols, pentachlorphenol,
and 2-chloro-*o*-phenol are good mildew-resisting agents, but because
of their pungent odour they are generally undesirable; they may,
however, be condensed with morpholine to form odourless products,
soluble in hot water, but almost insoluble in cold water, and giving
good resistance to mildew when applied from 3% solution. Salicylanilide (0·2%) gives excellent protection against mildew, provided
the fabric is not sterilised with steam; on the other hand, when
applied with a water-repelling mixture of wax and aluminium acetate
complete protection is afforded even after sterilisation. Two quaternary ammonium compounds, an alkylated dimethylbenzylammonium
phosphate and chloride (7 and 0·1% solutions respectively) gave
excellent protection against mildew.

Organo-metallic compounds

The organo-metallic compounds and metallic salts of organic
compounds include copper acetonate, mercury salicylate and oleate,
zinc and copper naphthenates, cadmium and copper soaps, and
morpholine and hydroquinoline condensation products. Copper
propionyl acetonate (3%), *p*-tolyl mercury salicylate (10%), and
phenyl mercury oleate (0·8%) resist mildew very effectively, as
applied from the commercial preparations on which the concentrations are based. Copper and zinc naphthenates may be applied in
water or from white spirit (Stoddard solvent) to give complete
protection; copper naphthenate (30%) is green, but zinc naphthenate
(20%) is colourless; both have a pungent odour and stiffen the fabric
slightly. Two-bath processes of soap (1%), followed by cadmium
chloride (1%) or copper sulphate (10%), form insoluble soaps in the
fabric and are easy to apply. The cadmium soap treatment is
colourless and affords excellent protection against mildew; 1% of
cadmium chloride appears better than 10% of copper sulphate.
Morpholine also combines with inorganic salts to form insoluble
products which are retained by the fibre; with cadmium chloride
and with copper sulphate, excellent protection against mildew is
obtained (U.S.P. 2,247,339). Aluminium acetate or magnesium
chloride may be used to form salts with 8-hydroxyquinoline to form
insoluble mildew-preventing agents.

Inorganic salts

With the inorganic salts, a treatment with cadmium chloride (5%),
followed by borax (4%), was found to be entirely satisfactory; copper

sulphate (5%), followed by sodium carbonate (5%), was also found
to be effective as a two-bath treatment, but the treated fabric was
reduced in strength about 9% before inoculation and incubation.

General

Goodavage (Am. Dyes. Rep., 1943, *32*, 265) has reviewed the
various fungicides used by the U.S. Army, and these include phenolic
derivatives, naphthenic acid derivatives, zinc compounds, copper
compounds, cuprammonium treatments, mercury compounds, and
quaternary amines.

Of the phenolic derivatives, dihydroxydichlorodiphenylmethane
is outstanding, as it inhibits all types of mould, and is non-toxic
and non-irritant. Many of the phenolic derivatives fall short of the
naphthenates in durability, as estimated by burial tests. Cuprammonium compounds require careful control to obviate stiffening and
glazing; they are sometimes apt to weaken the fabric. The outstanding mercury compound is stated to be phenylmercurotrinitriloethanol lactate, 0·4% on the fabric being non-toxic. Bertolet (ibid.,
1943, *32*, 214) also comments favourably on this compound. Basic
copper carbonate and copper oxides are less effective than copper
oleate or naphthenate; cadmium compounds are generally inferior
to zinc, and zinc soaps are inferior to copper soaps. Zinc dimethyldithiocarbonate (m.p. 248°C.) is stated to be quite promising; it is a
white, odourless, non-toxic substance, insoluble in water and in
petrol, but soluble in caustic soda or benzene.

The Dowicide mildewproofing compounds, which are popular in
the U.S.A., are mainly halogenated and phenylated phenols and
their water-soluble sodium salts; they have been discussed by
Stringfellow (Am. Dyes. Rep., 1939, *28*, 388).

Many of the fungicides applied from solvents are able to resist
leaching, but cannot withstand the mechanical beating of heavy
rainfall. It has therefore been considered better to treat the fabric
with a water-soluble fungicide to the extent of 3 to 4% of its weight,
and then pass the wet cloth through basic lead acetate solution, of
adequate concentration to ensure formation of the lead salt of the
fungicide. The greatest efficiency has been obtained with lead
pentachlorphenate obtained from the soluble sodium pentachlorphenate; this salt seems to be peculiar in that it is precipitated in
such a form that it is not readily removed and also appears
to be preferentially absorbed as the sodium salt. Many metallic
salts have been investigated, but the retention of the lead salt
is best.

Some of the various substances which have been suggested at
different times are summarised in the following table:

MILDEWPROOFING COMPOUNDS

Benzoic acid	. .	0·05%	Ammonium fluoride	.	0·04%
Cresylic acid	. .	0·1%	Borax .	. . .	0·9%
Dinitrophenol	. .	0·02%	Mercuric chloride .	.	0·02%
Formaldehyde	. .	0·05%	Sodium fluoride	. .	0·8%
Pentachlorphenol .	.	0·014%	Sodium silicofluoride	.	0·15%
Phenol	. .	0·13%			
Salicylanilide	. .	0·025%			
Phenyl mercuric nitrate .		0·01%			

Although zinc chloride was the commonest compound used for mildewproofing prior to 1920, only salicylanilide or paranitrophenol are used in England nowadays; the product known as G4 (2,2'-dihydroxy-5,5'-dichlordiphenylmethane) finds application in the U.S.A.

Rotproofing

Although rotproofing is primarily concerned with protection from bacterial decay, the exposure to the weather plays an important role; hence there must be some protection from the effects of air, light, and moisture. For these reasons, it is not easy to give a firm decision as to the "best" treatment.

Military and civil defence measures have aroused renewed interest in the rotproofing of heavy and coarse textile fabrics where considerations of treatment differ from those used on finer cloths. Metallic compounds containing copper are cheap and efficient, but cannot be universally employed on all fabrics. The iron-chromium treatment is fairly good to bacteria, and moderate to fungi; the efficient cadmium treatment is expensive for cheap and coarse cloths.

The following processes, therefore, are mainly of importance from the economic aspect and find application on low-quality textile products where preservation of the normal textile character is of minor importance.

Cuprammonium processes

The Willesden finish is effected by a cuprammonium process which imparts waterproof and mildewproof properties; it is famous as a treatment for canvas, tent-cloths, and the more robust cloths.

According to Matthews (Textile Fibres, 1924, 565) the solution is prepared in the following manner. A cold solution of copper sulphate is treated with rather less than the theoretically required amount of caustic soda solution; if the temperature is allowed to rise above 20°C., then the precipitate is black instead of blue. Prolonged washing of this hydroxide is carried out until the wash-waters no longer give a precipitate with barium chloride solution. The copper hydrate is then pressed to remove excess of water and dissolved in the minimum amount of ammonia of density 0·93.

The cuprammonia solution, when applied by padding methods to cellulosic material, partially dissolves the cellulose and forms a film over the fibres. The freedom from mildew is excellent, and is presumably due to the copper retained by the fabric, which assumes the greenish colour characteristic of this finish. The colour may be modified by a superficial treatment to produce copper sulphide, or, alternatively, the process may be applied to dyed material. The original green colour is not fast to light, but the change in colour does not seem to affect the mildewproof properties of the material.

The treated goods are rather harsh, but a softer finish may be produced by modifications of the standard process; the material may also be glazed during the treatment, if required, to give very lustrous effects. Although the process is apt to be expensive, its efficiency and the durability of the product, together with its waterproof nature, have maintained its place in textile finishing.

The solubility of cellulose in cuprammonia is generally assumed to have been discovered by Schweizer in 1857, but according to Cross and Bevan (Cellulose, Longmans, Green and Co., London, 1895, p. 13), the reaction was known to Mercer at an even earlier date; Mercer's method was to saturate ammonia of 0·92 specific gravity, with copper hydroxide, and then dilute it with 3 parts of water by volume.

The earliest patent for the proofing of fabrics was due to Scoffern (B.P. 1744 of 1859), who joined with A. E. Healey at Willesden in 1872. Greater prominence was given to the waterproofing effect than to the rotproofing, and this aspect was stressed in one of the first publications on the process by Alder Wright (Journal of the Society of Arts, 1884, *32*, 641). It was pointed out that when cellulose in the form of paper or cloth was impregnated with cuprammonia and the solution evaporated on the surface of the material by drying, a green varnish-like mass coats the fibres of the material, welding and cementing them together so that they become water-resistant. The presence of copper also renders the product immune to attack by insects and mildew.

Although mildew and rotproofing form a great part of the advantages of the cuprammonium process, particularly in cold or temperate climates, an additional feature is the resistance to the ravages of the white ants or termites in the tropics. There are over 1,200 species of the termite whose chief food is cellulose, but there is reason to believe that they do not attack the material until it has been decomposed to some extent by micro-organisms, with the formation of soluble carbohydrates. Hence, a rotproof material is also termite

33

resistant. The subject has been discussed in the Second Report of the Fabrics Co-ordinating Research Committee (1930).

The cuprammonium-proofing process was originally worked at Warrington by a company formed in 1868 by Elkanah Healey, but in 1873 an experimental factory was established at Willesden, and the name "Willesden-proofing" became famous. During the Boer War (1899–1902) considerable quantities of tent-cloth and other equipment was treated so as to withstand the severe climatic conditions. The characteristic green was the only colour which could be produced at that time, and became a familiar sight on suitcases, tents, lorry-covers, awnings, railway sheets, etc.

Within more recent times, stringent tests were carried out on canvas and discussed in the First Report of the Fabrics Co-ordinating Research Committee (1925). Fabrics treated by the cuprammonium process were shown to possess almost complete inhibition to the growth of moulds with which they were inoculated.

A further development in the proofing of canvas was made possible by combining the cuprammonium-proofing with bitumen, and although it is somewhat unsuitable for tents, yet it is largely used for covers for transports of various types, water-tanks, collapsible boats, and pontoons.

The Willesden cuprammonium process is specifically mentioned in several British Government specifications, sometimes in conjunction with bitumen.

The WILLESDEN FINISH is a controlled application of the cuprammonium solution which is capable of dissolving cellulose in certain circumstances; the difference in concentrations between solutions capable of swelling and of dissolving cellulose is small. This is utilised in the production of waterproof effects with cuprammonia, where the swollen cotton material is squeezed between rollers and the interstices closed, although not entirely blocked. The cloth remains air-porous; the effect varies with the woven structure, a closely-woven material giving better results than a loose weave.

The treatment of ropes and cordage by the Willesden process involves impregnating in the cuprammonia, followed by drying; the concentration of the solution and the duration of the treatment is partly determined by the nature of the cordage. Fabrics are treated in a very similar manner, being run through the impregnating bath and over drying cylinders.

Recent Work

The question of proofing came to the fore again at the beginning of the 1939 War in connection with sandbags, which had proved an important form of protection in the Boer War and the 1914–18 War. In the previous circumstances, however, sandbags were used in or near the front line and were only required to last from 3 to 4 months, so that rotproofing was not necessary.

In the Civil Defence precautions of 1938, sandbags played an important part, and by September 1938 some 70 million bags had been issued to local authorities by the Home Office. It was realised, however, that the sandbags would rot, especially when damp, and that they would rapidly deteriorate and collapse; revetments would soon become a danger instead of a protection. It was considered that untreated bags would only last about 3 or 4 months, whereas treated bags would last at least 18 months. Nevertheless, between August and December 1939, the Government ordered 700 million bags and by December 1939 at least 100 million bags were in position in Great Britain for civil defence purposes. It seems extraordinary that sandbags were almost the only textile articles for outdoor use which Government Departments did not have proofed. The question was discussed in the House of Commons on June 29, 1939, but by the middle of December 1939 in London alone 75% of the sandbags had been replaced on account of rot, many of the revetments having collapsed. The enormous waste and danger from rotting sandbags became so obvious to the "man in the street" that the Government started having sandbags proofed about 6 months after the start of the 1939 War. Some interesting details have been provided by C. J. Healey (The Romance of Willesden, London, 1941) of this rare Parliamentary interest in textile finishing processes.

A Sandbag Advisory Committee was formed to study the subject, and an account of its work has been given by Armstrong (Chem. and Ind., 1941, 60, 668). An earlier interim report was made giving details of the treatment of existing revetments to delay rotting, and in many instances this prolonged their life for 6 to 12 months. More time was required for the larger problem of finding the best process to prevent rotting.

The most important single factor in the micro-biological attack on cellulose is high humidity. Both fungi and bacteria take part in the attack, but fungi usually start to attack cellulose at a lower moisture content than required by bacteria; attack on jute by fungi is negligible where the jute contains less than 17% of moisture, and a moisture content of 22% is the minimum required for most strains of bacteria to become active. A good rotproofing reagent must have both fungicidal and bacterial properties; further, it should be neither acid nor alkaline. For obvious reasons, it should not volatilise on exposure to air nor should it be easily leached from the treated bag by rain. The possibility of photochemical action must also be considered in connection with the action of light on the reagent itself, as well as accelerated oxidation of fabric by the catalytic effect of the proofing medium, as, for instance, with an excess of copper. The rotproofing treatment should not diminish the tensile strength of the material on application or on subsequent exposure, nor should it cause more shrinkage than that normally encountered on wetting with water. The bags must not be rendered more inflammable by the treatment, and the reagents used should not be poisonous to human beings nor cause dermatitis to those working with them.

For reasons of economics the rotproofing medium must be readily available, cheap, and easy to apply, preferably at room temperatures. The reagent should dry quickly after application, and be free from stickiness and objectionable odours when dry.

Part of the deterioration of bags may be due to agencies other than rotting; for instance, expansion of the sand or earth on wetting may burst the bag, the pressure due to a high revetment may break the material, and there is also the abrasion caused by contact with pedestrians.

The life of unproofed unfilled bags was examined over a period of 22 months, the time of decay being measured in garden soil. The figures varied from 82 days in winter to 21 days in summer, the rotting times varying with the soil temperature. With filled bags, the time of rotting was taken as that of the under-side of a bag filled with earth and placed on earth. Where the upper surface was exposed to air and weather, it had a life from three to six times that of the lower surface, with a maximum of about 200 days under the most favourable weather conditions. Where the upper surface is in contact with another bag, the life of the interface is about 1·5 times that of the lowest surface. This explains why a pile of sandbags which has almost rotted internally may appear sound externally on casual examination. The exposed faces are dry or wet according to the weather, and are subject to temperature variations, so that the conditions favouring rotting and preservation vary continually.

The possibility of a chemical treatment to form an immune derivative of cellulose was considered, and although acetylation is most effective, the process is very costly, particularly on a cheap material such as jute.

A very large range of products has been suggested, including phenols, cresols, chlorophenols, crude coal-tar distillates, naphthenic acids and their metallic salts, derivatives of thiourea, and so forth. Many of the processes involve the use of organic solvents, and other methods are expensive; a simple technique with cheap water-soluble reagents is naturally of greatest interest.

Three main lines of treatment are considered to be practicable: (a) cuprammonium, (b) organic copper salts, and (c) creosote or specified tar distillates.

CUPRAMMONIA

The cuprammonia process has already been mentioned, and has a great deal to recommend it, but nevertheless is not quite as effective as the other two in respect of length of life; it also has the disadvantage of reducing the strength of the jute fibre by 10 to 15%. When proofing with cuprammonia, a range of from 1 to 1·5% of copper is required, the higher figure being usual in practice; there is some evidence that the life of the bag increases with increasing copper up to 2%, but not proportionately.

One method of using cuprammonia is to prepare a solution containing about 4% of metallic copper by dissolving 20 lb. of copper sulphate in water and making up the solution to 10 gallons, to which 2·1 gallons of strong ammonia (*sp. gr.* 0·88) are added. This solution may be diluted to give the required copper content.

ORGANIC COPPER SALTS

A cutch/cuprammonium process has been used in a two-bath process. The first bath should contain boiling cutch, about 1% of which is left on the fibre; the second bath contains cuprammonia, so as to deposit 0·8 to 1% of copper calculated on the weight of the fibre.

Organic copper salts are quite satisfactory as rotproofing agents. Organic acids may be used with mercury, cadmium, chromium, zinc, or iron, as well as copper; only the two last-mentioned are plentiful, but are less efficient than copper. The only suitable acids are those of high molecular weight, but they must not be too highly unsaturated, and liable to oxidation as, for instance, linoleic acid. Oleic, stearic, and naphthenic acids are very suitable, but the two former are generally required for other purposes. The copper soaps can be applied in solution in organic solvents, particularly white spirit.

Alternatives to the cuprammonium method of rotproofing cotton canvas and duck have been given by Fullerton (Rev. Appl. Mycol., 1942, *21*, 451). A copper formate solution is prepared by dissolving 60 lb. of copper sulphate in water, adding 40 lb. of soda ash, and dissolving the precipitate in 2·5 gallons of 85% formic acid; a solution of aluminium formate is also made from 60 lb. of aluminium sulphate, 50 lb. of soda ash, and 4 gallons of formic acid. The fabric is impregnated with a mixture of the two solutions, dried, impregnated with ammonia, and again dried.

A simple proofing treatment may be carried out with the following reagents: 50 parts of paraffin wax and 50 parts of wax-copper oleate, together with 10 parts of oleine and 10 parts of rosin in 140 parts of water, to which are added 20 parts of water, 10 parts of ammonia, and 10 parts of Amoa O.M. This mixture should be thoroughly blended and then added to 30 parts of lime green and water, and 10 parts of Amoa O.M. A fixing bath for the treated material consists of a mixture of 25 lb. of copper sulphate in 200 of water, and 25 lb. of lead oleate in 20 gallons of water acidified with acetic acid.

Emulsions of metallic naphthenates are available under the trade name of Micronil; zinc or copper naphthenate may be supplied. Micronil Green consists of copper naphthenate in which the concentration of metallic copper is 3·5%; this solution imparts a green colour to the treated fabric. Micronil Clear, however, is colourless and consists of zinc naphthenate, in which the concentration of metallic zinc is 5·2%. The Micronils only require dilution to the required concentration with water to be ready for application.

The manufacture of these emulsions is described in B.P. 491,501. A suitable solvent is added to the solid metallic salt or ester, and the solution then emulsified; white spirit, naphtha, kerosene, petrol, or creosote may be used as solvents. In most cases, 30% of the solvent is adequate, but 50% is sometimes required, estimated on the weight of the naphthenate. A typical example includes 60 parts of zinc naphthenate, 17·5 parts of naphtha, or of white spirit, 2·5 parts of an emulsifying agent such as Emulphor O, and 20 parts of water.

It appears that in all cases a minimum value of 0·35% metallic copper, estimated on the weight of the fibre, must be present to stop micro-biological action. As the organic copper soaps are very slightly soluble in water, a certain amount is removed periodically by leaching, and this has been estimated as 0·06% per month. Under adverse conditions the loss can amount to nearly 0·2% of copper in 3 months, so that proofing with 0·5% of copper, advocated at one time, is of no permanent value. An initial figure of 1% of copper is desirable, and an initial minimum of 0·8% of copper has been specified for Government contracts. Jute bags proofed in this manner should last from 18 months to 2 years.

CREOSOTE

Creosote or specified tar distillates have been defined in BSI/ARP–57, and in British Standard Specification 144/1936, with a tar-acid content of between 5 and 10%. Many tar distillates have been rejected on account of their tar-acid content or inferior toxicity; a suitable material is the distillate from Mond gas tar. Creosote alone was found to be effective in amounts ranging from 20 to 25% on the weight of the fibre.

The best results of all appear to come from proofing with a mixture of creosote and copper naphthenate, where the tar compound, in addition to its toxicity, exerts a waterproofing action and delays the loss of copper by leaching. Bags treated in this manner have a useful life well in excess of 2 years. The copper and creosote method gives a better fireproofing than copper naphthenate in white spirit.

British Standard Specifications, A.R.P. 56, 57, and 58 have been prepared for the rotproof treatment of various textiles. No. 56 refers to the rotproofing of canvas, yarn, and cordage, and deals with the application of copper and of zinc, together with methods of determining the copper and zinc contents of the material. No. 57 concerns jute and hessian sandbags; where copper naphthenate is used, its copper content should lie between 10 and 13%, the acids isolated should have a molecular weight of 200, assuming basicity, and the copper naphthenate should not leave more than 5% of an orange-coloured residue when extracted with thirty times its weight of cold acetone. No. 58 deals with rotproofing jute canvas; the copper content of the proofed fabric should lie between 0·5 and 1·0, expressed as metallic copper. If zinc compounds are used for colourless proofing, then the fabric should contain not less than 5% of metallic zinc.

A good copper and creosote water emulsion may be made on the basis of the cuprammonia described on page 517, which contains 4% of copper. The acids in the creosote are neutralised with a trace of caustic soda to ensure stability of the final emulsion; 5 gallons of creosote B.S.S. 144/1936 is mixed with 0·5 gallons of 10% sodium hydroxide. To make 10 gallons of a copper/creosote emulsion containing 50% creosote and 1·5% metallic copper, it is necessary to take 3·8 gallons of the cuprammonium solution and add 0·7 gallons of a 14% solution of carpenter's glue; this mixture is added gradually to 5 gallons of the neutralised creosote with continuous stirring. The whole mass is then heated to 50°C. with vigorous stirring or treatment in an emulsifying machine. The bags may be treated by impregnation or spraying.

The specified contents of the various proofing media advised by the Sandbag Advisory Committee are shown in the following table:

PROOFING OF JUTE SANDBAGS

Organic copper soaps . . .	0·8 to 1% of copper
Cuprammonia	1 to 1·5% of copper
Creosote	25%
Copper-creosote . . .	0·5% copper, 20% creosote

INORGANIC COMPOUNDS

Goods treated with cuprammonia or with creosote cannot be used for garments for obvious reasons, and many of the organic antiseptics are leached by rain; hence there is a large demand for the simple hydroxides of copper or chromium.

Perhaps the best-known chromium proofing treatment is that given by mineral khaki; it depends on the application of iron and chromium salts (usually the acetates) followed by precipitation of the hydrous oxides with warm alkali. It is necessary to wash thoroughly after the fixation with alkali, for otherwise the goods would deteriorate on storage. An alternative method of fixing the iron and chromium on the fibre is to use potassium chromate instead of the alkaline treatment; according to Race, Rowe, and Speakman (J.S.D.C., 1945, 61, 310), the only really toxic principle in cotton treated with chrome-iron is hexavalent chromium. As hexavalent chromium produced only by the chromate method is not resistant to leaching by water, the proof is not permanent, but an added resistance to attack may be imparted by wax.

A very simple process is known as "chrome-tinting" and involves impregnating the fabric with basic chromium sulphate or acetate, followed by treatment with alkali; a subsequent treatment with copper sulphate solution not only neutralises the free alkali, but forms basic copper salts which impart additional powers of resisting decay.

Opinions are divided as to the relative merits of copper and chromium; burial tests indicate the superiority of copper, but it is less resistant to weathering than chromium.

The I.C.I. developed the method of using a basic copper carbonate suspension which is simple and cheap, both in preparation and application. The method advised is to dissolve 4·5 lb. of soda ash or 11·5 lb. of washing soda in 5 gallons of water and slowly add this solution to another solution of 10 lb. of copper sulphate in 30 gallons of water with stirring. A 50-gallon vessel should be used, preferably made of wood, and not iron or galvanised iron. The solution should be made up to 40 gallons with water and 2 oz. of Calsolene Oil HS added as a wetting agent.

Sandbags may be immersed in this mixture until thoroughly saturated, and excess liquor removed, so that the weight of the bag is increased 100%; the bags should then be dried at a relatively low temperature. Experience has shown that about 5 minutes' immersion is necessary if the solution is cold, but the process may be hastened by warming the liquor to 30° to 40°C.

Although basic copper carbonate dispersions have been used as horticultural sprays, in the form of Burgundy mixture, this appears to be their first application to textile materials.

The single bath process, as outlined above, is very suitable for loosely woven fabrics containing soft spun yarns, such as jute hessians, but a two-bath process is preferred for canvas duck. The goods are first thoroughly wetted in 2% copper sulphate solution at any temperature up to 100°C., and then squeezed to retain about

100% of liquor; a second immersion takes place in a cold aqueous solution of 5% soda ash or 14% sodium carbonate crystals. The goods are subsequently squeezed to remove excess liquor and dried at a temperature below 60°C. Penetration may be assisted by the addition of Calsolene Oil to the copper sulphate solution in the first bath.

In both of these processes, good rinsing is essential to avoid leaving any free alkali in the cloth, as jute is very susceptible to alkalis.

The efficiency of both processes may be increased by waterproofing, which may be carried out by any of the simple preparations such as Waxol W.

It is considered that the life of jute sandbags may be increased fivefold by these treatments.

A recent American development, "Protela SB" (Textile World, 1942, 92, 88), appears to contain copper fluoride as the active agent; the copper content is about 10%. In use, the reagent is diluted to 10 or 16 volumes with water at 15° to 38°C., and a wetting agent is added, together with 1 to 2% of ammonia. When the fabric is dried, ammoniacal copper fluoride is deposited as copper fluoride in the fibres.

CHAPTER XXI

FIREPROOFING

THE protection of inflammable material against fire dates back to about 400 B.C., but the earliest attempts to fireproof textile fabrics are of more recent date; about 1640 attention was drawn to the use of clay and plaster of Paris on canvas used in theatres. Alum was suggested in 1740 and ammonium phosphate in 1786.

The first systematic investigation on fireproofing was due to Gay Lussac in 1820, and the conclusion was reached that the most effective salts for fireproofing were those with a low melting-point and capable of covering the material with a glassy layer; alternatively, effective salts were those which gave rise to non-inflammable vapours on heating. These two ideas formed the basis of the theoretical aspect of the action of fireproofing agents for many years, and are still discussed, but neither of these explanations accounts for the experimental data and attention has been devoted more recently to the nature of the decomposition products of the fabric affected.

Now it must not be assumed that a fireproof fabric when brought into contact with flame will behave in the same way as asbestos, for instance; most fireproof fabrics char and decompose. As will appear later, they are actually *less* resistant to heat than the untreated material. A fireproof fabric may be defined as one which does not propagate flame beyond the charred area; this would appear a better definition than the use of terms such as flameproof, which are apt to be misleading. Fireproofing processes do not render textiles incombustible.

Cotton fabrics are the chief concern of those who deal with the fireproofing of textiles, for wool and silk materials rarely require a fireproofing treatment, as they do not readily propagate flame. Results obtained from the treatment of cotton may also be expected to apply to other vegetable fibres such as linen and hemp; cellulose acetate, on the other hand, behaves more like wool or silk on burning, for it chars and melts. Viscose rayon and cuprammonium rayon burn like cotton.

A valuable review of fireproofing methods has been given by Ramsbottom and Snoad (Second Report of the Fabrics Co-ordinating Research Committee, 1930, 16), including comprehensive references to the literature; a later bibliography with 208 references is due to Akin, Spencer, and Macormac (Am. Dyes. Rep., 1940, *29*, 418 and 445).

A suitable test devised by Ramsbottom and Snoad (*supra*) is to cut a strip about 1 inch wide, suspend the fabric vertically, and ignite the lower edge. A cotton strip burns rapidly with a flame about 8 inches long, leaving a black mass possessing fabric structure and still glowing at the edges; the glow gradually travels across the strip, finally consuming it. Linen behaves in a similar manner, but the rate of propagation of the flame is rather slower. Wool, however, first chars and melts, but after a short length has been consumed, the molten mass becomes detached and the strip ceases to burn; there is no afterglow. Silk behaves in a similar manner to wool, but appears to melt at a lower temperature.

Although the great majority of inorganic compounds will probably prevent flame propagation, if present in sufficiently large amount, they cannot be regarded as efficient fireproofing agents, because it is usually necessary to avoid the addition of large amounts of substances which alter the textile character of the fabric.

In general, there are two main types of fireproofing processes: (*a*) the deposition of soluble salts, and (*b*) the precipitation of insoluble compounds on or in the fabric.

Early processes were almost entirely of the first type, and about 1875 both sodium tungstate and ammonium phosphate were regarded as most efficient "soluble" fireproofing agents; other useful salts were ammonium sulphate, ammonium chloride, borax, sodium silicate, and zinc chloride. Many mixtures of soluble salts have been suggested, borax often being one constituent in conjunction with an ammonium salt. With these mixtures, the general plan was based on the old theories—to provide a mixture which gave an easily fusible deposit or readily evolved non-inflammable gases. Numerous ideas were put forward to bind these salts to the fabric, the use of glue and starch being well known; synthetic resins have been utilised for this purpose, and drying oils have also been proposed.

Without some method of fixing the soluble salts to the fabric, the danger of removal by leaching with water was always present, and this gave rise to the second broad method whereby the so-called permanent fireproofing effect was obtained by double decomposition between two soluble salts. The common process was to impregnate the fabric with a soluble salt, dry the goods, and then impregnate in a second salt solution to give an insoluble precipitate. It seems to have been generally accepted that almost any insoluble compound would act as a fireproofing agent. One of the best-known "permanent" fireproofing processes was that based on hydrated stannic oxide and utilised by Perkin (Text. Manuf., 1913, *39*, 39, 424; 1914, *40*, 27); his processes include B.P. 9695, 23556, 23557 (1901), 6421, 8509, 9620 (1902), 24222 (1903), 22169 (1904), 17814 and 17815 (1913).

In Perkin's process, flannelette was impregnated with sodium stannate, dried, and immersed in ammonium sulphate solution, which precipitated stannic oxide on the fibre. The hydroxides of aluminium, zirconium, titanium, silicon, zinc, and magnesium were also investigated, but did not appear to be so successful as the tin compound. In a later examination of this type of fireproofing by Ramsbottom and Snoad (Second Report of the Fabrics Co-ordinating Research Committee, 1930, 16) it was found that fabrics containing 40% of hydrated stannic oxide burned readily after a short exposure to rain. Further, although stannic oxide and similar substances may prevent flame propagation, they do not prevent destruction of the fabric by flameless combustion—the afterglow effect.

It is possible to produce "permanent" fireproofing by a one-bath process; for instance, Perkin (B.P. 9695 of 1901) used a solution of sodium tungstate and aluminium acetate containing enough acetic acid to dissolve the precipitate, the aluminium tungstate being precipitated when the acetic acid was removed by evaporation.

It has been suggested that these insoluble precipitates act in virtue of conducting and radiating the heat so that the fabric cannot maintain the temperature of combustion.

SOLUBLE COMPOUNDS

Ramsbottom and Snoad (loc. cit.) made a comprehensive survey of substances which had been suggested for fireproofing and were able to divide them into three main classes:

(a) Substances which prevent flame propagation by the fabric, the flame persisting for a short time and not travelling beyond the charred area; the afterglow ceases when the uncharred fabric is reached. Ammonium phosphate is particularly valuable in that the charred fabric does not glow.

(b) Substances which prevent flame propagation by the fabric, but the charred fabric glows vigorously and the glow extends to the unchanged fabric, which is consumed by flameless combustion.

(c) Substances which do not prevent flame propagation, but reduce the rate.

Consideration of the chemical composition of these various compounds enables them to be classified in three groups:

(1) Caustic alkalis and compounds giving alkaline solutions; this includes alkali salts of weak inorganic acids and sodium orthophosphate. The neutral and acid phosphates, the alkali sulphates, and chlorides are not effective fireproofers.

(2) Strong mineral acids and potentially acid substances; the simple ammonium salts of inorganic acids are good examples, but it seems that the availability of acid from alums is insufficient. Neutral salts, which are stable when heated, do not possess fireproofing properties.

(3) Easily reducible oxides and oxidising agents; oxides such as silica and alumina are not easily reduced and show little fireproofing. Many easily reducible oxides do not prevent flame propagation, but in these cases adhesion to the fabric was not good. Potassium nitrate is a flame-proofing agent, but the fabric is rapidly destroyed by flameless combustion.

EFFICIENCY OF FIREPROOFING AGENTS

Flameproof and Glowproof		Flameproof	
Ammonium borate	24		
Borax	60		
Borax and boric acid (1 : 1)	10		
Ammonium phosphate	12	Sodium orthophosphate	20
Guanidine phosphate	19		
Ammonium sulphate	8		
Ammonium bromide	7		
Ammonium chloride	38		
Ammonium iodide	14		
Calcium chloride	14		
Magnesium chloride	16		
Zinc chloride	12		
Sodium hydrate	10		
Phosphoric acid	10		
Sodium carbonate	12	Potassium nitrate	13
Sodium bicarbonate	23		
Sodium tungstate	9		
Sodium silicate	20		
Sodium stannate	18		
Ammonium molybdate	7		
Sodium molybdate	6		
Sodium aluminate	19	Potassium permanganate	22
Sodium arsenate	33	Potassium thiocyanate	25

The figures in the table are the approximate minimum amounts to give the required effect, estimated as percentages of the weight of the fabric, and represent the relative efficiencies of the compounds. The chief conclusion to be drawn from this classification is that good fireproofing agents are compounds which may be expected rapidly to destroy the fabric under the influence of heat.

Although many of the fireproofing agents fuse on heating, few appear to form a coating on the fabric; the degree of permeability to air is indicated by the amount of afterglow, and boric acid seems to form an impervious coating. There is also an absence of glow with ammonium phosphate.

It is also noteworthy that the most efficient fireproofing agents are only required in small amounts, and this fact is difficult to reconcile with the theory that non-inflammable gases are evolved for no great volume of gas can be given off; further, substances such as sodium bicarbonate are less efficient than sodium carbonate, which in its turn is less efficient than sodium hydroxide. Any theory of fireproofing based on heat conductivity or endothermic changes is also incapable of accounting for fireproofing with the small amounts of the most efficient compounds.

Assuming, therefore, that the main action of the most efficient fireproofing agents is associated with rapid destruction of the fabric on heating, a series of tests was carried out by Ramsbottom and Snoad. In many cases, it was found that the initial treatment caused an apparent increase in tensile strength of the fabric, but in all cases there was a reduction in the ripping strength. Storage at room temperatures for 300 days was without serious deterioration, but heating at 40°C. caused a considerable loss in strength in many cases, particularly with samples containing ammonium sulphate. Exposure to sunlight for 200 days deteriorated most samples, but there was no relation between the results of the action of heat and sunlight.

LOSS IN STRENGTH ON EXPOSURE OF TREATED FABRICS

Proofing agent	Loss after 300 days at 40°C.	Loss after 200 days in sunlight
Ammonium bromide	59%	91%
Ammonium chloride	55%	93%
Ammonium phosphate . . .	46%	49%
Ammonium sulphate	74%	61%
Borax	—	41%
Calcium chloride	—	86%
Guanidine phosphate	—	71%
Sodium silicate	7%	49%
Sodium tungstate	9%	82%
Zinc chloride	12%	53%
Untreated fabric	—	30%

Borax, sodium silicate, and ammonium phosphate were found to have the least destructive action.

Now when cotton is slowly heated in air it becomes a yellow-brown colour, which darkens to black before ignition; these colour changes are accompanied by a loss of tensile strength. Examination of various fabrics showed that the untreated material started to discolour at about 200°C. and turned black at 340°C., whereas the most efficient fireproofing treatments caused the discoloration to start at 120° to 200°C., further increase in temperature causing blackening much more rapidly than with the untreated fabric. It was also established that those substances which caused considerable discoloration also produced great deterioration in strength on heating.

The action of heat seems to increase the rate of decomposition of the fabric at temperatures below the ignition point, so that the blackening which precedes ignition occurs at a lower temperature. The amount of volatile inflammable matter is also less, so that the propagation of the flame is reduced; it appears, therefore, that the action of fireproofing agents is mainly chemical.

The problem of fireproofing cotton goods bears certain similarities to the fireproofing of timber, and here again it has been found that the effect of efficient fireproofing agents is mainly chemical. Richardson (J.S.C.I., 1937, 56, 202) found that fireproofed timber, when carbonised at temperatures above 300°C., yields considerably more charcoal than untreated wood, and similar results have been published by Forest Products Research Board (Annual Report, 1938-9, p. 40). In short, treated timber yields 50% charcoal and 35% water, whereas untreated timber gives 25% charcoal and 20% water; hence, the treatment results in a decrease in the amount of inflammable gases and induces the formation of carbon and water. The most efficient compounds in this respect are those which dissociate on heating to provide free acid radicals; this was confirmed by Metz (Holz, 1938, 1, 217), who also found that alkalis or substances which produce alkalis on heating also accelerate carbonisation, but not to the same extent as acids, whereas neutral salts have little effect.

It appears, therefore, that compounds capable of rapid degradation of cellulose to hydrocellulose, and hence to glucose, are more effective than those which oxidise cellulose.

Before leaving the treatment of wood, it is interesting to note that ammonium phosphate is highly effective in reducing both flaming and glowing, and surpasses ammonium bromide, which has been widely used in Germany according to Eichengrun (Z. angew. Chem., 1929, 42, 214). Many mixtures for wood owe their efficiency to the presence of these ammonium salts.

Ammonium sulphamate has recently received attention as a fireproofing agent, particularly in the U.S.A. Sulphamic acid, HSO_3NH_2, is prepared by the reaction of urea with fuming sulphuric acid, and its properties have been described in some detail by Cupery (Ind. Eng. Chem., 1938, 30, 627). One of the special features of ammonium sulphamate is that when applied to the textile material it does not cause stiffening or otherwise adversely affect the handle of the cloth; there is no tendency to efflorescence on storage. The sulphamates are not removed by treatment with the solvents commonly employed in dry-cleaning processes. Ammonium sulphamate alone does not adequately prevent afterglow, but this may be effected by the addition of ammonium phosphate; a mixture of 85% ammonium sulphamate and 15% ammonium phosphate is satisfactory. Criticisms have also been made that the sulphamate produces tendering on rayon and is not readily absorbed by sized goods, but the Du Pont product, "Fire Retardant CM," is stated to have overcome these difficulties; it is mainly ammonium sulphamate, but also contains "certain modifying agents."

In a very large number of fireproofing agents ammonium salts form the chief constituent; in particular ammonium phosphate is often used, but ammonium sulphate is fairly common. These ammonium salts suffer from the disadvantage of instability and are apt to become acid with subsequent damage to the cloth.

A new flameproofing agent, known as "Abopon," is stated to overcome some of these difficulties as it combines in natural and stable form two of the most efficient ingredients of the old mixtures; chemically this product is an inorganic complex boro-phosphate which may be regarded as a resin. This product is soluble in water at 55°C. and dries to form a smooth, glossy, transparent film which is non-hygroscopic. The product, therefore, contains borate and phosphate radicals without the disadvantages of acidity, and the usual solutions employed in practice were found to lie between pH 7·3 and 7·9. The proper concentration of the flameproofing agent depends on the type of fabric to which it is applied, but solutions containing from 9 to 17% of the resinous product meet most requirements. Examination of the treated product shows that colours are hardly affected and that the boro-phosphate does not crystallise or dust out. The finish is permanent to non-aqueous solvents used for dry-cleaning and there is also some resistance to cold water. The specific gravity of the boro-phosphate (1·68) is such that it may be used for weighting as well as fireproofing.

MIXTURES

A number of fireproofing processes employ mixtures of various compounds, many of which can be explained on the assumption that the constituents act independently of each other, but a mixture of borax and boric acid (1 : 1) acts differently. Small amounts of such a mixture decrease the rate of flame propagation to a much greater extent than an equal weight of either constituent, and when the amount was increased to about 10% on the fabric there was no flame propagation.

Borax alone prevents flame propagation when present in amounts of the order of 60% of the weight of the fabric, but boric acid is ineffective even with 90% on the fabric. On the other hand, a mixture of equal parts of boric acid and borax prevents flame propagation when only 10% is present on the fabric. Examination of other mixtures revealed that any mixture containing not less than 20% boric acid or not more than 60% is more effective than the separate constituents; the most efficient mixture was that with 30 to 35% boric acid. Except when boric acid alone was used, the charred mass remaining after ignition glowed, and the intensity of the glow increased as the amount of borax was increased.

A mixture of 30% boric acid and 70% borax prevents flame propagation when present to the extent of about 6%; the treated fabric retains its softness and flexibility and does not feel damp nor "dusty." This proofing does not promote the growth of micro-organisms, nor is there any deterioration of strength on storage or exposure to light as compared with the untreated material.

Borax solution alone leaves a badly distributed deposit on the fabric, and one that does not adhere well; the mixture, however, adheres firmly and shows no tendency to dust off. The improved contact with the textile material facilitates chemical reaction. Although boric acid attacks the fabric at a lower temperature than the mixture, the deposit from boric acid solution adheres badly. Boric acid melts on the application of flame and covers the surface of the cloth with a glassy layer, but the reaction between boric acid and the fabric takes place comparatively slowly, which may account for the relative inefficiency of the acid as a fireproofing agent. The melting-point of boric acid is 185°C., but that of the mixture is 105°C.

As previously stated, an effective mixture is one containing 30% boric acid, and when applied to fabrics so as to leave 6% of the mixture on the cloth, it prevents both flame propagation and afterglow.

Some ternary mixtures have been suggested, and have a slight advantage over the binary mixture in that their efficiency is slightly greater on a weight basis. For example, 5% of a mixture of 50 parts of borax, 35 parts of boric acid, and 15 parts of sodium phosphate is very successful in use.

INSOLUBLE COMPOUNDS

Any attempt to produce a permanent fireproof effect is more difficult than with temporary fireproofing agents, as the former will have to withstand prolonged exposure to rain, wind, and sunshine. Water-soluble deposits are, therefore, not suitable for fabrics used in awnings, tents, and other material exposed to the open air.

Ramsbottom (loc. cit.) has classified a number of insoluble substances as effective fireproofing agents on the same basis as that given on page 525.

EFFICIENCY OF FIREPROOFING AGENTS

Fireproof and Glowproof		Fireproof		
Antimony oxychloride .	. 30	Aluminium stannate .	.	54
		Antimonious oxide	.	79
		Ferric chromate .	.	24
		Ferric oxide	.	19
		Lead chromate .	.	37
		Lead monoxide .	.	21
		Manganese dioxide	.	22
		Stannic oxide .	.	20
		Tin tungstate .	.	77
		Zinc stannate .	.	47

It will be seen that the only good fireproofing agent in the list is antimony oxychloride; when afterglow is not considered, ferric oxide, stannic oxide, lead oxide, and manganese dioxide may be of value.

These substances are generally deposited in the fabric by double decomposition, and the material washed in running water for an hour after impregnation.

The effect of weathering on the impregnated fabrics was examined by exposure for 6 months, when it was found that only two of the treated cloths resisted the propagation of flame; these contained ferric oxide and lead oxide. Nearly all the specimens suffered a greater decrease in strength than the untreated fabric when exposed, and complete destruction was observed with fabrics containing stannic oxide and titanium oxide. Whereas substances such as silica and alumina afford no measure of flameproofing, yet they have a protective action to weathering, and may be useful in mixtures on that account; they do not give rise to afterglow.

Although the most effective insoluble flameproofing agent seems to be ferric oxide, which is only required in relatively small amounts, the treated material suffers from afterglow which is sufficient to destroy the fabric by flameless combustion.

It is interesting to note that ferric oxide treatments are resistant to weathering, and this is not the case with the stannic oxide method, sometimes referred to as Perkin's process (see page 523). The loss of flameproofing properties after exposure to rain, however, may be restored by treatments with dilute alkali. Numerous other inert deposits are capable of preventing flame spreading in presence of a small amount of an adsorbed alkaline salt which is tenaciously held by cotton and may explain why many insoluble compounds, such as borates, tungstates, silicates, and hydroxides, have been suggested for flameproofing, whereas in actual fact their efficiency is influenced by the alkali salts which take part in the process of double decomposition and are often retained in the fabric.

Perhaps one of the most interesting points in connection with the comparison of soluble and insoluble fireproofing agents is the inferiority of the latter when estimated on a weight basis.

The insoluble fireproofing agents comprise a large number of oxides, many of which are easily reduced, and it has been suggested that their action may be one of catalytic oxidation.

U.S.P. 2,167,278 of Leatherman utilises a mixture of a plurality of mutually precipitated oxides, including at least one of the oxides, stannic oxide, copper oxide, manganese dioxide, or lead dioxide, in suspension in a chlorinated resin or a chlorinated wax/oil mixture which will liberate hydrochloric acid when heated. According to Leatherman (U.S. Dept. Agric. Circ. 466, 1938) stannic oxide and basic stannic salts owe their efficiency to catalysis of the thermal decomposition of cellulose, so that a protective sheath of charred material is formed. The precipitation of the oxide is best effected by acid decomposition, as this catalytic effect is weakened by the presence of alkali (cf. page 530). This type of fireproofing agent requires an additional compound to prevent afterglow, and chlorinated hydrocarbons of high molecular weight have been suggested in U.S.P. 2,012,686 and 1,990,292; similarly with the inorganic salts of the ethanolamines whose application preserves the smoothness and pliability of the fabric, as described in B.P. 437,226.

Leatherman has also protected the impregnation of fabrics with a metal alkyl sulphate, followed by a treatment with sodium stannate solution, and then with a solution of a salt which readily hydrolyses to form an insoluble hydroxide of the metal. This process has been described in U.S.P. 2,017,805.

Chlorinated compounds

Within recent years, more attention has been paid to the possible use of chlorinated hydrocarbon compounds as fireproofing agents. B.P. 465,500 protects the use of chlorinated polyphenyls; U.S.P. 2,028,715 utilises halogenated hydrocarbons, diphenyls, acenaphthenes, or phenanthrenes to which resinous or viscous aromatic compounds may be added to ensure adhesion to the fabric or yarn. Treatments of this type may not be suitable for curtains and upholstery fabrics, but are satisfactory for the textile insulating material on wires.

Chlorinated aromatic hydrocarbons for flameproofing have also received attention in B.P. 428,873, U.S.P. 1,777,776, 1,825,248, and 1,975,072.

Chlorinated rubber has been suggested for fireproof finishes by

Ellis in U.S.P. 1,852,998; the fire-retarding effect of the rubber varies with the degree of chlorination. The fabric is treated with a composition consisting of chlorinated rubber in benzene or carbon tetrachloride, to which has been added an aryl phosphate to impart flexibility and a softener such as diethyl phthalate; vegetable oils may also be used.

B.P. 390,097 of the I.G. gives an interesting application of chlorinated rubber for flameproofing; latex or other rubber dispersion is mixed with a wetting agent, and well oxidised before chlorination, when it becomes soluble in hydrocarbon solvents. Without oxidation, the chlorinated latex is stated to remain insoluble. B.P. 414,072 of the I.C.I. describes the use of chlorinated rubber in trichlorethylene, together with resin soap, casein, and sulphonated sulphoricinoleic acid.

More recent developments in the U.S.A. appear to rely on a mixture of a chlorinated product with a substantial amount of an oxide or sulphide of arsenic, antimony, or bismuth. (U.S.P. 2,299,612 is an example of this tendency.) It has been stated by van Tuyle (Am. Dyes. Rep., 1943, *32*, 297) that the U.S.A. War Department has developed a fireproofing process which depends on impregnation with a dispersion of antimony oxide (120 lb.) in a solution of Vinylite VYHH (60 lb.) in sufficient methyl ethyl ketone to give a suitable viscosity and an increase in weight of 35% of that of the cloth. According to Redmond (ibid., 1943, *32*, 375), where chlorinated paraffins are used they should contain 40 to 60% of chlorine; the decomposition of the compound is accelerated by the presence of ferric oxide, zinc oxide, zinc carbonate, and zinc borate, antimony oxide having only a slight action.

Zinc borate is particularly effective in catalysing the decomposition of the chlorinated material so that the resultant decomposition product accelerates decomposition of the cellulose below flame temperature, bringing about the formation of carbon through charring without burning. Suitable compounds are chlorinated paraffins, chlorinated rubber, chlorinated diphenyl, vinyl chloride, chloroprene, and chlorinated naphthalene to 100 parts, to which may be added 10 to 60 parts of zinc borate; the mass is mixed with a little triethanolamine to bind any residual hydrochloric acid which may be present, and also some calcium carbonate to neutralise any acid developed on ageing. The mixture may be applied from solvents by the spreading method or it may be used as an emulsion.

It is usual to test the efficiency of chlorinated products of the above type at a temperature of the order of 175°C.

Resins

Certain attempts have been made to fix the most efficient fireproofing agents to the fabric and so prevent the soluble salts being removed by water; the use of synthetic resins is a somewhat obvious line of approach. B.P. 334,408 states that it is possible to suspend or dissolve the fire-retardant in a condensation product of urea and formaldehyde which may then be applied to fabric or to timber; the resin adheres to the substrata and prevents crystallisation. In one example, from 10 to 20% of $(NH_4)_2HPO_4$ may be mixed with 1 to 2% of urea-formaldehyde solution in presence of a little starch or glue, and applied to fabric in the usual way. Alternatively, 20 parts of dimethylolurea may be mixed with 60 parts of diammonium phosphate and 1 part of 10% sulphuric acid solution; the fabric may be impregnated in this solution, squeezed, dried, and warmed.

B.F. 791,983 utilises the condensation products of formaldehyde and dicyandiamides to fix the usual ammonium salts which are flameproofing agents.

Urea-formaldehyde condensation products have also been suggested in B.P. 435,240 for the fixation of a mixture of fireproofing agents such as 5 to 10 parts of diammonium sulphate, 1 to 4 parts of ammonium chloride, 2 to 5 parts of boric acid, and 1 to 3 parts of borax; this mixture was recommended for fireproofing "electric" blankets.

B.P. 476,043 outlines the proofing of textiles by the application of resins from diamines and formaldehyde, in the presence of acids from groups which are known to possess fireproofing properties, such as boric, phosphoric, and so forth.

Fireproofing may also be effected by coating or impregnation with urea phosphates and synthetic resins as described in B.P. 446,379. This process is chiefly concerned with electric equipment which is frequently insulated with textile materials. The previous suggestions for the use of ammonium phosphate in conjunction with urea and formaldehyde which later form a resin on heating, and also the use of a mixture of urea and thiourea in an aqueous solution of formaldehyde and phosphoric acid, possess certain disadvantages mainly in connection with aqueous solutions; the application of urea phosphate in alcohol obviates these disadvantages. A typical recipe is to mix 2·4 Kg. of 84% phosphoric acid with 3·7 Kg. of urea by rubbing; the product is then added to 3 Kg. of phenol formaldehyde condensation product in the "A" state and dissolved in 24 Kg. of methyl or ethyl alcohol at 40° to 50°C. The textile material is saturated with this solution and then dried at 110° to 120°C. for 15 to 30 minutes to harden the resin.

A different type of resin has been suggested by Snyder in U.S.P. 1,885,870. The fabric is first made fireproof by the deposition of SnO_2, and then made resistant to weathering by impregnation with a solution in toluene of some 3% of a chlorine-containing vinyl resin,

1% of tritolyl phosphate, and 1% of tung oil fatty acid. Although this bears a superficial resemblance to the processes discussed on page 532, it will be noted that the amount of vinyl resin is quite small.

The gelatin-formaldehyde reaction may also be employed to fix fireproofing agents. B.P. 440,026, by Leroy, outlines a process in which the fabric is first treated with an insoluble salt of a higher fatty acid by impregnation with a soluble salt followed by double decomposition with a salt of a metal which forms a precipitate; the fabric is then treated at 30° to 75°C., when the fatty acid salt loses its water-repellency, with a fireproofing solution and gelatin, followed by hardening in the usual manner. For example, zinc stearate is formed in the fabric, which is then passed into a bath containing 10% of a mixture of 1% borax, 3% sodium phosphate, 2% ammonium phosphate, 1·3% sodium tungstate, and 0·5% of phosphotriamide formed by dissolving phosphorus oxychloride in ammonia solution; gelatin is also added to this solution and the impregnated fabric is finally treated with formaldehyde to insolubilise the gelatin and fix the fireproofing compounds.

GENERAL

Some of the commoner successful preparations are perhaps worth summarising.

Two recipes recommended by the London County Council for the treatment of curtains are of interest. The first is a solution of 10 oz. of borax and 8 oz. of boric acid in a gallon of water; the alternative method is to impregnate the fabric with a solution of 1 lb. of ammonium phosphate and 2 lb. of ammonium chloride in 1·5 gallons of water.

As mentioned elsewhere, the use of ammonium bromide is very popular in Germany, and is the main constituent of "Cellon," which may be the subject-matter of U.S.P. 1,612,104 by Eichengrun, as ammonium bromide and phosphate in suitable admixture are stated to prevent the propagation of flame and also the afterglow.

Mixtures of ammonium salts which act as flameproofing compounds, together with wetting agents form the basis of the proprietory products Intramon and Intravan of the I.G.; the Locron preparation of the same concern is believed to contain a urea-formaldehyde condensation product.

Calex F of the I.C.I. also contains a mixture of ammonium salts, probably phosphate and sulphate, but in addition there is a special softening agent which obviates the stiff and boardy handle associated with most fireproof finishes; this is an important point when finished goods have to be stitched. The amount of Calex applied depends to some extent on the construction of the fabric and in general 12 to

15% on the weight of the cloth is adequate; the expression of the padding mangle should be regulated accordingly. A typical recipe for gabardines is 250 lb. of Calex F, 50 gallons of water at 70°C., and 3 gallons of ammonia (d 0·91), the whole being diluted to a total bulk of 100 gallons.

The British Fire Prevention Committee Red Books, Nos. 128, 148, 159, 162, 167, and 245, outline non-flam processes; results which are reasonably fast to washing are given by a two-stage treatment. The fabric is first steeped in a solution of 3 lb. of sodium stannate per gallon of water (*sp. gr.* 1·21), squeezed, dried, and then passed through a second solution containing 1·25 lb. of ammonium sulphate per gallon of water (*sp. gr.* 1·07), followed by squeezing, drying, thorough rinsing, and final drying. Treated flannelettes show little change after 20 washes subsequent to the above process.

A less permanent treatment is obtained by using a solution of 2 lb. of ammonium sulphate and 4 lb. of ammonium chloride in 3 gallons of water.

Sodium silicate is stated to be fairly effective for interior decorations where change of colour or lustre is of no importance. The recommended method is to use commercial water-glass (*sp. gr.* 1·39) diluted with 1 to 5 volumes of water, according to the degree of fireproofing required.

An American process due to Bancroft (B.P. 604,197) has recently aroused very considerable interest; it depends on impregnating the textile material with an aqueous solution of phosphoric acid and urea followed by heating at 130-135° C. until combination takes place with the fibre. The effect is stated to be resistant to laundering. The chemistry of this process has attracted attention and has been discussed by Davis, Findlay and Rogers (J.T.I. 1949, *40*, 836.)

Heat resistance

Although not strictly a fireproof fabric, an interesting wartime development in Germany resulted in the production of protective clothing. The chief barrier to approaching a fierce fire is radiation of the heat, but fire-protection suits were made from material composed of aluminium foil (0·01 mm. thick) bonded with cellulose acetate to an open mesh fabric. The fabric was first coated with the acetate by spreading, after which bonding was effected by calendering. A wearer of a suit of this material could approach within two yards of a fire, whereas, without it, he could only come within 40 yards of the same fire.

APPENDIX

DENSITY TABLES

Baumé.	Twaddell.	Sp. Gr.	H_2SO_4 %	HCl %	HNO_3 %	NaOH %	KOH %
0	0	1·00	0·09	0·16	0·10	0	0
1·4	2	1·01	1·57	2·14	1·9	0·86	1·18
2·7	4	1·02	3·03	4·13	3·7	1·69	2·28
4·1	6	1·03	4·49	6·15	5·5	2·60	3·36
5·4	8	1·04	5·96	8·16	7·26	3·50	4·44
6·7	10	1·05	7·36	10·17	8·99	4·34	5·53
8·0	12	1·06	8·77	12·19	10·68	5·20	6·6
9·4	14	1·07	10·19	14·17	12·33	6·13	7·68
10·6	16	1·08	11·60	16·15	13·95	7·05	8·76
11·9	18	1·09	12·99	18·11	15·53	7·95	9·82
14·2	20	1·10	14·35	21·92	18·67	8·78	10·87
15·4	24	1·12	17·01	23·82	20·33	10·56	12·96
17·7	28	1·14	19·61	27·66	23·31	12·49	15·04
19·8	32	1·16	22·19	31·52	26·36	14·19	17·13
22·0	36	1·18	24·76	35·59	29·38	16·00	19·15
24·0	40	1·20	27·32	39·11	32·36	17·81	21·17
26·0	44	1·22	29·84		35·28	19·65	23·15
27·9	48	1·24	32·28		38·29	21·47	25·13
29·7	52	1·26	34·57		41·34	23·23	27·07
31·5	56	1·28	36·87		44·41	25·04	29·0
33·3	60	1·30	39·19		47·49	26·85	30·91
35·0	64	1·32	41·50		50·71	28·83	32·78
36·6	68	1·34	43·74		54·07	30·74	34·63
38·2	72	1·36	45·88		57·57	32·79	36·46
39·8	76	1·38	48·0		61·27	34·71	38·28
41·2	80	1·40	50·11		65·30	36·67	40·09
42·7	84	1·42	52·15		69·80	38·67	41·89
44·1	88	1·44	54·07		74·68	40·68	43·63
45·4	92	1·46	55·97		79·98	42·75	45·37
46·8	96	1·48	57·83		86·05	44·33	47·09
48·1	100	1·50	59·70		94·09	46·94	48·78
49·4	104	1·52	61·59		99·67	49·05	50·48
50·6	108	1·54	63·43				52·15
51·8	112	1·56	65·08				
53·0	116	1·58	66·71				
54·1	120	1·60	68·51				
55·2	124	1·62	70·32				
56·3	128	1·64	71·99				
57·4	132	1·66	73·64				
58·4	136	1·68	75·42				
59·5	140	1·70	77·17				
60·4	144	1·72	78·92				
61·4	148	1·74	80·68				
62·3	152	1·76	82·44				
63·2	156	1·78	84·50				
64·2	160	1·80	86·90				
65·0	164	1·82	90·50				
65·9	168	1·84	95·60				
		1·841	97·0				
		1·8415	97·7				
		1·841	98·2				
		1·840	99·2				
		1·839	99·7				

The acid and alkali percentages are by weight—for grams per 100 c.cs., multiply the percentage figure by the specific gravity.

SOME COMMON INDICATORS

	pH	pH	Colour change	
Thymol Blue . .	1·2 to	2·8	Red	Yellow
Bromo-phenol Blue .	2·8 ,,	4·6	Yellow	Violet
Methyl Orange . .	3·1 ,,	4·4	Red	Yellow
Bromo-cresol Green .	3·6 ,,	5·2	Yellow	Blue
Methyl Red . .	4·2 ,,	6·3	Red	Yellow
Litmus . . .	5·0 ,,	7·0	Red	Blue
Bromo-cresol Purple .	5·2 ,,	6·8	Yellow	Violet
Bromo-thymol Blue .	6·0 ,,	7·6	Yellow	Blue
Phenol Red . .	6·8 ,,	8·4	Yellow	Red
Cresol Red . .	7·2 ,,	8·8	Yellow	Violet-red
Thymol Blue . .	8·0 ,,	9·6	Yellow	Blue
Phenolphthalein .	8·3 ,,	10·5	None	Red
Alizarine Blue . .	9·0 ,,	11·0	Brown	Green
Alizarine Blue . .	11·0 ,,	13·0	Green	Violet

CENTIGRADE AND FAHRENHEIT

C.	F.	C.	F.	C.	F.
200	392	120	248	40	104
195	383	115	239	35	95
190	374	110	230	30	86
185	365	105	221	25	77
180	356	100	212	20	68
175	347	95	203	15	59
170	338	90	194	10	50
165	329	85	185	5	41
160	320	80	176	0	32
155	311	75	167	—5	23
150	302	70	158	—10	14
145	293	65	149	—15	5
140	284	60	140	—20	—4
135	275	55	131	—25	—13
130	266	50	122	—30	—22
125	257	45	113	—35	—31

NOTE

Throughout this book the *gallon* to which
reference is made is the British Imperial gallon
and not the U.S. gallon. The British gallon
is equivalent to 1·2 U.S. gallons.

BIBLIOGRAPHY OF FINISHING

COTTON FINISHING, by the Dyer and Calico Printer (*Heywood*, London, 1906).

CLOTH FINISHING, by the Dyer and Calico Printer (*Heywood*, London, 1909).

DRESSINGS AND FINISHINGS FOR TEXTILE FABRICS, by F. Polleyn (*Scott, Greenwood*, London, 1911).

THE CHEMISTRY AND PRACTICE OF FINISHING, by P. Bean and W. McCleary (Manchester, 1912).

FINISHING OF JUTE AND LINEN FABRICS, by T. Woodhouse (*Emmott*, Manchester, 1916).

THE CHEMICAL TECHNOLOGY OF TEXTILE FIBRES, by G. Georgievics (*Scott, Greenwood*, London, 1920).

TEXTILE FIBRES, by J. M. Matthews (*Chapman & Hall*, London, 1924).

THE BLEACHING, DYEING AND CHEMICAL TECHNOLOGY OF TEXTILE FIBRES, by S. R. and E. R. Trotman (*Griffin*, London, 1925).

TEXTILE BLEACHING, DYEING AND FINISHING MACHINERY, by A. J. Hall (*Benn*, London, 1926).

THE FINISHING OF TEXTILE FABRICS, by R. Beaumont (*Scott, Greenwood*, London, 1926).

THE BLEACHING AND FINISHING OF COTTON, by S. R. Trotman and E. L. Thorpe (*Griffin*, London, 1927).

THE FINISHING OF WOVEN FABRICS, by E. Midgley (*Arnold*, London, 1929).

THE FINISHING OF WOOL GOODS, by J. and J. C. Schofield (Huddersfield, 1935).

PROCESSING AND FINISHING COTTONS, by J. F. Monaghan (*Bennett*, Boston, 1935).

BLEACHING, DYEING, PRINTING AND FINISHING, by J. W. McMyn and J. W. Bardsley (*Pitman*, London, 1932).

FINISHING MATERIALS, by J. A. Clark (*W. R. C. Smith*, Atlanta, Ga., 1940).

A DICTIONARY OF APPLIED CHEMISTRY, by Thorpe and Whiteley (*Longmans, Green*, London, Fourth Edition, Vol. V, 1941).

OILSILK, by F. Warner (*Harlequin Press Co.*, Manchester, 1939).

WATERPROOFING OF FABRICS, by S. Mierzinski (*Scott, Greenwood*, London, 1914).

WATERPROOFING OF TEXTILE FABRICS, by H. P. Pearson (Chemical Catalogue Co., New York, 1924).

NOUVEAUX PROCÉDÉS DANS LA TECHNIQUE DE L'ENNOBLISSMENT DES FIBRES TEXTILES, by Diserens (*Edition Teintex*, Paris, 1940).

TRAITÉ DES APPRÊTS, by J. Depierre (*Baudry*, Paris, 1887).

BLANCHIMENT, TEINTURE, IMPRESSION ET APPRÊTS, by P. Lederlin (*Baillière*, Paris, 1923).

L'Apprêt des Tissus, by P. Montavon (*Davy*, Paris, 1924).

Technologie Chemico-Textile, by G. Capron (*L'Edition Textile*, Paris, 1938).

Progrès réalisés dans L'application des Matières Colorantes, by L. Diserens (*Edition Teintex*, Paris, 1937).

Les Apprêts Textiles, by Chaplet (*Gauthier-Villars*, Paris, 1914).

Les Apprêts Textiles, by A. Lambrette (*L'Edition Textile*, Paris, 1939).

L'Apprêt des Tissus, by Lejeune (*Industrie Textile*, Paris).

Tissus Imperméables, by D. de Prat (*Béranger*, Paris, 1925).

Enzyklopadie der Textilchemischen Technologie, by P. Heermann (*Springer*, Berlin, 1930).

Textilhilfsmittel, by A. Chwala (*Springer*, Vienna, 1939).

Handbuch der Appretur, by Bergmann (*Springer*, Berlin, 1928).

Technologie der Textilveredelung, by Heermann (*Springer*, Berlin, 1921).

Appretur mittelkunde, by Herzinger (*Ziemsen*, Wittenberg, 1930).

Appretur verfahren, by Herzinger (*Ziemsen*, Wittenberg, 1930).

Veredlung der Baumwollfasern, by Herzinger (*Ziemsen*, Wittenberg, 1926).

Fabrikation von Wachstuch, by W. Jacobi (*Hartleben*, Leipzig, 1931).

Die Gaufrage, by W. Kleinewefers (*Springer*, Berlin, 1925).

Mechanischehilfsmittel zur Veredlung, by Haller and Glafey (*Herzog's Techn. der Textilf*, Band IV, Pt. 3).

Praxis der Baumwollwaren Appretur, by E. Ruf (*Springer*, Berlin, 1930).

Verarbeitung der Faserstoffe, by E. v. Hoyer (*Kriedel*, Wiesbaden, 1900).

Vor- und Nach-appretur der Moebelstoffe, Teppiche und verwandter Waren, by M. R. Koehler (*Ziemsen*, Wittenberg, 1914).

Feuersicher- Geruchlos- und Wasserdichtmachen, by L. Andes (*Hartleben*, Vienna, 1922).

Imprägnierungstechnik, by T. Koller (*Hartleben*, Vienna, 1923) 2 vols.

Wasserdichtimpragnieren von Textilerzengnissen, by R. Buckleim (*Ziemsen*, Wittenberg, 1936).

Chemische Technologie der Gespinstfasern, by Ristenpart and others (*Krayn*, Berlin).

Teil. i. Die Chemische Hilfsmittel zur Veredlung der Gespinstfasern (1923).

ii. Die Gespinstfasern, 1928.

iii. Die Praxis der Färberei, 1926.

iv. Die Praxis der Bleicherei, 1928.

v. Die Ausrüstung (Appretur), 1932.

vi. Die Druckerei, 1934.

These are regarded also as the 3rd edition of Herzfeld's Das Färben und Bleichen.

The following volumes from the well-known series TECHNOLOGIE DER TEXTILFASERN,[1] edited by Herzog are concerned with finishing.

IV. 3 CHEMISCHE TECHNOLOGIE DER BAUMWOLLE, by Haller.
VI. 2 TECHNOLOGIE UND WIRTSCHAFT DER SEIDE, by Ley.
VIII. 3 CHEMISCHE TECHNOLOGIE DER WOLLE AND DIE ZUGEHORIGEN MASCHINEN, by Ultrich and Glafey.

The following journals and magazines are also of some interest:

The Journal of the Society of Dyers and Colourists.
The Journal of the Textile Institute.
The Journal of the Society of Chemical Industry.
The Transactions of the Faraday Society.
The Paper Trade Journal.
The Textile Recorder.
The Textile Manufacturer.
The Silk Journal and Rayon World.
The Dyer.
Silk and Rayon.
The Textile Mercury.
The Textile Weekly.
American Dyestuffs Reporter.
Textile World.
Rayon Textile Monthly.
The Textile Colorist.
Revue Générale des Matières Colorantes.
Teintex.
T.I.B.A. (Teinture, Impression, Blanchiment, Apprêts).
R.U.S.T.A. (Revue Universelle de la Soie et des Textiles Artificiels).
Cellulosechemie.
Textilberichte.
Kunstseide.
Seide.
Zellwolle.
Deutscher Fabrer Zeitung.
Leipziger Farber Zeitung.

---

[1] These books were published by Springer of Berlin between 1928 and 1938.

NAME INDEX

SUBJECT INDEX